74

Stanley Gibbons
STAMP CATALOGUE
PART 5
Czechoslovakia & Poland

Fifth edition, 1994

Stanley Gibbons Ltd
London and Ringwood

By Appointment to Her Majesty The Queen
Stanley Gibbons Ltd., London
Philatelists

Published by **Stanley Gibbons Ltd.**
Publications Editorial, Sales Offices and
Distribution Centre:
5 Parkside, Christchurch Road, Ringwood,
Hants, BH24 3SH

1st Edition in this form – June 1980
2nd Edition – March 1982
3rd Edition – October 1985
4th Edition – January 1991
5th Edition – December 1994

© Stanley Gibbons Ltd. 1994

ISBN: 0-85259-383-X

Item No. 2834 (94)

Made and printed in Great Britain by Black Bear Press Limited, Cambridge

Stanley Gibbons Foreign Catalogue Parts 2–22

Edward Stanley Gibbons published his first catalogue of postage stamps from Plymouth in November 1865. Its unillustrated twenty pages listed stamps and postal stationery from Antigua to Wurttemburg with price columns provided for unused or used, either as singles or by the dozen.

Since 1865 the catalogue range has grown to over forty current titles, all profusely illustrated and reflecting current research and price information.

The foreign listings, of which this volume forms a part, were published as Part II of the Stanley Gibbons catalogue from 1897 to 1945. Circumstances were difficult in the austerity period following the Second World War so the foreign listings were split into seven smaller catalogues. From 1951 to 1970 these were consolidated into Part II Europe and Colonies and Part III America, Asia and Africa.

Collecting patterns do change, however, so in 1970–71 an experimental series of Sectional catalogues appeared which were, in turn, replaced by a series of three alphabetical volumes covering Europe and four covering Overseas.

The present system of twenty-one catalogues, covering individual countries or collecting groups, was initiated in 1979. Full details of each volume and its contents are provided on the back cover. The scheme has the advantage of allowing flexibility in response to changing collecting habits with the listings being continually improved, currently by notes covering certain postal history aspects and by the addition of stamp booklet listings.

About this edition

With the dissolution of the Czech and Slovak Federative Republic (Czechoslovakia) this edition sees the emergence of the Czech Republic and the resumption of Slovakia as current stamp-issuing countries.

In Poland further perforation varieties have been added thanks to Mr C. V. Davies and Mr R. E. Tinkel, who also provided helpful comments on the text.

With the freer market following the collapse of the Communist regimes, prices are more volatile than in more previous editions, particularly for more modern issues.

Addresses of specialist societies for this area are given overleaf.

David J. Aggersberg
Pam Basley

New issues

The first supplement to this catalogue appeared in *Gibbons Stamp Monthly* for February 1995.

Catalogue numbers altered

The following are alterations made to catalogue numbers used in the Fourth Edition (1991) of Part 5.

Old	New
Poland	
521a	521b
636	636a
638	638a
969	969a
1188	1188a
1575	1575a
1577	1577a
2564	2564a

Stamps added to this edition

Items added to this catalogue, not previously published in *Gibbons Stamp Monthly* supplements.

Czechoslovakia: 227ab

Poland: 521a, 522a, 636, 637a, 638, 643a, 666a, 667d, 672a, 695b/c, 700a, 725a, 727a, 774a, 789a, 908a/12a, 917a, 969, 1188, 1465a, 1575, 1576a, 1577, 1579a, 1581a, 2564

Stanley Gibbons Holdings Plc.

Stanley Gibbons Ltd, Stanley Gibbons Auctions
399 Strand, London WC2R 0LX

Auction Room and Specialist Stamp Departments: Open Monday–Friday, 9.30 a.m. to 5 p.m.
Shop: Open Monday–Friday 8.30 a.m. to 6 p.m. and Saturday 10 a.m. to 4 p.m.
  Telephone 071-836 8444 and Fax 071-836 7342 for all departments.

Stanley Gibbons Publications
5 Parkside, Christchurch Road, Ringwood, Hants BH24 3SH.

Telephone 0425 472363 (24 hour answer phone service) and Fax 0425 470247
Publications Showroom: Open Monday–Friday 9 a.m. to 3 p.m.
Publications Mail Order: FREEPHONE 0800 611622 Monday–Friday 8.30 a.m. to 5 p.m.

Stanley Gibbons Publications has overseas licensees and distributors for Australia, Austria, Belgium, Canada, Denmark, Finland, France, Germany, Hong Kong, Israel, Italy, Japan, Luxembourg, Netherlands, New Zealand, Norway, Singapore, South Africa, Sweden, Switzerland, United States, West Indies and Caribbean. Please contact the Ringwood address for details.

Urch Harris & Co. (A division of Stanley Gibbons Ltd)
1 Osprey Court, Hawkfield Way, Bristol BS14 0BE

UH New Issue Service, Osprey Postal Auctions, UH Digest
  Telephone 0272 465656 and Fax 0272 465225 Monday–Friday 8.30 a.m. to 5 p.m.

Specialist Societies

**The Czechoslovak Philatelic
  Society of Great Britain**
Hon. Secretary: Mrs. D. Y. Gren
146 Old Shoreham Road
Shoreham-by-Sea
West Sussex
BN43 5TE

**Society for Czechoslovak
  Philately Inc.**
Secretary: R. T. Cossaboom
Box 25332
Scott AFB
IL 62225-0332
U.S.A.

**Society for Polish Pilately
  in Great Britain**
Hon. Secretary: A. T. Blunt
Riber House
13 Auden Close
Osbaston
Monmouth
Gwent
NP5 3NW

Polonus Philatelic Society
President: R. H. Strzelecki
P.O. Box 458
Berwyn
Illinois 60402
U.S.A.

General Philatelic Information
and Guidelines to the Scope of the Foreign Catalogue

The notes which follow seek to reflect current practice in compiling the Foreign Catalogue.

It scarcely needs emphasising that the *Stanley Gibbons Stamp Catalogue* has a very long history and that the vast quantity of information it contains has been carefully built up by successive generations through the work of countless individuals. Philately itself is never static and the Catalogue has evolved and developed during this long time-span. Thus, while these notes are important for today's criteria, they may be less precise the farther back in the listings one travels. They are not intended to inaugurate some unwanted series of piecemeal alterations in a widely respected work, but it does seem to us useful that Catalogue users know as exactly as possible the policies currently in operation.

THE CATALOGUE IN GENERAL

Contents. The Catalogue is confined to adhesive postage stamps, including miniature sheets. For particular categories the rules are

(a) Revenue (fiscal) stamps or telegraph stamps are listed only where they have been expressly authorised for postal duty.

(b) Stamps issued only precancelled are included, but normally issued stamps available additionally with precancel have no separate precancel listing unless the face value is changed.

(c) Stamps prepared for use but not issued, hitherto accorded full listing, are nowadays footnoted with a price (where possible).

(d) Bisects (trisects, etc.) are only listed where such usage was officially authorised.

(e) Stamps issued only on first day covers and not available separately are not listed but priced (on the cover) in a footnote.

(f) New printings, as such, are not listed, though stamps from them may qualify under another category, e.g. when a prominent new shade results.

(g) Official and unofficial reprints are dealt with by footnote.

(h) Stamps from imperforate printings of modern issues which also occur perforated are covered by footnotes or general notes, but are listed where widely available for postal use.

Exclusions. The following are excluded: (a) non-postal revenue or fiscal stamps; (b) postage stamps used fiscally; (c) local carriage labels and private local issues; (d) telegraph stamps; (e) bogus or phantom stamps; (f) railway or airline letter fee stamps, bus or road transport company labels; (g) cut-outs; (h) all types of non-postal labels; (i) documentary labels for the postal service, e.g. registration, recorded delivery, airmail etiquettes, etc.; (j) privately applied embellishments to official issues and privately commissioned items generally; (k) stamps for training post officers; (l) specimen stamps.

Full listing. "Full listing" confers our recognition and implies allotting a catalogue number and (wherever possible) a price quotation.

In judging status for inclusion in the catalogue broad considerations are applied to stamps. They must be issued by a legitimate postal authority, recognised by the government concerned, and must be adhesives valid for proper postal use in the class of service for which they are inscribed. Stamps, with the exception of such categories as postage dues and officials, must be available to the general public, at face value, in reasonable quantities without any artificial restrictions being imposed on their distribution.

We record as abbreviated Appendix entries, without catalogue numbers or prices, stamps from countries which either persist in having far more issues than can be justified by postal need or have failed to maintain control over their distribution so that they have not been available to the public in reasonable quantities at face value. Miniature sheets and imperforate stamps are not mentioned in these entries.

The publishers of this catalogue have observed, with concern, the proliferation of "artificial" stamp-issuing territories. On several occasions this has resulted in separately inscribed issues for various component parts of otherwise united states or territories.

Stanley Gibbons Publications have decided that where such circumstances occur, they will not, in the future, list these items in the SG catalogue without first satisfying themselves that the stamps represent a genuine political, historical or postal division within the country concerned. Any such issues which do not fulfil this stipulation will be recorded in the Catalogue Appendix only.

For errors and varieties the criterion is legitimate (albeit inadvertent) sale over a post office counter in the normal course of business. Details of provenance are always important; printers' waste and fraudulently manufactured material is excluded.

Certificates. In assessing unlisted items due weight is given to Certificates from recognised Expert Committees and, where appropriate, we will usually ask to see them.

New issues. New issues are listed regularly in the Catalogue Supplement published in *Gibbons Stamp Monthly*, whence they are consolidated into the next available edition of the Catalogue.

Date of issue. Where local issue dates differ from dates of release by agencies, "date of issue" is the local date. Fortuitous stray usage before the officially intended date is disregarded in listing.

Catalogue numbers. Stamps of each country are catalogued chronologically by date of issue. Subsidiary classes (e.g. postage due stamps) are integrated into one list with postage and commemorative stamps and distinguished by a letter prefix to the catalogue number.

The catalogue number appears in the extreme left column. The boldface Type numbers in the next column are merely cross-references to illustrations. Catalogue numbers in the *Gibbons Stamp Monthly* Supplement are provisional only and may need to be altered when the lists are consolidated. Miniature sheets only purchasable intact at a post office have a single **MS** number; sheetlets – individual stamps available – number each stamp separately. The catalogue no longer gives full listing to designs, originally issued in normal sheets, which subsequently appear in sheetlets showing changes of colour, perforation, printing process or face value. Such stamps will be covered by footnotes.

Information (contd.)

Once published in the Catalogue, numbers are changed as little as possible; really serious renumbering is reserved for the occasions when a complete country or an entire issue is being rewritten. The edition first affected includes cross-reference tables of old and new numbers.

Our catalogue numbers are universally recognised in specifying stamps and as a hallmark of status.

Illustrations. Stamps are illustrated at three-quarters linear size. Stamps not illustrated are the same size and format as the value shown unless otherwise indicated. Stamps issued only as miniature sheets have the stamp alone illustrated but sheet size is also quoted. Overprints, surcharges, watermarks and postmarks are normally actual size. Illustrations of varieties are often enlarged to show the detail.

CONTACTING THE CATALOGUE EDITOR

The editor is always interested in hearing from people who have new information which will improve or correct the Catalogue. As a general rule he must see and examine the actual stamps before they can be considered for listing; photographs or photocopies are insufficient evidence. Neither he nor his staff give opinions as to the genuineness of stamps.

Submissions should be made in writing to the Catalogue Editor, Stanley Gibbons Publications, 5 Parkside, Christchurch Road, Ringwood, Hants BH24 3SH. The cost of return postage for items submitted is appreciated, and this should include the registration fee if required.

Where information is solicited purely for the benefit of the enquirer, the editor cannot undertake to reply if the answer is already contained in these published notes or if return postage is omitted. Written communications are greatly preferred to enquiries by telephone and the editor regrets that he or his staff cannot see personal callers without a prior appointment being made.

The editor welcomes close contact with study circles and is interested, too, in finding reliable local correspondents who will verify and supplement official information in overseas countries where this is deficient.

We regret we do not give opinions as to the genuineness of stamps, nor do we identify stamps or number them by our Catalogue.

TECHNICAL MATTERS

The meanings of the technical terms used in the Catalogue will be found in *Philatelic Terms Illustrated* by James Mackay, published by Gibbons (Price £7.50 plus postage).

1. Printing

Printing errors. Errors in printing are of major interest to the Catalogue. Authenticated items meriting consideration would include background, centre or frame inverted or omitted; centre or subject transposed; error of colour; error or omission of value; double prints and impressions; printed both sides; and so on. Designs *tête-bêche*, whether intentionally or by accident, are listable. *Se-tenant* arrangements of stamps are recognised in the listings or footnotes. Gutter pairs (a pair of stamps separated by blank margin) are excluded unless they have some philatelic importance. Colours only partially omitted are not listed, neither are stamps printed on the gummed side.

Printing varieties. Listing is accorded to major changes in the printing base which lead to completely new types. In recess-printing this could be a design re-engraved, in photogravure or photolithography a screen altered in whole or in part. It can also encompass flat-bed and rotary printing if the results are readily distinguishable.

To be considered at all, varieties must be constant.

Early stamps, produced by primitive methods, were prone to numerous imperfections; the lists reflect this, recognising re-entries, retouches, broken frames, misshappen letters, and so on. Printing technology has, however, radically improved over the years, during which time photogravure and lithography have become predominant. Varieties nowadays are more in the nature of flaws and these, being too specialised for a general catalogue, are almost always outside the scope. We therefore do not list such items as dry prints, kiss prints, doctor-blade flaws, blanket set-offs, doubling through blanket stretch, plate cracks and scratches, registration flaws (leading to colour shifts), lithographic ring flaws, and so on. Neither do we recognise fortuitous happenings like paper creases or confetti flaws.

Overprints (and surcharges). Overprints of different types qualify for separate listing. These include overprints in different colours; overprints from different printing processes such as litho and typo; overprints in totally different typefaces, etc.

Overprint errors and varieties. Major errors in machine-printed overprints are important and listable. They include overprint inverted or omitted; overprint double (treble, etc.); overprint diagonal; overprint double, one inverted; pairs with one overprint omitted, e.g. from a radical shift to an adjoining stamp; error of colour; error of type fount; letters inverted or omitted, etc. If the overprint is handstamped, few of these would qualify and a distinction is drawn.

Varieties occurring in overprints will often take the form of broken letters, slight differences in spacing, rising spacers, etc. Only the most important would be considered for footnote mention.

Sheet positions. If space permits we quote sheet positions of listed varieties and authenticated data is solicited for this purpose.

2. Paper

All stamps listed are deemed to be on "ordinary" paper of the wove type and white in colour; only departures from this are mentioned.

Types. Where classification so requires we distinguish such other types of paper as, for example, vertically and horizontally laid; wove and laid bâtonné; card(board); carton; cartridge; enamelled; glazed; GC (Grande Consommation); granite; native; pelure; porous; quadrillé; ribbed; rice; and silk thread.

Our chalky (chalk-surfaced) paper is specifically one which shows a black mark when touched with a silver wire. This and other coatings are easily lost or damaged through immersion in water.

The various makeshifts for normal paper are listed as appropriate. They include printing on: unfinished banknotes, war maps, ruled paper, Post Office forms, and the unprinted side of glossy magazines. The varieties of double paper and joined paper are recognised.

Descriptive terms. The fact that a paper is handmade (and thus probably of uneven thickness) is mentioned where necessary. Such descriptive terms as "hard" and "soft"; "smooth" and "rough"; "thick", "medium" and "thin" are applied where there is philatelic merit in classifying papers.

Coloured, very white and toned papers. A coloured paper is one that is coloured right through (front and back of the stamp). In the Catalogue the colour of the paper is given in *italics*, thus

black/*rose* = black design on rose paper.

Papers have been made specially white in recent years by, for example, a very heavy coating of chalk. We do not classify shades of whiteness of paper as distinct varieties. There does exist, however, a type of paper from early days called toned. This is off-white, often brownish or buffish, but it cannot be assigned any definite colour. A toning effect brought on by climate, incorrect storage or gum staining is disregarded here, as this was not the state of the paper when issued.

Safety devices. The Catalogue takes account of such safety devices as varnish lines, grills, burelage or imprinted patterns on the front or moiré on the back of stamps.

Modern developments. Two modern developments also affect the listings, printing on self-adhesive paper and the tendency, philatelic in origin, for conventional paper to be reinforced or replaced by different materials. Some examples are the use of foils in gold, silver, aluminium, palladium and steel; application of an imitation wood veneer; printing on plastic moulded in relief; and use of a plastic laminate to give a three-dimensional effect. Examples also occur of stamps impregnated with scent; printed on silk; and incorporating miniature gramophone records.

3. Perforation and Rouletting

Perforation gauge. The gauge of a perforation is the number of holes in a length of 2 cm. For correct classification the size of the holes (large or small) may need to be distinguished; in a few cases the actual number of holes on each edge of the stamp needs to be quoted.

Measurement. The Gibbons *Instanta* gauge is the standard for measuring perforations. The stamp is viewed against a dark background with the transparent gauge put on top of it. Though the gauge measures to decimal accuracy, perforations read from it are generally quoted in the Catalogue to the nearest half. For example:

Just over perf. 12¾ to just under perf. 13¼ = perf. 13
Perf. 13¼ exactly, rounded up = perf. 13½
Just over perf. 13¼ to just under perf. 13¾ = perf. 13½
Perf. 13¾ exactly, rounded up = perf. 14

However, where classification depends on it, actual quarter-perforations are quoted.

Notation. Where no perforation is quoted for an issue it is imperforate. Perforations are usually abbreviated (and spoken) as follows, though sometimes they may be spelled out for clarity. This notation for rectangular stamps (the majority) applies to diamond shapes if "top" is read as the edge to the top right.

P 14: perforated alike on all sides (read: "perf. 14").

P 14×15: the first figure refers to top and bottom, the second to left and right sides (read: "perf. 14 by 15"). This is a compound perforation. For an upright triangular stamp the first figure refers to the two sloping sides and the second to the base. In inverted triangulars the base is first and the second figure refers to the sloping sides.

P 14–15: perforation measuring anything between 14 and 15: the holes are irregularly spaced, thus the gauge may vary along a single line or even along a single edge of the stamp (read: "perf. 14 to 15").

P 14 *irregular*: perforated 14 from a worn perforator, giving badly aligned holes irregularly spaced (read "irregular perf. 14").

P comp(ound) 14×15: two gauges in use but not necessarily on opposite sides of the stamp. It could be one side in one gauge and three in the other, or two adjacent sides with the same gauge (Read: "perf. compound of 14 and 15"). For three gauges or more, abbreviated as "*P* 14, 14½, 15 *or compound*" for example.

P 14, 14½: perforated approximately 14¼ (read: "perf. 14 or 14½"). it does *not* mean two stamps, one perf. 14 and the other perf. 14½. This obsolescent notation is gradually being replaced in the Catalogue.

Imperf: imperforate (not perforated).

Imperf × *P* 14: imperforate at top and bottom and perf 14 at sides.

P 14 × *imperf:* perf 14 at top and bottom and imperforate at sides.

Such headings as "*P* 13 × 14 (*vert*) and *P* 14 × 13 (*horiz*)" indicate which perforations apply to which stamp format – vertical or horizontal.

Some stamps are additionally perforated so that a label or tab is detachable; others have been perforated suitably for use as two halves. Listings are normally for whole stamps, unless stated otherwise.

Other terms. Perforation almost always gives circular holes; where other shapes have been used they are specified, e.g. square holes; lozenge perf. Interrupted perfs are brought about by the omission of pins at regular intervals. Perforations have occasionally been simulated by being printed as part of the design. With few exceptions, privately applied perforations are not listed.

Perforation errors and varieties. Authenticated errors, whre a stamp normally perforated is accidentally issued imperforate, are listed provided no traces of perforation (blind holes or indentations) remain. They must be provided as pairs, both stamps wholly imperforate, and are only priced in that form.

Stamps merely imperforate between stamp and margin (fantails) are not listed.

Imperforate-between varieties are recognised, where one row of perfs has been missed. They are listed and priced in pairs:

Imperf between (*horiz pair*): a horizontal pair of stamps with perfs all around the edges but none between the stamps.

Imperf between (*vert pair*): a vertical pair of stamps with perfs all around the edges but none between the stamps.

Where several of the rows have escaped perforation the resulting varieties are listable. Thus:

Imperf vert (*horiz pair*): a horizontal pair of stamps perforated top and bottom; all three vertical directions are imperf – the two outer edges and between the stamps.

Imperf horiz (*vert pair*): a vertical pair perforated at left and right edges; all three horizontal directions are imperf – the top, bottom and between the stamps.

Straight edges. Large sheets cut up before issue to post offices can cause stamps with straight edges, i.e. imperf on one side or on two sides at right angles. They are not usually listable in this condition and are worth less than corresponding stamps properly perforated all round. This does not, however, apply to certain stamps, mainly from coils and booklets, where straight edges on

Information (contd.)

various sides are the manufacturing norm affecting every stamp. The listings and notes make clear which sides are correctly imperf.

Malfunction. Varieties of double, misplaced or partial perforation caused by error or machine malfunction are not listable, neither are freaks, such as perforations placed diagonally from paper folds. Likewise disregarded are missing holes caused by broken pins, and perforations "fading out" down a sheet, the machinery progressively disengaging to leave blind perfs and indentations to the paper.

Centering. Well-centred stamps have designs surrounded by equal opposite margins. Where this condition affects the price the fact is stated.

Types of perforating. Where necessary for classification, perforation types are distinguished. These include:

Line perforation from one line of pins punching single rows of holes at a time.

Comb perforation from pins disposed across the sheet in comb formation, punching out holes at three sides of the stamp a row at a time.

Harrow perforation applied to a whole pane or sheet at one stroke.

Rotary perforation from the toothed wheels operating across a sheet, then crosswise.

Sewing-machine perforation. The resultant condition, clean-cut or rough, is distinguished where required.

Pin-perforation is the commonly applied term for pin-roulette in which, instead of being punched out, round holes are pricked by sharp-pointed pins and no paper is removed.

Punctured stamps. Perforation holes can be punched into the face of the stamp. Patterns of small holes, often in the shape of initial letters, are privately applied devices against pilferage. These "perfins" are outside the scope. Identification devices, when officially inspired, are listed or noted; they can be shapes, or letters or words formed from holes, sometimes converting one class of stamp into another.

Rouletting. In rouletting the paper is cut, for ease of separation, but none is removed. The gauge is measured, when needed, as for perforations. Traditional French terms descriptive of the type of cut are often used and types include:

Arc roulette (*percé en arc*). Cuts are minute, spaced arcs, each roughly a semicircle.

Cross roulette (*percé en croix*). Cuts are tiny diagonal crosses.

Line roulette (*percé en ligne* or *en ligne droite*). Short straight cuts parallel to the frame of the stamp. The commonest basic roulette. Where not further described, "roulette" means this type.

Rouletted in colour or *coloured roulette* (*percé en lignes colorées* or *en lignes de couleur*). Cuts with coloured edges, arising from notched rule inked simultaneously with the printing plate.

Saw-tooth roulette (*percé en scie*). Cuts applied zigzag fashion to resemble the teeth of a saw.

Serpentine roulette (*percé en serpentin*). Cuts as sharply wavy lines.

Zigzag roulettes (*percé en zigzags*). Short straight cuts at angles in alternate directions, producing sharp points on separation. U.S. usage favours "serrate(d) roulette" for this type.

Pin-roulette (originally *percé en points* and now

4. Gum

All stamps listed are assumed to have gum of some kind; if they were issued without gum this is stated. Original gum (o. g.) means that which was present on the stamp as issued to the public. Deleterious climates and the presence of certain chemicals can cause gum to crack and, with early stamps, even make the paper deteriorate. Unscrupulous fakers are adept in removing it and regumming the stamp to meet the unreasoning demand often made for "full o. g." in cases where such a thing is virtually impossible.

Until recent times the gum used for stamps has been gum arabic, but various synthetic adhesives – tinted or invisible-looking – have been in use since the 1960s. Stamps existing with more than one type of gum are not normally listed separately, though the fact is noted where it is of philatelic significance, e.g. in distinguishing reprints or new printings.

The distinct variety of grilled gum is, however, recognised. In this the paper is passed through a gum breaker prior to printing to prevent subsequent curling. As the patterned rollers were sufficient to impress a grill into the paper beneath the gum we can quote prices for both unused and used examples.

Self-adhesive stamps are issued on backing paper from which they are peeled before affixing to mail. Unused examples are priced as for backing paper intact. Used examples are best kept on cover or on piece.

5. Watermarks

Stamps are on unwatermarked paper except where the heading to the set says otherwise.

Detection. Watermarks are detected for Catalogue description by one of four methods: (1) holding stamps to the light; (2) laying stamps face down on a dark background; (3) adding a few drops of petroleum ether 40/60 to the stamp laid face down in a watermark tray; or (4) by use of the Morley-Bright Detector, or other equipment, which works by revealing the thinning of the paper at the watermark. (Note that petroleum ether is highly inflammable in use and can damage photogravure stamps.)

Listable types. Stamps occurring on both watermarked and unwatermarked papers are different types and both receive full listing.

Single watermarks (devices occurring once on every stamp) can be modified in size and shape as between different issues; the types are noted but not usually separately listed. Fortuitous absence of watermark from a single stamp or its gross displacement would not be listable.

To overcome registration difficulties the device may be repeated at close intervals (a *multiple watermark*), single stamps thus showing parts of several devices. Similarly a large *sheet watermark* (or *all-over watermark*) covering numerous stamps can be used. We give informative notes and illustrations for them. The designs may be such that numbers of stamps in the sheet automatically lack watermark; this is not a listable variety. Multiple and all-over watermarks sometimes undergo modifications, but if the various types are difficult to distinguish from single stamps notes are given but not separate listings.

Papermakers' watermarks are noted where known but not listed separately, since most stamps in the sheet will lack them. Sheet watermarks which are nothing more than officially adopted papermakers' watermarks are, however, given normal listing.

Marginal watermarks, falling outside the pane of stamps, are ignored except where misplacement causes the adjoining row to be affected, in which case they are footnoted.

Watermark errors and varieties. Watermark errors are recognised as of major importance. They comprise stamps intended to be on unwatermarked paper but issued watermarked by mistake, or stamps printed on paper with the wrong watermark. Watermark varieties, on the other hand, such as broken or deformed bits on the dandy roll, are not listable.

Watermark positions. Paper has a side intended for printing and watermarks are usually impressed so that they read normally when looked through from that printed side.

Illustrations in the Catalogue are of watermarks in normal positions (from the front of the stamps) and are actual size where possible.

Differences in watermark position are collectable as distinct varieties. In this Catalogue, however, only normal and sideways watermarks are listed (and "sideways inverted" is treated as "sideways"). Inverted and reversed watermarks have always been outside its scope: in the early days of flat-bed printing sheets of watermarked paper were fed indiscriminately through the press and the resulting watermark positions had no particular philatelic significance. Similarly, the special make-up of sheets for booklets can in some cases give equal quantities of normal and inverted watermarks.

6. Colours

Stamps in two or three colours have these named in order of appearance, from the centre moving outwards. Four colours or more are usually listed as multicoloured.

In compound colour names the second is the predominant one, thus:

orange-red = a red tending towards orange;

red-orange = an orange containing more red than usual.

Standard colours used. The 200 colours most used for stamp identification are given in the Stanley Gibbons Colour Key. The Catalogue has used the Key as a standard for describing new issues for some years. The names are also introduced as lists are rewritten, though exceptions are made for those early issues where traditional names have become universally established.

Determining colours. When comparing actual stamps with colour samples in the Key, view in a good north daylight (or its best substitute: fluorescent "colour-matching" light). Sunshine is not recommended. Choose a solid portion of the stamp design; if available, marginal markings such as solid bars of colour or colour check dots are helpful. Shading lines in the design can be misleading as they appear lighter than solid colour. Postmarked portions of a stamp appear darker than normal. If more than one colour is present, mask off the extraneous ones as the eye tends to mix them.

Errors of colour. Major colour errors in stamps or overprints which qualify for listing are: wrong colours; one colour inverted in relation to the rest; albinos (colourless impressions), where these have Expert Committee certificates; colours completley omitted, but only on unused stamps (if found on used stamps the information is footnoted).

Colours only partially omitted are not recognised. Colour shifts, however spectacular, are not listed.

Shades. Shades in philately refer to variations in the intensity of a colour or the presence of differing amounts of other colours. They are particularly significant when they can be linked to specific printings. In general, shades need to be quite marked to fall within the scope of this Catalogue; it does not favour nowadays listing the often numerous shades of a stamp, but chooses a single applicable colour name which will indicate particular groups of outstanding shades. Furthermore, the listings refer to colours as issued: they may deteriorate into something different through the passage of time.

Modern colour printing by lithography is prone to marked differences of shade, even within a single run, and variations can occur within the same sheet. Such shades are not listed.

Aniline colours. An aniline colour meant originally one derived from coal-tar; it now refers more widely to colour of a particular brightness suffused on the surface of a stamp and showing through clearly on the back.

Colours of overprints and surcharges. All overprints and surcharges are in black unless stated otherwise in the heading or after the description of the stamp.

7. Luminescence

Machines which sort mail electronically have been introduced in recent years. In consequence some countries have issued stamps on fluorescent or phosphorescent papers, while others have marked their stamps with phosphor bands.

The various papers can only be distinguished by ultraviolet lamps emitting particular wavelengths. They are separately listed only when the stamps have some other means of distinguishing them, visible without the use of these lamps. Where this is not so, the papers are recorded in footnotes or headings. (Collectors using the lamps, nevertheless, should exercise great care in their use as exposure to their light is extremely dangerous to the eyes.)

Phosphor bands are listable, since they are visible to the naked eye (by holding stamps at an angle to the light and looking along them, the bands appear dark). Stamps existing with and without phosphor bands or with differing numbers of bands are given separate listings. Varieties such as double bands, misplaced or omitted bands, bands printed on the wrong side, are not listed.

8. Coil Stamps

Stamps issued only in coil form are given full listing. If stamps are issued in both sheets and coils the coil stamps are listed separately only where there is some feature (e.g. perforation) by which singles can be distinguished. Coil strips containing different stamps *se-tenant* are also listed.

Coil join pairs are too random and too easily faked to permit of listing; similarly ignored are coil stamps which have accidentally suffered an extra row of perforations from the claw mechanism in a malfunctioning vending machine.

9. Booklet Stamps

Single stamps from booklets are listed if they are distinguishable in some way (such as watermark or perforation) from similar sheet stamps. Booklet panes, provided they are distinguishable from blocks of sheet stamps, are listed for most countries; booklet panes containing more than one value *se-tenant* are listed under the lowest of the values concerned.

Information (contd.)

Lists of stamp booklets are given for certain countries and it is intended to extend this generally.

10. Forgeries and Fakes

Forgeries. Where space permits, notes are considered if they can give a concise description that will permit unequivocal detection of a forgery. Generalised warnings, lacking detail, are not nowadays inserted since their value to the collector is problematic.

Fakes. Unwitting fakes are numerous, particularly "new shades" which are colour changelings brought about by exposure to sunlight, soaking in water contaminated with dyes from adherent paper, contact with oil and dirt from a pocketbook, and so on. Fraudulent operators, in addition, can offer to arrange: removal of hinge marks; repairs of thins on white or coloured papers; replacement of missing margins or perforations; reperforating in true or false gauges; removal of fiscal cancellations; rejoining of severed pairs, strips and blocks; and (a major hazard) regumming. Collectors can only be urged to purchase from reputable sources and to insist upon Expert Committee certification where there is any kind of doubt.

The Catalogue can consider footnotes about fakes where these are specific enough to assist in detection.

PRICES

Prices quoted in this Catalogue are the selling prices of Stanley Gibbons Ltd at the time when the book went to press. They are for stamps in fine average condition; in issues where condition varies they may ask more for the superb and less for the sub-standard.

All prices are subject to change without prior notice and Stanley Gibbons Ltd may from time to time offer stamps at other than catalogue prices in consequence of special purchases or particular promotions.

No guarantee is given to supply all stamps priced, since it is not possible to keep every catalogued item in stock. Commemorative issues may, at times, only be available in complete sets and not as individual values.

Quotations of prices. The prices in the left-hand column are for unused stamps and those in the right-hand column are for used.

Prices are expressed in pounds and pence sterling. One pound comprises 100 pence (£1 = 100p).

The method of notation is as follows: pence in numerals (e.g. 10 denotes ten pence); pounds and pence up to £100, in numerals (e.g. 4·25 denotes four pounds and twenty-five pence); prices above £100 expressed in whole pounds with the "£" sign shown.

Unused stamps. Prices for stamps issued up to the end of the Second World War (1945) are for lightly hinged examples and more may be asked if they are in unmounted mint condition. Prices for all later unused stamps are for unmounted mint. Where not available in this condition, ligthly hinged stamps supplied are often at a lower price.

Used stamps. The used prices are normally for stamps postally used but may be for stamps cancelled-to-order where this practice exists.

A pen-cancellation on early issues can sometimes correctly denote postal use. Instances are individually noted in the Catalogue in explanation of the used price given.

Prices quoted for bisects on cover or on large piece are for those dated during the period officially authorised.

Stamps not sold unused to the public but affixed by postal officials before use (e.g. some parcel post stamps) are priced used only.

Minimum price. The minimum price quoted is ten pence. This represents a handling charge rather than a basis for valuing common stamps for which the 10p price should not be reckoned automatically since it covers a variation in real scarcity.

Set prices. Set prices are generally for one of each value, excluding shades and varieties, but including major colour changes. Where there are alternative shades, etc, the cheapest is usually included. The number of stamps in the set is always stated for clarity.

Where prices are given for se-tenant blocks or strips, any mint set price quoted for such an issue is for the complete se-tenant strip plus any other stamps included in the set. Used set prices are always for a set of single stamps.

Repricing. Collectors will be aware that the market factors of supply and demand directly influence the prices quoted in this Catalogue. Whatever the scarcity of a particular stamp, if there is no one in the market who wishes to buy it it cannot be expected to achieve a high price. Conversely, the same item actively sought by numerous potential buyers may cause the price to rise.

All the prices in this Catalogue are examined during the preparation of each new edition by expert staff of Stanley Gibbons and repriced as necessary. They take many factors into account, including supply and demand, and are in close touch with the international stamp market and the auction world.

GUARANTEE

All stamps are guaranteed genuine originals in the following terms:

If not as described, and returned by the purchaser, we undertake to refund the price paid to us in the original transaction. If any stamp is certified as genuine by the Expert Committee of the Royal Philatelic Society, London, or by B.P.A. Expertising Ltd, the purchaser shall not be entitled to make claim against us for any error, omission or mistake in such certificate. Consumers' statutory rights are not affected by this guarantee.

The established Expert Committees in this country are those of the Royal Philatelic Society, 41 Devonshire Place, London W1N 1PE, and B.P.A. Expertising Ltd, P.O. Box 137, Leatherhead, Surrey, KT22 0RG. They do not undertake valuations under any circumstances and fees are payable for their services.

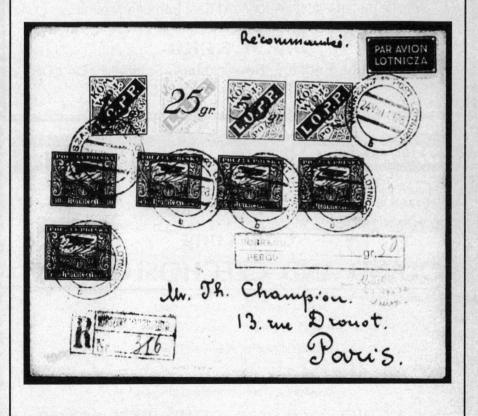

Czechoslovakia

100 Haleru=1 Koruna

CZECHOSLOVAK REPUBLIC
28 October 1918–11 July 1960

The Czechs of Bohemia and Moravia and the Slovaks of northern Hungary (both part of the Austrian-Hungarian Empire) supported a Czechoslovak National Council formed by Tomas Masaryk in Paris in February 1916. On 28 October 1918 the Council issued a declaration of independence and two days later the Slovak National Council voted for union with the Czechs; on 14 November a National Assembly in Prague confirmed the creation of a Czechoslovak Republic.

Unoverprinted Austrian and Hungarian stamps continued to be valid for use until 15 March 1919.

1

1918 (Oct). *Embossed. Arc roul. in colour. Greyish paper and yellow gum. P 12.*

1	**1**	10 h. bright blue (*shades*)	12·50	14·00
2		20 h. bright carmine (*shades*)	12·50	14·00

The above stamps were issued by the Revolutionary Committee of Prague. The distribution of the first revolutionary post was undertaken by Scouts. Reprints exist, on white paper with white gum. With commemorative overprint, 'PRIJEZD PRESIDENTA MASARYKA' (arrival of President Masaryk), they are scarce, but were made mainly for stamp collectors.

The Revolutionary Committee also applied a number of overprints to various stamps of Austria and Hungary but these were never put on sale at post offices, although some are known postally used. Also numerous Unpaid Letter stamps are known with overprint 'T', 'DOPLATIT' or 'PORTO', in various types, on Austrian or Czech stamps. These are purely local issues.

2	Hradčany, Prague 3

(T **2/5** Des A. Mucha. Eng M. Sula. Typo Czech Graphic Union, Prague)

1918–19 (*a*) *Imperf.*

3	**3**	1 h. chocolate (14.3.19)	10	10
4	**2**	3 h. reddish purple (21.12.18)	10	10
5		5 h. yellow-green (18.12.18)	10	10
		a. Olive-green	40	20
6		10 h. rose-carmine (*shades*) (18.12.18)	10	10
7		20 h. turquoise-green (30.12.18)	15	10
8		25 h. blue (*shades*) (30.12.18)	15	10
9		30 h. olive-bistre (17.1.19)	25	10
10		40 h. brown-orange (23.1.19)	25	10
11	**3**	50 h. purple (19.8.19)	25	10
12	**2**	100 h. red-brown (14.1.19)	75	10
13		200 h. bright blue (14.1.19)	1·25	10
		a. Ultramarine	1·25	10
		b. Violet-blue	25·00	1·50
14		400 h. violet (29.1.19)	1·50	15

(*b*) *P 13½* (1919)

15	**3**	1 h. chocolate	10	10
16	**2**	20 h. turquoise-green	20	10
17		25 h. blue	40	10
18		200 h. bright blue	2·50	15
		a. Violet-blue	2·75	15

(*c*) *P 11½* (1919)

19	**2**	5 h. light green	75	20
20		10 h. rose-carmine	25	10

21	**2**	20 h. turquoise-green	40	20
22		25 h. blue	1·25	75

(*d*) *P 11½×10½* (1919)

23	**2**	5 h. light green	1·50	40

In the 100 h., 200 h. and 400 h. the inscription is on a white instead of a coloured ground.

For T **2** in miniature sheet, see No. **MS**531*a*.

N **4** Windhover	D **4**	E **4**

(Des A. Mucha. Typo)

1918 (18 Dec)–**20** *NEWSPAPER. Imperf.*

N24	N **4**	2 h. green	10	10
N25		5 h. green (20.9.20)	10	10
		a. Greenish slate (28.12.20)	40	10
N26		6 h. red (7.6.19)	20	20
N27		10 h. lilac	10	10
N28		20 h. blue (4.7.19)	10	10
N29		30 h. brown (9.8.19)	15	10
N30		50 h. orange-yellow (28.12.20)	15	10
N31		100 h. red-brown (28.12.20)	50	10

The 20 h. in violet and 30 h. in olive were prepared but not issued (*Price £5 each*).

(Des A. Mucha. Typo)

1919 (1 Feb)–**20** *POSTAGE DUE. Imperf.*

D24	D **4**	5 h. olive-bistre	10	10
D25		10 h. olive-bistre	10	10
D26		15 h. olive-bistre	10	10
D27		20 h. olive-bistre (5.2.19)	15	10
D28		25 h. olive-bistre (22.3.19)	20	15
D29		30 h. olive-bistre (17.2.19)	40	10
D30		40 h. olive-bistre (24.2.19)	40	25
D31		50 h. olive-bistre (11.2.19)	40	10
D32		100 h. deep brown (6.3.19)	1·50	10
D33		250 h. bright orange (25.10.20)	5·50	1·00
D34		400 h. bright carmine (21.10.20)	7·00	1·00
D35		500 h. green (24.4.19)	3·00	20
D36		1000 h. violet (20.3.19)	4·00	40
D37		2000 h. blue (20.10.20)	18·00	90

Type D **4** perf 11½ or 13½ were not officially issued.

(Des A. Mucha. Typo)

1919 (10 Feb)–**20**. *NEWSPAPER EXPRESS. Imperf.*
A. *On yellow paper.* B. *On white paper*

			A		B	
E24	E **4**	2 h. brown-lilac	10	10	8·75	5·00
E25		5 h. green	10	10	6·25	3·75
		a. Brt grn (20.9.20)	10	10		†
E26		10 h. lake-brown (20.12.20)	50	50	£300	

4	5

T **5** differs from T **3** in having no sun and in the tree being shaded instead of white.

1919-20. (a) *Imperf.*

24	**4**	5 h. blue-green (*shades*) (1.8.19)	20	10
25		10 h. yellow-green (1920)	38·00	25·00
26		15 h. rose-red (*shades*) (7.6.19)	20	10
		a. Vermilion	50	15
27		20 h. carmine (1920)	£150	£100
28		25 h. deep purple (9.7.19)	20	10
		a. Reddish purple	50·00	2·50
29		30 h. mauve (1920)	£200	£170
		a. Deep violet	£200	£180
30		50 h. blue (15.8.19)	25	10
31	**5**	60 h. yellow-orange (10.4.19)	75	10
32	**4**	75 h. grey-green (3.7.19)	1·00	10
		a. Greyish slate	3·25	25
33	**5**	80 h. yellow-olive (22.4.19)	1·50	15
		a. Yellow-green	1·60	15
34	**4**	120 h. slate-black (28.7.19)	1·25	15
35	**5**	300 h. dull green (22.4.19)	5·00	15
36	**4**	500 h. lake-brown (9.8.19)	2·50	15
37	**5**	1000 h. purple (2.6.19)	12·50	50
		a. Reddish violet	30·00	1·25

(b) *P* 13½ (1919-20)

38	**4**	5 h. blue-green	15	10
39		10 h. yellow-green (3.1.20)	20	10
40		15 h. rose-red	15	10
41		20 h. carmine (*shades*) (3.1.20)	20	10
42		25 h. purple	75	15
43		30 h. mauve (12.4.20)	£325	£150
44	**5**	60 h. yellow-orange	15·00	10·00

(c) *P* 11½ (1919-20)

45	**4**	5 h. blue-green	20	10
46		10 h. yellow-green (3.1.20)	10·00	1·50
47		15 h. rose-red	1·00	10
48		25 h. purple	50	10
49		30 h. mauve (*shades*) (12.4.20)	15	10
50	**5**	60 h. yellow-orange	25	10
51	**4**	120 h. slate-black	5·00	1·25

(d) *P* 13½ × 11½ (1919)

52	**4**	5 h. turquoise-green	3·00	25
53		15 h. rose-red	1·50	15
54		25 h. purple	2·50	50

(e) *P* 11½ × 10½ (1919)

55	**4**	5 h. blue-green	1·50	25
56		15 h. rose-red	20·00	4·50
57		25 h. purple	3·00	1·00

(f) *P* 11½ × 13½ (1919-20)

58	**4**	15 h. rose-red	35·00	20·00
59		30 h. mauve (12.4.20)	£550	£450

(g) *P* 13½ × 10½ (1919)

60	**4**	15 h. rose-red	70·00	40·00
60a		25 h. purple	20·00	15·00

Varieties of colour and perforation of the "Hradčany" types, not listed above, are unofficial, or printers' waste.

6	7	(8)

(Des J. Obrovský. T **6** typo, T **7** photo Cartographic Section, Czechoslovak Army)

1919 (27 Oct). *First Anniv of Independence, and Czechoslovak Legion Commemoration.* (a) *P* 13½

61	**6**	15 h. olive-green/*pinkish*	10	10
		a. Bright green/*pinkish*	20·00	20·00
62		25 h. brown/*pinkish*	10	10
		a. Yellow-brown/*pinkish*	7·50	7·50
63		50 h. blue/*pinkish*	10	10
64	**7**	75 h. slate	10	10
65		100 h. purple-brown	10	10
		a. Blackish brown	1·90	1·90
66		120 h. reddish violet/*yellow*	10	10
61/66		Set of 6	35	35

(b) *P* 10½

61b	**6**	15 h. olive-green/*pinkish*	8·75	8·75
62b		25 h. brown/*pinkish*	2·50	2·50
63b		50 h. blue/*pinkish*	£110	£110
64b	**7**	75 h. slate	£150	£150
65b		100 h. purple-brown	£190	£190
66b		120 h. reddish violet/*yellow*	£300	£300

(c) *P* 11½

61c	**6**	15 h. olive-green/*pinkish*	2·00	2·00
62c		25 h. brown/*pinkish*	2·75	2·75
64c	**7**	75 h. slate	7·50	7·50
65c		100 h. reddish violet/*yellow*	12·50	12·50

(d) *P* 10½ × 13½ (*T* **6**) or 13½ × 10½ (*T* **7**)

61d	**6**	15 h. olive-green/*pinkish*	75	75
		da. Bright green/*pinkish*	32·00	32·00
62d		25 h. brown/*pinkish*	3·75	3·75
63d		50 h. blue/*pinkish*	50·00	50·00
64d	**7**	75 h. slate	30·00	30·00
65d		100 h. purple-brown	7·50	7·50
66d		120 h. reddish violet/*yellow*	38·00	38·00

(e) *P* 11½ × 10½ (*T* **6**) or 10½ × 11½ (*T* **7**)

61e	**6**	15 h. olive-green/*pinkish*	1·25	1·25
62e		25 h. brown/*pinkish*	1·25	1·25
63e		50 h. blue/*pinkish*	32·00	32·00
64e	**7**	75 h. slate	30·00	30·00
65e		100 h. purple-brown	4·50	4·50
66e		120 h. reddish violet/*yellow*	32·00	32·00

(f) *P* 11½ × 13½ (*T* **6**) or 13½ × 11½ (*T* **7**)

61f	**6**	15 h. olive-green/*pinkish*	10	10
		fa. Bright green/*pinkish*	42·00	42·00
62f		25 h. brown/*pinkish*	10	10
		fa. Yellow-brown/*pinkish*	90·00	90·00
63f		50 h. blue/*pinkish*	25·00	
64f	**7**	75 h. slate	10	10
65f		100 h. purple-brown	10	10
		fa. Blackish brown	60	60
66f		120 h. reddish violet/*yellow*	10	10

For 5 k. red as T **6** see No. **MS**1782.

1919 (12 Dec). *Charity. Various stamps (some already optd or surch) optd diagonally as T* **8** *in varying sizes, by A. Haase, Prague.*

A. *Stamps of Austria*

(a) *Postage stamps of 1916-18*

67	**49**	3 h. violet (Imperial Crown)	15	10
68		5 h. yellow-green	15	10
69		6 h. orange (B.)	40	50
		a. Black overprint	£1400	£1100
70		10 h. claret	50	65
71		12 h. greenish blue	50	50
72	**60**	15 h. Venetian red (Charles I)	15	15
73		20 h. blue-green	15	15
		a. Yellow-green	£100	85·00
75		25 h. blue	20	15
76		30 h. dull violet	20	15
77	**51**	40 h. olive (Arms)	20	20
78		50 h. deep green	20	15
79		60 h. deep blue	25	25
80		80 h. red-brown	20	20
81		90 h. claret	45	45
82		1 k. red/*yellow* (B.)	30	30
		a. Black overprint	£100	85·00
83	**52**	2 k. deep blue (Arms)	£1800	£2000
		a. Light blue	2·00	2·00
		aa. Granite paper	1·50	1·25
85		3 k. lake	£1000	£1100
		a. Bright carmine	50·00	50·00
		aa. Granite paper	6·25	5·00
87		4 k. deep green	60·00	50·00
		a. Yellowish green	12·50	6·25
		aa. Granite paper	£17000	
89		10 k. deep violet	£450	£450
		a. Violet	£250	£300
		aa. Granite paper	£15000	

(b) *Air stamps of 1918 (optd "FLUGPOST" or surch also)*

91	**52**	1 k. 50 on 2 k. mauve	£170	£150
92		2 k. 50 on 3 k. ochre	£200	£170
93		4 k. grey	£650	£600

(c) *Newspaper stamp of 1908. Imperf*

94	**N 43**	10 h. rose-carmine (Mercury)	£1600	£1400

(d) *Newspaper stamps of 1916. Imperf*

95	N 53	2 h. brown (Mercury)		10	10
96		4 h. green		25	25
97		6 h. blue		25	25
98		10 h. orange		3·75	3·75
99		30 h. claret		1·50	1·25

(e) *Newspaper Express stamps of 1916 (Mercury — triangular stamps)*

100	N 54	2 h. carmine/yellow (B.)		30·00	30·00
101		5 h. green/yellow (Bk.)		£1200	£1000

(f) *Newspaper Express stamps of 1917 (Mercury — rectangular). P 11½ or 12½*

102	N 61	2 h. carmine/yellow (B.)		10	10
		a. Black overprint		75·00	80·00
103		5 h. green/yellow (Bk.)		10	10

(g) *Postage Due stamps of 1908–13 (Numeral and Arms)*

104	D 44	2 h. rose-carmine		£3000	£2500
105		4 h. rose-carmine		25·00	25·00
106		6 h. rose-carmine		12·50	7·50
108		14 h. rose-carmine		75·00	75·00
109		25 h. rose-carmine		50·00	50·00
110		30 h. rose-carmine		£425	£425
111		50 h. rose-carmine		£1000	£1000

(h) *Postage Due stamps of 1916 (Numeral)*

112	D 55	5 h. carmine		10	15
113		10 h. carmine		15	20
114		15 h. carmine		15	20
115		20 h. carmine		2·00	2·00
116		25 h. carmine		1·25	1·25
117		30 h. carmine		45	45
118		40 h. carmine		1·25	1·25
119		50 h. carmine		£450	£375
120	D 56	1 k. blue		12·50	12·50
121		5 k. blue		50·00	50·00
122		10 k. blue		£350	£300

(i) *Postage Due stamps, Nos. D284/5 (optd "PORTO" or surch also)*

123	36	1 h. black (R.)		25·00	20·00
124	—	15 h. on 2 h. violet (Bk.)		£150	£130

(j) *Postage Due stamps of 1917 (Francis Joseph I optd "PORTO" and surch)*

125	50	10 h. on 24 h. violet		85·00	£100
126		15 h. on 36 h. violet		50	50
127		20 h. on 54 h. orange		90·00	£100
128		50 h. on 42 h. brown		60	65

B. Stamps of Hungary

(a) *Postage stamps of 1913. W 11. P 15*

129	7	1 f. grey (Turul and Crown)		£1600	£1200
130		2 f. olive-yellow		4·25	3·75
131		3 f. orange		65·00	65·00
132		6 f. olive-green		5·00	5·00
133		50 f. lake/blue		60	55
134		60 f. green/rose		60·00	25·00
135		70 f. brown/green		£1800	£1500

(b) *Postage stamps of 1916 inscr "MAGYAR KIR POSTA". W 11. P 15 or 14 (T 19)*

136	18	2 f. yellow-brown (Harvesters)		10	10
137		3 f. dull claret		10	10
138		5 f. green		10	10
139		6 f. greenish blue		50	50
140		10 f. rose-red		1·00	1·50
141	17	10 f. rose-red (Harvesters)		£400	£325
142	18	15 f. plum		20	15
143	17	15 f. purple		£170	£180
144	18	20 f. grey-brown		8·50	7·50
145		25 f. blue		60	50
146		35 f. brown		8·75	8·75
147		40 f. olive-green		2·00	1·60
148	19	50 f. dull purple (Parliament Buildings)		75	65
149		75 f. turquoise-green		65	50
150		80 f. yellow-green		1·25	1·00
151		1 k. lake		1·50	1·25
152		2 k. bistre-brown		8·75	8·75
153		3 k. grey and dull violet		50·00	55·00
154		5 k. pale brown and brown		£120	£110
155		10 k. magenta and chocolate		£1300	£1200

T **17** has white figures of value, and T **18** has coloured figures.

(c) *Charles and Zita stamps of 1918. W 11*

156	27	10 f. rose		15	15
157		20 f. deep brown		25	20
158		25 f. blue		1·50	1·00
159	28	40 f. olive-green		2·50	2·00
160		50 f. purple		55·00	75·00

(d) *War Charity stamps of 1916–17. W 11*

161	20	10 + (2 f.) red		40	50
162	21	15 + (2 f.) deep lilac		55	75
163	22	40 + (2 f.) brown-lake		5·00	4·50

(e) *Postage stamps of 1919 inscr "MAGYAR POSTA". W 11*

164	30	10 f. rose-red (Harvesters)		8·75	7·50
165		20 f. grey-brown		£3750	£3750

(f) *Newspaper stamp of 1908. W 10. Imperf*

166	N 9	(2 f.) orange (Arms)		10	10

(g) *Express Letter stamp of 1916. W 11*

167	E 18	2 f. olive and red (Crown)		10	10

(h) *Postage Due stamps (Numeral). Figures in black*

(i) *W 9 (Crown)*

168	D 9	12 f. black and green		£3250	£2750
169		50 f. black and green		£325	£250

(ii) *W 10 (Crown)*

170	D 9	1 f. black and green		£1000	£650
171		12 f. black and green		£3250	£2750
172		50 f. black and green		£325	£250

(iii) *W 11 (Crosses)*

173	D 9	2 f. black and green		£500	£450
174		5 f. black and green		£900	£750
175		50 f. black and green		£325	£250

(i) *Postage Due stamps of 1915–18. Figures in red*

176	D 9	1 f. red and green		£200	£180
177		2 f. red and green		70	50
178		5 f. red and green		15·00	13·00
179		6 f. red and green		1·50	1·50
180		10 f. red and green		40	40
181		12 f. red and green		2·00	2·00
182		15 f. red and green		8·50	5·50
183		20 f. red and green		75	1·00
184		30 f. red and green		50·00	50·00

The purpose of the stamps overprinted as T **8** was to exchange them for Austrian and Hungarian stamps which had become invalid but they were supplied at a premium of 50 per cent above face value for the benefit of charity. All were available for ordinary postal use without regard to their original purpose.

The overprinted stamps were valid for use until 31 January 1920. Sales continued to collectors until 1928.

Care should be exercised in purchasing the rarer items as these overprints have been dangerously forged.

9 President Masaryk

(Des M. Švabinský. Eng E. Karel. Typo)

1920 *P 13½*

185	9	125 h. slate-blue (23.9)		45	20
		a. Ultramarine		17·00	22·00
186		500 h. black/bluish (7.3)		2·50	2·50
187		1000 h. brown/buff (7.3)		5·00	5·00

125 h. "E. KAREL" is omitted from the bottom right-hand corner.

10 I II I II

20 h. I. Long foot to "2"; interior of "0" angular.
II. Short foot; interior rounded.

25 h. I. Upturned top to "2".
II. Top curved downwards.

(Des J. Benda. Typo Czech Graphic Union, Prague)

1920–25. *P* 14.
188	**10**	5 h. deep blue (1.6.20)			10	10
189		5 h. violet (*shades*) (3.1.21)			10	10
		a. Tête-bêche (pair)			1·50	1·00
190		10 h. blue-green (1.6.20)			10	10
191		10 h. olive-bistre (13.11.20)			10	10
		a. Tête-bêche (pair)			1·50	1·25
192		15 h. red-brown (5.6.20)			10	10
193		20 h. orange (I) (3.1.21)			25	10
		b. Type II			10	10
		ba. Tête-bêche (pair)			15·00	15·00
194		25 h. blue-green (I) (1.9.20)			15	10
		a. Type II (8.2.21)			15	10
195		30 h. magenta (20.5.25)			1·75	10
188/195		*Set of* 8 (*cheapest*)			2·00	35

The *tête-bêche* pairs, which are all horizontal, from this and the following set come from special sheets produced for intended booklets. These booklets were not made and the sheets were put on normal sale at post offices.

11 Allegories of Republic **11***a*   **12** Hussite

 14 Kč

13   **(14)**

(Des V. Brunner (**11**, **11***a*), A. Mucha (**12**), J. Obrovský (**13**). T **12** photo, others typo Czech Graphic Union, Prague)

1920–22 *P* 14.
196	**11**	20 h. rose-carmine (22.6.20)			10	10
197	**11***a*	25 h. grey-brown (18.6.20)			10	10
198	**11**	30 h. purple (22.6.20)			10	10
199		40 h. red-brown (16.8.20)			15	10
		a. Tête-bêche (pair)			1·50	1·50
200		50 h. rose-red (17.9.20)			15	10
201		50 h. apple-green (23.1.22)			15	10
		a. Tête-bêche (pair)			38·00	30·00
202		60 h. blue (16.8.20)			15	10
		a. Tête-bêche (pair)			4·50	3·75
203	**12**	80 h. violet (1.6.20)			20	25
204		90 h. sepia (10.6.20)			40	70
205	**13**	100 h. blue-green (17.6.20)			30	10
206	**11**	100 h. deep brown (15.10.20)			30	10
207		150 h. carmine (10.4.22)			2·25	70
208		185 h. bright orange (17.9.20)			85	20
209	**13**	200 h. bright purple (17.6.20)			60	10
210	**11**	250 h. deep myrtle-green (15.10.20)			2·25	40

211	**13**	300 h. scarlet (*shades*) (23.6.20)		1·50	10
212		400 h. grey-brown (23.6.20)		4·00	50
213		500 h. green (*shades*) (24.8.20)		6·25	50
214		600 h. purple (*shades*) (24.8.20)		7·50	50
196/214		*Set of* 19		25·00	4·00

500 h. and 600 h. "J. OBROVSKY" is omitted from the bottom left-hand corner.
See note on *tête-bêche* pairs below No. 195.
For T **13** re-engraved, see Nos. 227/9b.

1920. *AIR*. Surch as T **14**.

(a) Imperf (11 Aug)
215	**2**	14 k. on 200 h. bright blue (R.)	22·00	25·00
		a. Surch inverted	60·00	
216	**4**	24 k. on 500 h. lake-brown (B.)	50·00	50·00
		a. Surch inverted	80·00	
217	**5**	28 k. on 1000 h. purple (G.)	50·00	50·00
		a. Surch inverted	80·00	
		b. Surch double	85·00	

(b) P 13½ (14 Sept)
218	**2**	14 k. on 200 h. bright blue (R.)	25·00	27·00
219	**4**	24 k. on 500 h. lake-brown (B.)	60·00	60·00
220	**5**	28 k. on 1000 h. purple (G.)	45·00	45·00
		a. Surch inverted	75·00	75·00

(15)

 + 25 +

(16)

1920 (15 Dec). *Red Cross Fund*. Surch with T **15** or **16**, in red.
P 13½
221	**2**	40 h. + 20 h. olive-bistre	1·00	1·00
222	**5**	60 h. + 20 h. yellow-green	1·00	1·00
223	**9**	125 h. + 25 h. slate-blue	2·50	2·50

100 DOPLATIT 50

(D 17)   **(17)**

1922–23. *POSTAGE DUE*. Stamps of 1918–19 surch as Type D **17**. *Imperf*.

(a) In blue (1922)
D224	**2**	20 on 3 h. reddish purple (10.2)		25	20
		a. Violet-blue surch		10	10
D225	**4**	50 on 75 h. grey-green (20.1)		25	10
		a. Violet-blue surch		75	10
D226	**5**	60 on 80 h. yellow-green (17.2)		20	10
D227		100 on 80 h. yellow-green (18.1)		30	10
		a. Violet-blue surch		19·00	15
D228	**2**	200 on 400 h. violet (18.2)		50	15

(b) In violet-blue (1923)
D229	**2**	10 on 3 h. reddish purple (15.6)		10	10
D230		30 on 3 h. reddish purple (15.6)		10	10
D231		40 on 3 h. reddish purple (15.6)		10	10
D232	**4**	60 on 75 h. grey-green (15.5)		40	10
D233		100 on 120 h. slate-black (1.4)		70	10

See also Nos. D257/65.

1922 (15 June). *AIR*. Surch as T **17**.
224	**13**	50 on 100 h. blue-green	1·90	1·75
		a. Surch inverted	15·00	
225		100 on 200 h. bright purple	5·00	3·75
		a. Surch inverted	27·00	
226		250 on 400 h. grey-brown (B.)	7·50	7·50
		a. Surch inverted	40·00	

A   B   C

Three Types of re-engraved T **13**

A. The stem of the upper right leaf extends to the tip of the leaf; the white triangle over the book appears only to the left of the stalk; the "P" of "POSTA" has a short extra leg.
B. The leaf stem is shorter and "s" shaped; the triangle extends to the right of the stalk; the "P" is as Type A.
C. The leaf stem is now quite short; the triangle is as Type B; the extra leg has been removed from the "P".

1923–25. *Re-engraved. Typo. P 14.*

227	**13**	100 h. red/yellow (A) (14.1)		2·00	10
		a. Type B (3.23)		2·00	10
		ab. *Se-tenant* pair. Types B and C			
		b. Type C (5.24)		8·00	15
228		200 h. blue/yellow (B.) (24.2)		7·50	10
		a. Type C (1.25)		8·00	25
229		300 h. purple/yellow (A) (1.2)		6·00	15
		b. Type B (7.23)		24·00	25
		b. Type C (8.24)		18·00	50

The different Types for each value occurred in separate sheets. On one plate of the 100 h. Type C, however, positions 81-85 were damaged and were replaced with clichés of Type B, giving No. 227ab.

18 President Masaryk,   **19** Linden leaf—*vertical*   (D **20**)
after portrait by
M. Švabinský

(Des M. Švabinský. Eng K. Wolf. Recess)

1923 (28 Oct). *Fifth Anniv of Republic. W* **19** *(horiz). P* 14, 14½ *or* 14½×14.

230	**18**	50 h. (+50 h.) green		1·00	75
231		100 h. (+100 h.) carmine		1·25	1·00
232		200 h. (+200 h.) blue		6·00	6·25
233		300 h. (+300 h.) sepia		9·00	7·00
230/233		*Set of* 4		15·00	13·50

The gum is quadrille, and shows a monogram "C.S.P." on each stamp.

1924. *POSTAGE DUE No.* D34 *surch as Type* D **20**, *in violet.*

D234	D **4**	50 on 400 h. bright carmine (6.11)	50	10
D235		60 on 400 h. bright carmine (30.11)	1·75	45
D236		100 on 400 h. bright carmine (30.11)	1·25	20

20   **21**   I   II

Two types of 1 k

I. Shading of crossed lines on shoulder at right
II. Shading of horizontal lines only

A   B

Two types of moustache
A. Normal   B. Retouched, shorter at left

(Des M. Švabinský. Photo)

1925 (7 Mar). *W* **19** *(vert). P* 13½.

234	**20**	40 h. orange		1·00	15
235		50 h. yellow-green		1·75	10
236		60 h. purple		2·40	10

For similar design but recess-printed see Nos. 253/54c.

(Des M. Švabinský. Eng J. Goldschmied. Recess)

1925 (7 Mar)–27.
I. *Name and value tablets shaded horiz, shaded lettering. W* **19**.

A. *Size* 19×23 mm. Wmk vertical. P 13½.
B. *Size* 19½×22 mm. Wmk horizontal. P 13½.

				A	B	
237	**21**	1 k. carmine (I)	70·00	3·75	90	10
238		2 k. blue	95·00	20·00	3·50	25
239		3 k. brown	£190	16·00	5·50	75
240		5 k. blue-green	3·25	75	1·50	25

(*c*) *Size* 18½×21½ mm. Wmk horizontal. P 13½

241	**21**	1 k. carmine (I)		70·00	65
		a. Type II		10·00	15
242		2 k. blue		3·50	25
243		3 k. brown		5·00	30

(*d*) *Size* 19×22 mm. Wmk horizontal. P 9½

243a	**21**	1 k. carmine (II)		90	10

II. *Name and value tablets shaded horiz and vert; lettering unshaded*

(*a*) *Size* 19×22 mm. P 9½
(i) *W* **19** *(horiz)*

244	**21**	1 k. carmine (I) (1.26)		90	10
		a. Thick line at bottom of portrait*		90	10

(ii) *No wmk*

244b	**21**	1 k. carmine (I) (A) (1927)		10·00	90
		c. Retouched moustache (B) (1927)	1·25		10

(*b*) *Size* 18½×21½ mm. *W* **19** *(horiz). P* 13½

245	**21**	3 k. pale brown (1.26)		4·50	15

*On Nos. 244a and 244b/c the bottom of the portrait ends in a thick line, and the inner vertical frame line of the right-hand value tablet is also thick. On previous issues, including No. 244, these lines are very thin.

(**22**)   (N **23**)   (D **23**)

1925 (11 May). *International Olympic Congress. With embossed opt, T* **22**.

246	**18**	50 (+50 h.) green (B.)		5·00	10·00
247		100 (+100 h.) carmine (B.)		10·00	15·00
248		200 (+200 h.) blue (R.)		70·00	£100

1925 (18 May)–26. *NEWSPAPER. Surch with Type* N **23**.

N249	N **4**	5 on 2 h. green (V.)		50	50
N250		5 on 6 h. red (V.) (1.7.26)		20	75

1925 (1 July)–**27.** *POSTAGE DUE. Surch as Type D* **20** *or* D **23** *(No. D256), in violet.*

D249	D **4**	10 on 5 h. olive-bistre	10	10
D250		20 on 5 h. olive-bistre	10	10
D251		30 on 15 h. olive-bistre (8.7.25)	10	10
D252		40 on 15 h. olive-bistre (8.7.25)	15	10
D253		50 on 250 h. bright orange	70	10
D254		60 on 250 h. brt orge (20.9.25)	1·00	20
D255		100 on 250 h. brt orge (15.7.25)	1·25	15
D256		200 on 500 h. green (26.9.27)	3·00	1·75
D249/256		*Set of 8*	5·75	2·00

(N **24**)

(D **24**)

1926. *NEWSPAPER. Nos. E24/6A optd "NOVINY", as in Type N* **24**, *in violet, and 2 h. surch also.*

N251	E **4**	5 on 2 h. brown-lilac/yellow (1.3)	10	10
N252		5 h. green/yellow (1.3)	45	45
N253		5 h. bright green/yellow	20	20
N254		10 h. lake-brown/yellow (1.2)	10	15
N251/254		*Set of 4*	70	70

1926 (2 Feb). *POSTAGE DUE. Surch with Type D* **17**, *in violet.*

(a) Perf 13½

D257	**4**	30 on 15 h. rose-red	35	15
D258	**4**	40 on 15 h. rose-red	30	15

(b) Perf 11½

D259	**4**	30 on 15 h. rose-red	35	15
D260	**4**	40 on 15 h. rose-red	40	15

(c) Perf 13½ × 11½

D261	**4**	40 on 15 h. rose-red	·30·00	38·00

(d) Imperf

D262	**3**	60 on 50 h. purple	3·00	1·25
D263	**4**	60 on 50 h. blue	3·25	1·50
D264	**2**	100 on 400 h. violet	40	10
D265	**5**	100 on 1000 h. purple	85	25

1926 (1 Apr–15 July). *POSTAGE DUE. Nos. 205, 209 and 211/14 surch as Type D* **24**, *in violet.*

D266	**13**	30 on 100 h. blue-green (15.7)	10	10
D267		40 on 200 h. bright purple (15.7)	15	10
D268		40 on 300 h. scarlet	1·00	25
D269		50 on 500 h. deep green	50	10
D270		60 on 400 h. grey-brown	40	10
D271		100 on 600 h. bright purple	2·00	25
D266/271		*Set of 6*	3·75	65

On all, except No. D269, the bars at top left are longer and not separated by thin lines.

(23)   23a   24

T **24** differs from T **21** in the frame ornaments.

1926 (1 June). *"VIII All-Sokol Display, Prague". With embossed opt. T* **23.**

249	**18**	50 (+50 h.) green (B.)	6·00	6·50
250		100 (+100 h.) carmine (B.)	6·00	6·50
251		200 (+200 h.) blue (R.)	25·00	25·00
252		300 (+300 h.) sepia (R.)	45·00	55·00
249/252		*Set of 4*	75·00	85·00

1926–27 *Re-engraved types. Moustache as Types* A *or* B

(a) W **19** *(horiz). (i) P 9½*

253	**23**a	50 h. green (A) (20.7.26)	60	10
		a. Retouched moustache (B) (4.27)	2·00	10
254		60 h. purple (B) (20.9.26)	70	10

(ii) Imperf × perf 9½ (coils)

254a	**23**a	50 h. green (A) (27.10.26)	20	10

(b) No wmk. P 9½

254b	**23**a	50 h. green (B) (10.27)	15	10
254c		60 h. purple (B) (9.27)	50	10
254d	**24**	1 k. deep carmine (1.10.27)	25	10

25 Karluv Tyn Castle   26 Strahov

27 Pernstyn Castle   28 Orava Castle   29 Statue of St. Wenceslas, Prague

30 Hradčany, Prague   31 Upper Tatra

(Des T. F. Šimon (T **25, 28, 30**), A. Kalvoda (T**26/27**), J. Šetelik (T **29**), O. Štáfl (T **31**). Eng K. Seizinger. Recess)

1926–31 A. *W* **19** *(horiz). (a) Imperf × perf 9½ (coils).*

255	**25**	20 h. brown-red (16.10.26)	50	40
256	**27**	30 h. myrtle (16.10.26)	25	15

(b) P 9½

257	**27**	30 h. myrtle (22.3.27)	1·00	10
258	**28**	40 h. brown (16.10.26)	40	10
259	**25**	1 k. 20, purple (1.6.26)	50	40
260	**26**	1 k. 20, purple (1.6.27)	3·50	1·75
261	**25**	1 k. 50, carmine (1.6.26)	40	10
262		2 k. 50, blue (1.6.26)	5·00	40

(c) P 13½

263	**30**	2 k. ultramarine (19.10.26)	90	10
264		3 k. scarlet (Pl I) (19.10.26)	2·10	10
		a. Plate II. Clouds heavily shaded	1·75	10
265	**31**	4 k. deep purple (25.9.27)	7·00	65
266		5 k. deep blue-green (1.6.27)	24·00	3·25
255/266		*Set of 12*	42·00	6·50

B. *No wmk (a) Imperf × perf 9½ (coils)*

267	**25**	20 h. brown-red (25.2.28)	25	10

(b) P 9½

268	**27**	30 h. myrtle (20.7.27)	15	10
269	**28**	40 h. brown (27.1.28)	50	10
270	**26**	1 k. 20, purple (15.11.27)	25	10
271	**25**	1 k. 50, carmine (10.9.29)	25	10
272	**27**	2 k. blue-green (30.6.29)	30	10
273	**25**	2 k. blue (11.11.27)	4·00	25
273a	**29**	2 k. 50, blue (12.6.29)	35	10
273b	**28**	3 k. chocolate (15.5.31)	50	10

(c) P 13½

274	**30**	2 k. blue (20.5.28)		90	15
275		3 k. scarlet (10.4.28)		2·25	75
276	**31**	4 k. deep purple (27.6.28)		6·00	1·00
277		5 k. deep blue-green (10.7.27)		6·50	60
267/277		*Set of* 13		20·00	3·00

No. 255 has a white background in value tablets similar to T **27/28**. No. 265 is inscribed "KORUNY" as in T **30**. In No. 272 the word "KORUNY" and figures "2" are white on a quadrille lined blue-green background.

(D **32**)   (D **33**)   D **34**

1927. *POSTAGE DUE. (a) Optd with Type D* **32.**

D278	**11**	100 h. deep brown (V.) (10.1)		35	10

(b) Surch as Type D **33,** *in violet*

D279	**11**	40 on 185 h. bright orange (17.1)		10	10
D280		50 on 20 h. rose-carmine (24.9)		15	10
		a. Error. 50 on 50 h. rose-red		—	£10000
D281		50 on 150 h. carmine (17.1)		20	10
D282	**11a**	60 on 25 h. grey-brown (24.9)		20	20
D283	**11**	60 on 185 h. bright orange (17.1)		15	10
D284	**11a**	100 on 25 h. grey-brown (24.9)		30	10
D278/284		*Set of* 7		1·25	50

(Des J. Vlček. Typo)

1928 (1 Feb–17 July). *POSTAGE DUE. P* 13½.

D285	D **34**	5 h. carmine (17.7)		10	10
D286		10 h. carmine		10	10
D287		20 h. carmine (29.3)		10	10
D288		30 h. carmine (29.3)		10	10
D289		40 h. carmine		10	10
D290		50 h. carmine		10	10
D291		60 h. carmine		10	10
D292		1 k. bright ultramarine		15	10
D293		2 k. bright ultramarine		30	10
D294		5 k. bright ultramarine (29.3)		60	10
D295		10 k. bright ultramarine (29.3)		1·25	10
D296		20 k. bright ultramarine (29.3)		2·50	10
D285/296		*Set of* 12		5·00	75

ENGRAVERS AND PRINTERS. Eng K. Seizinger (T **32** to **51, 53, 56, 64, 65, 70, 72a, 77** to **78**). Bohumil Heinz (**52, 54, 55, 57** to **63, 66** to **69, 71, 73** to **76** and **79**). Recess. T **30** to **80**, Czech Graphic Union, Prague.

32 Hradek Castle   33 President Masaryk

1928 (22 Oct). *10th Anniv of Independence. T* **32/3** *and similar types inscr* "1918–1928". *P* 13½.

278		30 h. grey-black		10	10
279		40 h. chocolate		10	15
280		50 h. green		15	10
281		60 h. vermilion		15	20
282		1 k. carmine		25	15
283		1 k. 20, slate-purple		45	80
284		2 k. deep ultramarine		50	75
285		2 k. 50, blue		1·60	2·50
286		3 k. sepia		1·25	1·40
287		5 k. violet		1·60	2·50
278/287		*Set of* 10		5·75	7·75

Designs: *Horiz*—40 h. Town Hall, Levoca; 50 h. Telephone Exchange Prague; 60 h. Village of Jasina; 1 k. Hluboka Castle; 1 k. 20, Pilgrim's House, Velehrad; 2 k. 50, The Grand Tatra. *Vert*—2 k. Brno Cathedral; 5 k. Town Hall, Prague.

34 National Arms   35 St. Wenceslas on Horseback

1929 (10 Apr)–**37.** *P* 9½.

287a	**34**	5 h. deep ultramarine (2.2.31)		10	10
287b		10 h. brown (2.2.31)		10	10
288		20 h. vermilion		10	10
289		25 h. blue-green		10	10
290		30 h. purple		10	10
291		40 h. red-brown		50	15
291a		40 h. sepia (1937)		10	10

Imperf × perf 9½ *(coils)*

292	**34**	20 h. vermilion (2.11.29)		10	10
287a/292		*Set of* 8		90	45

(From paintings by Aleš, Jenewein and Mánes)

1929 (14 May). *Death Millenary of St. Wenceslas. T* **35** (*and similar types). P* 13½.

293	**35**	50 h. green		15	10
294		60 h. grey-violet		35	10
295		2 k. blue		70	50
296		3 k. chocolate		95	25
297		5 k. purple		4·75	2·75
293/297		*Set of* 5		6·25	3·25

Designs:—2 k. Foundation of St. Vitus's Church; 3 k. and 5 k. Martyrdom of St. Wenceslas.

36 Brno Cathedral   37 Tatra Mountain Scene

1929 (15 Oct)–**31.** *T* **36/7** *and similar vert designs. P* 13½.

298		3 k. brown		1·60	10
299		4 k. deep blue		3·75	50
300		5 k. deep green		4·50	25
301		10 k. deep violet-blue (15.5.31)		8·00	2·75
298/301		*Set of* 4		16·00	3·25

Designs:—5 k. Town Hall, Prague; 10 k. St. Nicholas Church, Prague.

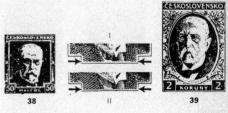

50 h.   I. Gap between shading of coat, etc., and bottom frame-line.
       II. Additional horizontal frame-line, against which shading terminates.

1930 (2 Jan)–**31.** *P* 9½.

302	**38**	50 h. green (Type I)		40	10
		a. Type II		15	10
303		60 h. purple		50	10
304		1 k. carmine		20	10

Imperf × perf 9½ (coils)

304a **38** 1 k. carmine (24.1.31) 60 45
For 50 h. black, see No. 373.

1930 (1 Mar). *80th Birthday of Pres. Masaryk. P 13½.*
305 **39** 2 k. blue-green 70 40
306 3 k. claret .. .. 1·25 40
307 5 k. deep blue .. .. .. 4·00 2·50
308 10 k. slate-black .. .. .. 7·50 5·00
305/308 *Set of 4* .. .. 12·00 7·50
The top and bottom rows of the sheets have their marginal
tablets inscribed with the dates "1850*1930" in fancy scrollwork
above (or below) each stamp.

40 Fokker F.IXD   **41** Smolik S.19

42 Fokker F.IXD over Prague

1930 (16 Dec). *AIR. P 13½.*
309 **40** 50 h. green 10 15
    a. Perf 12 .. .. .. 2·50 3·75
310 1 k. carmine 20 30
    a. Perf 12 .. .. .. 22·00 30·00
    b. Perf 12×13½ .. .. 3·75 6·25
311 **41** 2 k. slate-green 50 70
    a. Perf 12 .. .. .. 15·00 21·00
    b. Perf 13½×12 .. .. 12·00 15·00
312 3 k. purple .. .. .. 1·00 1·00
313 – 4 k. deep blue .. .. .. 75 1·00
    a. Perf 12 .. .. .. 7·00 7·50
314 – 5 k. red-brown .. .. .. 1·60 2·25
    a. Perf 12 .. .. .. £850
315 **42** 10 k. ultramarine .. .. 3·75 5·00
316 20 k. violet .. .. .. 3·75 4·50
    a. Perf 12 .. .. .. 4·75 4·50
    b. Perf 13½×12 .. .. £850
309/316 *Set of 8* .. .. .. 10·50 13·50
Design: *Horiz*—4, 5 k. Smolik S.19 with tree in foreground.
Specialists distinguish two types of the 50 h. and three types of
the 3 k., whilst the 50 h. to 4 k. each exist in slightly different
sizes.
For 30 h. stamp as Type **40**, see No. 394.

43 Krumlov   **44** Dr. Miroslav Tyrs **45**

1932 (2 Jan). *T 43 and similar types. P 9½.*
317 3 k. 50, purple (Krivoklat) .. .. 1·25 90
318 4 k. blue (Orlik) .. .. 1·75 50
319 5 k. green .. .. .. 3·00 50

1932 (16 Mar). *Birth Centenary of Dr. Tyrs, Founder of
"Sokol" Movement. P 9½.*
320 **44** 50 h. yellow-green 30 10
321 1 k. carmine 50 10
322 **45** 2 k. bright blue .. .. 6·00 40
323 3 k. red-brown .. .. 11·00 45
320/323 *Set of 4* .. .. .. 16·00 95

46 Dr. M. Tyrs   **47** Church and   **49** Frederic
                Episcopal Palace, Nitra   Smetana

1933 (1 Feb). *P 9½.*
324 **46** 60 h. bright violet 10 10

1933 (20 June). *1100th Anniv of Foundation of First Christian
Church at Nitra. T 47 and similar type. P 9½.*
325 50 h. yellow-green 30 10
326 1 k. carmine (Church Gateway) .. 3·50 25

1934 (24 Mar). *Fiftieth Anniv of Smetana's death. P 9½.*
327 **49** 50 h. yellow-green 15 10

50 Consecrating Colours   (N **51** "O (bchodni) T(iskovina)"
at Kiev   Commercial printed matter)

O.T.

1934 (15 Aug). *20th Anniv of Czechoslovak Foreign Legions
T 50 and similar designs inscr "1914–1934". P 9½.*
328 50 h. green 25 10
329 1 k. claret 30 10
330 2 k. blue .. .. .. 1·75 30
331 3 k. brown .. .. .. 3·00 30
328/331 *Set of 4* .. .. .. 4·75 60
Designs: *Horiz*—1 k. French battalion enrolling at Bayonne.
Vert—2 k. Standard of Russian Legion; 3 k. French, Russian
and Serbian legionaries.

1934 (15 Nov). *COMMERCIAL PRINTED MATTER. Optd
with Type N 51, in violet.*
N332 N **4** 10 h. lilac 10 10
N333 20 h. blue 10 10
N334 30 h. brown 15 15

52 Antonin Dvořák   **53** "Where is my
                                Fatherland?"

1934 (22 Nov). *30th Anniv of Dvořak's Death. P 9½.*
332 **52** 50 h. blue-green 20 10

(Eng from drawing by J. Mánes)
1934 (17–21 Dec). *Centenary of Czech National Anthem.
P 9½.*
333 **53** 1 k. purple 30 15
334 2 k. blue 90 40
MS334a. Special souvenir sheets of 15 stamps were issued
21.12.34 on thick carton paper, perf 13½, ungummed and
with the words and music of the Czech National Anthem
printed above and below the stamps.
Price per pair of sheets £1500 £1600
Pair from sheet .. .. .. 70·00 45·00
Beware of forged sheets.
Nos. 333/4 were each issued in sheets of 100 stamps and
12 blank labels.

54 Autograph portraits of Pres. Masaryk **55**

1935 (1 Mar). *85th Birthday of Pres. Masaryk. Toned paper.*
P 9½.

335	**54**	50 h. green			20	10
336		1 k. claret			35	10
337	**55**	2 k. blue			90	40
338		3 k. brown			1·75	40
335/338	Set of 4				3·00	80

Nos. 337/8 were each issued in sheets of 100 stamps and 12 blank labels.
See also No. 374.

56 Czech Monument at Arras	**57** Gen. M. R. Štefánik	**58** St. Cyril and St. Methodius

(Des J. Hruška)

1935 (4 May). *20th Anniv of Battle of Arras.* P 9½.

339	**56**	1 k. rose-carmine		35	10
340		2 k. blue		90	40

Each issued in sheets of 100 stamps and 12 blank labels.

1935 (18 May). *16th Death Anniv of Gen. M. R. Štefánik.*
P 9½.

341	**57**	50 h. green		10	10

(Des J. Köhler)

1935 (22 June). *Prague Catholic Congress.* P 9½.

342	**58**	50 h. green		20	10
343		1 k. claret		30	10
344		2 k. blue		95	40

59 J. A. Komensky (Comenius)	**60** Dr. Edward Beneš	**60a** Gen. M. R. Štefánik	**61** Pres. Masaryk

1935–36. P 12½.

345	**59**	40 h. Prussian blue (1.7.36)		10	10
346	**60**	50 h. deep green (27.5.36)		10	10
347	**60a**	60 h. slate-lilac (27.5.36)		10	10
348	**61**	1 k. claret (20.10.35)		10	10
345/348	Set of 4			30	30

For other stamps in Type **60a**, see Nos. 390/1; and for stamp as
Type **61**, see No. 395.

62 Symbolic of Infancy	**63** K. H. Macha

(Eng after painting by J. Mánes)

1936 (1 Apr). *Child Welfare.* T **62** *and similar type.* P 12½.

349		50 h.+50 h. green		30	40
350		1 k.+50 h. claret		50	65
351		2 k.+50 h. blue		1·25	1·90

Design:—50 h., 2 k. Grandfather, mother and child, enlarged,
from centre of T **62**.
Each issued in sheets of 100 stamps and 12 blank labels.

1936 (30 Apr). *Death Centenary of Macha (poet).* P 12½.

352	**63**	50 h. green		10	10
353		1 k. claret		25	10

Each issued in sheets of 100 stamps and 12 blank labels.

64 Banska Bystrica	**65** Podebrady

(Des K. Vik)

1936 (1 Aug)–**37.** T **64/5** *and similar views.* P 12½.

354		1 k. 20, purple		10	10
355		1 k. 50, carmine		10	10
355a		1 k. 60, olive-green (4.12.37)		10	10
356		2 k. green		10	10
357		2 k. 50, blue		15	10
358		3 k. chocolate		20	10
359		3 k. 50, violet		70	40
360		4 k. violet		25	10
361		5 k. grey-green		30	10
362		10 k. blue		70	40
354/362	Set of 10			2·40	1·25

Designs: as T **64**—1 k. 20 Palanok Castle; 1 k. 60 St.
Barbara's Church, Kutna Hora; 2 k. Zvikov (Klingen Berg)
Castle; 2 k. 50 Strecno Castle; 3 k. Hruba Skala Castle (Cesky
Raj); 3 k. 50 Slavkov Castle. As T **64**, but 23½ × 29½ mm.—5 k.
Town Hall, Olomouc. As T **65**—10 k. Bratislava and Danube.
Nos. 360/2 were each issued in sheets of 100 stamps and 12
blank labels.

P **66**	**66** Pres. Beneš	N **67** Dove

(Des V. Cuban. Photo)

1937 (1 Mar). *PERSONAL DELIVERY.* P 12–13½.
For Prepayment. "V" in each corner

P363	P **66**	50 h. blue		20	45

For Payment on Delivery. "D" in each corner

P364	P **66**	50 h. carmine		20	45

No. P363 prepaid a special additional fee which ensured
personal delivery to the addressee. It was affixed to correspondence by the sender.
No. P364 represented a special fee payable by an addressee
who required all his mail to be delivered to him personally. It was
affixed to correspondence by the P.O. delivering such mail.
Each issued in sheets of 100 stamps and 12 blank labels.

1937 (26 Apr). P 12½.

363	**66**	50 h. green		10	10

(Des J. Benda. Typo)

1937 (30 April). *NEWSPAPER. Imperf.*

N364	N **67**	2 h. yellow-brown		10	10
N365		5 h. pale blue		10	10
N366		7 h. orange-vermilion		10	10
N367		9 h. emerald-green		10	10
N368		10 h. brown-lake		10	10
N369		12 h. bright ultramarine		10	10
N370		20 h. deep green		10	10
N371		50 h. red-brown		10	10
N372		1 k. grey-olive		10	10
N364/72	Set of 9			40	40

For No. N368 in miniature sheet, see No. **MS**377b.

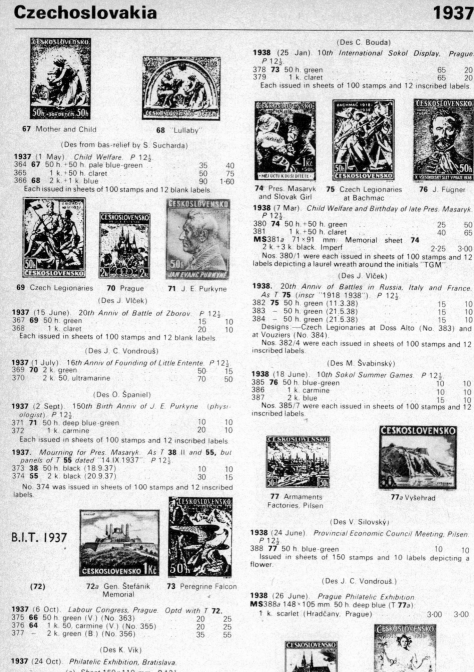

67 Mother and Child   **68** "Lullaby"

(Des from bas-relief by S. Sucharda)

1937 (1 May). *Child Welfare.* P 12½.
364	**67**	50 h. + 50 h. pale blue-green		35	40
365		1 k. + 50 h. claret		50	75
366	**68**	2 k. + 1 k. blue		90	1·60

Each issued in sheets of 100 stamps and 12 blank labels.

69 Czech Legionaries   **70** Prague   **71** J. E. Purkyne

(Des J. Vlček)

1937 (15 June). *20th Anniv of Battle of Zborov.* P 12½.
367	**69**	50 h. green		15	10
368		1 k. claret		20	10

Each issued in sheets of 100 stamps and 12 blank labels.

(Des J. C. Vondrouš)

1937 (1 July). *16th Anniv of Founding of Little Entente.* P 12½.
369	**70**	2 k. green		50	15
370		2 k. 50, ultramarine		70	50

(Des O. Španiel)

1937 (2 Sept). *150th Birth Anniv of J. E. Purkyne (physiologist).* P 12½.
371	**71**	50 h. deep blue-green		10	10
372		1 k. carmine		20	10

Each issued in sheets of 100 stamps and 12 inscribed labels.

1937. *Mourning for Pres. Masaryk.* As T **38** II and **55**, *but panels of T **55** dated "14.IX.1937".* P 12½.
373	**38**	50 h. black (18.9.37)		10	10
374	**55**	2 k. black (20.9.37)		30	15

No. 374 was issued in sheets of 100 stamps and 12 inscribed labels.

B.I.T. 1937

(72)   **72a** Gen. Štefánik Memorial   **73** Peregrine Falcon

1937 (6 Oct). *Labour Congress, Prague. Optd with T **72**.*
375	**66**	50 h. green (V.) (No. 363)		20	25
376	**64**	1 k. 50, carmine (V.) (No. 355)		20	25
377	–	2 k. green (B.) (No. 356)		35	55

(Des K. Vik)

1937 (24 Oct). *Philatelic Exhibition, Bratislava.*
   (a) *Sheet 150×110 mm.* P 12½
MS377a 50 h. deep ultramarine (Poprad Lake, Tatra Mts.), 1 k. crimson (T **72a**)   1·90   2·00
   (b) *Sheet 150×165 mm. containing 25 of No.* N368
MS377b N **67** 10 h. brown-lake   2·50   8·50
No. **MS**377b was printed at the Exhibition.
See also No. **MS**388a.

(Des C. Bouda)

1938 (25 Jan). *10th International Sokol Display, Prague.* P 12½.
378	**73**	50 h. green		65	20
379		1 k. claret		65	20

Each issued in sheets of 100 stamps and 12 inscribed labels.

74 Pres. Masaryk and Slovak Girl   **75** Czech Legionaries at Bachmac   **76** J. Fügner

1938 (7 Mar). *Child Welfare and Birthday of late Pres. Masaryk.* P 12½.
380	**74**	50 h. + 50 h. green		25	50
381		1 k. + 50 h. claret		40	65
MS381a	71×91 mm. Memorial sheet **74**				
	2 k. + 3 k. black. Imperf			2·25	3·00

Nos. 380/1 were each issued in sheets of 100 stamps and 12 labels depicting a laurel wreath around the initials "TGM".

(Des J. Vlček)

1938. *20th Anniv of Battles in Russia, Italy and France.* As T **75** (inscr "1918 1938"). P 12½.
382	**75**	50 h. green (11.3.38)		15	10
383	–	50 h. green (21.5.38)		15	10
384	–	50 h. green (21.5.38)		15	10

Designs:—Czech Legionaries at Doss Alto (No. 383) and at Vouziers (No. 384).
Nos. 382/4 were each issued in sheets of 100 stamps and 12 inscribed labels.

(Des M. Švabinský)

1938 (18 June). *10th Sokol Summer Games.* P 12½.
385	**76**	50 h. blue-green		10	10
386		1 k. carmine		10	10
387		2 k. blue		15	10

Nos. 385/7 were each issued in sheets of 100 stamps and 12 inscribed labels.

77 Armaments Factories, Pilsen   **77a** Vyšehrad

(Des V. Silovský)

1938 (24 June). *Provincial Economic Council Meeting, Pilsen.* P 12½.
388	**77**	50 h. blue-green		10	10

Issued in sheets of 150 stamps and 10 labels depicting a flower.

(Des J. C. Vondrouš.)

1938 (26 June). *Prague Philatelic Exhibition.*
MS388a 148×105 mm. 50 h. deep blue (T **77a**):
1 k. scarlet (Hradčany, Prague)   3·00   3·00

78 St. Elizabeth's Cathedral, Košice   **79** "Peace"

(Des K. Vik)

1938 (16 July). *Košice Cultural Exhibition.* P 12½.
389 **78** 50 h. blue-green   . . .   10   10
Issued in sheets of 150 stamps and 10 labels depicting bunches of grapes.

LOCAL ISSUES FOR SUDETENLAND. As Czech authorities evacuated this area and German authorities moved in, a number of local issues appeared but they were unofficial.

For Asch No. 289 was surcharged "50 h." and Nos. 287b, 288, 363 and 348 were surcharged "1.20". For Karlsbad a number of stamps were overprinted "Karlsbad 1 X 1938" and swastika. Numerous stamps were overprinted "Sudetenland" for Konstantinsbad, other stamps were surcharged in "Kc" for Niklasdorf and finally many stamps were overprinted with a swastika and "Wir sind frei" for Reichenberg-Maffersdorf and Rumburg. Similar overprints were made for Mährisch-Ostrau in Bohemia. The Sudeten districts were incorporated in Germany from 1 October 1938 till the German defeat in 1945.

1938 (21 Nov)–**39.** P 12½.
390 **60**a 50 h. green   . . .   10   10
391   60 h. blue (30.3.39)   . . .   9·00   14·00
No. 391 could only be used in Slovakia.

(Des M. Švabinský)

1938 (19 Dec). *20th Anniv of Czech Republic.* P 12½.
392 **79** 2 k. ultramarine   . . .   20   15
393   3 k. chocolate   . . .   40   15
MS393a 71×90 mm. 2 k. (+8 k.) blue (T **79**)
(15.12.38)   . . .   2·00   2·75
Nos. 392/3 were each issued in sheets of 100 stamps and 12 blank labels.

300 h
(79a)   80 Jasina

1939 (18 Jan). *Inauguration of Slovak Parliament.* No. 362 surch with T **79**a.
393b   300 h. on 10 k. blue (O.)   . . .   75   90
No. 393b was only issued in Slovakia. It was formerly listed under Slovakia but was withdrawn from use on 31 January, before the state of Slovakia was established. The used price is for the stamp cancelled to order. *Price postally used* £2·50.

On 14 March 1939. the Slovak Diet declared Slovakia to be an independent state and the Hungarians occupied Carpatho-Ukraine (Ruthenia). On 15 March the Germans invaded Bohemia and Moravia. making them a German protectorate the following day.

1939 (15 Mar). *Inauguration of Carpatho-Ukrainian Parliament.* P 12½.
393c **80** 3 k. ultramarine   . . .   10·00   30·00
Issued in sheets of 100 stamps and 12 blank labels.
No. 393c was only valid for use in Carpatho-Ukraine. It was placed on sale in Prague and Chust but was withdrawn the next day when these towns were occupied; it is known postally used from Chust. Used price is for cancelled-to-order.

1939 (23 Apr). *AIR. As T* **40** *but "CESKO-SLOVENSKO" hyphenated.*
394   30 h. violet   . . .   10   15

1939 (23 Apr). *As No. 348, but "CESKO-SLOVENSKO" hyphenated and "1 K" substituted for "1 Kc" in value tablets.*
395   1 k. claret   . . .   15   10

> See under Bohemia and Moravia for the stamps issued between 1939 and 1944 and under Slovakia for the stamps of the same period. Hungarian stamps were used in Ruthenia.

In 1943 a souvenir sheet comprising four values similar to Type **65** and another showing Beneš, Masaryk and Štefánik, all inscribed "1918–1943", was issued in connection with an Exhibition of Czechoslovak stamps in London. This had no franking value.

Military conquest by the Red Army was completed between October 1944 and 9 May 1945, the independent Slovak state ceasing to exist in April and the protectorate on 5 May. Sovereignty reverted to Czechoslovakia except for Ruthenia which was transferred to Russia on 29 June 1945. The Government in Exile returned to Prague on 10 May 1945.

After the cease-fire a number of German issues with Hitler's head and stamps of Bohemia and Moravia were handstamped with the names of places, arms and "1945" etc. but these were produced privately without authority.

In Ruthenia in December 1944 the Government in Exile's delegation at Chust overprinted Hungarian stamps "ČSP 1944". Meanwhile in November 1944 the People's Council of Carpatho-Ukraine had been set up at Uzhgorod and gradually took over all the area. It established a postal service from January 1945 and surcharged Hungarian stamps (including those already overprinted by the Chust administration) "Poshta Zakarpatska Ukraina" (in Cyrillic) with numeral. From May 1945 until the territory's incorporation into Russian Ukraine similarly inscribed stamps were issued.

81 Clasped Hands   82 Arms and Soldier

(Des J. Gajzer (T **81**), L. Gajdzica (T **82**). Litho Wiko, Košice)

1945. *Košice Issue.* T **81** roul 12½ (*percé en lignes*). T **82** imperf.
396 **81** 1 k. 50, maroon (9.5)   . . .   1·90   1·90
397 **82** 2 k. scarlet (26.3)   . . .   15   15
398   5 k. slate-green (26.3)   . . .   1·50   1·50
399   6 k. blue (26.3)   . . .   40   40
400 **81** 9 k. vermilion (2.4)   . . .   40   40
401   13 k. chestnut (2.4)   . . .   75   75
402   20 k. light blue (2.4)   . . .   1·75   1·75
396/402   Set of 7   . . .   6·25   6·25
MS402a 132×120 mm. Nos. 397/9 (25.6)   3·25   3·25

83 Arms and   84 Linden Leaf   85 Linden Leaf
Linden Leaf   and Buds   and Flower

(Des L. Csáder. Photo Tiskárna Andrej, later Grafia, Bratislava)

1945 (30 Apr–Dec). *Bratislava Issue. Imperf.*
403 **83** 50 h. grey-green   . . .   10   10
404   1 k. bright purple (16.7)   . . .   10   10
405   1 k. 50, carmine   . . .   10   10
406   2 k. blue   . . .   10   10
407   2 k. 40, brown-red (1.12)   . . .   35   20
408   3 k. red-brown   . . .   10   10
409   4 k. blue-green (16.7)   . . .   15   10
410   6 k. violet   . . .   15   10
411   10 k. sepia (16.7)   . . .   35   20
403/11   Set of 9   . . .   1·00   70
The Grafia printing was in sheets of 200, fine impression, thick white paper; Andrej printing in sheets of 100, coarse impression, thin hard paper. Only the 50 h. 1 k. 50, 2 k. 3 k. and 6 k. were printed by Andrej; all values were printed by Grafia.

(Des A. Schaumann. Eng J. Goldschmied (T **85**). Photo (**84**), recess (**85**))

1945. *Prague Issue.* P 14 (*T* **84**) *or* 12½ (*T* **85**).

412 **84**	10 (h.) black (8.10)	10	10
413	30 (h.) brown (8.6)	10	10
414	50 (h.) blue-green (26.5)	10	10
415	60 (h.) blue (23.5)	10	10
416 **85**	60 (h.) blue (19.6)	10	10
417	80 (h.) vermilion (8.10)	10	10
418	120 (h.) carmine (26.5)	10	10
419	300 (h.) brown-purple (11.6)	10	10
420	500 (h.) sage-green (11.6)	10	10
412/420	*Set of 9*	45	30

This issue was adapted from the 1939/40 issue of Bohemia and Moravia.

86 Pres. Masaryk

87 Staff Capt. Ridky

(Photo State Printing Works, Moscow)

1945 (5 July)–46. P 12½.

421 **86**	5 h. violet (5.3.46)	10	10
422	10 h. yellow (5.3.46)	10	10
423	20 h. brown (5.3.46)	10	10
424	50 h. emerald	10	10
425	1 k. red	10	10
426	2 k. ultramarine	10	10
421/426	*Set of 6*	40	30

Nos. 424/6 were not issued in Slovakia until 16 July 1945.

(Recess. De La Rue, London)

1945 (18 Aug). *War Heroes.* *T* **87** *and similar designs (portraits).* P 11½×12½.

427	5 h. blue-grey	10	10
428	10 h. brown	10	10
429	20 h. red	10	10
430	25 h. carmine	10	10
431	30 h. violet	20	10
432	40 h. sepia	10	10
433	50 h. grey-green	10	10
434	60 h. violet	20	15
435	1 k. carmine	10	10
436	1 k. 50, claret	10	10
437	2 k. ultramarine	10	10
438	2 k. 50, violet	10	10
439	3 k. purple-brown	10	10
440	4 k. mauve	10	10
441	5 k. blue-green	20	10
442	10 k. ultramarine	40	10
427/442	*Set of 16*	1·50	75

Portraits:—10 h., 1 k. 50, Dr. Novak; 20 h., 2 k. Capt. O Jaros; 25 h., 2 k. 50, Staff Capt. S. Zimprich; 30 h., 3 k. Lt. J. Kral. 40 h., 4 k. J. Gabcik (parachutist); 50 h., 5 k. Staff Capt. Vasatko; 60 h., 10 k. Fr. Adamek; 1 k. T **87**.

88 Allied Flags

89 Russian Soldier and Slovak Partisan

(Des Št. Bednár (443/4). L. Varga (445). V. Chmel (446/7). Photo Bratislava)

1945 (29 Aug). *First Anniv of Slovak Rising.* T **88/9** *and similar designs.* P 10.

443	1 k. 50, scarlet	10	10
444	2 k. blue	10	10
445	4 k. brown	20	20
446	4 k. 50, violet	20	20
447	5 k. blue-green	30	35
443/447	*Set of 5*	75	80
MS447a	148×210 mm. Nos. 443/7 Imperf	25·00	40·00

Designs: *Vert*—2 k. Banska Bystrica. *Horiz*—4 k. 50, Sklabina; 5 k. Strecno and partisan.

90 Pres. Masaryk

91 Pres. Beneš

O **92**

(Des Jindra Schmidt)

1945–47. *T* **90/1** *and similar portrait of Gen. M. R. Štefánik.*

(*a*) *Photo.* P 14

448 **90**	50 h. sepia (10.12.45)	10	10
449 —	80 h. deep green (10.12.45)	10	10
450 **91**	60 h. yellow-green (10.12.45)	10	10
451 **90**	15 k. purple (20.12.45)	50	10

(*b*) *Recess.* P 12½

452 —	30 h. reddish purple (28.10.45)	10	10
453 **91**	60 h. blue (28.10.45)	15	10
454 —	1 k. red-orange (5.4.47)	10	10
455 **90**	1 k. 20, carmine-red (28.10.45)	15	10
456	1 k. 20, mauve (25.2.46)	10	10
457 —	2 k. 40, scarlet (14.12.45)	10	10
458 **91**	3 k. reddish purple (15.11.45)	20	10
459 **90**	4 k. deep blue (5.3.46)	15	10
460	5 k. deep blue-green (15.11.45)	20	10
461 **91**	7 k. grey-black (10.12.45)	25	10
462	— 10 k. grey-blue (15.11.45)	55	10
462a	— 20 k. purple-brown (5.2.46)	85	10
448/462a	*Set of 16*	3·25	60

(Des A. Erhardt. Litho)

1945 (1 Nov–Dec). *OFFICIAL: Size* 16½×21½ *mm.* P 10.

O463 O **92**	50 h. dull green	10	10
O464	1 k. indigo	10	10
O465	1 k. 20, reddish purple (1.12)	15	15
O466	1 k. 50, vermilion	10	10
O467	2 k. 50, ultramarine	15	15
O468	5 k. brown-purple	25	25
O469	8 k. carmine (1.12)	40	40
O463/469	*Set of 7*	1·00	1·00

See also Nos. O490/7.

92

93 J. S. Kozina Monument

(Des J. Sejpka. Eng J. Goldschmied. Recess)

1945 (14 Nov). *Student's World Congress, Prague.* P 12½.

463 **92**	1 k. 50+1 k. 50, carmine	10	10
464	2 k. 50+2 k. 50, blue	20	20

(Des J. Sejpka. Eng J. Goldschmied. Recess)

1945 (28 Nov). *Execution of Jan Stadky Kozina, 1695.* P 12½.

465 **93**	2 k. 40, carmine	15	10
466	4 k. blue	20	20

N **94** Messenger D **94**

(Des A. Erhardt. Typo)

95 Capt. F. Novak **96** Lockhead
and Westland Constellation over
Lysander Bratislava

1945 (20 Dec)–**47**. *NEWSPAPER. Imperf.*

N467	N **94**	5 h. light blue	10	10
N468		10 h. rose-red	10	10
N469		15 h. emerald-green	10	10
N470		20 h. deep green	10	10
N471		25 h. bright purple (5.4.47)	15	15
N472		30 h. yellow-brown	10	10
N473		40 h. vermilion	10	10
N474		50 h. red-brown	10	10
N475		1 k. grey	10	10
N476		5 k. ultramarine	15	15
N467/476		*Set of 10*	45	45

(Des and eng J. Schmidt (T **95**); des A. Erhardt, eng J. Goldschmied (T **96**). Recess)

1946 (4 July)–**47**. *AIR. P 12½.*

469	**95**	1 k. 50, scarlet	15	10
470		5 k. 50, indigo	45	15
471		9 k. brown-purple (5.4.47)	75	15
472	**96**	10 k. blue-green	65	35
473	**95**	16 k. violet (17.6.46)	75	45
474	**96**	20 k. light blue	1·00	75
475	**94**a	24 k. claret	1·25	75
476		50 k. blue	2·10	1·40
469/476		*Set of 8*	6·50	3·75

Nos. 472 and 474/6 were each issued in sheets of 100 stamps and 12 labels as for No. 468b.

(Des A. Erhardt. Photo Bratislava)

1946 (1 May)–**48**. *POSTAGE DUE. P 14.*

D467	D **94**	10 h. blue	10	10
D468		20 h. blue	10	10
D469		50 h. blue	15	10
D470		1 k. carmine	30	10
D471		1 k. 20, carmine	35	10
D472		1 k. 50, carmine (30.9.48)	40	10
D473		1 k. 60, carmine	45	10
D474		2 k. carmine (30.9.48)	55	10
D475		2 k. 40, carmine	60	10
D476		3 k. carmine	75	10
D477		5 k. carmine	1·40	10
D478		6 k. carmine (30.9.48)	1·75	10
D467/478		*Set of 12*	6·25	50

97 K. H. Borovsky **98** Brno **99** Hodonin

(Eng J. Schmidt from a daguerrotype. Recess)

1946 (5 July). *90th Death Anniv of Borovsky (independence advocate). P 12½.*

477 **97** 1 k. 20, greenish grey ... 15 15

Issued in sheets of 100 stamps and 12 inscribed labels.

(Des J. C. Vondrouš. Eng J. Schmidt. Recess)

1946 (3 Aug). *P 12½.*

478	**98**	2 k. 40, carmine	35	15
479	**99**	7 k. 40, dull violet	20	10
MS479a		69×89 mm. No. 478. Imperf (sold at 10 k.)	55	45

94 St. George **94**a Lockheed
and Dragon Constellation over
 Charles Bridge, Prague

(Eng J. Schmidt, after painting by J. Mánes. Recess)

1946 (5 May). *Victory. P 12½.*

467 **94** 2 k. 40+2 k. 60, carmine ... 10 15
468 4 k.+6 k. grey-blue ... 15 15
MS468a 70×91 mm. T **94** 4 k.+6 k. deep greyblue. Imperf ... 75 75

Nos. 467/8 were each issued in sheets of 100 stamps and 12 inscribed labels.

(Des A. Erhardt. Eng J. Goldschmied. Recess)

1946 (12 June). *AIR. First Prague–New York Flight. P 12½.*

468b **94**a 24 k. grey-blue/buff ... 75 75

Issued in sheets of 100 stamps and 12 labels depicting a plane and the globe.

See also Nos. 475/6.

100 Emigrants **101** Pres. Beneš

(Des A. Kajlich. Photo)

1946 (15 Oct). *Repatriation Fund. T **100** and similar designs. P 14.*

480		1 k. 60+1 k. 40, brown	50	50
481		2 k. 40+2 k. 60, scarlet	25	25
482		4 k.+4 k. blue	40	40

Designs:—1 k. 60, Emigrants' departure; 4 k. Emigrants return.

(Des M. Švabinský. Eng J. Schmidt. Recess)

1946 (28 Oct). *Independence Day. P 12½.*

483	**101**	60 h. indigo	10	10
484		1 k. 60, deep bluish green	10	10
485		3 k. brown-purple	10	10
486		8 k. slate-purple	20	10
483/486		*Set of 4*	45	20

P **95**

(Des V. Cuban. Photo)

1946 (1 July). *PERSONAL DELIVERY. P 13½.*

P469 P **95** 2 k. blue ... 20 20

102 Flag and Symbols of Transport, Industry, Agriculture and Learning

O 103

103 St. Adalbert

(Des L. Horák. Eng J. Schmidt. Recess)

1947 (1 Jan). *"Two Year Plan". P* 12½.
487	**102**	1 k. 20, grey-green	10	10
488		2 k. 40, carmine	10	10
489		4 k. blue	50	20

Each issued in sheets of 100 stamps and 12 labels depicting a posthorn.

1947 (1 April). *OFFICIAL. Photo. Size* 18 × 21½ *mm. P* 14.
O490	**O 103**	60 h. scarlet	10	10
O491		80 h. deep olive	10	10
O492		1 k. indigo	10	10
O493		1 k. 20, maroon	10	10
O494		2 k. 40, carmine	10	10
O495		4 k. ultramarine	15	15
O496		5 k. brown-purple	15	15
O497		7 k. 40, violet	25	25
O490/497		*Set of 8*	80	80

(Des K. Dvořák. Eng J. Schmidt. Recess)

1947 (23 Apr). *950th Anniv of Death of St. Adalbert (Bishop of Prague). P* 12½.
490	**103**	1 k. 60, black	45	35
491		2 k. 40, carmine	65	50
492		5 k. greyish green	75	40

Each issued in sheets of 100 stamps and 12 labels bearing a monogram.

104 "Grief"

105 Rekindling Flame of Remembrance

(Des K. Svolinský (T **104**), J. Kaplický (T **105**). Eng J. Schmidt. Recess)

1947 (10 June). *Fifth Anniv of Destruction of Lidice. P* 12½.
493	**104**	1 k. 20, black	30	25
494		1 k. 60, blue-black	40	40
495	**105**	2 k. 40, mauve	50	45

Each issued in sheets of 100 stamps and 12 labels bearing a commemorative inscription.

106 Congress Emblem

107 Pres. Masaryk

(Des J. Liesler. Eng J. Schmidt. Recess)

1947 (20 July). *Youth Festival. P* 12½.
496	**106**	1 k. 20, purple	40	25
497		4 k. blue-grey	40	15

(Des K. Svolinský. Eng J. Schmidt. Recess)

1947 (14 Sept). *10th Death Anniv of Pres. Masaryk. P* 12½.
498	**107**	1 k. 20, black/*buff*	15	15
499		4 k. grey-blue/*cream*	25	25

Each issued in sheets of 100 stamps and 12 inscribed labels.

108 Stefan Moyses

109 "Freedom"

(Des K. Svolinský. Eng J. Schmidt. Recess)

1947 (19 Oct). *150th Birth Anniv of Stefan Moyses (Slavonic Society organizer). P* 12½.
500	**108**	1 k. 20, purple	15	15
501		4 k. blue	25	25

Each issued in sheets of 100 stamps and 12 labels bearing a floral decoration.

(Des J. Benda. Photo)

1947 (26 Oct). *30th Anniv of Russian Revolution. P* 14.
502	**109**	2 k. 40, carmine	25	20
503		4 k. ultramarine	40	20

110 Pres. Beneš

111 "Athletes Paying Homage to Republic"

(Des K. Svolinský. Photo)

1948 (15 Feb). *P* 14. *(a)* 17¼ × 21½ *mm.*
504	**110**	1 k. 50, brown	10	10

(b) Larger design 19 × 23 *mm.*
505	**110**	2 k. purple	10	10
506		5 k. ultramarine	15	10

(Des M. Švabinský. Eng J. Schmidt. Recess)

1948 (7 Mar). *11th Sokol Congress, Prague. First Issue. P* 12½.
507	**111**	1 k. 50, purple-brown	10	10
508		3 k. carmine	15	10
509		5 k. blue	40	10

Each issued in sheets of 100 stamps and 12 labels depicting a bouquet.
See also Nos. 515/18.

112 Charles IV

113 St. Wenceslas and Charles IV

(Des K. Svolinský. Eng J. A. Švengsbír. Recess)

1948 (7 Apr). *600th Anniv of Charles IV University, Prague. P* 12½.
510	**112**	1 k. 50, sepia/*buff*	10	10
511	**113**	2 k. brown/*buff*	15	10
512		3 k. lake/*buff*	15	10
513	**112**	5 k. deep blue/*buff*	20	15
510/513		*Set of 4*	50	35

Each issued in sheets of 100 stamps and 12 inscribed labels.

114 Insurgents   **115** Dr. J. Vanicek   **117** Fr. Palacky and Dr. F. L. Rieger

(Des J. Alexy. Photo)

1948 (14 May). *Centenary of Abolition of Serfdom.* P 14.
514 **114** 1 k. 50, olive-black .. 10 10

(Des M. Švabinský. Eng J. Schmidt. Recess)

1948 (10 June). *11th Sokol Congress, Prague. Second Issue. T 115 and similar vert design.* P 12½
515 **115** 1 k. deep bluish green 10 10
516 – 1 k. 50, agate 15 10
517 – 2 k. slate-blue 15 10
518 **115** 3 k. claret 25 10
515/518 *Set of 4* 55 30
Portrait:—1 k. 50, 2 k. Dr. J. Scheiner.
Each issued in sheets of 100 stamps and 12 labels depicting a sunflower.

(Des M. Švabinský. Eng J. Schmidt. Recess)

1948 (20 June). *Centenary of Constituent Assembly at Kromeriz.* P 12½
519 **117** 1 k. 50, slate-violet/*buff* .. 10 10
520 3 k. claret/*buff* .. 15 10
Each issued in sheets of 100 stamps and 12 labels depicting a wreath.

118 J. M. Hurban   **119** Pres. Beneš   **120** "Independence"

(Des K. Svolinský. Eng J. A. Švengsbir, L. Jirka and J. Mráček. Recess)

1948 (27 Aug). *Centenary of Slovak Insurrection. T 118 and portraits of insurrectionists.* P 12½
521 1 k. 50, brown/*buff* 10 10
522 3 k. carmine/*buff* (L. Stur) .. 10 10
523 5 k. blue *cream* (M. Hodza) .. 25 15
On the 1 k. 50 Hurban's initials have been transposed.
Nos. 521/3 were each issued in sheets of 100 stamps and 12 labels bearing a signature.

(Des after K. Svolinský. Eng J. A. Švengsbír. Recess)

1948 (28 Sept). *Death of Pres. Beneš.* P 12½
524 **119** 8 k. black .. 15 10

(Des V. Sivko. Eng J. A. Švengsbir. Recess)

1948 (28 Oct). *30th Anniv of Independence.* P 12½
525 **120** 1 k. 50, blue .. 10 10
526 3 k. carmine .. 15 15
Each issued in sheets of 100 stamps and 12 labels depicting leaves.

121 Pres. Gottwald   **122** Czech and Russian Workers

(Des K. Hájek. Eng J. Schmidt. Recess)

1948 (28 Oct)–**53.** *Size 19×24 mm.* P 12½
526a **121** 1 k. blackish green (2.6.52) .. 10 10
527 1 k. 50, purple-brown .. 10 10
528 3 k. carmine .. 25 10
    a. Claret (25.2.49) .. 70 10
    b. Brown-lake. Perf 11½ (15.4.53) 15 10
529 5 k. blue .. 20 10
See also Nos. 530/**MS**530*a*, 538 and 772/5.

1948 (23 Nov). *Pres. Gottwald's 52nd Birthday. Size 23×30 mm.* P 12½
530 **121** 20 k. deep violet .. 60 10
MS530*a* 66×99 mm. 30 k. carmine-red (T **121**)
    Imperf .. 3·50 3·00
No. 530 was issued in sheets of 100 stamps and 12 labels bearing a monogram.

(Des B. Němec. Eng J. Schmidt. Recess)

1948 (11 Dec). *5th Anniv of Alliance with Russia.* P 12½
531 **122** 3 k. carmine .. 15 10
Issued in sheets of 100 stamps and 12 labels depicting flags.

1948 (18 Dec). *30th Anniv of First Czechoslovak Stamps. Recess. Imperf.*
MS531*a* 70×90 mm. 10 k. deep violet-blue (T **2**) 1·75 1·50

123 Girl and Birds   **124** V. I. Lenin

(Des K. Svolinský. Eng L. Jirka (1 k. 50), J. Mráček (2 k.), J. A. Švengsbír (3 k.). Recess)

1948 (18 Dec). *Child Welfare. T* **123** *and similar types.* P 12½
532 1 k. 50+1 k. purple .. 30 10
533 2 k.+1 k. blue .. 15 10
534 3 k.+1 k. carmine .. 25 10
Designs:—1 k. 50, Boy and birds; 2 k., Mother and child.
Each issued in sheets of 100 stamps and 12 labels bearing various motifs.

(Des and eng J. Schmidt. Recess)

1949 (21 Jan). *25th Anniv of Death of Lenin.* P 12½
535 **124** 1 k. 50, dull purple .. 25 15
536 5 k. deep blue .. 25 20
Each issued in sheets of 100 stamps and 12 labels depicting a flaming torch.

125 Pres. Gottwald   **126** P. O. Hviezdoslav
Addressing Rally

(T **125** des B. Němec. Photo (**125**), recess (**121**))

1949 (25 Feb). *First Anniv of Gottwald Government.*

    (*a*) T **125.** P 14
537 **125** 3 k. lake-brown .. 10 10

(*b*) As T **121** (23×30 mm.) but inscr "ÚNOR 1948". P 12½
538 **121** 10 k. green .. 40 15
No. 538 was issued in sheets of 100 stamps and 12 inscribed labels.

(Des and eng L. Jirka (4 k.); des M. Svabinský, eng J. Schmidt (8 k.); recess. Des A. Strnadel (2 k.), K. Svolinský (others); photo *Pravda* Ptg Office, Bratislava)

1949. *As T* **126** *(poets).* P 14 *or* 12½ *(4 k., 8 k.).*

539	50 h. plum (20.3)		10	10
540	80 h. scarlet (V. Vančura) (20.3)		10	10
541	1 k. blackish green (J. Šverma) (20.3)		10	10
542	2 k. bright blue (J. Fučík) (30.9)		30	10
543	4 k. violet (J. Wolker) (4.5)		30	10
544	8 k. violet-black (A. Jirásek) (4.5)		45	10
539/544	*Set of 6*		1·10	15

127 Mail Coach and Steam Train

(Des K. Lhoták. Eng J. Mráček (3 k.), J. Schmidt (5 k.) and L. Jirka (13 k.). Recess)

1949 (20 May). *75th Anniv of Universal Postal Union. T* **127** *and similar horiz designs.* P 12½.

545	3 k. lake/*cream*		2·40	1·75
546	5 k. dull blue/*cream*		65	25
547	13 k. grey-green/*cream*		2·00	55

Designs:—5 k. Mounted postman and mail van; 13 k. Sailing ship and Douglas DC-2 airliner.

128 Girl Agricultural Worker

129 Workers and Flag

130 Industrial Worker

131 F. Smetana and National Theatre, Prague

(Des V. Polášek (1 k. 50), V. Kovarík (3 k.) and J. Kotík (5 k.). Eng J. A. Švengsbír (1 k. 50, 3 k.), J. Mráček (5 k.). Recess)

1949 (24 May). *Ninth Meeting of Czechoslovak Communist Party.* P 12½.

548	**128**	1 k. 50, green	45	45
549	**129**	3 k. claret	25	25
550	**130**	5 k. blue	45	45

Each issued in sheets of 100 stamps and 12 inscribed labels.

(Des and eng B. Heinz. Recess)

1949 (4 June). *125th Birth Anniv of Smetana (composer).* P 12½.

551	**131**	1 k. 50, bluish green/*cream*	15	10
552		5 k. greenish blue/*cream*	60	20

ALBUM LISTS

Write for our latest lists of albums and accessories.

These will be sent free on request.

132 A. S. Pushkin

133 F. Chopin and Warsaw Conservatoire

(Des K. Svolinský. Eng J. Mráček. Recess)

1949 (6 June). *150th Birth Anniv of A. S. Pushkin (poet).* P 12½.

553	**132**	2 k. grey-green/*cream*	20	20

(Des and eng J. Schmidt. Recess)

1949 (24 June). *Death Centenary of Chopin (composer).* P 12½.

554	**133**	3 k. claret/*cream*	50	20
555		8 k. slate-purple/*cream*	50	40

134 Globe and Ribbon

135 Zvolen Castle

(136)

(Des F. Tichý. Eng J. Schmidt. Recess)

1949 (20 Aug). *50th Sample Fair, Prague.* P 12½.

556	**134**	1 k. 50, brown-purple	25	25
557		5 k. ultramarine	75	75

(Des and eng J. A. Švengsbír. Recess)

1949 (28 Aug). P 12½.

558	**135**	10 k. lake	60	15

1949 (1 Sept). *AIR. Nos.* 469/76 *surch as T* **136.**

559	**95**	1 k. on 1 k. 50, scarlet (B.)	15	10
560		3 k. on 5 k. 50, indigo (R.)	25	10
561		6 k. on 9 k. brown-purple (Br.)	45	10
562		7 k. 50 on 16 k. violet (R.)	55	20
563	**96**	8 k. on 10 k. blue-green (G.)	55	50
564		12 k. 50 on 20 k. light blue (B.)	75	40
565	**94a**	15 k. on 24 k. claret (B.)	2·25	70
566		30 k. on 50 k. blue (B.)	1·50	70
559/566	*Set of 8*		6·00	2·50

137 Mediaeval Miners

138 Modern Miner

(Des A. Strnadel (1 k. 50), J. Hudeček (3 k.), J. A. Švengsbír (5 k.). Eng B. Housa (1 k. 50), J. Mráček (3 k.), J. A. Švengsbír (5 k.). Recess)

1949 (11 Sept). *700th Anniv of Czechoslovak Mining Industry and 150th Anniv of Miners' Laws. T* **137/8** *and similar horiz type inscr* "DEN HORNIKU II. IX. 1949". P 12½.

567		1 k. 50, blackish violet	65	40
568		3 k. carmine	5·25	1·75
569		5 k. blue	4·00	1·60

Design:—5 k. Miner with cutting-machine.

> **BLOCKED VALUES.** From October 1949 one value of some commemorative issues could only be obtained on purchase of the complete set. These values were produced in small quantities and are priced accordingly.

139 Carpenters   **140** Dove and Buildings

(Des J. Kotik. Eng L. Jirka (1 k.) and J. Mráček (2 k.). Recess)

1949 (11 Dec). *Second Trades' Union Congress, Prague.*
T **139** *and similar type inscribed* "II. VSEODBOROVY SJEZD
1949". *P* 12½.

570	1 k. blue-green		2·25	1·00
571	2 k. slate-purple (Mechanic)		1·50	50

(Des T. Nováková. Eng B. Housa. Recess)

1949 (18 Dec). *Red Cross Fund. T* **140** *and similar vert type
inscr* "CS. CERVENY KRIZ". *P* 12½.

572	1 k. 50+50 h. claret		3·00	1·75
573	3 k.+1 k. scarlet (Dove and globe)		3·00	1·75

141 Mother and Child   **142** Joseph Stalin

(Des R. Šváb. Eng J. Schmidt (1 k. 50), B. Housa (3 k.).
Recess)

1949 (18 Dec). *Child Welfare Fund. T* **141** *and similar type
inscr* "DETEM 1949". *P* 12½.

574	1 k. 50+50 h. grey-green		3·00	1·50
575	3 k.+1 k. claret (Father and child)		4·50	1·75

(Des and eng J. Mráček (1 k. 50), J. Schmidt (3 k.). Recess)

1949 (21 Dec). *70th Birth Anniv of Joseph Stalin. T* **142** *and
similar type inscr* "J. V. STALIN 21.XII.1879 1949". *P* 12½.

576	1 k. 50, grey-green/*buff*		80	50
577	3 k. claret/*buff* (Stalin facing left)		3·25	1·50

143 Skier   **144** Efficiency Badge   **145** V. Mayakovsky

(Des K. Hochman (1 k. 50, 5 k.), J. Benda (3 k.). Eng J. Schmidt.
Photo (3 k.); recess (others))

1950 (15 Feb). *Tatra Cup Ski Championship. P* 13½ (3 k.),
12½ (*others*).

578	**143** 1 k. 50, grey-blue		2·00	80
579	**144** 3 k. claret and buff		2·00	1·25
580	**143** 5 k. ultramarine		2·75	1·50

(Des K. Svolinský. Eng J. Mráček. Recess)

1950 (14 Apr). *20th Death Anniv of V. Mayakovsky (poet).*
P 12½.

581	**145** 1 k. 50, purple-brown		1·60	70
582	3 k. brown-red		1·60	70

146 Soviet Tank Driver   **147** Workers and Factory
and Hradčany, Prague

(Des K. Oberthor (1 k. 50), V. Němeček (2 k.), B. Doleželová
(3 k.), V. Sukdolák (5 k.). Eng J. Schmidt (1 k. 50), L. Jirka
(2 k.), B. Housa (3 k.) and J. Švengsbír (5 k.). Recess)

1950 (5 May). *5th Anniv of Republic (first issue). T* **146** *and
similar types. P* 12½.

583	1 k. 50, blue-green		25	20
584	2 k. purple-brown		80	50
585	3 k. red		20	10
586	5 k. blue		45	15
583/586	*Set of 4*		1·50	85

Designs:—2 k. "Hero of Labour" Medal; 3 k. Workers and
Town Hall; 5 k. "The Košice Programme" (part of text).

(Des J. Adamcová (1 k. 50), B. Dolezelová (2 k., 3 k.),
O. Androsvá (5 k.). Photo)

1950 (9 May). *5th Anniv of Republic (second issue). T* **147**
and similar types. P 14.

587	1 k. 50, blue-green		1·50	90
588	2 k. brown		1·50	75
589	3 k. carmine		90	40
590	5 k. blue		90	40
587/590	*Set of 4*		4·25	2·25

Designs:—2 k. Crane and Tatra mountains; 3 k. Labourer and
tractor; 5 k. Three workers.

148 S. K. Neumann   **149** Bozena Němcová

(Des and eng J. A. Švengsbír. Recess)

1950 (5 June). *75th Birth Anniv of S. K. Neumann (writer).*
P 12½.

591	**148** 1 k. 50, blue		25	10
592	3 k. purple		90	75

(Des K. Svolinský. Eng J. Mráček. Recess)

1950 (21 June). *130th Birth Anniv of Bozena Němcová
(authoress). P* 12½.

593	**149** 1 k. 50, blue		1·00	75
594	7 k. brown-purple		25	20

150 "Liberation of   **151** Miner, Soldier and
Colonial Nations"   Farmer

(Des and eng 1 k. 50 B. Doleželová and J. Mráček; 2 k. O. Andrsová and L. Jirka; 3 k. J. Adamcová and B. Housa; 5 k. J. Mikula and J. Schmidt. Recess)

1950 (14 Aug). *Second International Students' World Congress, Prague. As T* **150** (*inscr* "II. KONGRES MSS"). *P* 12½.

595	1 k. 50, blue-green		15	10
596	2 k. slate-purple		1·25	50
597	3 k. carmine		20	15
598	5 k. blue		40	35
595/598	*Set of 4*		1·75	1·00

Designs: *Horiz*—2 k. Woman, Globe and Dove ("Fight for Peace"); 3 k. Group of students ("Democratisation of Education"); 5 k. Students and Banner ("International Students' Solidarity").

(Des and eng 1 k. 50 V. Sivko and J. A. Švengsbir; 3 k. F. Hudeček and L. Jirka. Recess)

1950 (6 Oct). *Army Day. T* **151** *and similar type inscr* "6.X.1950 DEN ČS. ARMÁDY". *P* 12½.

599	1 k. 50, slate-blue		75	70
600	3 k. carmine		25	20

Design:—3 k. Czechoslovak and Russian soldiers.

152 Z. Fibich

153 "Communications"

(Des K. Svolinský. Eng J. Mráček. Recess)

1950 (15 Oct). *Birth Centenary of Zdenek Fibich* (*composer*). *P* 12½.

601	**152**	3 k. claret	90	50
602		8 k. yellow-green	25	15

(Des P. Dillinger. Eng J. A. Švengsbir. Recess)

1950 (25 Oct). *First Anniv of League of Postal, Telephone and Telegraph Employees. P* 12½.

603	**153**	1 k. 50, purple-brown	20	10
604		3 k. claret	75	30

154 J. G. Tajovský

155 Reconstruction of Prague

(Des K. Svolinský. Eng J. Schmidt. Recess)

1950 (26 Oct). *Tenth Death Anniv of J. Gregor Tajovský* (*writer*). *P* 12½.

605	**154**	1 k. 50, brown	75	40
606		5 k. ultramarine	75	55

(Des and eng J. A. Švengsbir. Recess)

1950 (28 Oct). *Philatelic Exhibition, Prague. P* 12½.

607	**155**	1 k. 50, slate-blue	35	15
608		3 k. claret	60	45
MS608*a*	120×101 mm. No. 607 in imperf block of four		35·00	22·00

A set comprising 1 k. 50, 2, 3 and 5 k. values showing historical views of Prague was printed arranged in blocks of four. They were sold at 20 k. including entrance to the Exhibition but only to subscribers to the inland new issue service of the Philatelic Bureau and to members of Czechoslovak Philatelic Societies, one per applicant. *Price £22 un., £12 us.*

156 Czech and Russian Workers

157 Dove (after Picasso)

(Des F. Hudeček. Eng J. Mráček. Recess)

1950 (4 Nov). *Czechoslovak-Soviet Friendship. P* 12½.

609	**156**	1 k. 50, purple-brown	35	25
610		5 k. violet-blue	65	45

(Des J. A. Švengsbir. Photo)

1951 (20 Jan). *Czechoslovak Peace Congress. P* 14.

611	**157**	2 k. blue	4·75	2·75
612		3 k. claret	3·00	1·50

158 Julius Fučík

159 Mechanical Hammer

160 Industrial Workers

(Des M. Švabinský. Eng J. Mráček. Recess)

1951 (17 Feb). *Peace Propaganda. P* 12½ (1 k. 50). *P* 14 (5 k.).

613	**158**	1 k. 50, grey	50	30
614		5 k. grey-blue	1·75	1·00

(Des and eng J. A. Švengsbir. Recess)

1951 (24 Feb). *Five Year Plan* (*heavy industry*). *T* **159** *and horiz type inscr* "TAŽKY PRIEMYSEL ZÁKLAD PATROČNICE". *P* 12½.

615	**159**	1 k. 50, black	10	10
616	—	3 k. brown-purple (Installing machinery)	15	10
617	**159**	4 k. deep blue	65	45

(Des V. Šprungl (1 k. 50, 5 k.), Z. Kadrnožková (3 k.). Photo)

1951 (8 Mar). *International Women's Day. T* **160** *and similar types inscr* "8. III. 1951 MEZINARODNI DEN ZEN". *P* 14.

618	1 k. 50, brown-olive		25	10
619	3 k. claret		1·40	55
620	5 k. blue		50	10

Designs:—3 k. Woman driving tractor; 5 k. Korean woman and group.

161 Karlovy Vary

162 Miners

(Des Z. Pokorný. Eng J. Schmidt. Recess)

1951 (2 Apr). *AIR. T* **161** *and similar vert designs showing Ilyushin Il-12 over spas. P* 14.

621	6 k. green			2·50	75
622	10 k. purple (Pieštany)			2·25	95
623	15 k. blue (Mariánské Lázne)			5·00	1·50
624	20 k. purple-brown (Silač)			6·75	1·60
621/624	*Set of* 4			15·00	4·25

(Des V. Šprungl. Eng J. Schmidt. Recess)

1951 (12 Apr). *Mining Industry. P* 12½.

625	**162**	1 k. 50, black		75	20
626		3 k. reddish purple		10	10

163 Ploughing   **164** Tatra Mountains

(Des J. Kaiser (1 k. 50), Z. Kadrnožková (2 k.). Photo)

1951 (28 Apr). *Agriculture. T* **163** *and similar horiz design inscr* "SPOLOČNÝ CHOV DOBYTKA". *P* 14.

627	1 k. 50, yellow-brown		50	50
628	2 k. green (Woman and cows)		1·75	60

(1 k. 50, 2 k. des J. Blažek, eng B. Roule. 3 k. des H. Hrubešová, eng J. Goldschmied. Recess)

1951 (5 May). *Recreation Centres. T* **164** *and similar designs inscr* "ROH". *P* 12½.

629	1 k. 50, green		20	10
630	2 k. brown (Beskydy Mts)		1·00	50
631	3 k. carmine (Krkonoše Mts)		25	10

165 Partisan and Soviet Soldier   **166** Gottwald and Stalin

(Des J. Čumpelík (2 k., 3 k.), J. Horník (8 k.). Eng L. Jirka (2 k.), B. Roule (3 k.), J. Mráček (8 k.). Recess)

1951 (17 May). *Thirtieth Anniv of Czechoslovak Communist Party* (*first issue*). *T* **165** *and designs inscr* "30 LET", *etc. P* 12½.

632	2 k. lake-brown		25	10
633	3 k. lake		30	10
634	8 k. black		75	30

Designs: *Horiz*—8 k. Marx, Engels, Lenin and Stalin. *Vert*—2 k. Factory Militia-man.

(Des and eng J. Schmidt. Recess)

1951 (30 May). *Thirtieth Anniv of Czechoslovak Communist Party* (*second issue*). *P* 12½.

635	**166**	1 k. 50, greenish grey		75	25
636		5 k. blue		2·00	1·00

167 Dvořák   **168** Gymnast   **169** B. Šmeral

(Des K. Svolínský. Eng J. Schmidt (1 k., 2 k.), J. Mráček (1 k. 50, 3 k.). Recess)

1951 (30 May). *Prague Music Festival. T* **167** *and similar portrait. P* 12½.

637	**167**	1 k. red-brown			25	10
638	–	1 k. 50, olive-grey			1·00	50
639	**167**	2 k. reddish brown			1·00	65
640	–	3 k. brown-purple			25	15
637/640		*Set of* 4			2·25	1·25

Portrait:—1 k. 50, 3 k. F. Smetana.

(Des and eng J. Švengsbir. Recess)

1951 (21 June). *Ninth Sokol Congress. Sporting designs as T* **168**. *P* 12½.

641	1 k. green/cream		60	20
642	1 k. 50, brn/cream (Woman discus thrower)		55	25
643	3 k. carmine/cream (Footballers)		1·25	25
644	5 k. blue/cream (Skier)		2·50	1·00
641/644	*Set of* 4		4·50	1·50

(Des V. Sprungl. Eng L. Jirka. Recess)

1951 (21 June). *Tenth Death Anniv of B. Šmeral* (*Communist leader*). *P* 12½.

645	**169**	1 k. 50, greenish grey		45	30
646		3 k. reddish purple		45	15

170 Scene from *Fall of Berlin*   **171** J. Hybeš

(Des K. Perman, eng J. Mráček (80 h., 4 k.). Des J. Figer, eng J. Schmidt (1 k. 50). Recess)

1951 (14 July). *International Film Festival, Karlovy Vary. T* **170** *and similar type inscr* "SE SOVETSKYM FILMEM" *etc. P* 12½.

647	**170**	80 h. claret		35	20
648	–	1 k. 50, greenish black		35	20
649	**170**	4 k. grey-blue		1·25	90

Design: *Horiz*—1 k. 50, Scene from *The Great Citizen*.

(Des J. Hlina. Eng L. Jirka. Recess)

1951 (21 July). *Thirtieth Death Anniv of Hybeš* (*politician*). *P* 12½.

650	**171**	1 k. 50, purple-brown		10	10
651		2 k. brownish carmine		90	40

172 A. Jirásek **173** "Fables and Fates" (M. Aleš)

178 Stalin and Gottwald **179** P. Jilemnický

(Des K. Svolinský. Eng J. Schmidt. Recess (1 k. 50, 5 k.), photo (others)

(Des and eng J. Schmidt (T **178**). Recess. Des A. Kibrik and J. A. Švengsbir (3 k.). Photo)

1951 (19 Aug). *Birth Centenary of A. Jirasek (author).* T **172/3** *and similar horiz design inscr* "1851–1951/23 . VIII". P 12½ (1 k. 50) *or* 14 *(others).*

652	**172**	1 k. 50, black	40	10
653	**173**	3 k. brown-red	40	10
654	—	4 k. black	40	10
655	**172**	5 k. blue	1·50	85
652/655		Set of 4	2·40	1·00

Design:—4 k. "The Region of Tabor" (M. Aleš).

1951 (3 Nov). *Czechoslovak-Soviet Friendship.* T **178** *and similar vert type.* P 14 (3 k.) *or* 12½ *(others).*

664	**178**	1 k. 50, brownish black	10	10
665	—	3 k. claret	15	10
666	**178**	4 k. blue	1·00	50

Design (23½×31½ mm.):—3 k. Lenin, Stalin and Russian soldiers.

(Des L. Ilečko. Eng J. Mráček. Recess)

1951 (5 Dec). *50th Birth Anniv of Jilemnický (writer).* P 12½.

667	**179**	1 k. 50, purple-brown	20	15
668		2 k. grey-blue	70	40

174 Miner and Pithead **175** Miners Drilling

180 L. Zápotocký **181** J. Kollár

(Des and eng B. Roule (T **174**) and J. A. Švengsbir (T **175**). Recess)

(Des K. Svolinský. Eng J. Schmidt. Recess)

1951 (8 Sept). *Miners' Day.* P 12½.

656	**174**	1 k. 50, purple-brown	15	10
657	**175**	3 k. claret	15	10
658	**174**	5 k. blue	1·00	85

1952 (12 Jan). *Birth Centenary of Zápotocký (socialist pioneer).* P 11×11½.

669	**180**	1 k. 50, orange-red	10	15
670		4 k. black	50	40

(Des K. Svolinský. Eng J. Schmidt. Recess)

1952 (30 Jan). *Death Centenary of J. Kollar (poet).* P 11×11½.

671	**181**	3 k. lake	10	10
672		5 k. deep ultramarine	45	45

176 Soldiers parading **177** President Gottwald

182 Lenin Hall, Prague **183** Dr. E. Holub and Negro

(Des V. Šprungl (80 h., 1 k.), K. Svolinský (1 k. 50), D. Křováková (3 k.), and J. Blažek (5 k.). Eng L. Jirka (80 h., 1 k., 5 k.), J. Schmidt (1 k. 50) and J. A. Švengsbir (3 k.). Photo (80 h., 5 k.); recess (others))

(Des J. Vávrová and J. Landa. Eng J. Mráček. Recess)

1951 (6 Oct). *Army Day.* T **176** *and similar vert designs, inscr* "DEN ČS ARMÁDY 1951", *and* **177**. P 14 (80 h., 5 k.) *or* 12½ *(others).*

659		80 h. yellow-brown	25	15
660		1 k. green	25	25
661		1 k. 50, brownish black	40	25
662		3 k. purple	45	25
663		5 k. blue	2·00	95
659/663		Set of 5	3·00	1·75

Designs:—1 k. Gunner and field-gun; 3 k. Tank driver and tank; 5 k. Two pilots and aircraft.

1952 (30 Jan). *40th Anniv of Sixth All-Russian Party Conference.* P 12½.

673	**182**	1 k. 50, claret	10	20
674		5 k. deep blue	90	35

(Des K. Svolinský. Eng J. Mráček. Recess)

1952 (21 Feb). *50th Death Anniv of Dr. Holub (explorer).* P 11½×11.

675	**183**	3 k. brown-lake	40	25
676		5 k. indigo	1·75	1·10

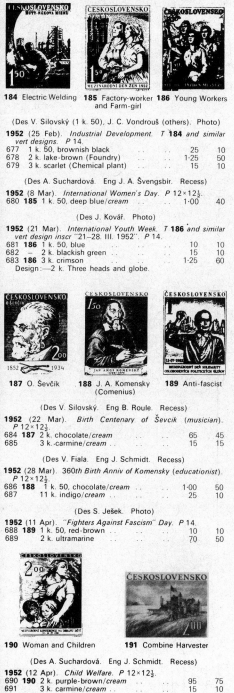

184 Electric Welding **185** Factory-worker **186** Young Workers and Farm-girl

(Des V. Silovský (1 k. 50), J. C. Vondrouš (others). Photo)

1952 (25 Feb). *Industrial Development. T 184 and similar vert designs.* P 14.
677 1 k. 50, brownish black   25   10
678 2 k. lake-brown (Foundry)   1·25   50
679 3 k. scarlet (Chemical plant)   15   10

(Des A. Suchardová. Eng J. A. Švengsbir. Recess)

1952 (8 Mar). *International Women's Day.* P 12 × 12½.
680 **185** 1 k. 50, deep blue/*cream*   1·00   40

(Des J. Kovář. Photo)

1952 (21 Mar). *International Youth Week. T 186 and similar vert design inscr "21–28. III. 1952".* P 14.
681 **186** 1 k. 50, blue   10   10
682 – 2 k. blackish green   15   10
683 **186** 3 k. crimson   1·25   60
Design:—2 k. Three heads and globe.

187 O. Ševčík   **188** J. A. Komensky (Comenius)   **189** Anti-fascist

(Des V. Silovský. Eng B. Roule. Recess)

1952 (22 Mar). *Birth Centenary of Ševcik (musician).* P 12 × 12½.
684 **187** 2 k. chocolate/*cream*   65   45
685 3 k. carmine/*cream*   15   15

(Des V. Fiala. Eng J. Schmidt. Recess)

1952 (28 Mar). *360th Birth Anniv of Komensky (educationist).* P 12 × 12½.
686 **188** 1 k. 50, chocolate/*cream*   1·00   50
687 11 k. indigo/*cream*   25   10

(Des S. Ješek. Photo)

1952 (11 Apr). *"Fighters Against Fascism" Day.* P 14.
688 **189** 1 k. 50, red-brown   10   10
689 2 k. ultramarine   70   50

190 Woman and Children   **191** Combine Harvester

(Des A. Suchardová. Eng J. Schmidt. Recess)

1952 (12 Apr). *Child Welfare.* P 12 × 12½.
690 **190** 2 k. purple-brown/*cream*   95   75
691 3 k. carmine/*cream*   15   10

(Des V. Polášek (T **191**), J. Podhajský (3 k.). Photo)

1952 (30 Apr). *Agriculture Day. T 191 and similar horiz design.* P 14.
692 **191** 1 k. 50, blue   90   75
693 2 k. brown   25   20
694 – 3 k. red (Combine drill)   25   20

192 May Day Parade

(Des V. Šprungl. Photo)

1952 (1 May). *Labour Day.* P 14.
695 **192** 3 k. red   35   35
696 4 k. lake-brown   1·10   85

193 Russian Tank and Crowd   **194** Boy Pioneer and Children

(Des V. Šprungl. Photo)

1952 (9 May). *Seventh Anniv of Liberation.* P 14.
697 **193** 1 k. 50, red   60   50
698 5 k. bright blue   1·75   1·25

(Des M. Kazdová. Eng L. Jirka (T **194**), J. Goldschmied (3 k.). Recess)

1952 (31 May). *International Children's Day. T 194 and similar horiz design inscr "PIONYŘI DRUHÁ SMĚNA ČSM".* P 12½.
699 **194** 1 k. 50, sepia/*cream*   10   10
700 2 k. deep green/*cream*   1·25   60
701 – 3 k. carmine/*cream*   15   10
Design:—3 k. Pioneers and teacher.

195 J. V. Myslbek   **196** Beethoven   **197** "Rebirth of Lidice"

(Des K. Svolinský. Eng J. Schmidt (T **195**), J. Mráček (8 k.). Recess)

1952 (2 June). *Thirtieth Death Anniv of Myslbek (sculptor). T 195 and similar vert design inscr "JOS. V. MYSLBEK HUDBA".* P 11½.
702 **195** 1 k. 50, chestnut   20   10
703 2 k. chocolate   90   80
704 – 8 k. dull green ("Music" (statue))   15   10

(Des K. Svolinský. Eng J. Schmidt (T **196**). Des and eng J. A. Švengsbír (3 k.). Recess)

1952 (7 June). *International Music Festival, Prague. T 196 and horiz design inscr "PRAZSKE JARO 1952" etc.* P 11½.
705 **196** 1 k. 50, blackish brown   30   25
706 3 k. brown-lake   30   25
707 **196** 5 k. indigo   1·60   90
Design:—3 k. House of Artists, Prague.

(Des P. Šimon. Eng B. Roule. Recess)

1952 (10 June). *Tenth Anniv of Destruction of Lidice.* P 12½.
| 708 | **197** | 1 k. 50, black/cream | 10 | 10 |
| 709 | | 5 k. indigo/cream | 1·00 | 50 |

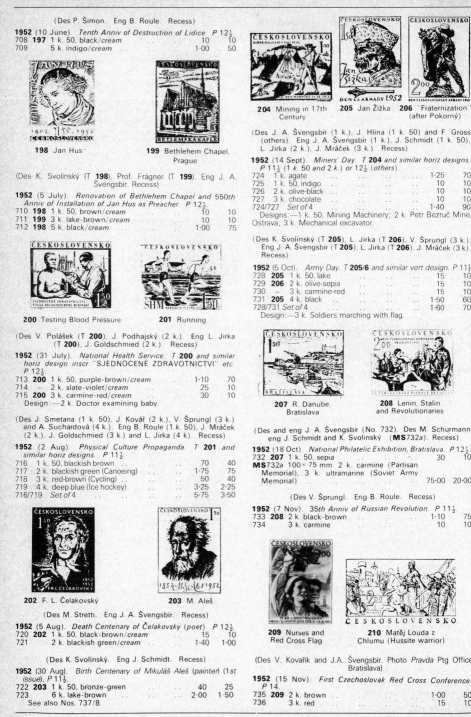

198 Jan Hus

199 Bethlehem Chapel, Prague

(Des K. Svolinský (T **198**), Prof. Frágner (T **199**). Eng J. A. Švengsbir. Recess)

1952 (5 July). *Renovation of Bethlehem Chapel and 550th Anniv of Installation of Jan Hus as Preacher.* P 12½.
710	**198**	1 k. 50, brown/cream	10	10
711	**199**	3 k. lake-brown/cream	10	10
712	**198**	5 k. black/cream	1·00	75

200 Testing Blood Pressure

201 Running

(Des V. Polášek (T **200**), J. Podhajský (2 k.). Eng L. Jirka (T **200**), J. Goldschmied (2 k.). Recess)

1952 (31 July). *National Health Service.* T **200** and similar horiz design inscr "SJEDNOCENÉ ZDRAVOTNICTVI" etc. P 12½.
713	**200**	1 k. 50, purple-brown/cream	1·10	70
714		2 k. slate-violet/cream	25	10
715	**200**	3 k. carmine-red/cream	30	10
Design:—2 k. Doctor examining baby.

(Des J. Smetana (1 k. 50), J. Kovář (2 k.), V. Šprungl (3 k.) and A. Suchardová (4 k.). Eng B. Roule (1 k. 50), J. Mráček (2 k.), J. Goldschmied (3 k.) and L. Jirka (4 k.). Recess)

1952 (2 Aug). *Physical Culture Propaganda.* T **201** and similar horiz designs. P 11½.
716		1 k. 50, blackish brown	70	40
717		2 k. blackish green (Canoeing)	1·75	75
718		3 k. red-brown (Cycling)	50	40
719		4 k. deep blue (Ice hockey)	3·25	2·25
716/719		Set of 4	5·75	3·50

202 F. L. Čelakovský

203 M. Aleš

(Des M. Stretti. Eng J. A. Švengsbir. Recess)

1952 (5 Aug). *Death Centenary of Čelakovsky (poet).* P 12½.
| 720 | **202** | 1 k. 50, black-brown/cream | 15 | 10 |
| 721 | | 2 k. blackish green/cream | 1·40 | 1·00 |

(Des K. Svolinský. Eng J. Schmidt. Recess)

1952 (30 Aug). *Birth Centenary of Mikuláš Aleš (painter)* (1st issue). P 11½.
| 722 | **203** | 1 k. 50, bronze-green | 40 | 25 |
| 723 | | 6 k. lake-brown | 2·00 | 1·50 |
See also Nos. 737/8.

204 Mining in 17th Century

205 Jan Žižka

206 "Fraternization" (after Pokorný)

(Des J. A. Švengsbir (1 k.), J. Hlina (1 k. 50) and F. Gross (others). Eng J. A. Švengsbir (1 k.), J. Schmidt (1 k. 50), L. Jirka (2 k.), J. Mráček (3 k.). Recess)

1952 (14 Sept). *Miners' Day.* T **204** and similar horiz designs. P 11½ (1 k. 50 and 2 k.) or 12½ (others).
724		1 k. agate	1·25	70
725		1 k. 50, indigo	10	10
726		2 k. olive-black	10	10
727		3 k. chocolate	10	10
724/727		Set of 4	1·40	90
Designs:—1 k. 50, Mining Machinery; 2 k. Petr Bezruč Mine, Ostrava; 3 k. Mechanical excavator.

(Des K. Svolinský (T **205**), L. Jirka (T **206**), V. Šprungl (3 k.). Eng J. A. Švengsbir (T **205**), L. Jirka (T **206**), J. Mráček (3 k.). Recess)

1952 (5 Oct). *Army Day.* T **205**/6 and similar vert design. P 11½.
728	**205**	1 k. 50, lake	15	10
729	**206**	2 k. olive-sepia	15	10
730		3 k. carmine-red	15	10
731	**205**	4 k. black	1·50	60
728/731		Set of 4	1·60	70
Design:—3 k. Soldiers marching with flag.

207 R. Danube, Bratislava

208 Lenin, Stalin and Revolutionaries

(Des and eng J. A. Švengsbir (No. 732). Des M. Schurmann, eng J. Schmidt and K. Svolinský (**MS**732a). Recess)

1952 (18 Oct). *National Philatelic Exhibition, Bratislava.* P 12½.
| 732 | **207** | 1 k. 50, sepia | 30 | 10 |
MS732a 100 × 75 mm. 2 k. carmine (Partisan Memorial), 3 k. ultramarine (Soviet Army Memorial) ... 75·00 20·00

(Des V. Šprungl. Eng B. Roule. Recess)

1952 (7 Nov). *35th Anniv of Russian Revolution.* P 11½.
| 733 | **208** | 2 k. black-brown | 1·10 | 75 |
| 734 | | 3 k. carmine | 10 | 10 |

209 Nurses and Red Cross Flag

210 Matěj Louda z Chlumu (Hussite warrior)

(Des V. Kovařík and J.A. Švengsbir. Photo *Pravda* Ptg Office, Bratislava)

1952 (15 Nov). *First Czechoslovak Red Cross Conference.* P 14.
| 735 | **209** | 2 k. brown | 1·00 | 50 |
| 736 | | 3 k. red | 15 | 10 |

(Des K. Svolinský. Eng J. Schmidt. Recess)

1952 (18 Nov). *Birth Centenary of Mikuláš Aleš (2nd issue).*
T **210** *and similar horiz design. P* 11½.

737	2 k. purple-brown		20	10
738	3 k. greenish black		50	10

Design:—3 k. "Trutnov" (warrior fighting dragon).

211	**212** "Dove of Peace" (after Picasso)	**213** Smetana Museum, Prague

(Des B. Němec and J. A. Švengsbir. Photo)

1952 (12 Dec). *Peace Congress, Vienna. P* 14.

739	**211** 3 k. brown-red		20	10
740	4 k. blue		1·00	65

(Des J. A. Švengsbir. Photo)

1953 (17 Jan). *Second Czechoslovak Peace Congress, Prague.*
T **212** *and another vert design inscr* "PRAHA LEDEN 1953".
P 14.

741	1 k. 50, sepia		10	10
742	4 k. Prussian blue		50	30

Design:—4 k. Workman, woman and child (after Lev Haas).

PRINTERS. All stamps from No. 743 were printed by the Post
Office Ptg Wks at Prague or Bratislava, *unless otherwise stated.*

(Des and eng J. A. Švengsbir (1 k. 50), L. Jirka (4 k.). Recess)

1953 (10 Feb). *75th Birth Anniv of Prof. Z. Nejedlý (founder
of museums). T* **213** *and similar vert design inscr* "10.11.1878
10.11.1953". *P* 11½.

743	1 k. 50, chocolate		10	10
744	4 k. grey-black (Jirásek Museum, Prague)	1·00	60

214 Marching Soldiers	**215** M. Kukučin	**216** Torch and Open Book

(Des B. Němec (3 k.), J. Schmidt (1 k. 50, 8 k.). Photo *Pravda* Ptg
Office, Bratislava)

1953 (25 Feb). *Fifth Anniv of Communist Govt. T* **214** *and
similar designs inscr* "PÁTÉ VÝROČI VÍTÉZNÉHO UNORA".
P 14.

745	1 k. 50, blue		15	10
746	3 k. red		15	10
747	8 k. deep brown		1·60	75

Designs: *Vert*—3 k. Pres. Gottwald addressing meeting.
Horiz—8 k. Stalin, Gottwald and crowd with banners.

(Des V. Šprungl (1 k.), M. Stretti (3 k.), K. Svolinský (others).
Eng B. Housa (1 k.), J. Mráček (3 k.), J. Schmidt (others).
Recess)

1953 (28 Feb). *Czech Writers and Poets. T* **215** *and other
vert portraits inscr* "1953". *P* 11½.

748	1 k. olive-grey		10	10
749	1 k. 50, olive-brown (J. Vrchlický)		10	10
750	2 k. carmine-lake (K. J. Erben)		10	10
751	3 k. deep orange-brown (V. M. Kramerius)	50	35
752	5 k. blue (J. Dobrovský)		1·25	70
748/752	*Set of 5*		1·90	1·25

(Des and eng J. Liesler and B. Roule (1 k.); J. Schmidt and
J. Goldschmied (3 k.). Recess)

1953 (5 Mar). *Tenth Death Anniv of Vaclavek (writer). T* **216**
and vert portrait inscr "1897*1943". *P* 11½.

753	1 k. purple-brown		1·00	50
754	3 k. chestnut (B. Václavek)		15	10

217 Woman Revolutionary	**218** Stalin

(Des V. Šprungl (1 k. 50), J. Flejšar and J. Mráček (2 k.).
Eng B. Roule (1 k. 50), J. Goldschmied (2 k.). Recess)

1953 (8 Mar). *International Women's Day. T* **217** *and vert
design inscr* "MEZINARODNI DEN ZEN 8. III. 1953". *P* 11½.

755	1 k. 50, ultramarine (Mother and baby)		15	10
756	2 k. brown-red		90	45

(Des and eng J. Mráček. Recess)

1953 (12 Mar). *Death of Stalin. P* 11½.

757	**218** 1 k. 50, grey-black		30	15

219 President Gottwald	**220** Pecka, Zápotocký and Hybeš

(Des J. Schmidt. Eng K. Svolinský. Recess)

1953 (19 Mar). *Death of President Gottwald. P* 11½.

758	**219** 1 k. 50, black		20	10
759	3 k. black		20	10
MS759a	67×100 mm. 5 k. black (T **219**) Imperf	2·25	1·60

(Des J. Kaiser and J. Koukolský. Eng B. Housa. Recess)

1953 (7 Apr). *75th Anniv of First Czech Social Democratic
Party Congress. P* 11½.

760	**220** 2 k. chocolate		20	10

221 Cyclists	**222** 1890 May Day Medal

223 Marching Crowds

(Des J. Blažek. Eng B. Housa. Recess)

1953 (29 Apr). *Sixth International Cycle Race. P* 11½.

761	**221** 3 k. grey-blue		50	25

(Des J. Kaiser and J. Koukolský (1, 3 k.), V. Šprungl and J. Schmidt
(1 k. 50, 8 k.). Eng L. Jirka (1 k.), B. Roule (1 k. 50), J. Schmidt
(8 k.). Photo *Pravda* Ptg Office, Bratislava (3 k.), recess (others))

1953 (30 Apr). *Labour Day. T* **222** *and similar horiz designs
inscr "1 MÁJ 1953" and T* **223**. *P* 14 (3 k.) *or* 11½ *(others)*.
762	**222**	1 k. chocolate		1·60	75
763	–	1 k. 50, indigo		10	10
764	**223**	3 k. lake		20	10
765	–	8 k. deep grey-green		25	15
762/765		*Set of 4*		2·00	1·00

Designs:—1 k. 50, Lenin and Stalin; 8 k. Marx and Engels.

224 Hydro-electric Barrage   **225** Seed-drills

(Des V. Hájek (1 k. 50), J. Schmidt (2 k.), B. Vančura (3 k.). Eng
J. Mráček (1 k. 50), L. Jirka (2 k.), B. Roule (3 k.). Recess)

1953 (8 May). *T* **224** *and similar designs inscr "STAVBA
SOCIALISMU". P* 11½.
766	1 k. 50, blackish green		90	40
767	2 k. indigo		15	10
768	3 k. red-brown		15	10

Designs: *Vert*—2 k. Welder and blast furnaces, Kunčice.
Horiz—3 k. Gottwald foundry, Kunčice.

(Des J. Blažek. Photo *Pravda* Ptg Office, Bratislava)

1953 (8 May). *Agriculture Day. T* **225** *and similar horiz design.*
P 14
769	1 k. 50, brown		20	10
770	7 k. deep blue-green (Combine-harvester)	1·25	85

Currency revalued

(Recess at Bratislava (15 h., 1 k.) or Prague (others))

1953 (19 June). *P* 12½ (15 h., 1 k.) *or* 11½ *(others)*.
772	**121**	15 h. green		25	10
773	–	20 h. purple-brown		45	10
774	–	1 k. slate-lilac		90	10
775	–	3 k. black		60	10
772/775		*Set of 4*		2·00	30

226 President   **227**   **228**
Zápotocký   J. Slavík   L. Janáček

(Des J. Poš. Photo *Pravda* Ptg Office, Bratislava)

1953 (19 June). *P* 14.
776	**226**	30 h. ultramarine		50	10
777		60 h. carmine		25	10

(Des J. Liesler (T **227**), K. Svolínský (T **228**). Eng J. Schmidt.
Recess)

1953 (19 June). *Prague Music Festival. P* 11½.

    (*a*) *120th Death Anniv of Slavík (violinist)*
778	**227**	75 h. indigo		50	15

    (*b*) *25th Death Anniv of Janacek (composer)*
779	**228**	1 k. 60, sepia		1·00	10

229 Pres. Zápotocký   **230** Charles Bridge, Prague

(Des J. Poš. Eng J. Schmidt. Recess at Prague (30 h.) or Bratislava
(60 h.))

1953–56. *P* 12×11½ (30 *h.*) *or* 12½ (60 *h.*).
780	**229**	30 h. deep ultramarine (18.7.53)		25	10
		a. Perf 12½. *Blue* (10.7.56)		60	10
		b. Perf. 12½. *Ultramarine*		40	10
		c. Perf 12½. *Violet-blue*		60	10
781		60 h. carmine-pink (22.7.53)		55	10

(Des B. Heinz. Eng J. Goldschmied. Recess)

1953 (15 Aug)**–59.** *P* 11½.
782	**230**	5 k. blue-grey		2·75	10
		a. *Grey-black* (1959)		2·75	10

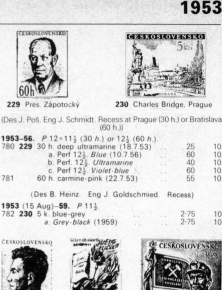

231 Fučík   **232** Book, Carnation   **233** Miner and Banner
           and Laurels

(Des M. Švabinský (40 h.), T. Nováková (60 h.). Eng J.
Mráček (40 h.), J. Švengsbir (60 h.). Recess)

1953 (8 Sept). *Tenth Death Anniv of Julius Fučík (writer). P* 12½.
783	**231**	40 h. brownish black		20	10
784	**232**	60 h. magenta		45	25

(Des M. Stretti. Eng L. Jirka (30 h.), J. Švengsbir (60 h.).
Recess)

1953 (10 Sept). *Miners' Day. T* **233** *and similar horiz design
inscr "NAFTA ZAKLADNI SUROVINA", etc. P* 11½.
785	**233**	30 h. black		20	10
786		60 h. plum		1·10	50

Design:—60 h. Miners and colliery shafthead.

234 Volleyball   **235** Hussite Warrior   **236** "Friendship"
                       (after T. Bartfay)

(Des J. Kovář. Eng L. Jirka (30 h.), B. Housa (40 h.), B. Roule
(60 h.). Recess)

1953 (15 Sept). *Sports. T* **234** *and similar designs. P* 11½.
787		30 h. brown-lake		2·00	1·50
788		40 h. slate-purple		3·75	90
789		60 h. deep purple		3·75	90

Designs: *Horiz*—40 h. Motor cycling. *Vert*—60 h. Throwing
the javelin.

(Des P. Hlava (30 h.), J. Schmidt (60 h.), B. Matějiček (**1 k.**).
Eng J. Mráček (30 h.), J. Goldschmied (60 h.), L. Jirka (1 k.).
Recess)

1953 (3 Oct). *Army Day. T* **235** *and similar vert designs. P* 11½.
790		30 h. sepia		25	10
791		60 h. claret		30	10
792		1 k. red		85	80

Designs:—60 h. Soldier presenting arms; 1 k. Czechoslovak
Red Army soldiers.

(Des and eng J. Schmidt. Recess)

1953 (11 Oct). *Czechoslovak-Korean Friendship.* P 11½
793 **236** 30 h. sepia .. .. 2·25 1·25

237 Hradčany, Prague and Kremlin, Moscow

(Des A. Jonáš. Eng B. Housa (30 h.). Des and eng B. Roule (60 h.), B. Housa (1 k. 20). Recess)

1953 (7 Nov). *Czechoslovak-Soviet Friendship.* T **237** and similar horiz designs. P 11½.
794 30 h. greenish black .. .. 1·00 65
795 60 h. sepia .. .. .. 1·25 85
796 1 k. 20, violet-blue .. .. 3·25 2·00
Design:—60 h. Lomonosov University Moscow; 1 k. 20, Lenin Ship-canal.

238 Ema Destinnova (opera singer)
239 National Theatre, Prague

(Des and eng J. Švengsbir (60 h.). Des K. Svolinský, eng J. Schmidt (others). Recess)

1953 (18 Nov). *70th Anniv of National Theatre, Prague.* T **238** and similar portrait and T **239.** P 11½ (60 h.) or 14 (others).
797 30 h. blue-black .. .. 1·00 90
798 60 h. bistre-brown 25 10
799 2 k. black-brown (E. Vojan (actor)) .. 2·50 1·25

240 J. Mánes (painter)
241 Vaclav Hollar (etcher)

(Des K. Svolinský. Eng J. Schmidt. Recess)

1953 (28 Nov). P 11½.
800 **240** 60 h. brown-lake 25 10
801 1 k. 20, deep blue .. .. 1·10 90

(Des and eng J. Švengsbir (30 h.), J. Schmidt (1 k. 20). Recess)

1953 (5 Dec). T **241** and another vert design inscr "1607 1677". P 11½.
802 30 h. black 25 10
803 1 k. 20, brownish black 95 50
Design:—1 k. 20, Hollar and engraving tools.

242 Leo Tolstoy
243 Locomotive

(Des J. Horník. Eng J. Mráček. Recess)

1953 (29 Dec). *125th Birth Anniv of Tolstoy (writer).* P 11½.
804 **242** 60 h. deep green 15 10
805 1 k. sepia .. .. 1·40 45

(Des F. Postránecký (60 h.), A. Jonáš (1 k.). Centres photo; frame recess)

1953 (29 Dec). T **243** and similar horiz design. P 11½.
806 60 h. indigo and orange-brown .. 50 25
807 1 k. new blue and yellow-brown .. 2·00 1·00
Design:—1 k. Ilyushin Il-12 (30th anniv of Czech airmail services).

244 Lenin (after J. Lauda)
245 Lenin Museum, Prague

(Des K. Svolinský and eng J. Schmidt (30 h.). Des and eng J. Švengsbir (1 k. 40). Recess)

1954 (21 Jan). *30th Death Anniv of Lenin.* P 11½.
808 **244** 30 h. blackish brown 45 10
809 **245** 1 k. 40, brown .. .. 1·40 90

246 Gottwald Speaking
247 Gottwald Mausoleum, Prague

248 Gottwald and Stalin (after relief by O. Španiel)

(Des M. Stretti (60 h.), I. Strnad (2 k. 40). Eng J. Schmidt (60 h.), L. Jirka (2 k. 40). Recess)

1954 (18 Feb). *25th Anniv of Fifth Czechoslovak Communist Party Congress.* T **246** and similar vert design inscr "1929 1954". P 11½ (60 h.) or 14 (2 k. 40).
810 60 h. deep brown 25 10
811 2 k. 40, carmine-lake .. .. 3·25 1·25
Design:—2 k. 40, Revolutionary and flag.
See also No. **MS**2917.

(Des K. Svolinský (60 h.), P. Sukdolák (others). Eng J. Švengsbir (30 h.), J. Schmidt (60 h.), B. Housa (1 k. 20). Recess)

1954 (5 Mar). *First Anniv of Deaths of Stalin and Gottwald. T **247** and similar horiz design and T **248**. P 14 (1 k. 20) or 11½ (others)*.

812	30 h. sepia	25	10
813	60 h. deep blue	30	10
814	1 k. 20, brown lake	1·40	1·00

Design—1 k. 20. Lenin-Stalin Mausoleum. Moscow

249 Girl and Sheaf of Corn   **250** Athletics

(Des J. C. Vondrouš (15 h.), A. Podzemná-Suchardová (20 h., 40 h.), I. Strnad (45 h.), B. Matějíček (50 h.), V. Němeček (75 h.), Z. Adámek (80 h., 1 k. 20), A. V. Hrska (1 k.), V. Silovský (1 k. 60), M. Stretti (2 k., 3 k.), C. Bouda (2 k. 40). Eng J. Goldschmied (15 h.), J. Mráček (20 h., 75 h., 1 k. 20), J. A. Švengsbir (40 h., 50 h.), L. Jirka (45 h.), B. Housa (80 h., 1 k. 60), B. Roule (1 k., 2 k. 40, 3 k.), J. Schmidt (2 k.). Recess at Prague (1 k. 60 to 3 k.) or Bratislava (others))

1954 (15 Mar–25 Sept). *T **249** and similar designs (18½ × 32 mm.). P 12½ (15 h. to 1 k. 20) or 11½ (others)*.

815	15 h. slate-green (25.9)	20	10
816	20 h. lilac	25	10
817	40 h. purple-brown (25.9)	35	10
818	45 h. deep blue	10	10
819	50 h. grey-green (15.5)	25	10
820	75 h. blue (25.9)	25	10
821	80 h. chocolate (15.5)	25	10
822	1 k. deep yellow-green	50	10
823	1 k. 20, deep violet-blue (15.5)	25	10
824	1 k. 60, brownish black	90	10
825	2 k. orange-brown	1·10	10
826	2 k. 40, deep violet-blue (15.5)	1·25	10
827	3 k. carmine-red (15.5)	1·10	10
815/827	*Set of 13*	6·00	65

Designs:—15 h. Labourer; 20 h. Nurse; 40 h. Postwoman; 45 h. Foundry worker; 50 h. Soldier; 75 h. Metal worker; 80 h. Mill girl; 1 k. 20, Scientist; 1 k. 60. Miner; 2 k. Doctor and baby; 2 k. 40, Engine-driver; 3 k. Chemist.

(Des J. Běhounek (1 k.), M. Stretti (others). Eng J. Goldschmied (30 h.), J. Mráček (80 h.), L. Jirka (1 k.). Recess)

1954 (24 Apr). *Sports. T **250** and similar designs. P 14 (80 h.) or 11½ (others)*.

828	30 h. sepia	2·00	60
829	80 h. green	6·75	3·25
830	1 k. deep blue	1·25	40

Designs: *Horiz*—80 h. Hiking. *Vert*—1 k. Girl diving

251 Dvořák   **252** Prokop Divis (physicist)

(Des K. Svolinský. Eng J. Schmidt. Recess)

1954 (22 May). *Czechoslovak Musicians. T **251** and similar vert portraits inscr "ROK ČESKÉ HUDBY". P 11½*.

831	30 h. brown-lake	90	20
832	40 h. brown-red (Janáček)	1·40	20
833	60 h. deep blue (Smetana)	75	15

(Des C. Bouda. Eng B. Roule. Recess)

1954 (15 June). *Bicentenary of Invention of a Lightning Conductor by Diviš. P 11½*.

834	**252** 30 h. black	25	10
835	75 h. brown-lake	1·00	40

253 Partisan   **254** A. P. Chekhov   **255** Soldiers in Battle

(Des M. Medvecká. Eng J. Goldschmied (30 h.), B. Housa (1 k. 20). Recess)

1954 (28 Aug). *Tenth Anniv of Slovak National Uprising. T **253** and similar portrait. P 11½*.

836	30 h. Venetian red	20	10
837	1 k. 20, deep blue	90	85

Portrait: *Vert*—1 k. 20, Woman partisan.

(Des and eng B. Roule. Recess)

1954 (24 Sept). *50th Death Anniv of Chekhov (playwright). P 11½*.

838	**254** 30 h. bronze-green	20	10
839	45 h. brown	1·00	40

(Des J. Schoř. Eng L. Jirka (60 h.), J. A. Švengsbir (2 k.). Recess)

1954 (3 Oct). *Army Day. T **255** and similar vert design inscr "DEN ČS ARMÁDY 1954". P 11½*.

840	60 h. deep dull green	20	10
841	2 k. brown (Soldier carrying girl)	1·10	1·00

256 Farm Workers in Cornfield

(Des V. Fiala. Eng B. Roule (30 h.), J. Goldschmied (60 h.), J. Schmidt (2 k.). Recess)

1954 (6 Nov). *Czechoslovak-Russian Friendship. T **256** and similar horiz designs. P 11½*.

842	30 h. yellow-brown	15	10
843	60 h. deep blue	25	10
844	2 k. red-orange	1·50	1·10

Designs:—60 h. Factory workers and machinery; 2 k. Group of girl folk dancers.

D 257   **D 258**   **257** J. Neruda

(Des and eng B. Roule (D **257**), J. A. Švengsbir (D **258**). Recess at Bratislava (D845/57) or Prague (D858/67))

1954 (22 Nov)–**63**. *POSTAGE DUE. (a) P 12½ (1954–55)*

D845	D **257**	5 h. bronze-green (15.4.55)	10	10
D846		10 h. bronze-green (15.4.55)	10	10
D847		30 h. bronze-green	15	10
D848		50 h. bronze-green (15.4.55)	15	10
D849		60 h. bronze-green (15.4.55)	15	10
D850		95 h. bronze-green	35	10

D851	D **258**	1 k. violet	35	10
D852		1 k. 20, violet (15.4.55)	35	10
D853		1 k. 50, violet	70	10
D854		1 k. 60, violet (15.4.55)	40	10
D855		2 k. violet (10.12.54)	75	10
D856		3 k. violet (10.12.54)	1·00	20
D857		5 k. violet (15.4.55)	1·40	25
D845/857		*Set of 13*	5·50	85

(b) P 11½ (1963)

D858	D **257**	5 h. green	10	10
D859		10 h. green	10	10
D860		30 h. green	10	10
D861		50 h. green	15	10
D862		60 h. green	15	10
D863	D **258**	1 k. violet	25	10
D864		1 k. 20, violet	30	10
D865		1 k. 50, violet	45	10
D866		3 k. violet	75	20
D867		5 k. violet	1·25	30
D858/867		*Set of 10*	3·25	75

Since April 1985 postage due stamps have been used as normal postage stamps.

(Des A. Nauman (1 k. 60), K. Stika (others). Eng J. Schmidt (30 h.), J. Goldschmied (60 h.), L. Jirka (1 k. 60). Recess)

1954 (25 Nov). *Czechoslovak Poets.* T **257** *and similar vert portraits.* P 11½

845		30 h. deep blue	90	15
846		60 h. red (J. Jesensky)	1·25	50
847		1 k. 60, deep slate-purple (J. Wolker)	40	15

PRINTING PROCESS. Recess* = Printed by a combination of recess-printing and photogravure.

258 České Budějovice   **259** President Zápotocký

(Des C. Bouda. Eng B. Roule (30 h.), B. Housa (others). Recess*)

1954 (10 Dec). *Czechoslovak Architecture.* T **258** *and similar horiz designs.* P 11½

848		30 h. black and buff (Telč)	40	10
849		60 h. brown and buff (Levoča)	40	10
850		3 k. indigo and buff	2·00	1·40

(Des and eng J. Schmidt. Recess)

1954 (18 Dec). *70th Birthday of Zápotocky.* P 11½

851	**259**	30 h. black-brown	45	10
852		60 h. deep blue	20	10
MS852a		65 × 100 mm. 2 k. lake (T **259**) Imperf	7·50	4·25

For similar stamps, in black, see Nos. 1006/7.

260 "Spirit of the Games"   **261** University Building

(Des M. Stretti. 30 h. eng J. Schmidt, Recess; 45 h. eng J. A. Švengsbir, Recess*)

1955 (20 Jan). *First National Spartacist Games (first issue).* T **260** *and similar vert design inscr* "1 CELOSTÁTNÍ SPARTAKIÁDA." P 11½

853		30 h. rose-red	2·25	30
854		45 h. black and blue (Ski-jumper)	3·00	25

See also Nos. 880/2.

(Des P. Sukdolák (60 h.), J. Běhounek (75 h.), Eng B. Housa (60 h.), L. Jirka (75 h.). Recess)

1955 (28 Jan). *35th Anniv of Comenius University, Bratislava.* T **261** *and another horiz design inscr* "UNIVERZITY KOMEN-SKÉHO". P 11½

855		60 h. deep dull green	25	10
856		75 h. chocolate	90	50

Design:—75 h. Comenius Medal (after O. Španiel).

262 Český Krumlov

(Des C. Bouda (1 k. 55, 10 k.), K. Vik (2 k. 75). Eng J. Goldschmied (1 k. 55), B. Housa (2 k. 75), J. Schmidt (10 k.). Des and eng J. Švengsbir (80 h., 2 k. 35). Recess)

1955 (20 Feb–28 Mar). AIR. T **262** *and similar horiz designs.* P 11½

857		80 h. bronze-green/buff (28.3)	1·60	30
858		1 k. 55, deep brown/buff (28.3)	1·60	25
859		2 k. 35, deep ultramarine/buff (28.3)	1·60	20
860		2 k. 75, brown-purple/buff (28.3)	3·00	40
861		10 k. indigo/buff	5·50	1·50
857/861		*Set of 5*	12·00	2·40

Designs:—1 k. 55, Olomouc; 2 k. 35, Bánská Bystrica; 2 k. 75, Bratislava; 10 k. Prague.

263 Skoda Motor-car   **264** Russian Tank-driver

(Des J. Běhounek. Eng B. Roule (60 h.), L. Jirka (others). Recess)

1955 (15 Mar). *Czechoslovak Industries.* T **263** *and similar horiz designs.* P 11½

862		45 h. deep dull green	70	45
863		60 h. deep blue	15	10
864		75 h. black	25	10

Designs:—60 h. Shuttleless jet loom; 75 h. Skoda machine tool.

(Des J. Švengsbir (868), Z. Brdlík (others). Eng J. Goldschmied (30 h.), L. Jirka (35 h.), J. Mráček (867). Photo (868), recess (others))

1955 (5 May). *Tenth Anniv of Liberation.* T **264** *and similar designs inscr* "DESÁTÉ VÝROČI OSVOBOZENI ČESKO-SLOVENSKA". P 11½

865		30 h. blue	25	10
866		35 h. chocolate	1·00	50
867		60 h. carmine	25	10
868		60 h. olive-black	25	10
865/868		*Set of 4*	1·60	70

Designs: *Vert*—30 h. Girl and Russian soldier; 60 h. (No. 867), Children and Russian soldier. *Horiz*—60 h. (No. 868), Stalin Monument, Prague.

265 Agricultural Workers

266 "Music and Spring"

267 A. S. Popov (60th anniv of radio discoveries)

(Des B. Doležalová. Eng B. Housa (30 h.), B. Roule (45 h.). Recess)

1955 (12 May). *Third Trades' Union Congress.* T **265** and similar vert design. P 11½.
869	30 h. deep violet-blue (Foundry worker)	15	10
870	45 h. green	65	45

(Des K. Svolinský. Eng J. Schmidt. Recess*)

1955 (12 May). *International Music Festival, Prague.* T **266** and similar vert design. P 11½.
871	30 h. indigo and light blue	35	10
872	1 k. indigo and pink	1·25	75
Design:—1 k. "Music" playing a lyre.

(Des V. Sivko (20 h., 1 k. 40), M. Švabinský (30 h., 1 k. 60), R. Klimovič (40 h., 75 h.), V. Stretti (60 h.). Eng B. Housa (20 h.), J. Schmidt (30 h., 60 h., 1 k. 60), J. Goldschmied (40 h., 75 h.), B. Roule (1 k. 40). Recess)

1955 (25 May–2 July). *Cultural Anniversaries.* T **267** and similar vert portraits. P 11½.
873	20 h. chocolate (2.7)	25	10
874	30 h. brown-black (2.7)	25	10
875	40 h. grey-green (2.7)	75	10
876	60 h. black	40	10
877	75 h. maroon	90	50
878	1 k. 40, black/yellow	50	20
879	1 k. 50, deep blue (2.7)	50	15
873/879	Set of 7	3·25	1·00
Portraits:—20 h. Jakub Arbes (writer); 30 h. Jan Štursa (sculptor); 40 h. Elena Maróthy-Šoltésová (writer); 60 h. Josef V. Sládek (poet); 1 k. 40, Ján Holly (poet); 1 k. 60, Pavel J. Šafařík (philologist).

268 Folk Dancers

269 "Friendship"

270 Očová Woman, Slovakia

(Des K. Svolinský. Eng J. Schmidt. Recess)

1955 (21 June). *First National Spartacist Games (second issue).* T **268** and similar vert designs inscr "1955 V. PRAZE" etc. P 11½.
880	20 h. deep ultramarine (Girl athlete)	75	40
881	60 h. deep green	25	10
882	1 k. 60, red (Male athlete)	80	20

(Des J. Černý. Eng L. Jirka. Recess)

1955 (20 July). *Fifth World Youth Festival, Warsaw* P 11½.
883	**269** 60 h. deep ultramarine	25	10

(Des K. Svolinský. Eng J. Schmidt. Recess)

1955 (25 July). *National Costumes (first issue).* T **270** and similar vert designs. P 14.
884	60 h. black-brown, rose and red	11·00	7·00
885	75 h. sepia, orange and carmine	6·50	3·75
886	1 k. 60, sepia, bright blue and orange	11·00	6·50

887	2 k. sepia, lemon and carmine	14·00	7·00
884/887	Set of 4	38·00	22·00
Designs:—75 h. Detva man, Slovakia; 1 k. 60, Chodsko man, Bohemia; 2 k. Haná woman, Moravia.
See also Nos. 952/5 and 1008/11.

271 Swallowtail

(Des Z. Seydl. Eng J. Schmidt (20 h., 30 h.), L. Jirka (others). Recess*)

1955 (8 Aug). *Animals and Insects.* T **271** and similar horiz designs. P 11½.
888	20 h. black and pale blue	70	15
889	30 h. black-brown and rose	70	10
890	35 h. black-brown and pale bistre	70	20
891	1 k. 40, black and pale yellow	5·25	2·50
892	1 k. 50, black and pale green	70	20
888/892	Set of 5	7·50	2·75
Designs:—20 h. Carp; 30 h. Stag beetle; 35 h. Grey partridge; 1 k. 50, Brown hare.

272 Tábor

273 Motor Cyclists and Trophy

(Des V. Fiala. Eng B. Housa (30 h.), J. Goldschmied (45 h.), J. Mráček (60 h.). Recess)

1955 (26 Aug). *Towns of Southern Bohemia.* T **272** and similar horiz designs. P 11½.
893	30 h. dull purple	20	10
894	45 h. rose-carmine (Prachatice)	75	65
895	60 h. green (Jindřichuv Hradec)	20	10

(Des M. Stretti. Eng B. Roule. Recess)

1955 (28 Aug). *30th International Motor Cycle Six-Day Trial.* P 11½.
896	**273** 60 h. deep dull purple	3·00	50

273a Round Chapel

274 Soldier and Family

275 Hans Andersen

(Des J. Švengsbir. Eng V. Stretti (30 h.), P. Sukdolak (75 h.), J. Švengsbir (others). Recess)

1955 (10 Sept). *Prague International Philatelic Exhibition.* Sheets 145×111 mm. P 14.
MS896a 30 h. black (T **273a**)
45 h. black (Brick tower)	
60 h. lake (Fountain)	
75 h. lake (Winter Palace)	
1 k. 60, black (Hradčany, 50×31 mm.)	30·00 30·00
MS896b As above but imperf | 65·00 65·00 |

(Des E. Kotrba (30 h.), J. Šebek (60 h.). Eng L. Jirka (30 h.), B. Housa (60 h.). Recess)

1955 (6 Oct). *Army Day. T* **274** *and similar vert design inscr* "DEN ČS. ARMÁDY 1955". *P* 11½.
897	30 h. blackish brown			25	10
898	60 h. deep grey-green (Tank attack)			2·40	2·00

(Des K. Svolinský. Eng J. Schmidt. Recess)

1955 (27 Oct). *Famous Writers. Vert portraits as T* **275**. *P* 11½.
899	30 h. brown-red			15	10
900	40 h. deep blue (Schiller)			1·60	75
901	60 h. brown-purple (Mickiewicz)			25	10
902	75 h. black (Walt Whitman)			50	10
899/902	Set of 4			2·25	85

276 Railway Viaduct

277 "Electricity"

(Des F. Hudeček. Eng J. Mráček (20 h.), L. Jirka (30 h.), J. Schmidt (60 h.), B. Housa (1 k. 60). Recess)

1955 (15 Dec). *Building Progress. T* **276** *and similar horiz designs. P* 11½.
903	20 h. deep grey-green			25	20
904	30 h. purple-brown			25	10
905	60 h. indigo			25	10
906	1 k. 60, carmine-red			40	10
903/906	Set of 4			1·00	40

Designs:—30 h. Train crossing viaduct; 60 h. Train approaching tunnel; 1 k. 60, Housing project, Ostrava.

(Des F. Hudeček. Eng B. Roule (5 h.), L. Jirka (10 h. and 30 h.), J. Mráček (25 h.), B. Housa (60 h.). Recess)

1956 (20 Feb). *Five Year Plan. T* **277** *and similar horiz designs inscr* "1956–1960". *P* 11½.
907	5 h. brown-purple			20	10
908	10 h. black ("Mining")			20	10
909	25 h. carmine ("Building")			20	10
910	30 h. deep green ("Agriculture")			20	10
911	60 h. violet-blue ("Industry")			30	10
907/911	Set of 5			1·00	20

278 Karlovy Vary

279 Jewellery

280 "We Serve our People" (after J. Cumpelik)

(Des M. Stretti. Eng J. Mráček (30 h.), J. Schmidt and J. Goldschmied (45 h.), J. Schmidt (others). Recess)

1956 (17 Mar). *Czechoslovak Spas. T* **278** *and similar vert designs. P* 11½.
912	30 h. bronze green			1·40	25
913	45 h. deep brown			1·10	40
914	75 h. brown-purple			7·00	4·25
915	1 k. 20, deep ultramarine			65	15
912/915	Set of 4			9·00	4·75

Designs:—45 h. Mariánské Lazně; 75 h. Piešťany; 1 k. 20, Vyšné Ružbachy, Tatra Mountains.

(Des and eng J. Švengsbir. Recess)

1956 (17 Mar). *Czechoslovak Products. T* **279** *and similar vert designs. P* 11½.
916	30 h. deep dull green			25	10
917	45 h. deep blue (Glassware)			5·00	2·50
918	60 h. brown-purple (Ceramics)			75	10
919	75 h. black (Textiles)			25	10
916/919	Set of 4			5·50	2·50

(Designs adapted F. Hudeček. Photo)

1956 (9 Apr). *Defence Exhibition. T* **280** *and similar vert designs. P* 11½.
920	30 h. sepia			35	10
921	60 h. bright carmine-red			35	10
922	1 k. bright blue			5·75	3·50

Designs:—60 h. Liberation Monument, Berlin; 1 k. "Tank Soldier with Standard" (after J. Schoř).

281 Cyclists

282 Discus Thrower, Hurdler and Runner

(Des J. Černý (30 h., 45 h.), E. Kotrba (60 h.), A. Podzemná-Suchardová (75 h., 80 h., 1 k. 20). Eng L. Jirka (30 h.), J. Mráček (45 h., 75 h., 1 k. 20), J. Švengsbir (60 h., 80 h.). Recess*)

1956 (25 Apr–8 Sept). *Sports Events of 1956. T* **281** *and similar designs and T* **282**. *P* 11½.
923	30 h. deep dull green and blue			2·50	20
924	45 h. deep blue and rose-red			1·25	20
925	60 h. indigo and buff (8.9)			1·90	25
926	75 h. deep brown and yellow			1·10	20
927	80 h. maroon and lavender (8.9)			1·10	15
928	1 k. 20, dp grey-green & yell-orge (8.9)			75	25
923/928	Set of 6			8·00	10

Designs: *Vert as T* **281**—30 h. *T* **281** (Ninth International Cycle Race); 45 h. Basketball players (Fifth European Women's Basketball Championship, Prague. *Horiz as T* **281**—60 h. Horsemen jumping (Pardubice Steeplechase); 80 h. Runners (International Marathon, Košice). *T* **282**—75 h., 1 k. 20, (Sixteenth Olympic Games, Melbourne).

283 Mozart

284

(Des K. Svolinský. Eng J. Schmidt. Recess*)

1956 (12 May). *Birth Bicentenary of Mozart and Prague Music Festival. T* **283** *and similar vert designs. P* 11½.
929	30 h. black and orange-yellow			80	35
930	45 h. black and pale grey-green			17·00	11·00
931	60 h. black and pale reddish purple			60	10
932	1 k. black and salmon			1·40	20
933	1 k. 40, black and light blue			3·50	70
934	1 k. 60, black and lemon			80	15
929/934	Set of 6			22·00	11·50

Designs:—30 h. J. Mysliveček; 60 h. J. Benda; 1 k. "Bertramka" (Dušek's villa in Prague where Mozart composed some of his music); 1 k. 40, Mr. and Mrs. Dušek; 1 k. 60, Nostic Theatre.

(Des Z. Brdlik. Eng B. Housa. Recess)

1956 (25 May). *First National Meeting of "Svarzarm"* (*Home Guard*). *P* 11½.
935 **284** 60 h. ultramarine 75 15

285 J .K. Tyl	**286** Naval Guard	**287** Picking Grapes

(Des M. Švabinský. Eng J. Schmidt. Recess)

1956 (23 June). *Czech Writers (first issue). T* 285 *and similar vert portraits. P* 11½.
936 20 h. deep purple (L. Stur) .. 60 10
937 30 h. deep blue (F. Srámek) .. 40 10
938 60 h. black 30 10
939 1 k. 40, purple-brown (K. H. Borovský) .. 5·00 2·50
936/939 *Set of 4* .. 5·75 2·50
See also Nos. 956/9.

(Des Z. Brdlik. Eng. B. Roule (30 h.), J. Mráček (60 h.). Recess)

1956 (8 July). *Frontier Guards' Day. T* 286 *and similar vert design, inscr* "DEN POHRANIČNI STRÁŽE". *P* 11½.
940 30 h. deep bright blue 90 35
941 60 h. dull green 15 10
Design:—60 h. Military guard and watchdog.

(Des M. Stretti. Eng J. Mráček (30 h.), J. Schmidt (35 h.), J. Schmidt and J. Goldschmied (80 h.), L. Jirka (95 h.). Recess)

1956 (20 Sept). *National Products. T* 287 *and similar designs. P* 11½.
942 30 h. brown-lake 25 10
943 35 h. deep dull green 30 20
944 80 h. grey-blue 60 15
945 95 h. deep brown .. .. 1·75 1·40
942/945 *Set of 4* .. .. .. 2·50 1·60
Designs: *Vert*—35 h. Picking hops. *Horiz*—80 h. Fishing; 95 h. Logging.

288 *Kladno,* 1855

(Des F. Hudeček. Eng B. Roule (10 h.), J. A. Švengsbir (30 h.), J. Schmidt (40 h.), B. Housa (1 k.), J. Schmidt and J. Goldschmied (others). Recess)

1956 (9 Nov). *European Freight Services Timetable Conference. T* 288 *and similar designs showing railway engines. P* 11½.
946 10 h. deep brown .. .. 1·25 10
947 30 h. brownish black 70 10
948 40 h. deep green .. .. 3·25 20
949 45 h. brown- purple .. .. 18·00 11·00
950 60 h. indigo 70 10
951 1 k. deep blue .. .. 1·25 20
946/951 *Set of 6* .. .. 22·00 11·00
Designs: *Vert*—10 h. Zbraslav, 1846. *Horiz*—40 h. Class "534.0", 1945; 45 h. Class "556.0" 1952; 60 h. Class "477.0", 1955; 1 k. Electric locomotive "E499.0", 1954.

(Des K. Svolinský. Eng L. Jirka (1 k. 40), J. Schmidt (others). Recess)

1956 (15 Dec). *National Costumes (second issue). Vert designs as T* 270. *P* 14.
952 30 h. sepia, carmine and blue .. 2·50 80
953 1 k. 20, sepia, blue and carmine .. 1·90 15
954 1 k. 40, brown, ochre and red .. 5·25 2·00
955 1 k. 60, black-brown, green and carmine 2·50 40
952/955 *Set of 4* .. .. 11·00 3·00
Designs:—30 h. Slovácko woman; 1 k. 20, Blata woman; 1 k. 40, Čičmany woman; 1 k. 60, Novohradsko woman.

(Des M. Švabinský. Eng J. Schmidt. Recess)

1957 (18 Jan). *Czech Writers (second issue). Vert portraits as T* 285. *P* 11½.
956 15 h. red-brown/*buff* (I. Olbracht) .. 25 10
957 20 h. deep green/*buff* (K. Toman) .. 25 10
958 30 h. sepia/*buff* (F. X. Šalda) .. 25 10
959 1 k. 60, deep blue/*buff* (T. Vansová) .. 40 10
956/959 *Set of 4* .. .. 1·00 30

289 Forestry Academy, Banská Stiavnica	**290** Girl Harvester

(Des J. C. Vondrouš (Nos. 960, 963/4); J. Lipanská-Kolářová (Nos. 962, 965). Des and eng J. Švengsbir (No. 961). Eng J. Goldschmied (Nos. 960, 964); L. Jirka (Nos. 962/3); B. Housa (No. 965). Recess)

1957 (23 Feb). *Towns and Monuments Anniversaries. T* 289 *and similar horiz designs. P* 11½.
960 30 h. deep blue (Kolin) 20 10
961 30 h. reddish purple 20 10
962 60 h. carmine-red (Uherské Hradišté) .. 40 10
963 60 h. sepia (Charles Bridge, Prague) .. 40 10
964 60 h. green (Karlstejn Castle) .. 40 10
965 1 k. 25, black (Moravská Trebova) .. 2·75 2·00
960/965 *Set of 6* .. .. 4·00 2·10

(Des F. Hudeček. Eng J. Mráček. Recess)

1957 (22 Mar). *Third Agricultural Collective Farming Congress, Prague. P* 11½.
966 **290** 30 h. blue-green 55 10

291 Komenský's Mausoleum	**292** J. A. Komenský (Comenius)

(Des M. Švabinský, eng J. Schmidt (60 h.). Des and eng J. A. Švengsbir (others). Recess)

1957 (28 Mar). *300th Anniv of Publication of Komenský's "Opera Didactica Omnia". As T* **291** *(horiz designs inscr "300-VYROCI-VYDANI-SPISU") and T* **292**. *P* 14 (60 h.) or 11½ (others).

967	30 h. bistre-brown			45	15
968	40 h. deep grey-green			45	15
969	60 h. deep brown			1·50	80
970	1 k. rose-red			60	10
967/970	*Set of 4*			2·75	1·10

Designs:—40 h. Komenský at work; 1 k. Illustration from *Opera Didactica Omnia.*

293 Racing Cyclists   294 J. B. Foerster

(Des Z. Brdlik (Nos. 971/2, 976), R. Klimovič (Nos. 973/4), J. Černý (No. 975). Eng L. Jirka (Nos. 971/2, 974), B. Housa (No. 973), J. Mráček (Nos. 975/6). Recess*)

1957 (30 Apr–5 July). *Sports Events of 1957. T* **293** *and similar designs. P* 12×11½ *or* 11½×12 *(vert).*

971	30 h. slate-purple and blue		30	10
972	60 h. grey-green and bistre		1·75	1·50
973	60 h. slate-violet and brown		30	10
974	60 h. dull purple and orange-brown		30	10
975	60 h. black and emerald		30	10
976	60 h. grey-black and blue (5.7)		90	10
971/976	*Set of 6*		3·25	1·75

Designs: *Horiz*—Nos. 971/2, T **293** (Tenth International Cycle Race); 973, Rescue squad (Mountain Rescue Service); 975, Archer (World Archery Championships, Prague); 976, Motor cyclists (32nd International Motor Cycle Six-Day Trial). *Vert*—No. 974, Boxers (European Boxing Championships, Prague); 976, Motor cyclists (32nd International Motor Cycle Six-Day Trial).

(Des M. Švabinský. Eng J. Schmidt. Recess)

1957 (12 May). *International Music Festival Jubilee. Portraits of musicians as T* **294**. *P* 11½×12.

877	60 h. reddish violet (J. V. Stamic)		25	10
978	60 h. black (F. Laub)		25	10
979	60 h. slate-blue (F. Ondříček)		25	10
980	60 h. deep brown (Type **294**)		25	10
981	60 h. brown-lake (V. Novák)		95	10
982	60 h. deep bluish green (J. Suk)		25	10
977/982	*Set of 6*		2·00	50

295 J. Bozek (founder)

296 Young Collector Blowing Posthorn

(Des V. Kolařík (1 k.), I. V. Kozák (1 k. 40). J. Podhajský (others). Eng J. Mráček (30 h.), L. Jirka (60 h. 1 k.), B. Roule (1 k. 40). Recess)

1957 (25 May). *250th Anniv of Polytechnic Engineering Schools, Prague. T* **295** *and similar designs inscr "INZENYRSKYCH SKOL V PRAZE". P* 11½.

983	30 h. slate-black		15	10
984	60 h. deep brown		30	10
985	1 k. brown-purple		30	15
986	1 k. 40, deep violet		45	15
983/986	*Set of 4*		1·10	35

Designs: *Vert*—60 h. F. J. Gerstner and 1 k. R. Skuherský (school professors). *Horiz*—1 k. 40, Polytechnic Engineering Schools Building, Prague.

(Des M. Stretti. Eng J. Švengsbir. Recess* (30 h.) or recess (60 h.))

1957 (8 June). *Junior Philatelic Exhibition, Pardubice. T* **296** *and similar vert design. P* 11½ *(30 h.) or* 14 *(60 h.).*

987	30 h. salmon and bronze-green		50	10
988	60 h. grey-blue and brown		2·00	90

Design:—60 h. Young girl sending letter by pigeon. No. 988 was issued in sheets of four.

297 Rose of Friendship and Peace"   298 Karel Klič and Printing Press   299 Chamois

(Des K. Svolinský. Eng J. Schmidt. Recess)

1957 (8 June). *15th Anniv of Destruction of Lidice. T* **297** *and similar vert design. P* 11½ *or* 14 *(60 h.).*

989	30 h. black (Veiled woman)		35	10
990	60 h. rose-red and black		55	25

(Des J. Poš. Eng B. Roule (30 h.). Des K. Tondl. Eng J. Mráček (60 h.). Recess)

1957 (5 July). *Czech Inventors. T* **298** *and similar vert design. P* 11½.

991	30 h. black		15	10
992	60 h. violet-blue		25	10

Design:—60 h. Joseph Ressel and propeller.

(Des J. Balaš (20 h., 30 h., 40 h.), A. Hollý (others). Eng B. Roule (20 h.), J. Schmidt and J. Goldschmied (30 h.), J. Švengsbir (40 h., 60 h.), J. Schmidt (1 k. 25). Recess*)

1957 (28 Aug). *Tatra National Park. T* **299** *and similar designs inscr "TATRANSKY NARODNY PARK". P* 11½×12 (20 h 30 h.) or 12×11½ (40 h., 60 h.) or 11½ (1 k. 25).

993	20 h. grey-black and bright green		65	50
994	30 h. chocolate and cobalt		65	10
995	40 h. deep violet-blue and yellow-brown		1·10	10
996	60 h. deep green and yellow		50	10
997	1 k. 25, greenish black and ochre		1·25	1·50
993/997	*Set of 5*		3·75	2·00

Designs: *Vert*—30 h. Brown bear. *Horiz*—40 h. Gentian; 60 h. Edelweiss; 1 k. 25 (49×29 *mm*.). Tatra Mountains.

300 Maryčka Magdonová   301 Worker with Banner

(Des K. Svolinský. Eng J. Schmidt. Recess*)

1957 (15 Sept). *90th Birthday of Petr Bezruč (poet). P 11½.*
998 **300** 60 h. black and red 45 10

(Des V. Polášek. Eng J. Mráček. Recess)

1957 (28 Sept). *Fourth World Trade Unions Congress, Leipzig. P 11½.*
999 **301** 75 h. rose-red 45 15

302 Tupolev Tu-104A and
Paris–Prague–Moscow Route

(Des F. Hudeček. Eng B. Housa (75 h.), B. Roule (2 k. 35). Recess*)

1957 (28 Sept). *AIR. Opening of Czechoslovak Airlines. T 302 and similar horiz design. P 11½.*
1000 75 h. blue and pale red . . 90 10
1001 2 k. 35, blue and orange-yellow . . 1·10 20
Design.—2 k. 35, "Prague—Cairo—Beirut—Damascus".

303 Television
Tower and Aerials

304 Youth, Globe
and Lenin

(Des F. Hudeček. Eng B. Housa. Recess*)

1957 (19 Oct). *Television Development. T 303 and similar vert design. P 11½.*
1002 40 h. deep blue and carmine . . 20 10
1003 60 h. brown and green . . 25 10
Design:—60 h. Family watching television.

(Des V. Fiala. Eng J. Schmidt. Recess)

1957 (7 Nov). *40th Anniv of Russian Revolution. T 304 and similar horiz design inscr "1917 1957". P 12×11½.*
1004 30 h. lake . . 20 10
1005 60 h. deep blue . . 25 10
Design:—60 h. Lenin, refinery and Russian emblem.

(Des and eng J. Schmidt. Recess)

1957 (18 Nov). *Death of President Zápotocký. As T 259 but dated "19 XII 1884–13 XI 1957" and colours changed. P 11½.*
1006 30 h. black . . 10 10
1007 60 h. black . . 20 10
MS1007a 70×100 mm. 2 k. blk (as 1006) Imperf 2·50 2·10

(Des K. Svolinský. Eng L. Jirka (1 k. 95), J. Schmidt (others). Recess)

1957 (18 Dec). *National Costumes (third issue). Similar designs to T 270. P 14.*
1008 45 h. sepia, red and blue . . 3·25 1·40
1009 75 h. sepia, red and green . . 2·25 90
1010 1 k. 25, sepia, red and yellow . . 3·25
1011 1 k. 95, sepia, blue and red . . 3·75 2·50
1008/1011 *Set of 4* . . 11·00 5·00
Designs:—45 h. Pilsen woman; 75 h. Slovácko man; 1 k. 25, Haná woman; 1 k. 95, Těšín woman.

305 Artificial Satellite
("Sputnik" 2)

306 Figure Skating
(European Champion-
ships, Bratislava)

(Des F. Hudeček. Eng B. Roule (30 h.), B. Housa (45 h.), L. Jirka (75 h.). Recess*)

1957 (20 Dec). *International Geophysical Year. Designs as T 305 inscr "MEZINÁRODNÍ GEOFYSIKÁLNI ROK 1957–1958". P 11½.*
1012 30 h. purple-brown and yellow . . 1·75 45
1013 45 h. sepia and light blue . . 30 25
1014 75 h. lake and blue . . 2·25 65
Designs:—*Horiz*—30 h. Radio-telescope and observatory. *Vert*—45 h. Lomnický Stit meteorological station.

(Des J. Běhounek (30 h.), J. Kovár (40 h.), M. Stretti (60 h., 80 h.), J. Černý and J. Schmidt (1 k. 60). Eng J. Švengsbir (30 h.), J. Mráček (40 h.), B. Roule (60 h.), B. Housa (80 h.), J. Goldschmied (1 k. 60). Recess)

1958 (25 Jan). *Sports Events of 1958. T 306 and similar vert designs. P 11½×12.*
1015 30 h. reddish purple . . 1·40 25
1016 40 h. deep blue . . 30 20
1017 60 h. brown . . 30 10
1018 80 h. deep violet-blue . . 1·90 80
1019 1 k. 60, emerald . . 50 15
1015/1019 *Set of 5* . . 4·00 1·25
Designs:—40 h. Canoeing (World Canoeing Championships, Prague); 60 h. Volleyball (European Volleyball Championships, Prague); 80 h. Parachuting (Fourth World Parachute-jumping Championships, Bratislava); 1 k. 60, Football (World Cup Football Championship, Stockholm).

307 Litomysl Castle
(birthplace of Nejedly)

308 Soldiers guarding Shrine
of "Victorious February"

(Des and eng J. Švengsbir. Recess)

1958 (10 Feb). *80th Birthday of Zdenek Nejedly (musician). T 307 and similar horiz design. P 11½.*
1020 30 h. deep green . . 20 10
1021 60 h. red-brown . . 20 10
Design:—60 h. Bethlehem Chapel, Prague.

(Des J. Liesler. Eng B. Housa (30 h.), B. Roule (60 h.), J. Mráček (1 k. 60). Recess*)

1958 (25 Feb). *Tenth Anniv of Communist Govt. T 308 and similar designs inscr "1948–1958". P 11½.*
1022 30 h. deep grey-blue and pale yellow . . 30 10
1023 60 h. sepia and carmine . . 30 10
1024 1 k. 60, deep green and pale orange . . 45 10
Designs:—*Vert*—30 h. Giant mine-excavator. *Horiz*—1 k. 60, Combine-harvester.

HAVE YOU READ THE NOTES AT THE BEGINNING OF THIS CATALOGUE?

These often provide answers to the enquiries we receive.

309 Jewellery

310 George of Pode-
brady and his Seal

(Des F. Hudeček (1 k. 95), K. Svolinský (others). Eng
J. Schmidt (45 h., 1 k. 20), L. Jirka (others). Recess*)

1958 (25 Mar–15 July). *Brussels International Exhibition.
Designs as T 309 inscr "Bruxelles 1958". P 11½.*
1025	30 h. carmine and pale blue	..	..	20	10
1026	45 h. red and lilac		..	45	10
1027	60 h. violet and turquoise-green		..	20	10
1028	75 h. blue and orange		..	1·40	75
1029	1 k. 20, blue-green and carmine		..	45	10
1030	1 k. 95, yellow-brown & lt blue (15.7)			70	15
1025/1030	Set of 6	..	..	2·75	1·10

Designs: *Vert*—45 h. Toy dolls; 60 h. Draperies; 75 h.
Kaplan turbine; 1 k. 20, Glassware. *Horiz* (48½×29½ mm.)—
1 k. 95, Czech pavilion.

(Des and eng J. Švengsbir. Recess)

1958 (19 May). *National Exhibition of Archive Documents.
T 310 and similar horiz design inscr as in T 310.* P 12×11½.
| 1031 | 30 h. carmine-red | .. | .. | 30 | 10 |
| 1032 | 60 h. deep violet-blue | .. | | 25 | 10 |

Design:—60 h. Prague, 1628 (from engraving).

311 Hammer and
Sickle

312 "Towards the
Stars" (after sculpture
by G. Postnikov)

(Des F. Hudeček (30 h., 60 h.), V. Polášek (45 h.). Eng B. Housa
(30 h.), B. Roule (45 h.), L. Jirka (60 h.). Recess)

1958 (26 May). *11th Czech Communist Party Congress, and
15th Anniv of Czech-Soviet Friendship Treaty. T 311 and
similar horiz designs inscr "XI. SJEZD KSČ 1958" (45 h.) or
"VÝOČÍ UZAVŘENÍ" etc. (60 h.).* P 12×11½.
1033	30 h. brown-red	..	..	20	10
1034	45 h. green	..	..	20	10
1035	60 h. indigo	..	..	20	10

Designs:—45 h. Map of Czechoslovakia, with sickle and
hammer; 60 h. Atomic reactor, Rež (near Prague).

(Des J. Schmidt (30 h.), J. Černý (45 h., 60 h.), Eng. J. Schmidt
and J. Goldschmied (30 h.). L. Jirka (45 h.), B. Housa (60 h.).
Recess)

1958 (26 May). *Cultural and Political Events. Designs as
T 312 inscr "IV KONGRES MEZINÁRODNI" etc. (45 h.) or
"I. SVETOVA ODBOROVA" etc. P 12×11½ (60 h.) or
11½×12 (others).*
1036	30 h. carmine-red	..	..	65	40
1037	45 h. purple	..	..	20	20
1038	60 h. blue	..	..	20	10

Designs: *Vert*—45 h. Three women of different races standing
before globe (Fourth International Democratic Women's Federa-

tion Congress, Vienna). *Horiz*—60 h. Boy and girl with globes
(First World T.U. Conference of Working Youth, Prague).
T **312** represents the Society for the Dissemination of Cultural
and Political Knowledge.

313 President Novotny

314 Telephone Operator

(Des and eng J. Schmidt. Recess)

1958 (18 June)—**59.** *T 313.*
A. *Ptd in Bratislava.* P 12½ (18.6.58).
B. *Ptd in Prague.* P 12×11½.

		A		B	
1039	30 h. bluish violet	20	10	20	10
1039a	30 h. deep reddish violet				
	(7.12.59)	2·50	1·00	†	
1040	60 h. rose-carmine	20	10	20	10

There are variations in size between the two printings and
also the figures of value in the 60 h. are finer in the Prague
printing.

(Des M. Stretti. Eng L. Jirka and J. Goldschmied (30 h.),
B. Housa and J. Goldschmied (45 h.). Recess*)

1958 (20 June). *Communist Postal Conference, Prague.
T 314 and similar vert designs inscr "KONFERENCE
MINISTRU SPOJU SOCIALISTICKYCH ZEMI-PRAHA-
1958". P 11½×12.*
| 1041 | 30 h. sepia and pale orange-brown | | 25 | 10 |
| 1042 | 45 h. black and pale blue-green | | 25 | 20 |

Design:—45 h. Aerial mast.

315 Karlovy Vary
(600th Anniv)

316 "The Poet and the Muse"
(after Max Švabinský)

(Des V. Šprungl (30 h.), A. Homolka (40 h., 80 h.), K. Tondl
(60 h.), J. Chovan (1 k. 20, 1 k. 60). Eng B. Roule (30 h.,
40 h.), J. Mráček (60 h., 1 k. 20 and 1 k. 60), B. Housa (80 h.).
Recess)

1958 (25 June). *Czech Spas. Horiz designs as T 315.*
P 12×11½.
1043	30 h. lake	..	..	10	10
1044	40 h. red-brown	..	..	10	10
1045	60 h. deep grey-green	..	..	15	10
1046	80 h. sepia	..	..	25	10
1047	1 k. 20, deep ultramarine	..	40	15
1048	1 k. 60, violet	..	..	1·00	90
1043/1048	Set of 6	..	..	1·90	1·10

Spas:—40 h. Poděbrady; 60 h. Mariánské Lázně (150th
Anniv); 80 h. Luhačovice; 1 k. 20, Strbské Pleso; 1 k. 60,
Trenčiánske.

(Des M. Švabinský. Eng J. Schmidt. Recess)

1958 (20 Aug). *85th Birthday of Dr. Max Svabinský (artist).*
P 14.
1049 **316** 1 k. 60, brown-black . . . 3·00 1·25
Printed in sheets of four.

317 S. Cech

318 Children's Hospital. Brno

321 Božek's Steam   **322** Garlanded Woman
Car of 1815   ("Republic") with First
                           Czech Stamps

(Des M. Švabinský. Eng J. Schmidt. Recess)

1958 (20 Aug). *Writers' Anniversaries. Vert portrait designs as
T* **317**. *P* 11½.
1050 30 h. scarlet (Julius Fučík) . . . 25 10
1051 45 h. violet (Gustav K. Zechenter) . . 1·25 50
1052 60 h. indigo (Karel Čapek) . . . 15 10
1053 1 k. 40, black 50 15
1050/1053 *Set of 4* . . . . . . 1·90 75

(Des E. Milen. Eng J. Schmidt. Recess)

1958 (6 Sept). *National Stamp Exhibition, Brno. Horiz
designs as T* **318** *inscr* "BRNO 1958". *P* 14 (1 k. 60) *or*
12×11½ (*others*).
1054 30 h. reddish violet 20 10
1055 60 h. scarlet 20 10
1056 1 k. sepia 45 10
1057 1 k. 60, blackish green . . . 1·75 1·75
1054/1057 *Set of 4* . . . . . 2·40 2·25
Designs:—*As T* **318**—60 h. New Town Hall, Brno; 1 k. St.
Thomas's Church, Red Army Square, Brno. 50×28½ *mm*—1 k. 60,
Brno view.
No. 1057 was issued in sheets of four.

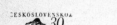

319 Parasol Mushroom   **320** Children sailing
(*Lepiota procera*)

(Des K. Švolinský. Eng L. Jirka. Recess)

1958 (6 Oct). *Mushrooms. Vert designs as T* **319**. *P* 14.
1058 30 h. buff, green and deep brown . . 40 15
1059 40 h. buff, red and purple-brown . . 40 15
1060 60 h. vermilion, buff and purple-black . . 40 15
1061 1 k. 40, scarlet, green & deep brown . 60 20
1062 1 k. 60, brown-red, green and black . . 6·50 1·60
1058/1062 *Set of 5* . . . . . 7·50 2·00
Designs:—40 h. Cep (*Boletus edulis*); 1 k. Red Cap
(*Krombholzia rufescens*); 1 k. 40, Fly agaric (*Amanita muscaria*);
1 k. 60, Boot-lace fungus (*Armillariella mellea*).

(Des after children's drawings. Eng J. Švengsbir. Recess)

1958 (24 Oct). *Inauguration of U.N.E.S.C.O Headquarters
Building, Paris. Vert designs as T* **320**. *P* 14.
1063 30 h. red, yellow and blue . . . 20 10
1064 45 h. carmine-red and bright blue . . 25 10
1065 60 h. blue, yellow and brown . . . 20 10
Designs:—45 h. Mother, child and bird; 60 h. Child skier.

(Des F. Hudeček. Eng L. Jirka (30 h.), B. Housa (45 h.),
B. Roule (60 h., 1 k. 25), J. Mráček (80 h.), J. Švengsbír
(1 k.). Recess*)

1958 (1 Dec). *Czech Motor Industry Commemoration. Horiz
designs as T* **321**. *P* 12×11½.
1066 30 h. slate-violet and yellow . . . 70 10
1067 45 h. sepia and apple-green . . . 50 10
1068 60 h. deep green and salmon . . . 70 10
1069 80 h. lake and blue-green . . . 50 10
1070 1 k. brown and pale green . . . 50 10
1071 1 k. 25, grey-green and yellow . . 2·25 75
1066/1071 *Set of 6* . . . . . 4·75 1·10
Designs:—45 h. "President" car of 1897; 60 h. Skoda "450"
car; 80 h. Tatra "603" car; 1 k. Skoda "706" motor coach;
1 k. 25, Tatra "III" and Praga "VS3" motor trucks in Tibet.

(Des M. Švabinský. Eng J. Schmidt. Recess)

1958 (18 Dec). *40th Anniv of First Czech Postage Stamps.*
P 11½×12.
1072 **322** 60 h. indigo 25 10

323 Ice Hockey Goalkeeper

324 U.A.C. Emblem

(Des M. Stretti. Eng. J. Švengsbir (20 h.), B. Roule (30 h.),
J. Schmidt (60 h.), B. Housa (1 k.), J. Mráček (1 k. 60).
J. Goldschmied and J. Schmidt (2 k.). Recess*)

1959 (14 Feb). *Sports Events of 1959. T* **323** *and similar
horiz designs. P* 12×11½.
1073 20 h. brown-purple and grey-green . . 30 10
1074 30 h. brown and orange . . . 30 10
1075 60 h. ultramarine and pale green . . 30 10
1076 1 k. lake and light greenish yellow . . 30 10
1077 1 k. 60, slate-violet and light blue . . 45 10
1078 2 k. red-brown and pale blue . . . 1·60 1·40
1073/1078 *Set of 6* . . . . . 3·00 1·60
Designs:—20 h. Ice hockey player (50th anniv of Czech Ice
Hockey Association); 30 h. Throwing the javelin; 60 h. T **323**
(World Ice Hockey Championships, 1959); 1 k. Hurdling; 1 k. 60,
Rowing; 2 k. High jumping.

(Des F. Hudeček. Eng J. Mráček (30 h.), J. Goldschmied (60 h.).
Recess*)

1959 (27 Feb). *Fourth National Unified Agricultural Co-operatives Congress, Prague. T* **324** *and a similar vert design inscr*
"IV CELOSTATNI SJEZD JZD". *P* 11½×12.
1079 30 h. brown-lake and light blue . . 15 10
1080 60 h. indigo and yellow . . . 30 10
Design:—60 h. Artisan shaking hands with farmer.

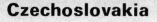

325 "Equal Rights" **326** Girl with Doll **327** F. Joliot-Curie
(scientist)

(Des M. Švabinský. Eng J. Schmidt. Recess)

1959 (23 Mar). *Tenth Anniv of Declaration of Human Rights.
T 325 and similar vert designs inscr* "DEN LIDSKYCH PRÁV"
etc. P 11½×12.
1081	60 h. deep slate-green	15	10
1082	1 k. blackish brown	25	10
1083	2 k. indigo	1·10	50

Designs:—1 k. "World Freedom" (girl with Dove of Peace).
2 k. "Freedom for Colonial peoples" (native woman with child).

(Des J. Baláž. Eng J. Schmidt (30 h., 40 h.), L. Jirka (60 h.,
80 h.). Recess*)

1959 (28 Mar). *Tenth Anniv of Young Pioneers Movement.
Vert designs as T **326**. P 11½×12.*
1084	30 h. deep bluish violet and yellow	30	10
1085	40 h. black and blue	30	20
1086	60 h. black and reddish violet	30	10
1087	80 h. brown and green	30	20
1084/1087	*Set of 4*	1·10	50

Designs:—40 h. Boy hiker; 60 h. Young radio technician; 80 h.
Girl planting tree.

(Des M. Švabinský. Eng J. Schmidt. Recess)

1959 (17 Apr). *Tenth Anniv of Peace Movement. P 11½×12*
1088	**327** 60 h. slate-purple	1·60	25

328 Man in outer space,   **329** Pilsen Town Hall
and Moon Rocket

(Des V. Němeček. Eng B. Housa. Recess)

1959 (17 Apr). *2nd Czech Political and Cultural Knowledge
Congress, Prague. P 11½×12.*
1089	**328** 30 h. deep violet-blue	1·25	25

(Des and eng J. Švengsbir. Recess; backgrounds photo on
60 h. and 1 k. 60)

1959 (2 May). *Skoda Works Centenary and National Stamp
Exhibition, Pilsen. T **329** and similar vert designs inscr*
"PLZEN 1959". *P 11½×12.*
1090	30 h. brown	15	10
1091	60 h. reddish violet and light green	15	10
1092	1 k. deep blue	25	15
1093	1 k. 60, black and yellow	1·25	1·10
1090/1093	*Set of 4*	1·60	1·25

Designs:—60 h. Part of steam turbine; 1 k. St. Bartholomew's
Church, Pilsen; 1 k. 60, Part of SR-1200 lathe.

330 Congress Emblem and Industrial Plant

(Des V. Polášek (30 h.), Z. Brdlik (60 h.). Eng J. Mráček.
Recess*)

1959 (13 May). *Fourth Trades Union Congress, Prague. T **330**
and similar horiz design. P 12×11½.*
1094	30 h. carmine and yellow	20	10
1095	60 h. brown-olive and blue (Dam)	20	10

331 Zvolen Castle   **332** F. Benda
(composer)

(Des and eng J. Švengsbir. Recess*)

1959 (13 June). *Slovak Stamp Exhibition, Zvolen. P 12×11½.*
1096	**331** 60 h. olive and pale yellow	50	10

(Des K. Švolinský (15 h., 30 h., 60 h. (1101), 1 k., 3 k.),
M. Švabinský (others). Eng J. Schmidt. Recess)

1959 (22 June–16 Oct). *Cultural Anniversaries. Vert portrait
designs as T **332**. P 11½×12.*
1097	15 h. deep blue	20	10
1098	30 h. brown-red	20	10
1099	40 h. slate-green	25	10
1100	60 h. chocolate	25	10
1101	60 h. violet-black (16.10)	45	15
1102	80 h. dull violet	25	10
1103	1 k. sepia	25	10
1104	3 k. chocolate (16.10)	1·25	75
1097/1104	*Set of 8*	2·75	1·10

Portraits:—30 h. Vaclav Klicpera (dramatist); 40 h. Aurel Stodola
(engineer); 60 h. Karel V. Rais (writer); 60 h. Haydn (composer);
80 h. Antonín Slaviček (painter); 1 k. Petr Bezruč (poet); 3 k.
Charles Darwin (naturalist).

333 "Z" Pavilion

(Des F. Hudeček (30 h., 1 k. 60), A. Pražsky (60 h.). Eng L. Jirka
(30 h.), B. Housa (60 h.), B. Roule (1 k. 60). Recess;
backgrounds photo (30 h., 1 k. 60).

1959 (20 July). *International Fair, Brno. T **333** and similar
horiz designs inscr* "MEZI. NÁRODNI VELETRH BRNO 6–20.
IX. 1959". *P 12×11½.*
1105	30 h. purple and yellow	15	10
1106	60 h. greenish blue	15	10
1107	1 k. 60, deep blue and yellow	40	10

Designs:—30 h. General view of Fair; 60 h. Fair emblem
and world map.

334 Revolutionary (after A. Holly)

(Des and eng B. Housa (30 h.), B. Roule (60 h.), J. Švengsbir (1 k. 60). Recess (60 h.) or recess* (others))

1959 (29 Aug). *15th Anniv of Slovak National Uprising, and 40th Anniv of Republic. T* **334** *and similar designs inscr "1944 29.8.1959". P* 11½×12 (60 h.) *or* 12×11½ *(others).*
1108   30 h. black and magenta   . .   15   10
1109   60 h. claret   20   10
1110   1 k. 60, indigo and yellow   . .   40   10
Designs:—*Vert*—60 h. Revolutionary with upraised rifle (after sculpture "Forward" by L. Snopka). *Horiz*—1 k. 60, Factory, sun and linden leaves.

335 Moon Rocket   **336** Lynx

(Des V. Polášek. Eng L. Jirka. Recess*)

1959 (23 Sept). *Landing of Russian Rocket on the Moon. P* 12×11½.
1111 **335** 60 h. scarlet and blue   . .   1·40   25

(Des J. Baláž. Eng B. Housa (30 h.), J. Mráček (40 h., 60 h.), B. Roule (1 k.), J. Goldschmied (1 k. 60). Recess*)

1959 (25 Sept). *Tenth Anniv of Tatra National Park. T* **336** *and similar horiz designs inscr "*1949 TATRANSKY NARODNY PARK 1959". P 11½×12 (60 h.) or 12×11½ *(others).*
1112   30 h. black and grey   . .   65   10
1113   40 h. chocolate and turquoise   . .   65   10
1114   60 h. brown-red and yellow   . .   1·40   10
1115   1 k. olive-brown and pale blue   . .   1·90   75
1116   1 k. 60, red-brown & pale red-brown   . .   1·40   10
1112/1116   *Set of* 5   . .   . .   5·50   1·00
Designs:—30 h. Alpine marmots; 40 h. European bison: 1 k. Wolf; 1 k. 60, Red deer.

337 Stamp Printing Works, Peking

(Eng B. Housa. Recess*)

1959 (1 Oct). *Tenth Anniv of Chinese People's Republic. P* 12×11½.
1117 **337** 30 h. brown-red & pale yellow-green   35   10

338 Blériot XI Monoplanes at First Czech Aviation School

339 Great Spotted Woodpecker

(Des K. Lhoták. Eng J. Švengsbir. Recess*)

1959 (15 Oct). *AIR. 50th Anniv of First Flight by Jan Kaspar. T* **338** *and similar horiz design inscr "*50 VYROČI PRVNIHO VZLETU INZ KAŠPARA". P 12×11½.
1118   1 k. black and yellow   20   10
1119   1 k. 80, black and pale blue   . .   1·00   10
Design:—1 k. 80, Jan Kašpar and Blériot XI in flight.

(Des K. Švolinský. Eng L. Jirka. Recess)

1959 (16 Nov). *Birds. Horiz designs as T* **339**. *P* 14.
1120   20 h. red, brown, blue and black   . .   90   20
1121   30 h. blue, yellow, brown and black   . .   90   20
1122   40 h. slate, orange, brown and sepia   . .   3·00   1·10
1123   60 h. red, brown, yellow and black   . .   90   20
1124   80 h. yellow, orange-brown, red & black   . .   90   20
1125   1 k. red, blue and black   90   20
1126   1 k. 20, orange-brn, bl, bl-grn & blk   . .   2·00   50
1120/1126   *Set of* 7   . .   . .   8·50   2·40
Designs:—30 h. Blue tit; 40 h. European nuthatch; 60 h. Golden oriole; 80 h. Goldfinch; 1 k. Bullfinch; 1 k. 20, Common kingfisher.

340 Nikola Tesla and   **341** Exercises
Electrical Apparatus

(Des C. Bouda. Eng J. Goldschmied (25 h.), L. Jirka (30 h.), B. Housa (35 h.), J. Mráček (60 h.), B. Roule (1 k.), J. Schmidt (2 k.). Recess*)

1959 (7 Dec). *Radio Inventors. Horiz portrait designs as T* **340**. *P* 12×11½.
1127   25 h. black and rose   . .   . .   1·25   25
1128   30 h. black and orange-brown   . .   15   10
1129   35 h. black and lilac   . .   20   10
1130   60 h. black and blue   . .   30   10
1131   1 k. black and turquoise-green   . .   20   10
1132   2 k. black and yellow-bistre   . .   90   70
1127/1132   *Set of* 6   . .   . .   2·75   1·00
Inventors (each with sketch of invention):—30 h. Aleksandr Popov; 35 h. Edouard Branly; 60 h. Guglielmo Marconi; 1 k. Heinrich Hertz; 2 k. Edwin Armstrong.

(Des Anna Podzemná. Eng J. Schmidt (30 h.), B. Housa (1 k. 60). Des M. Stretti. Eng L. Jirka (60 h.). Recess*)

1960 (20 Jan). *Second National Spartacist Games (first issue). T* **341** *and similar vert designs inscr "*II CELOSTÁTNI SPARTAKIÁDA 1960". P 11½×12.
1133   30 h. sepia and orange-red   . .   . .   1·00   10
1134   60 h. indigo and light blue (Skiing)   . .   50   15
1135   1 k. 60, sepia & yell-bistre (Basketball)   55   25
See also Nos. 1160/2.

342 Freighter *Lidice*

(Des F. Hudeček. Eng B. Roule (30 h., 60 h.), Jan Mráček (1 k.), J. Švengsbir (1 k. 20). Recess*)

1960 (22 Feb). *Czech Ships. T* **342** *and similar horiz designs. P* 12×11½.
1136   30 h. bronze-green and orange-red   . .   80   15
1137   60 h. lake and pale turquoise   . .   35   10

1138   1 k. violet and light yellow   80   20
1139   1 k. 20, purple and pale green   . .   1·90   1·50
1136/1139 Set of 4   . .   . .   3·50   1·75
Ships:—30 h. *Praha Liben* (dredger); 60 h. *Kharito Latjev* (tug);
1 k. *Komarno* (river boat).

343 Ice Hockey

(Des M. Stretti. Eng L. Jirka (60 h.), J. Schmidt (1 k. 80).
Recess*)

1960 (27 Feb). *Winter Olympic Games. T* **343** *and similar
horiz design. P* 11½.
1140   60 h. sepia and light blue   40   25
1141   1 k. 80, black & blue-green (Skating)   4·00   2·50
See also Nos. 1163/5.

344 Trenčin Castle   **344***a*

(Des A. Hollý (5 h., 40 h., 1 k.), J. Šváb (others). Eng J.
Švengsbir (5 h., 40 h.), B. Housa (10 h., 30 h., 50 h.),
J. Schmidt (20 h.), J. Mráček (60 h.), B. Roule (1 k.),
L. Jirka (1 k. 60). Recess)

1960 (21 Mar)–**63**. *Czechoslovak Castles. Vert designs as
T* **344**. *No wmk. P* 12×11½.
1142   5 h. deep violet-blue   15   10
1143   10 h. black (Bezděz)   15   10
1144   20 h. red-orange (Kost)   25   10
1145   30 h. deep emerald (Pernštejn)   . .   25   10
    a. Error. W **344***a* (10.61)   . .   1·50   50
1146   40 h. brown (Kremnica)   25   10
1146*a* 50 h. black (Křivoklát) (15.10.63)   . .   25   10
1147   60 h. rose-red (Karlštejn)   40   10
1148   1 k. purple (Smolenice)   30   10
1149   1 k. 60, blue (Kokořín)   60   10
1142/1149 Set of 9 . .   . .   2·40   40

345 Lenin   **346** Soldier and Child

(Des K. Svolinský. Eng L. Jirka. Recess)

1960 (22 Apr). *90th Birth Anniv of Lenin. P* 11½×12.
1150 **345** 60 h. deep olive   75   20

(Des M. Stretti (1151), Anna Podzemná (1152/3), V. Polášek
(1154/5). Eng B. Housa (1152), J. Mráček (1155), J. Švengsbir
(others). Recess*)
1960 (5 May). *15th Anniv of Liberation. T* **346** *and similar
designs inscr* "15 VÝROČI OSVOBOZENI" *etc. P* 11½×12
(*Nos.* 1151/53) *or* 12×11½ (*others*).
1151   30 h. lake and pale blue   30   10
1152   30 h. blackish green and lavender   . .   25   10
1153   30 h. red and pink   25   10
1154   60 h. blue and buff   25   10
1155   60 h. maroon and pale green   25   10
1151/1155 Set of 5 . .   . .   1·10   35
Designs: *Vert*—No. 1151, T **346**; 1152, Soldier with liberated
political prisoner; 1153, Child eating pastry. *Horiz*—1154,
Welder; 1155, Tractor-driver.

347 Smelter

(Des J. Podhajský. Eng J. Mráček. Recess*)

1960 (24 May). *Parliamentary Elections. T* **347** *and similar
horiz design inscr* "ZA DALSI ROZVOJ NASI VLASTI"
P 12×11½.
1156   30 h. brown-lake and grey   . .   15   10
1157   60 h. deep green and pale blue   . .   20   10
Design:—60 h. Countrywoman and child.

348 Red Cross Woman with Dove

(Des I. Vraná-Šnajdrova. Eng B. Roule. Recess*)

1960 (26 May). *Third Czechoslovak Red Cross Congress.
P* 12×11½.
1158 **348** 30 h. brown-red and pale blue   . .   20   10

349 Fire-prevention Team with Hose

(Des J. Lukavský. Eng B. Roule. Recess*)

1960 (26 May). *Second Firemen's Union Congress. P* 12 ×11½.
1159 **349** 60 h. deep blue and pink   . .   30   10

(Des Anna Podzemná. Eng J. Švengsbír. Recess*)

1960 (15 June). *Second National Spartacist Games* (*second
issue*). *Designs similar to T* **341**. *P* 11½×12.
1160   30 h. brown-red and light green   . .   45   10
1161   60 h. black and pink   45   10
1162   1 k. ultramarine and yellow-orange   . .   65   15
Designs: –30 h. Ball exercises; 60 h. Stick exercises;
1 k. Three girls with hoops.

(Des Z. Adámek. Eng B. Housa (1 k. 80), Des M. Stretti.
Eng J. Schmidt (others). Recess*)

1960 (15 June). *Olympic Games, Rome. Horiz designs similar to
T* **343**. *P* 11½.
1163   1 k. black and yellow-orange (Sprinting)   50   20
1164   1 k. 80, black and red (Gymnastics)   . .   1·25   25
1165   2 k. black and light blue (Rowing)   . .   2·50   80

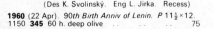

CZECHOSLOVAKIAN SOCIALIST REPUBLIC
11 July 1960–31 Dec 1968

350 Czech 10 k. stamp of 1936

(Des J. Baláž. Eng B. Roule. Recess*)

1960 (11 July). *National Philatelic Exhibition, Bratislava (first issue).* T **350** *and similar horiz design inscr* "BRATISLAVA 1960". P 12×11½.

| 1166 | 60 h. black and yellow | 45 | 15 |
| 1167 | 1 k. black and blue | 80 | 15 |

Design:—60 h. Hand of philatelist holding stamp T **350**. See Nos. 1183/4.

351 Stalin Mine, Ostrava-Heřmanice

(Des F. Hudeček. Eng J. Goldschmied (10 h.), J. Mráček (20, 40 h.), B. Housa (others). Recess*)

1960 (25 July). *Third Five Year Plan (first issue).* T **351** *and similar horiz designs inscr* "III PĚTILETKA-PLAN" *etc.* P 11½.

1168	10 h. black and light green	20	10
1169	20 h. lake and light blue	20	10
1170	30 h. indigo and rose	20	10
1171	40 h. deep bluish green and lilac	20	10
1172	60 h. deep ultramarine and yellow	20	10
1168/1172	Set of 5	90	30

Designs:—20 h. Hodonin Power Station; 30 h. Klement Gottwald Iron Works, Kunčice; 40 h. Excavator; 60 h. Naphtha refinery.
See Nos. 1198/1200.

352 V. Cornelius of Všehra (historian)

353 Zlin Trener 6 flying upside-down

(Des M. Švabinský (30, 60 h.), V. Silovský (others). Eng J. Schmidt. Recess)

1960 (23 Aug). *Cultural Anniversaries. Vert portrait designs as* T **352**. P 11½×12.

1173	10 h. black	20	10
1174	20 h. chocolate	30	10
1175	30 h. rose-red	40	10
1176	40 h. deep green	45	10
1177	60 h. bluish violet	50	10
1173/1177	Set of 5	1·60	40

Portraits—20 h. K. M. Capek-Chod (writer); 30 h. Hana Kvapilová (actress); 40 h. Oskar Nedbal (composer); 60 h. Otakar Ostrčil (composer).

(Des K. Vysušil. Eng J. Mráček. Recess*)

1960 (28 Aug). *First World Aviation Aerobatic Championships, Bratislava.* P 12×11½.

| 1178 | **353** | 60 h. violet and blue | 60 | 15 |

354 "New Constitution"

355 Worker with *Rudé Právo*

(Des K. Svolinský. Eng J. Schmidt. Recess*)

1960 (18 Sept). *Proclamation of New Constitution.* P 12×11½.

| 1179 | **354** | 30 h. ultramarine and rose-red | 20 | 10 |

(Des M. Kopřiva. Eng L. Jirka (30 h.), J. Goldschmied (60 h.). Recess*)

1960 (18 Sept). *Czechoslovak Press Day (30 h.) and 40th Anniv of newspaper "Rude Pravo" (60 h.).* T **355** *and similar design inscr* "DEN TISKU". P 12×11½ (30 h.) *or* 11½×12 (60 h.).

| 1180 | 30 h. indigo and red-orange | 10 | 10 |
| 1181 | 60 h. black and rose-red | 20 | 10 |

Design: Horiz—30 h. Steel-workers with newspaper.

356 Globes

(Des M. Hegar. Eng B. Housa. Recess*)

1960 (18 Sept). *15th Anniv of World Federation of Trades Unions.* P 12×11½.

| 1182 | **356** | 30 h. deep blue and bistre | 25 | 10 |

357 Mail Coach and Ilyushin II-18B

(Des J. Baláž. Eng B. Roule. Recess*)

1960 (24 Sept). *AIR. National Philatelic Exhibition, Bratislava (second issue).* T **357** *and similar horiz design.* P 11½.

| 1183 | 1 k. 60, indigo and grey | 3·00 | 1·25 |
| 1184 | 2 k. 80, deep green and cream | 4·50 | 1·60 |

Design:—2 k. 80, MIL Mi-4 helicopter over Bratislava.

358 Mallard

359 *Doronicum clusii Tausch*

(Des O. Janeček. Eng B. Housa (25, 30 h., 1 k. 60), J. Švengsbír (others). Recess*)

1960 (24 Oct). *Water Birds. Designs as T 358. P 12×11½ (1 k., 1 k. 60) or 11½×12 (others).*

1185	25 h. black and cobalt	40	10
1186	30 h. black and pale green	1·25	10
1187	40 h. black and turquoise-blue	60	15
1188	60 h. black and pink	95	10
1189	1 k. black and yellow	1·25	15
1190	1 k. 60, black and lilac	3·75	1·40
1185/1190	Set of 6	7·50	1·75

Designs: *Vert*—25 h. Black-crowned night heron; 30 h. Great crested grebe; 40 h. Lapwing; 60 h. Grey heron. *Horiz*—1 k. Greylag goose; 1 k. 60, T 358.

(Des K. Svolinský. Eng L. Jirka. Recess)

1960 (21 Nov). *Flowers. T 359 and similar vert designs. P 14.*

1191	20 h. yellow, orange, yellow-grn & blk	30	10
1192	30 h. carmine-red, blue-green & black	50	15
1193	40 h. yellow, emerald-green and black	50	10
1194	60 h. rose, green and black	55	10
1195	1 k. blue, violet, green and black	85	20
1196	2 k. yellow, green, purple and black	2·50	1·00
1191/1196	Set of 6	4·75	1·40

Flowers:—30 h. *Cyclamen europaeum* L.; 40 h. *Primula auricula* L.; 60 h. *Sempervivum mont.* L.; 1 k. *Gentiana clusii* Perr. et Song.; 2 k. *Pulsatilla slavica* Reuss.

360 A. Mucha (painter and stamp designer)

361 Automatic Machinery

(Des M. Švabinský. Eng J. Schmidt. Recess)

1960 (18 Dec). *Stamp Day and Birth Centenary of Mucha. P 11½×12.*

1197	360	60 h. indigo	60	10

(Des J. Podhajský. Eng J. Goldschmied (20 h.), J. Švengsbír (others). Recess)

1961 (20 Jan). *Third Five Year Plan (second issue). T 361 and similar vert designs inscr "TRETÍ PĚTILETY PLÁN". P 11½.*

1198	20 h. blue	10	10
1199	30 h. red	15	10
1200	60 h. emerald	15	10

Designs:—30 h. Turbo-generator and control desk; 60 h. Excavator.

362 Motor Cyclists (International Grand Prix, Brno)

(Des Anna Podzemná; eng B. Housa (30 h. (1201), 1 k. 20). Des A. Suchardová Podzemná; eng J. Mráček (30 h. (1202)). Des V. Kovářík; eng L. Jirka (40 h.). Des I. Strnad; eng L. Jirka (60 h., 1 k.). Des and eng V. Kovářík (1 k. 60). Recess*)

1961 (10 Feb). *Sports Events of 1961. T 362 and similar designs. P 12×11½ (Nos. 1201, 1203) or 11½×12 (others).*

1201	30 h. indigo and magenta	20	10
1202	30 h. brown-red and blue	20	10
1203	40 h. black and carmine	45	10
1204	60 h. reddish purple and blue	45	10
1205	1 k. ultramarine and yellow	45	10
1206	1 k. 20, green and salmon	45	15
1207	1 k. 60, brown and orange-red	2·00	1·25
1201/1207	Set of 7	3·75	1·50

Designs: *Horiz*—30 h. (No. 1201), T 362; 40 h. Rowing (European Rowing Championships, Prague). *Vert*—30 h. (1202), Athletes with banners (40th Anniv of Czech physical culture); 60 h. Figure skating (World Figure Skating Championships, Prague); 1 k. Rugger (35th Anniv of rugby football in Czechoslovakia); 1 k. 20, Football (60th anniv of football in Czechoslovakia); 1 k. 60, Running (65th anniv of Běchovice–Prague marathon race).

363 Exhibition Emblem

364 "Sputnik 3"

(Des M. Hegar. Eng J. Mráček. Recess*)

1961 (6 Mar). *"Praga 1962" International Stamp Exhibition (first issue). P 11½×12.*

1208	363	2 k. carmine and deep ultramarine	1·90	10

See also Nos. 1250/6, 1267/70, 1297/1300 and 1311/5b.

(Des F. Hudeček. Eng B. Housa (20 h., 40 h.), J. Švengsbír (30 h., 60 h.), J. Mráček (1 k. 60), L. Jirka (2 k.). Recess*)

1961 (6 Mar). *Space Research (1st series). T 364 and similar designs. P 11½×12 (20, 40 h.) or 12×11½ (others).*

1209	20 h. rose-red and deep violet	50	10
1210	30 h. turquoise-blue and yellow-buff	50	10
1211	40 h. carmine and light yellow-green	45	15
1212	60 h. violet and orange-yellow	30	10
1213	1 k. 60, grey-blue & pale yellow-green	50	10
1214	2 k. brown-purple and pale blue	2·10	1·25
1209/1214	Set of 6	4·00	1·50

Designs: *Horiz*—60 h. "Lunik 1"; 1 k. 60, "Lunik 3" and Moon; 2 k. Cosmonaut (similar to T 366). *Vert*—20 h. Launching cosmic rocket; 40 h. Venus rocket.

See also Nos. 1285/90 and 1349/54.

365 J. Mošna (actor)

366 Man in Space

(Des M. Švabinský. Eng J. Schmidt. Recess)

1961 (27 Mar). *Cultural Anniversaries. Vert portrait designs as T 365. P 11½×12.*

1215	60 h. deep green	25	10
1216	60 h. black	30	10
1217	60 h. indigo	30	10
1218	60 h. brown-lake	25	10
1219	60 h. sepia	25	10
1215/1219	Set of 5	1·25	25

Portraits:—No. 1215, T 365; 1216, J. Uprka (painter); 1217, P. O. Hviezdoslav (poet). 1218, A. Mrštik (writer); 1219, J. Hora (poet).

(Des F. Hudeček. Eng L. Jirka. Recess*)

1961 (13 Apr). *World's First Manned Space-flight.* P 12×11½.
1220 **366** 60 h. carmine-red and turquoise . . 50 10
1221 3 k. ultramarine and yellow . . 2·25 65

371 Gagarin
waving Flags

372 Woman's Head and
Map of Africa

367 Kladno Steel Mills

368 "Instrumental Music"

(Des C. Bouda. Eng L. Jirka. Recess)

1961 (24 April). *P.* 11½.
1222 **367** 3 k. brown-red . . 90 10

(Des K. Svolinský. Eng L. Jirka. Recess)

1961 (24 Apr). *150th Anniv of Prague Conservatoire.* T **368** *and similar vert designs inscr* "150 let pražske konservatoře". *P* 11½×12.
1223 30 h. deep sepia (Type **368**) . . 30 15
1224 30 h. deep brown-red (Dancer) . . 35 15
1225 60 h. deep blue (Girl playing lyre) . . 30 15

(Des C. Bouda. Eng J. Švengsbir (60 h.), J. Mráček (1 k. 60).
Recess*)

1961 (22 June). *Yuri Gagarin's (first man in space) Visit to Prague.* T **371** *and similar vert design.* P 11½×12.
1237 60 h. black and rose-red . . 25 10
1238 1 k. 80, black and blue . . 40 15
Design:—1 k. 80, Gagarin in space helmet, rocket and dove.

(Des V. Bauer. Eng L. Jirka. Recess*)

1961 (26 June). *Czecho-African Friendship.* P 12×11½.
1239 **372** 60 h. brown-red and light blue . . 25 10

373 Map of Europe and
Fair Emblem

374 Clover and Cow

369 "People's House"
(Lenin Museum), Prague

370 Manasek Doll

(Des R. Klimovič. Eng L. Jirka (Nos. 1226/7), J. Mráček
(others). Recess)

1961 (10 May). *40th Anniv of Czech Communist Party.* T **369** *and similar designs.* P 12×11½ (*Nos.* 1226/7) or 11½×12 (*others*).
1226 30 h. chocolate 20 10
1227 30 h. indigo 20 10
1228 30 h. deep violet 20 10
1229 60 h. carmine-red 20 10
1230 60 h. myrtle-green 20 10
1231 60 h. orange-red 20 10
1226/1231 Set of 6 . . . . 1·10 25
Designs: *Horiz*—No. 1226, T **369**; 1227, Gottwald's Museum, Prague. *Vert*—1228, Workers in Wenceslas Square, Prague; 1229, Worker, star and factory plant; 1230, Woman wielding hammer and sickle; 1231, May Day procession, Wenceslas Square.

(Des V. Cinybulk. Eng J. Švengsbir. Recess*)

1961 (20 June). *Czech Puppets.* T **370** *and similar vert designs.* P 11½×12.
1232 30 h. red and yellow . . 20 10
1233 40 h. sepia and turquoise . . 20 10
1234 60 h. ultramarine and salmon . . 20 10
1235 1 k. deep bluish green and light blue . . 20 10
1236 1 k. 60, brown-red and violet-blue . . 1·25 40
1232/1236 Set of 5 . . 1·90 55
Puppets:—40 h. "Dr. Faustus and Caspar"; 60 h. "Spejbl and Hurvinek"; 1 k. Scene from "Difficulties with the Moon" (Aškenazy); 1 k. 60, "Jasánek" of Brno.

(Des F. Hudeček. Eng L. Jirka (1 k.), J. Goldschmied (others).
Recess*)

1961 (14 Aug). *International Trade Fair, Brno.* T **373** *and similar designs inscr* "M.V.B. 1961". *P* 11½×12 (60 *h.*) or 12×11½ (*others*).
1240 30 h. ultramarine and pale green . . 15 10
1241 60 h. slate-green and salmon . . 25 10
1242 1 k. chocolate and pale blue . . 25 10
Designs: *Vert*—60 h. Horizontal drill. *Horiz*—1 k. Scientific discussion group.

(Des C. Bouda. Eng L. Jirka. Recess*)

1961 (18 Sept). *Agricultural Produce.* T **374** *and similar vert designs.* P 11½×12.
1243 20 h. reddish purple and indigo . . 15 10
1244 30 h. ochre and brown-purple . . 15 10
1245 40 h. orange and chocolate . . 15 10
1246 60 h. bistre and slate-green . . 20 10
1247 1 k. 40, orange-brown and chocolate . . 40 10
1248 2 k. blue and slate-purple . . 1·40 55
1243/1248 Set of 6 . . 2·10 85
Designs:—20 h. Sugar beet, cup and saucer; 40 h. Wheat and bread; 60 h. Hops and beer; 1 k. 40, Maize and cattle; 2 k. Potatoes and factory.

375 Prague   **376** Orlik Dam

(Des J. Šváb. Eng J. Goldschmied. Recess*)

1961 (25 Sept). *Twenty-sixth Session of Red Cross Societies League Governors' Council, Prague.* P 11½×12.
1249 **375** 60 h. slate-violet and red 85 10

(Des C. Bouda. Eng J. Švengsbir (20 h., 1 k. 20, 4 k.), L. Jirka (30 h.), J. Mráček (others). Recess*)

1961 (23 Oct). *"Praga* 1962" *International Stamp Exhibition (second issue). T* **376** *and similar horiz designs inscr* "PRAGA 1962" *within globe.* P 12×11½.
1250   20 h. black and blue 65 15
1251   30 h. blue and red 20 10
1252   40 h. grey-blue and pale green .. 65 15
1253   60 h. slate and pale bistre .. 65 15
1254   1 k. 20, deep bluish-green and pink .. 85 50
1255   3 k. blue and light yellow .. 2·00 50
1256   4 k. reddish violet and orange .. 2·50 1·25
1250/1256   *Set of 7* .. .. 7·00 2·50
Designs:—30 h. View of Prague; 40 h. Hluboka Castle from lake; 60 h. Karlovy Vary; 1 k. 20, North Bohemian landscape; 3 k. Brno; 4 k. Bratislava.
For other values, see Nos. 1267/70.

377 Orange-tip   **378** Congress Emblem
(*Anthocharis*   and World Map
cardamines)

(Des M. Švabinský. Eng J. Schmidt. Recess)

1961 (27 Nov). *Butterflies and Moths. T* **377** *and similar vert designs. Multicoloured.* P 14.
1257   15 h. Type **377** 50 10
1258   20 h. Southern festoon (*Zerynthia hypsipyle*) .. 70 10
1259   30 h. Apollo (*Parnassius apollo*) .. 1·00 15
1260   40 h. Swallowtail (*Papilio machaon*) .. 1·00 25
1261   60 h. Peacock (*Nymphalis io*) (wrongly inscr "Jo") .. 1·25 25
1262   80 h. Camberwell beauty (*Nymphalis antiopa*) 1·50 30
1263   1 k. Clifden's nonpareil (*Catocala fraxini*) 1·50 30
1264   1 k. 60 Red admiral (*Vanessa atalanta*) 1·75 40
1265   2 k. Brimstone (*Gonepteryx rhamni*) .. 4·50 2·00
1257/1265   *Set of 9* .. .. .. 12·50 3·50

(Des M. Juna. Eng J. Goldschmied. Recess*)

1961 (27 Nov). *Fifth World Federation of Trades Unions Congress, Moscow.* P 12×11½.
1266 **378** 60 h. blue and carmine-red .. 35 10

(Des C. Bouda. Eng L. Jirka (1, 2 k.), J. Mráček (1 k. 60), J. Schmidt (5 k.). Recess (5 k.) or recess* (others))

1961 (18 Dec). *"Praga* 1962" *International Stamp Exhibition (third issue). Horiz designs as T* **376**. P 14 (5 k.) or 12×11½ (others).
1267   1 k. brown-red and green 65 50
1268   1 k. 60, brown and bluish violet .. 1·10 70
1269   2 k. black and yellow-orange .. 1·50 1·25
1270   5 k. multicoloured .. .. 24·00 22·00
1267/1270   *Set of 4* .. .. 25·00 22·00
Views:—1 k. Pilsen; 1 k. 60, High Tatras; 2 k Gottwald Ironworks, Ostrava-Kunčice; 5 k. Prague (50×29 *mm*.).
No. 1270 was only issued in sheets of four.

379 Racing Cyclists   **380** K. Kovařovic
(Berlin–Prague–Warsaw   (composer, centenary
Cycle Race)   of birth)

(Des J. Černý (30 h., 1 k., 1 k. 20), Anna Podzemná (40 h., 60 h., 1 k. 60). Eng L. Mráček (30 h., 1 k. 60), J. Švengsbir (40 h., 1 k.), B. Housa (60 h.), L. Jirka (1 k. 20). Recess*)

1962 (5 Feb). *Sports Events of 1962. Vert designs as T* **379**. P 11½×12.
1271   30 h. black and violet-blue .. 25 10
1272   40 h. black and yellow . . 20 10
1273   60 h. slate-blue and light blue .. 30 10
1274   1 k. black and rose-pink .. 30 10
1275   1 k. 20, black and green .. 30 10
1276   1 k. 60, black and yellow-green .. 1·40 70
1271/1276   *Set of 6* .. . . 2·50 95
Designs:—40 h. Gymnastics (15th World Gymnastics Championships, Prague); 60 h. Figure skating (World Figure Skating Championships, Prague); 1 k. Bowling (World Bowling Championships, Bratislava); 1 k. 20, Football (World Cup Football Championship, Chile); 1 k. 60, Throwing the discus (7th European Athletic Championships, Belgrade).
For 1 k. 60 stamp as No. 1275, see No. 1306.

(Des M. Švabinský. Eng J. Schmidt. Recess)

1962 (26 Feb). *Cultural Celebrities and Anniversaries. T* **380** *and similar designs.* P 12×11½.
1277   10 h. orange-brown 10 10
1278   20 h. ultramarine 10 10
1279   30 h. brown 10 10
1280   40 h. purple 15 10
1281   60 h. black 15 10
1282   1 k. 60, black-green .. 40 10
1283   1 k. 80, indigo 50 10
1277/1283   *Set of 7* .. . . 1·25 30
Designs: *Vert* (*As T* **380**)—20 h. F. Škroup (composer, death centenary); 30 h. B. Němcová (writer, death centenary); 60 h. Rod of Aesculapius and Prague Castle (Medical Association and Journal centenary); 1 k. 60, L. Čelakovský (founder, 50th Anniv of Botanical Society). *Horiz*—(41×22½ *mm*.) 40 h. F. Záviška and K. Petr (Centenary of Czech Mathematics and Physics Union); 1 k. 80, M. Valouch and J. Hronec (as 40 h.).

381 Miner holding lamp

382 "Man Conquers Space"

(Des V. Polašek. Eng B. Housa. Recess*)

1962 (19 Mar). *30th Anniv of Miners' Strike. Most. P 12 × 11½*
1284 **381** 60 h. indigo and red 25 10

(Des F. Hudeček. Eng L. Jirka (30 h., 40 h.), L. Jirka and
J. Goldschmied (60 h.), J. Mráček (80 h., 1 k. 60), B. Housa
(1 k.). Recess*)

1962 (26 Mar). *Cosmic Space Research (2nd Series)* T **382**
and similar designs. P 11½ × 12 (vert) or 12 × 11½ (horiz)
1285   30 h. brown-red and pale blue .. 25 10
1286   40 h. deep blue and orange 25 10
1287   60 h. grey-blue and pink .. 25 10
1288   80 h. purple and pale green .. 60 10
1289   1 k. deep blue and pale greenish yellow 25 20
1290   1 k. 60, green and orange-yellow .. 2·00 75
1285/1290   Set of 6 .. .. .. 3·25 1·10
Designs:—*Vert*—40 h. Launching of Soviet Space Rocket.
1 k. Automatic station on Moon. *Horiz*—60 h. "Vostok 2";
80 h. Multi-stage automatic rocket; 1 k. 60, Television satellite
station.

383 Indian and African Elephants

384 Dove and Nest

(Des P. Rolčik. Eng L. Jirka (20 h., 30 h., 60 h.), J. Švengsbír
(others). Recess*)

1962 (24 Apr). *Animals of Prague Zoos. T **383** and similar
designs. P 11½ × 12 (vert) or 12 × 11½ (horiz)*
1291   20 h. black and turquoise-blue .. 30 10
1292   30 h. black and bluish violet .. 30 10
1293   60 h. black and yellow .. 30 10
1294   1 k. black and green 50 10
1295   1 k. 40, black and magenta .. 50 20
1296   1 k. 60, black and yellow-brown .. 2·00 80
1291/1296   Set of 6 .. .. 3·50 1·25
Animals:—*Vert*—20 h. Polar bear; 30 h. Chimpanzee; 60 h.
Bactrian camel. *Horiz*—1 k. 40, Leopard; 1 k. 60, Przewalski's
horses.

(Des V. Sivko. Eng J. Herčik. Recess)

1962 (14 May). *AIR. "Praga 1962" International Stamp
Exhibition (fourth issue). T **384** and similar vert designs.
P 14.*
1297   80 h. yellow, red, brown and black .. 50 25
1298   1 k. 40, red, blue and black .. 2·50 2·50
1299   2 k. 80, yellow, red, brown and black 4·00 3·00
1300   4 k. 20, red, black, yellow and brown 5·50 5·00
1297/1300   Set of 4 .. .. 11·00 10·00
Designs:—1 k. 40, Dove; 2 k. 80, Flower and bird; 4 k. 20,
Plant and bird. All designs show "Praga 62" emblem. Nos.
1297, 1299 are inscr in Slovakian; Nos. 1298, 1300 in Czech.

385 Girl of Lidice

386 Klary's Fountain, Teplice

(Des Anna Podzemná. Eng B. Housa (30 h.), J. Švengsbír (60 h.).
Recess*)

1962 (9 June). *20th Anniv of Destruction of Lidice and Lezaky.
T **385** and similar vert design inscr "1942–1962". P 11½*
1301   30 h. black and rose-red 30 10
1302   60 h. black and violet-blue 30 10
Design:—60 h. Flowers on Ležáky ruins.

(Des and eng J. Švengsbír. Recess*)

1962 (9 June). *1200th Anniv of Discovery of Teplice Springs.
P 11½.*
1303 **386** 60 h. grey-green and yellow .. 35 10

387 Campaign Emblem

388 Swimmer with Rifle

(Des J. Šváb. Eng J. Mráček. Recess*)

1962 (18 June). *Malaria Eradication. T **387** and similar vert
design. P 11½ × 12.*
1304   60 h. red and black 15 10
1305   3 k. blue and yellow .. .. 1·25 75
Design:—3 k. Campaign emblem and dove (*different*).

1962 (20 June). *Czechoslovakia's Participation in World
Football Championships' Final, Chile. Design as No. 1275,
but additionally inscr "ČSSR VE FINALE". Value and colours
changed.*
1306   1 k. 60, green and pale yellow .. 1·10 15

(Des J. Baláž. Eng J. Goldschmied (30 h.), J. Mráček (40 h.),
B. Housa (60 h.), L. Jirka (1 k.). Recess*)

1962 (20 July). *Second Military Spartacist Games. T **388** and
similar vert designs. P 11½ × 12.*
1307   30 h. deep green and violet-blue .. 15 10
1308   40 h. deep reddish violet and yellow .. 20 10
1309   60 h. brown and green .. 25 10
1310   1 k. deep blue and salmon-red .. 30 10
1307/1310   Set of 4 .. .. 80 30
Designs:—40 h. Soldier mounting obstacle; 60 h. Footballer;
1 k. Relay race.

389 "Sun" and Field (Socialized Agriculture)

390 Swallow, "Praga '62" and Congress Emblems

(Des J. Liesler. Eng J. Schmidt (30, 60 h.), J. Mráček (80 h.), J. Herčík (1 k.), J. A. Švengsbír (1 k. 40), L. Jirka (5 k.). Recess).

1962 (18 Aug). *"Praga 1962" International Stamp Exhibition (fifth issue). T 389 and similar designs. P 14.*

1311	30 h. red, black, yellow and grey		3·25	1·25
1312	60 h. red, black, green and yellow		80	40
1313	80 h. red, black, yellow and green		4·00	2·00
1314	1 k. red, black, yellow and blue		4·00	3·00
1315	1 k. 40, red, black, yellow and blue		4·00	3·50
1311/1315	Set of 5		14·50	9·00

MS1315*a* 96 × 75 mm. 5 k. multicoloured (View of Prague with Exhibition emblem). *P* 14 18·00 18·00
MS1315*b* As above but imperf 60·00 60·00
Designs: *Vert*—60 h. Astronaut in "spaceship"; 1 k. 40. Children playing under "tree". *Horiz*—80 h. Boy with flute, and peace doves; 1 k. Workers of three races. All designs feature the "Praga 62" emblem.
Four each of Nos. 1311/2 were printed together in a miniature sheet and sold at 5 k. only on production of an entrance ticket to the exhibition. *Price un.* £18

(Des J. Liesler. Eng B. Housa. Recess)

1962 (1 Sept). *F.I.P. Day (Féderation Internationale de Philatélie). P 14.*

1316	**390**	1 k. 60, black, red, blue, yellow & grn	5·50	4·75

391 Žinkovy Sanatorium and Sailing Dinghy

392 Cruiser *Aurora*

393 Astronaut and Worker

(Des R. Šváб. Eng J. Mráček. Recess*)

1962 (29 Oct). *Social Facilities for Czech Workers. T 391 and similar designs. P 12×11½ (30 h.) or 11½×12 (60 h.).*

1317	30 h. black and light blue		20	10
1318	60 h. sepia and ochre		30	10

Design: *Horiz*—30 h. Children in day nursery, and factory.

(Des J. Šalamoun. Eng B. Housa. Recess*)

1962 (7 Nov). *45th Anniv of Russian Revolution. P 11½.*

1319	**392**	30 h. sepia and light blue	25	10
1320		60 h. black and pink	40	10

(Des V. Polášek. Eng L. Jirka (30 h.). Des and eng J. Schmidt (60 h.). Recess*)

1962 (7 Nov). *40th Anniv of U.S.S.R. T 393 and similar vert design. P 11½.*

1321	30 h. brown-red and light blue		20	10
1322	60 h. black and pink (Lenin)		25	10

394 Crane ("Building Construction")

(Des R. Šváб. Eng J. Goldschmied (30 h.), J. Herčík (others). Recess*)

1962 (4 Dec). *12th Czech Communist Party Congress, Prague. T 394 and similar designs inscr "XII SJEZD KSC" etc. P 11½.*

1323	30 h. lake and yellow		25	10
1324	40 h. slate-blue and yellow		25	10
1325	60 h. black and rose		25	10

Designs: *Vert*—40 h. Produce ("Agriculture"). *Horiz*—60 h. Factory plants ("Industry").

395 Stag Beetle (*Lucanus cervus*)

396 Table Tennis (World Championships, Prague)

(Des Z. Bilková. Eng L. Jirka (20 h., 1 k.), J. Mráček (60 h.), B. Housa (1 k. 60). Des V. Sivko. Eng J. Herčík (30 h., 2 k.). Recess)

1962 (15 Dec). *Beetles. T 395 and similar multicoloured designs. P 14.*

1326	20 h. Caterpillar-hunter (*Calosoma sycophantha*) (horiz)		40	15
1327	30 h. Cardinal beetle (*Pyrochroa coccinea*) (horiz)		40	10
1328	60 h. Type **395**		40	15
1329	1 k. Great diving beetle (*Dytiscus marginalis*) (horiz)		90	25
1330	1 k. 60, Alpine longhorn beetle (*Rosalia alpina*)		1·10	25
1331	2 k. Blue ground beetle (*Carabus intricatus*)		3·00	1·25
1326/1331	Set of 6		5·50	2·00

(Des K. Hruška. Eng J. Švengsbír (30 h., 60 h.), B. Housa (80 h., 1 k. 20), J. Mráček (1 k.), J. Herčík (1 k. 60). Recess*)

1963 (28 Jan). *Sports Events of 1963. T 396 and similar vert designs. P 11½.*

1332	30 h. black and blue-green		25	10
1333	60 h. black and orange		25	10
1334	80 h. black and blue		25	10
1335	1 k. black and bluish violet		30	10
1336	1 k. 20, black and yellow-brown		30	15
1337	1 k. 60, black and scarlet		65	15
1332/1337	Set of 6		1·75	55

Designs: —60 h. Cycling (80th Anniv of Czech Cycling); 80 h. Skiing (First Czech Winter Games, 1963); 1 k. Motorcycle dirt-track racing (15th Anniv of "Golden Helmet" Race, Pardubice); 1 k. 20, Weightlifting (World Championships, Prague); 1 k. 60, Hurdling (First Czech Summer Games, 1963).

397 Industrial Plant

398 Guild Emblem

(Des C. Bouda. Eng B. Housa and J. Goldschmied (No. 1340). Des I. Strnad. Eng J. Mráček (others). Recess*)

1963 (25 Feb). *15th Anniv of "Victorious February" and Fifth Trade Union Congress. T 397 and similar designs. P 11½.*

1338	30 h. carmine and blue		15	10
1339	60 h. carmine and black		15	10
1340	60 h. black and vermilion		15	10

Designs: *Vert*—No. 1339, Sun and campfire. *Horiz*—No. 1340, Industrial plant and annual "stepping stones".

(Des J. Šváb (1341), C. Bouda (1342, 1345), M. Benka (1343), A. Kajlich (1344, 1346), M. Švabinský (1347), Eng. B. Housa (1341), J. Mráček (1342, 1343), J. A. Švengsbír (1344), L. Jirka (1345, 1347), J. Herčík (1346). Recess*. (1341, 1343, 1345) or recess (others))

1963 (25 Mar). *Cultural Anniversaries.* T **398** *and similar designs.* P 11½.

1341	20 h. black and light blue	..	10	10
1342	30 h. red	..	10	10
1343	30 h. carmine-red and light blue	..	10	10
1344	60 h. black	..	15	10
1345	60 h. brown-purple and grey-blue	..	15	10
1346	60 h. grey-green	..	15	10
1347	1 k. 60, brown	..	50	15
1341/1347	*Set of 7* ..		1·00	30

Designs:—No. 1341, T **398** (Artists' Guild centenary); 1342, E. Urx (journalist); 1343, J. Jánošík (national hero); 1344, J. Palkovič (author); 1346, Woman with book, and children (Centenary of Slovak Cultural Society, Slovenska Matice); 1347, M. Švabinsky (artist; after self-portrait). *Horiz*—1345, Allegorical figure and National Theatre, Prague (80th Anniv).

399 Young People   **400** Television Cameras and Receiver

(Des Z. Bílková. Eng J. Herčík. Recess*)

1963 (18 Apr). *Fourth Czech Youth Federation Congress, Prague.* P 11½.

1348	**399**	30 h. indigo and red	..	25	10

(Des F. Hudeček. Eng J. Švengsbír (30 h.), J. Herčík (50, 60 h.), B. Housa (1, 2 k.), B. Housa and J. Goldschmied (1 k. 60). Recess (3 k.) or recess* (others))

1963 (25 Apr). *Space Research* (3rd series). *Horiz designs as* T **364** *but inscr* "1963" *at foot.* P 12×11½.

1349	30 h. maroon, brown-red & pale yellow	15	10
1350	50 h. deep blue and turquoise-green	..	25	10
1351	60 h. deep bluish green & greenish yell	25	10
1352	1 k. black and light orange-brown	..	55	15
1353	1 k. 60, sepia and light green	..	40	15
1354	2 k. deep reddish violet & greenish yell	2·25	75
1349/1354	*Set of 6* ..	3·50	1·10

MS1354*a* 84×70 mm. 3 k. salmon and deep bluish green (Spacecraft and Mars) Imperf .. 5·00 4·00

Designs:—30 h. Rocket circling Sun; 50 h. Rockets and Sputniks leaving Earth; 60 h. Spacecraft and Moon; 1 k. "Mars 1" rocket and Mars; 1 k. 60, Rocket heading for Jupiter; 2 k. Spacecraft returning from Saturn.

(Des F. Hudeček. Eng B. Housa (40 h.), B. Housa and J. Goldschmied (60 h.). Recess*)

1963 (25 Apr). *Tenth Anniv of Czech Television Service.* T **400** *and similar design inscr* "10 LET CS. TELEVIZE". P 12×11½ (40 *h.*) or 11½×12 (60 *h.*).

1355	40 h. deep blue and light orange	20	10
1356	60 h. carmine and light blue	..	20	10

Design: *Vert*—60 h. Television transmitting aerial.

401 Broadcasting Studio, and Receiver   **402** Ancient Ring and Moravian Settlements Map

(Des F. Hudeček. Eng J. Švengsbír (30 h.), B. Housa (1 k.). Recess*)

1963 (18 May). *40th Anniv of Czech Radio Service.* T **401** *and similar design.* P 12×11½ (30 *h.*) or 11½×12 (1 *k.*).

1357	30 h. maroon and pale blue		15	10
1358	1 k. bright purple & light turquoise-grn	25	10

Design: *Vert*—1 k. Aerial mast, globe and doves.

(Des Ludmila Jiřincová. Eng J. Švengsbír. Recess*)

1963 (25 May). *1,100th Anniv of Moravian Empire.* T **402** *and similar vert design.* P 11½×12.

1359	30 h. black and green	..	20	10
1360	1 k. 60, black and yellow	..	40	10

Design:—1 k. 60, Ancient silver plate showing falconer with hawk.

403 Tupolev Tu-104A   **404** Singer

(Des H. Hudeček. Eng J. Herčík (80 h.), J. Mráček (1 k. 80). Recess*)

1963 (25 May). *40th Anniv of Czech Airlines.* T **403** *and similar horiz design.* P 12×11½.

1361	80 h. violet and pale blue	..	40	10
1362	1 k. 80, indigo and pale green	..	75	15

Design:—1k. 80, Ilyushin Il-18B.

(Des K. Švolinský. Eng L. Jirka. Recess)

1963 (25 May). *60th Anniv of Moravian Teachers Singing Club.* P 11½.

1363	**404**	30 h. red	..	35	10

405 Nurse and Child   **406** Wheatears and Kromeriz Castle

(Des Anna Podzemná. Eng L. Jirka. Recess*)

1963 (20 June). *Centenary of Red Cross.* P 11½.

1364	**405**	30 h. indigo and red	..	40	10

(Des Anna Podzemná. Eng J. Mráček. Recess*)

1963 (20 June). *National Agricultural Exhibition, Kromeriz.* P 11½.

1365	**406**	30 h. deep green and yellow	..	40	10

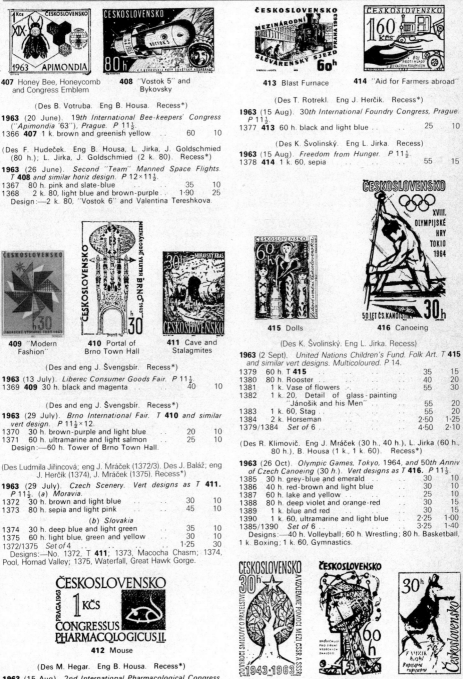

407 Honey Bee, Honeycomb and Congress Emblem   **408** "Vostok 5" and Bykovsky

(Des B. Votruba. Eng B. Housa. Recess*)

1963 (20 June). *19th International Bee-keepers' Congress* ("Apimondia '63"), Prague. P 11½.
1366 **407** 1 k. brown and greenish yellow   60   10

(Des F. Hudeček. Eng B. Housa, L. Jirka, J. Goldschmied (80 h.); L. Jirka, J. Goldschmied (2 k. 80). Recess*)

1963 (26 June). *Second "Team" Manned Space Flights. T* **408** *and similar horiz design.* P 12×11½.
1367   80 h. pink and slate-blue   35   10
1368   2 k. 80, light blue and brown-purple ..   1·90   25
Design:—2 k. 80, "Vostok 6" and Valentina Tereshkova.

409 "Modern Fashion"   **410** Portal of Brno Town Hall   **411** Cave and Stalagmites

(Des and eng J. Švengsbír. Recess*)

1963 (13 July). *Liberec Consumer Goods Fair.* P 11½.
1369 **409** 30 h. black and magenta ..   40   10

(Des and eng J. Švengsbír. Recess*)

1963 (29 July). *Brno International Fair. T* **410** *and similar vert design.* P 11½×12.
1370   30 h. brown-purple and light blue   20   10
1371   60 h. ultramarine and light salmon ..   25   10
Design:—60 h. Tower of Brno Town Hall.

(Des Ludmila Jiřincová; eng J. Mráček (1372/3). Des J. Baláž; eng J. Herčík (1374), J. Mráček (1375). Recess*)

1963 (29 July). *Czech Scenery. Vert designs as T* **411.** P 11½. (a) *Moravia.*
1372   30 h. brown and light blue   30   10
1373   80 h. sepia and light pink   45   10
     (b) *Slovakia*
1374   30 h. deep blue and light green   35   10
1375   60 h. light blue, green and yellow ..   30   10
1372/1375   *Set of* 4   1·25   30
Designs:—No. 1372, T **411**; 1373, Macocha Chasm; 1374, Pool, Hornad Valley; 1375, Waterfall, Great Hawk Gorge.

412 Mouse

(Des M. Hegar. Eng B. Housa. Recess*)

1963 (15 Aug). *2nd International Pharmacological Congress, Prague.* P 12×11½.
1376 **412** 1 k. carmine-red and black   40   10

413 Blast Furnace   **414** "Aid for Farmers abroad"

(Des T. Rotrekl. Eng J. Herčík. Recess*)

1963 (15 Aug). *30th International Foundry Congress, Prague.* P 11½.
1377 **413** 60 h. black and light blue ..   25   10

(Des K. Švolinský. Eng L. Jirka. Recess)

1963 (15 Aug). *Freedom from Hunger.* P 11½.
1378 **414** 1 k. 60, sepia   55   15

415 Dolls   **416** Canoeing

(Des K. Švolinský. Eng L. Jirka. Recess)

1963 (2 Sept). *United Nations Children's Fund. Folk Art. T* **415** *and similar vert designs. Multicoloured.* P 14.
1379   60 h. T **415**   35   15
1380   80 h. Rooster   40   20
1381   1 k. Vase of flowers   55   30
1382   1 k. 20, Detail of glass-painting "Jánošik and his Men"   55   20
1383   1 k. 60, Stag   55   20
1384   2 k. Horseman   2·50   1·25
1379/1384   *Set of* 6   4·50   2·10

(Des R. Klimovič. Eng J. Mráček (30 h., 40 h.), L. Jirka (60 h., 80 h.), B. Housa (1 k., 1 k. 60). Recess*)

1963 (26 Oct). *Olympic Games, Tokyo, 1964, and 50th Anniv of Czech Canoeing* (30 h.). *Vert designs as T* **416.** P 11½.
1385   30 h. grey-blue and emerald   30   10
1386   40 h. red-brown and light blue   30   10
1387   60 h. lake and yellow ..   25   10
1388   80 h. deep violet and orange-red   30   15
1389   1 k. blue and red   30   15
1390   1 k. 60, ultramarine and light blue ..   2·25   1·00
1385/1390   *Set of* 6   3·25   1·40
Designs:—40 h. Volleyball; 60 h. Wrestling; 80 h. Basketball; 1 k. Boxing; 1 k. 60, Gymnastics.

417 Linden Tree   **418** "Human Reason and Technology"   **419** Chamois

(Des A. Fuchs. Eng J. Schmidt. Recess*)

1963 (11 Dec). *20th Anniv of Czech–Soviet Treaty of Friendship.*
T **417** *and similar vert design.* P 11½×12.

1391	30 h. yellow-brown and pale blue	..	15	10
1392	60 h. carmine-red and grey-green		15	10

Design: 60 h. Hammer and sickle, and star.

(Des J. Lukavský. Eng J. Švengsbir. Recess)

1963 (12 Dec). *Technical and Scientific Knowledge Society*
Congress. P 11½×12

1393	**418**	60 h. deep slate-violet	40	10

(Des M. Hanák. Eng J. Schmidt (30 h., 60 h., 1 k. 20), L. Jirka
(others). Recess)

1963 (14 Dec). *Mountain Animals.* *Vert designs as T* **419**.
P 14.

1394	30 h. black, yellow, purple and blue	..	90	25
1395	40 h. black, yellow-brown, red & slate-bl	90	40
1396	60 h. sepia, yellow and green	..	1·10	30
1397	1 k. 20, black, orge-brn, red & yell-grn	1·10	25
1398	1 k. 60, black, chestnut, red & green	1·50	40
1399	2 k. chestnut, orange and green	..	4·25	2·00
1394/1399	*Set of 6*	..	9·00	3·25

Animals:—40 h. Ibex; 60 h. Mouflon; 1 k. 20, Roe deer; 1 k. 60,
Fallow deer; 2 k. Red deer.

420 Figure Skating

421 Ice Hockey

(Des N. Synecká. Eng B. Housa. Recess*)

1964 (20 Jan). *Sports Events of 1964.* *Designs as T* **420**.
P 12×11½ (80 h.) or 11½×12 (others).

1400	30 h. bluish violet and greenish yellow	25	10
1401	80 h. grey-blue and red-orange	..	25	10
1402	1 k. chocolate and lilac	..	75	15

Designs:—*Vert*—30 h. T **420** (Czech Students' Games);
1 k. Handball (World Handball Championships). *Horiz*—80 h.
Cross-country skiing (Students' Games).

(Des Anna Podzemná. Eng J. Mráček (2 k.), L. Jirka (others).
Recess*)

1964 (20 Jan). *Winter Olympic Games, Innsbruck.* *Designs as*
T **421**. P 11½.

1403	1 k. purple and turquoise-green	..	1·25	40
1404	1 k. 80, slate-green and lavender	..	1·10	60
1405	2 k. ultramarine and light green	..	2·75	2·00

Designs:—*Vert*—1 k. 80, Tobogganing. *Horiz*—2 k. Ski jumping.

422 Belanské Tatra Mountains,   **423** Magura Hotel,
       Skiers and Tree   Zdiar, High Tatra

(Des V. Sivko. Eng J. Herčik. Recess*)

1964 (19 Feb). *Tourist Issue.* *Horiz designs as T* **422**. P 11½.

1406	30 h. maroon and light blue	..	..	20	10
1407	60 h. indigo and carmine	..	..	30	10
1408	1 k. brown and yellow-olive	..	50	10
1409	1 k. 80, bronze-green & yellow-orange	90	25
1406/1409	*Set of 4*	..	..	1·75	45

Designs:—60 h. Telč (Moravia) and motor-camp; 1 k. Spiš

Castle (Slovakia) and angler; 1 k. 80, Ceský Krumlov (Bohemia)
and sailing dinghies. Each design includes a tree.

(Des A. Brunovský. Eng J. Schmidt (60 h.), J. Mráček (80 h.).
Recess*)

1964 (19 Feb). *Trade Union Recreation Hotels.* *T* **423** *and*
similar horiz design. P 11½.

1410	60 h. deep green and greenish yellow..	20	10
1411	80 h. blue and pink	..	20	10

Design:—80 h. "Slovak Insurrection" Hotel, Lower Tatra.

424 Statuary (after Michelangelo)

(Des J. Švengsbir (1 k. 60), J. Liesler (others). Eng J. Schmidt
(40 h., 1 k.), J. Švengsbir (others). Recess*)

1964 (20 Mar). *U.N.E.S.C.O. Cultural Anniversaries.* *T* **424** *and*
similar designs. P 11½×12 (1 k.) or 12×11½ (others).

1412	40 h. black and yellow-green	..	20	10
1413	60 h. black and carmine	..	20	10
1414	1 k. black and light blue	..	40	10
1415	1 k. 60, black and greenish yellow	40	10
1412/1415	*Set of 4*	..	1·00	35

Designs: *Horiz*—40 h. T **424** (400th death anniv of
Michelangelo); 60 h. Bottom, *Midsummer Night's Dream* (400th
birth anniv of Shakespeare); 1 k. 60, King George of Poděbrady
(500th anniv of his mediation in Europe). *Vert*—1 k. Galileo Galilei
(400th birth anniv).

See also No. **MS**2948.

425 Yuri Gagarin

(Des J. Lukavský. Eng J. Mráček (30 h., 60 h., 1 k. 60, 2 k.),
B. Housa (others). Recess*)

1964 (27 Apr). *"Space Exploration".* *Various designs as T* **425**.
Cream paper. P 11½.

1416	30 h. ultramarine and black	..	50	25
1417	60 h. crimson and deep green	..	25	10
1418	80 h. bluish violet and lake	..	50	20
1419	1 k. reddish violet and blue	..	75	25
1420	1 k. 20, bronze-green and vermilion	..	50	25
1421	1 k. 40, deep bluish green and black ..	1·25	75
1422	1 k. 60, turquoise and violet	..	4·00	1·90
1423	2 k. rose-red and deep blue	..	75	30
1416/1423	*Set of 8*	..	7·75	3·50

Astronauts: *Horiz*—60 h. Titov; 80 h. Glenn; 1 k. 20, Popovich
and Nikolaev. *Vert*—1 k. Carpenter; 1 k. 40, Schirra; 1 k. 60,
Cooper; 2 k. Tereshkova and Bykovsky.

426 Campanula
(*Campanula*
rapunculoides)

427 Miner of 1764

(Des K. Svolinský. Eng L. Jirka. Recess)

1964 (15 June). *Wild Flowers.* T **426** *and similar vert designs.*
P 14.

1424	60 h. purple, orange and deep green	1·60	20
1425	80 h. bright purple, red, green and black	1·60	20
1426	1 k. blue, pink and green	1·60	40
1427	1 k. 20, yellow, orange, green and black	80	25
1428	1 k. 60, violet and green	1·00	40
1429	2 k. red, blue-green and bluish violet	5·50	1·90
1424/1429	Set of 6	11·00	3·00

Flowers:—80 h. Musk thistle (*Carduus nutans*); 1 k. Chicory (*Cichorium intybus*); 1 k. 20, Yellow iris (*Iris pseudacorus*); 1 k. 60, Marsh gentian (*Gentiana pneumonanthe*); 2 k. Common poppy (*Papaver rhoeas*).

(Des F. Hudeček. Eng J. Herčík (1431). Des J. Šváb. Eng B. Housa (1430). Des E. Zmeták. Eng B. Housa (1432). Recess*)

1964 (20 June). *Czech Anniversaries.* T **427** *and other designs.*
P 12×11½ (*No.* 1431) *or* 11½ (*others*).

1430	30 h. black and yellow	25	10
1431	60 h. carmine-red and pale blue	50	10
1432	60 h. sepia and light green	25	10

Designs: *Horiz* (30½ × 22½ *mm.*)—30 h. Silesian coat-of-arms (stylised) (150th anniv of Silesian Museum, Opava); (41½ × 23 *mm.*)—No. 1431, Skoda ASC-16 fire engine (Centenary of Voluntary Fire Brigades). *Vert*—No. 1432, T **427** (Bicentenary of Banská Stiavnica Mining School).

428 Ciné-film "Flower"

429 Hradčany, Prague, and Black-headed Gulls

(Des J. Fišer. Eng L. Jirka. Recess)

1964 (20 June). *14th International Film Festival, Karlovy Vary.*
P 14.

1433	**428** 60 h. black, blue and red	1·50	15

(Des Ludmila Jiřinková. Eng B Housa. Recess*)

1964 (10 July). *Fourth Czech Red Cross Congress, Prague.*
P 11½.

1434	**429** 60 h. slate-violet and red	60	10

430 Human Heart

431 Slovak Girl and Workers

(Des J. Istler. Eng J. Mráček. Recess*)

1964 (10 July). *Fourth European Cardiological Congress, Prague.* P 12×11½.

1435	**430** 1 k. 60, carmine-red and blue	90	10

(Des A. Brunovsky. Eng J. Schmidt (1438). Des J. Baláž. Eng J. Švengsbír (others). Recess*)

1964 (17 Aug). *20th Anniv of Slovak Rising and Dukla Battles.*
T **431** *and similar horiz designs.* P 11½.

1436	30 h. red and brown	15	10
1437	60 h. blue and red	15	10
1438	60 h. deep sepia and red	15	10

Designs:—No. 1437, Armed Slovaks; No. 1438, Soldiers in battle at Dukla Pass.

432 Hradčany, Prague

433 Cycling

(Des J. Liesler. Eng L. Jirka. Recess* (60 h.) or recess (5 k.))

1964 (31 Aug). *Millenary of Prague.* P 11½×12.

1439	**432** 60 h. deep sepia and magenta	50	10
MS1439*a*	76×99 mm. 5 k. brown-lake (Charles Bridge and City) Imperf	1·75	1·25

(Des Anna Podzemná. Eng J. Švengsbír (60 h., 1 k.), J. Schmidt (80 h., 1 k. 60), L. Jirka (1 k. 20, 2 k. 80), Recess)

1964 (2 Sept). *Olympic Games, Tokyo.* T **433** *and similar designs. Multicoloured.* P 14.

1440	60 h. Type **433**	40	25
1441	80 h. Throwing the discus and pole vaulting (*vert*)	50	25
1442	1 k. Football (*vert*)	50	25
1443	1 k. 20, Rowing (*vert*)	65	40
1444	1 k. 60, Swimming	75	55
1445	2 k. 80, Weightlifting	4·50	2·50
1440/1445	Set of 6	6·50	3·75

433a "Voskhod", Astronauts and Globe

(Des J. Lukavský. Eng J. Schmidt and J. Goldschmied. Recess*)

1964 (12 Nov). *Three-manned Space Flight of October* 12–13.
P 11½.

MS1445*a*	**433a** 3 k. steel-blue & reddish lilac	6·25	4·50

434 Redstart

435 Brno Engineering Works (150th Anniv)

(Des V. Kovařík. Litho)

1964 (16 Nov). *Birds.* T **434** *and similar vert designs. Multi-coloured.* P 11.

1446	30 h. Type **434**	35	10
1447	60 h. Green woodpecker	55	10
1448	80 h. Hawfinch	1·10	15
1449	1 k. Black woodpecker	1·10	30

1450	1 k. 20, European robin	.. ..	70	40
1451	1 k. 60, Common roller	..	2·40	70
1446/1451	Set of 6 ..	..	5·50	1·60

(Des F. Hudeček. Eng J. Schmidt, recess (30 h.), recess* (60 h.))

1964 (16 Nov). *Czech Engineering.* T **435** *and similar horiz design.* P 11½.

1452	30 h. red-brown	.. ..	10	10
1453	60 h. deep bluish green and salmon	..	25	10

Design:—60 h. Diesel-electric shunter.

436 "Dancing Girl"   **437** Mountain Rescue Service (tenth anniv)

(Des K. Svolinský. Eng L. Jirka. Recess*)

1965 (3 Jan). *Third National Spartacist Games* (1st issue). P 12×11½.

1454	**436** 30 h. red and light blue	..	15	10

See also Nos. 1489/92.

(Des V. Kovařík. Eng J. Švengsbir. Recess*)

1965 (15 Jan). *Sports Events of 1965.* T **437** *and similar vert designs.* P 11½.

1455	60 h. violet and light blue	..	20	10
1456	60 h. lake and orange ..	..	20	10
1457	60 h. bronze-green and red ..	..	20	10
1458	60 h. deep green and greenish yellow ..		20	10
1455/1458	Set of 4 ..	..	70	30

Designs:—No. 1455, T **437**; 1456, Exercising with hoop (First World Artistic Gymnastics Championships, Prague); 1457, Cycling (World Indoor Cycling Championships, Prague); 1458, Hurdling (Czech University Championships, Brno).

438 Domažlice   **439** Exploration of Mars

(Des C. Bouda. Eng J. Mráček (1459, 1463), J. Herčík (1460, 1464), B. Housa (1461, 1465), L. Jirka (1462). Recess*)

1965 (15 Feb). *700th Anniv of Six Czech Towns and 20th Anniv of Terezin Concentration Camp* (No. 1465). T **438** *and similar horiz designs.* P 11½.

1459	30 h. reddish violet and yellow	..	20	10
1460	30 h. violet and light blue	..	20	10
1461	30 h. ultramarine and sage-green	..	20	10
1462	30 h. sepia and light yellow-olive	..	20	10
1463	30 h. bluish green and buff	..	20	10
1464	30 h. slate and light drab	..	20	10
1465	30 h. rose and black	..	20	10
1459/1465	Set of 7 ..	..	1·10	30

Towns:—No. 1459, T **438**; 1460, Beroun, 1461, Zatec, 1462, Polička; 1463, Lipnik and Bečvou; 1464, Frýdek-Mistek; 1465, Terezin concentration camp.

(Des J. Lukavský. Eng B. Housa (20 h., 30 h., 60 h., 1 k. 60), J. Herčík (1 k., 2 k.), J. Mráček (1 k. 40). Recess*)

1965 (15 Mar). *International Quiet Sun Years and Space Research.* T **439** *and similar designs.* P 12×11½ (horiz) or 11½×12 (vert).

1466	20 h. reddish purple and rose-red		30	10
1467	30 h. greenish yellow and scarlet		30	10
1468	60 h. indigo and pale greenish yellow ..		30	10
1469	1 k. reddish violet & pale turquoise-grn		65	10
1470	1 k. 40, deep slate-blue and salmon ..		65	20
1471	1 k. 60, black and pink	..	65	20
1472	2 k. indigo and pale turquoise	..	2·00	1·25
1466/1472	Set of 7 ..	..	4·25	1·90

Designs: *Horiz*—20 h. Maximum sun-spot activity; 30 h. Minimum sun-spot activity ("Quiet Sun"); 60 h. Moon exploration; 1 k. 40, Artificial satellite and space station; 2 k. Soviet "Kosmos" and U.S. "Tiros" satellites. *Vert*—1 k. Space-ships rendezvous.

440 Horse Jumping   **441** Leonov in Space
(Amsterdam, 1928)

(Des Anna Podzemná. Eng J. Herčík (20 h., 60 h., 2 k.), J. Schmidt (30 h., 1 k. 40, 1 k. 60), J. Mráček (1 k.). Recess*)

1965 (16 Apr). *Czechoslovakia's Olympic Victories.* T **440** *and similar vert designs.* P 11½×12.

1473	20 h. brown and gold	..	20	10
1474	30 h. deep violet and light emerald		20	10
1475	60 h. blue and gold	..	20	10
1476	1 k. chestnut and gold	..	40	20
1477	1 k. 40, deep green and gold	..	90	65
1478	1 k. 60, black and gold	..	90	65
1479	2 k. lake and gold	..	90	25
1473/1479	Set of 7 ..	..	3·25	1·90

Designs (each with city feature):—30 h. Throwing the discus (Paris, 1900); 60 h. Marathon (Helsinki, 1952); 1 k. Weight-lifting (Los Angeles, 1932); 1 k. 40, Gymnastics (Berlin, 1936); 1 k. 60, Rowing (Rome, 1960); 2 k. Gymnastics (Tokyo, 1964).

(Des J. Lukavský. Eng B. Housa (Nos. 1480, 1482), J. Herčík (Nos. 1481, 1483). Recess*)

1965 (17 Apr). *Space Achievements.* T **441** *and similar horiz designs.* P 11½.

1480	60 h. slate-purple and light blue	..	25	20
	a. Se-tenant pair. Nos. 1480 and 1482		50	40
1481	60 h. deep violet-blue and mauve	..	25	20
	a. Se-tenant pair. Nos. 1481 and 1483		3·00	2·50
1482	3 k. slate-purple and light blue	..	1·50	1·25
1483	3 k. deep violet-blue and mauve	..	1·50	1·25
1480/1483	Set of 4 ..	..	3·25	2·75

Designs:—No. 1480, T **441**; No. 1481, Grissom, Young and "Gemini 3"; No. 1482, Leonov leaving spaceship "Voskhod 2"; No. 1483, "Gemini 3" on launching pad at Cape Kennedy.

Nos. 1480 and 1482 were issued together in sheets of 25 (5×5), containing one vertical row of the 3 k., and four vertical rows of the 60 h. Nos. 1481/3 were issued in similar sheets.

442 Soldier

445 U.N. Emblem

(Des J. Lukavský. Eng J. Herčík (1484, 1487), J. Mráček (1485), J. Schmidt (1486), L. Jirka (1488). Recess)

1965 (5 May). *20th Anniv of Liberation. T* **442** *and similar horiz designs.* P 14.

1484	30 h. olive, black and red	20	10
1485	30 h. violet, blue and carmine	20	10
1486	60 h. black, red and blue	25	10
1487	1 k. deep violet, brown and orange	50	15
1488	1 k. 60, black-purple, red, orange & yell	75	40
1484/1488	Set of 5	1·60	60

Designs:—No. 1484, *T* **442**; 1485, Workers; 1486, Mechanic; 1487, Building worker; 1488, Peasant.

(Des L. Guderna (60 h., 1 k.), J. Králík (1 k. 60). Eng J. Goldschmied (60 h., 1 k. 60), B. Housa (1 k.). Recess*)

1965 (24 June). *U.N. Commemoration and International Co-operation Year. T* **445** *and similar horiz designs.* P 12×11½.

1499	60 h. red-brown and lemon	20	10
1500	1 k. blue and pale turquoise-blue	40	10
1501	1 k. 60, carmine-red and gold	40	35

Designs:—60 h. *T* **445** (The inscr reads: "Twentieth Anniversary of the Signing of the U.N. Charter"); 1 k. U.N. Headquarters ("20th Anniv of U.N."); 1 k. 60. I.C.Y. emblem.

443 Children's Exercises

444 Slovak "Kopov"

(Des Anna Podzemná. Eng J. Schmidt (30 h., 60 h.), J. Švengsbir (others). Recess*)

1965 (24 May). *Third National Spartacist Games (second issue). T* **443** *and similar vert designs inscr* "III CELOSTATNI SPARTAKIADÁ". P 11½×12.

1489	30 h. ultramarine and carmine	15	10
1490	60 h. brown and bright blue	20	10
1491	1 k. indigo and olive-yellow	35	10
1492	1 k. 60, Venetian red and light drab	40	25
1489/1492	Set of 4	1·00	40

Designs:—60 h. Young gymnasts; 1 k. Women's exercises; 1 k. 60, Start of race.

446 "SOF" and Linked Rings

447 Women of Three Races

(Des J. Šváb. Eng B. Housa. Recess*)

1965 (24 June). *20th Anniv of World Federation of Trade Unions.* P 12×11½.

1502	446	60 h. carmine-red and blue	40	10

(Des A. Brunovský. Eng J. Herčík. Recess)

1965 (24 June). *20th Anniv of International Democratic Women's Federation.* P 12×11½.

1503	447	60 h. ultramarine	40	10

(Des M. Hanák. Eng L. Jirka. Recess*)

1965 (10 June). *Canine Events. T* **444** *and similar horiz designs.* P 12×11½.

1493	30 h. black and orange-red	40	10
1494	40 h. black and yellow	40	10
1495	60 h. black and rose-red	35	10
1496	1 k. black and claret	90	15
1497	1 k. 60, black and orange-yellow	60	25
1498	2 k. black and yellow-orange	2·00	1·00
1493/1498	Set of 6	4·25	1·50

Dogs:—1 k. Poodle (Int. Dog-breeders' Congress, Prague, also 30 h.). 40 h. German sheep-dog; 60 h. Czech "fousek" (retriever) (both World Dog Exhibition, Brno). 1 k. 60, Czech terrier; 2 k. Afghan hound (both Plenary Session of F.C.I.—Int. Federation of Cynology, Prague).

448 Children's House

449 Marx and Lenin

(Des and eng J. Švengsbir. Recess)

1965 (25 June). *Prague Castle (first series). T* **448** *and similar vert design, inscr* "PRAHA HRAD" *etc.* P 11½.

1504	30 h. myrtle-green	20	10
1505	60 h. sepia (Mathias Gate)	25	10

See also Nos. 1572/4, 1656/8, 1740/2, 1827/8, 1892/3, 1959/60, 2037/8, 2103/4, 2163/4, 2253/4, 2305/6, 2337/8, 2404/5, 2466/7, 2543/4, 2599/2600, 2637/8, 2685/6, 2739/40, 2803/4, 2834/5, 2878/9, 2950/1, 2977/8 and 3026/7.

(Des J. Krátik. Eng J. Schmidt. Recess*)

1965 (1 July). *Sixth Organization of Socialist Countries' Postal Ministers Conference, Peking.* P 11½.

1506	449	60 h. carmine-red and gold	20	10

MINIMUM PRICE

The minimum price quoted is 10p which represents a handling charge rather than a basis for valuing common stamps. For further notes about prices see introductory pages.

450 Jan Hus

451 "Lady at her Toilet" (after Titian)

(Des J. Liesler (1507), C. Bouda (1508), J. Tyfa (1509), F. Hudeček (1510). Eng J. Schmidt (1507/8), J. Mráček (1509/10). Recess*)

1965 (10 July). *Various Anniversaries and Events (first issue). T 450 and other designs inscr "1965". P 11½×12 (1507), 12×11½ (1508) or 11½ (others).*

1507	60 h. black and rosine		20	10
1508	60 h. ultramarine and red		20	10
1509	60 h. slate-lilac and gold		20	10
1510	1 k. blue and red-orange		25	10
1507/1510	Set of 4		75	25

Designs:—No. 1507, T 450 (reformer—550th anniv of death). *Vert* (As T 450)—1508, G. J. Mendel (centenary of publication in Brno of his study of heredity). *Horiz* (30½×23 *mm.*)—1509, Jewellery emblems ("Jablonec 65" Jewellery Exhibition); 1510, Early telegraph and telecommunications satellite (I.T.U. centenary).

(Des and eng J. Švengsbir. Recess)

1965 (12 Aug). *Culture. 75×99 mm. P 11½.*
MS1511 **451** 5 k. multicoloured .. .. 3·50 2·50

(Des E. Zmeták. Eng J. Mráček (1512). Des K. Štika. Eng J. Schmidt (1513). Des O. Janeček. Eng J. Herčík (1514). Des V. Hložník. Eng B. Housa (1515). Des J. Fišer. Eng J. Herčík (1516). Recess (1515) or recess* (others))

1965 (20 Aug). *Various Anniversaries and Events (second issue). Designs as T 450 inscr "1965". P 11½×12 (1512/3), 12×11½ (1514) or 11½ (others).*

1512	30 h. black and emerald		15	10
1513	30 h. black and Venetian red		15	10
1514	60 h. black and orange-red		20	10
1515	60 h. brown/cream		20	10
1516	1 k. black and red-orange		20	10
1512/1516	Set of 5		80	15

Designs (As T 450) *Horiz*—No. 1512 L. Štúr (nationalist; 150th anniv of birth); 1513, J. Navrátil (painter; death centenary). *Vert*—1514, B. Martinu (composer; 75th anniv of birth). *Vert*—(23½×30½ *mm.*)—1515, Allegoric figure (500th anniv of Academia Istropolitana, Bratislava). *Horiz*—(30×22½ *mm.*)—1516, Emblem (IUPAC Macromolecular Symposium, Prague).

452 "Fourfold Aid"

453 Dotterel

(Des A. Brunovský. Eng J. Švengsbír; recess (30 h.). Eng J. Herčík; recess* (2 k.))

1965 (6 Sept). *Flood Relief. T 452 and similar design. P 11½×12 (30 h.) or 12×11½ (2 k.).*

| 1517 | 30 h. ultramarine | | 15 | 10 |
| 1518 | 2 k. black and yellow-olive | | 70 | 30 |

Design: *Horiz*—2 k. Rescue by boat.

(Des M. Hanák (30 h., 1 k. 20, 1 k. 60), J. Baláž (others). Litho)

1965 (20 Sept). *Mountain Birds. T 453 and similar designs. Multicoloured. P 11.*

1519	30 h. Type 453		55	10
1520	60 h. Wallcreeper (*vert*)		55	10
1521	1 k. 20, Redpoll		85	25
1522	1 k. 40, Golden eagle (*vert*)		1·25	30
1523	1 k. 60, Ring ousel		85	40
1524	2 k. Nutcracker (*vert*)		2·50	1·50
1519/1524	Set of 6		6·00	2·40

454 Levoča

455 Coltsfoot (*Tussilago farfara*)

(5 h. to 30 h. des L. Guderna. Eng B. Housa. 40 h. to 1 k. des J. Chudomel. Eng B. Housa (40 h., 50 h.), J. Herčík (60 h., 1 k.). 1 k. 20 to 5 k. des J. Liesler. Eng J. Mráček (1 k. 20), J. Herčík (others). Recess*)

1965–66. *Czech Towns. T 454 and similar horiz designs. P 11½×12*

(a) *Size 23×19 mm.* (i) (20.10.65)

1525	5 h. black and yellow		10	10
1526	10 h. blue and bistre		15	10
1527	20 h. sepia and light blue		15	10
1528	30 h. ultramarine and light green		15	10

(ii) (24.10.66)

1529	40 h. sepia and pale blue		15	10
1530	50 h. black and buff		20	10
	a. Black and olive-bistre		50	35
1531	60 h. red and pale blue		25	10
1532	1 k. reddish violet and pale green		35	10

(b) *Size 30½×23½ mm.* (20.11.65)

1533	1 k. 20, blackish olive and pale blue		30	10
1534	1 k. 60, chalky blue and pale yellow		50	10
1535	2 k. bronze-green and pale yellow-grn		65	10
1536	3 k. purple-brown & pale greenish yell		80	10
1537	5 k. black and pink		1·25	10
1525/1537	Set of 13		4·50	60

Towns:—10 h. Jindrichuv Hradec; 20 h. Nitra; 30 h. Košice; 40 h. Hradec Králové; 50 h. Telč; 60 h. Ostrava; 1 k. Olomouc; 1 k. 20, České Budejovice; 1 k. 60, Cheb; 2 k. Brno; 3 k. Bratislava; 5 k. Prague.

No. 1530 was issued on phosphorescent paper in 1979 (No. 1530a occurs only on this paper) and No. 1526 in 1984 (see note after No. 2384).

(Des K. Svolinský. Eng L. Jirka. Recess)

1965 (6 Dec). *Medicinal Plants. T 455 and similar vert designs. Multicoloured. P 14.*

1538	30 h. Type 455		25	10
1539	60 h. Meadow saffron (*Colchicum autumnale*)		45	15
1540	80 h. Common poppy (*Papaver rhoeas*)		50	15
1541	1 k. Foxglove (*Digitalis purpurea*)		60	20
1542	1 k. 20, Arnica (*Arnica montana*)		1·40	30
1543	1 k. 60, Cornflower (*Centaurea cyanus*)		80	40
1544	2 k. Dog rose (*Rosa canina*)		4·00	1·75
1538/1544	Set of 7		7·25	2·75

MINIMUM PRICE

The minimum price quoted is 10p which represents a handling charge rather than a basis for valuing common stamps. For further notes about prices see introductory pages.

456 Panorama of "Stamps"

(Des J. Liesler. Eng L. Jirka. Recess*)

1965 (18 Dec). *Stamp Day.* P 11½×12.
1545 **456** 1 k. brown-red and sage-green .. 3·75 3·50

457 "Music"   **458** Pair Dancing

(Des K. Svolinský. Eng L. Jirka. Recess*)

1966 (15 Jan). *70th Anniv of Czech Philharmonic Orchestra.*
P 11½×12.
1546 **457** 30 h. black and gold 50 20

(Des K. Pekarek. Eng J. Herčík (1547/8, 1552), B. Housa (1549/51). Recess*)

1966 (17 Jan). *Sports Events of 1966. T **458** and similar designs.* P 12×11½ (horiz) or 11½×12 (vert). (a) *European Figure Skating Championships, Bratislava.*
1547   30 h. crimson and light pink ..   15   10
1548   60 h. emerald and light yellow-green ..   20   10
1549   1 k. 60, brown and pale yellow   40   10
1550   2 k. lilac and pale turquoise-green ..   2·10   50
Designs: *Horiz*—60 h. Male skater leaping; 1 k. 60 Female skater leaping; 2 k. Pair-skaters taking bows.

(b) *World Volleyball Championships, Prague*
1551   60 h. rosine and light buff ..   20   10
1552   1 k. violet and pale blue ..   25   10
1547/1552   *Set of 6* .. .. ..   3·00   75
Designs: *Vert*—60 h. Player leaping to ball; 1 k. Player falling.

459 S. Sucharda (sculptor)

460 *Ajax,* 1841

(Des L. Šindelár. Eng J. Schmidt (1553, 1556), J. Mráček (1554/5). Recess)

1966 (14 Feb). *Cultural Anniversaries. Vert portrait designs as T **459**.* P 12×11½.
1553   30 h. myrtle green   10   10
1554   30 h. ultramarine   10   10
1555   60 h. lake   20   10
1556   60 h. brown   20   10
1553/1556   *Set of 4*   50   20
Portraits: No. 1553, Type **459** (birth centenary); 1554, Ignác J. Pešina (veterinary surgeon, birth bicentenary); 1555, Romain Rolland (writer, birth centenary); 1556, Donatello (sculptor, 500th death anniv).

(Des F. Hudeček. Eng B. Housa (20 h., 60 h., 1 k.), J. Schmidt (others). Recess)

1966 (21 Mar). *Czech Locomotives. T **460** and similar horiz designs.* P 12×11½.
1557   20 h. sepia/*cream*   35   10
1558   30 h. slate-violet/*cream* ..   35   10
1559   60 h. plum/*cream*   35   10
1560   1 k. ultramarine/*cream* ..   60   15
1561   1 k. 60, turquoise-blue/*cream*   80   15
1562   2 k. brown-lake/*cream* ..   3·50   1·40
1557/1562   *Set of 6* .. ..   5·50   1·75
Locomotives:—30 h. *Karlštejn,* 1865; 60 h. 423.0 type, 1946; 1 k. 498.0 type, 1946; 1 k. 60, E699.0 (electric) type, 1964; 2 k. T699.0 (diesel-electric) type, 1964.

461 Dancer   **462** Trout

(Des K. Svolinský. Eng L. Jirka. Recess)

1966 (21 Mar). *Centenary of Bedřich Smetana's Bartered Bride* (opera). *Sheet* 84×106 mm. *Imperf.*
MS1563 **461** 3 k. red, blue & deep greenish blue   2·00   1·60

(Des V. F. Vingler. Litho Cartographical and Reproduction Institute, Bratislava)

1966 (25 Apr). *World Angling Championships, Svit. T **462** and similar designs but horiz. Multicoloured.* P 13½.
1564   30 h. Type **462**   30   10
1565   60 h. Perch   45   10
1566   1 k. Carp   60   15
1567   1 k. 20, Pike   60   20
1568   1 k. 40, Grayling   90   30
1569   1 k. 60, Eel .. ..   3·25   1·25
1564/1569   *Set of 6* ..   5·50   1·75

463 "Solidarity of Mankind"   **464** W.H.O. Building

(Des J. Šváb. Eng B. Housa. Recess*)

1966 (25 Apr). *20th Anniv of United Nations Children's Fund.* P 11½.
1570 **463** 60 h. black and yellow   25   10

(Des M. Hegar. Eng J. Schmidt. Recess*)

1966 (25 Apr). *Inauguration of World Health Organization Headquarters, Geneva.* P 12×11½.
1571 **464** 1 k. ultramarine and light blue ..   45   10

465 Belvedere Palace   **466** St. Wenceslas' Crown

(Des C. Bouda. Eng L. Jirka (30 h.). Des J. Šváb. Eng B. Housa (60 h.). Des and eng J. Švengsbír (5 k.). Recess* (60 h.), recess (others))

1966 (9 May). *Prague Castle (second series). T 465 and similar vert design and T 466.* P 11½.
1572   30 h. deep blue   ..   25   10
1573   60 h. black and yellow-bistre   ..   40   15
MS1574 75×97½ mm. 5 k. multicoloured   3·25   2·75
Design:—60 h. Wood triptych, "Virgin and Child" (St. George's Church).
See also Nos. 1656/**MS**1658 and 1740/**MS**1742.

467 Scarce Swallowtail   **468** Flags
(*Iphiclides podalirius*)

(Des J. Švengsbír. Eng J. Herčík (60 h., 80 h.), J. Švengsbír (others). Recess)

1966 (23 May). *Butterflies and Moths. T 467 and similar horiz designs. Multicoloured.* P 14.
1575   30 h. Type **467**   ..   40   10
1576   60 h. Moorland clouded yellow (*Colias palaeno*)   70   10
1577   80 h. Lesser purple emperor (*Apatura ilia*)   70   15
1578   1 k. Apollo (*Parnassius apollo*)   70   25
1579   1 k. 20 Scarlet tiger moth (*Panaxia dominula*)   ..   1·50   35
1580   2 k. Cream-spot tiger moth (*Epicallia villica*)   ..   3·75   1·90
1575/1580   Set of 6   ..   7·00   2·50

(Des L. Guderna. Eng J. Mráček (30 h.), L. Jirka (60 h.), J. Schmidt (1 k. 60). Recess*)

1966 (31 May). *13th Czechoslovakian Communist Party Congress. T 468 and similar horiz designs.* P 12×11½.
1581   30 h. red and blue   ..   15   10
1582   60 h. red and blue   ..   15   10
1583   1 k. 60, red and blue   ..   40   10
Designs:—60 h. Hammer and sickle; 1 k. 60, Girl.

469 Indian Village   **470** Atomic Symbol

(Des L. Šindelář (20 h., 1 k., 1 k. 40), P. Sukdolák (others). Eng J. Herčík (20 h., 1 k. 40), L. Jirka (30, 40 h.), J. Schmidt (60 h., 1 k.), J. Mráček (1 k. 20). Recess* (1 k. 40) or recess (others).

1966 (20 June). *"North-American Indians". Centenary of Náprstek's Ethnographic Museum, Prague. T 469 and similar designs.* P 12×11½ (20 h., 1 k.) or 11½×12 (others).
1584   20 h. deep blue and orange   20   10
1585   30 h. black and orange-brown   20   10
1586   40 h. sepia and light blue   20   10
1587   60 h. deep green & light orange-yellow   25   10
1588   1 k. purple and light green   ..   35   10
1589   1 k. 20, deep blue and mauve   50   20
1590   1 k. 40, multicoloured   ..   2·00   90
1584/1590   Set of 7   ..   3·25   1·25
Designs: *Vert*—30 h. Tomahawk; 40 h. Haida totem pole; 60 h. Katchina, "good spirit" of Hopi tribe; 1 k. 20, Dakota calumet (pipe of peace); 1 k. 40, Dakota Indian chief. *Horiz*—1 k. Hunting American bison.

(Des F. Gross. Eng J. Goldschmied. Recess*)

1966 (4 July). *Centenary of Czech Chemical Society.* P 11½.
1591 **470** 60 h. black and light blue   ..   30   10

471 "Guernica", after Picasso

(Eng J. Herčík. Recess*)

1966 (5 July). *30th Anniv of International Brigade's War Service in Spain.* P 11½.
1592 **471** 60 h. black and pale blue   ..   1·60   1·60
No. 1592 was issued in sheets of 15 stamps and 5 labels (⅓ stamp size) depicting Picasso's signature and a hand grasping a broken sword.

472 Pantheon,   **473** Fair Emblem   **474** "Atomic Age"
    Bratislava

(Des V. Hložník. Eng J. Mráček and J. Goldschmied (1593), L. Jirka (1594/5). J. Mráček (1596). Recess)

1966 (25 July). *Cultural Anniversaries. T 472 and similar vert designs.* P 11½.
1593 **472** 30 h. slate-lilac   15   10
1594   60 h. ultramarine   20   10
1595   60 h. grey-green   20   10
1596   60 h. sepia   20   10
1593/1596   Set of 4   ..   70   20
Designs:— No 1593, T **472** (21st anniv of liberation of Bratislava); 1594, L. Stur (Slovak leader) and Devin Castle; 1595, Nachod (700th anniv); 1596, Arms, globe, books and view of Olomouc (400th anniv of State Science Library)

(Des J. Fišer. Eng B. Housa. Recess*)

1966 (29 Aug). *Brno International Fair.* P 11½.
1597 **473** 60 h. black and rose-red   ..   25   10

(Des F. Hudeček. Eng L. Jirka. Recess*)

1966 (29 Aug). *Jáchymov (source of pitch-blende).* P 11½.
1598 **474** 60 h. black and red   ..   30   10

475 Olympic Coin   **476** Missile-carrier, Tank and
Mikoyan Gurevich MiG-21D Fighter

(Des J. Fišer. Eng J. Schmidt (60 h.), J. Herčik (1 k.). Recess*)
1966 (29 Aug). *70th Anniv of Olympic Committee. T* **475** *and similar vert design.* P 11½×12.
1599   60 h. black and gold   20   10
1600   1 k. deep blue and red   . .   80   25
Design:—1 k. Olympic flame and rings.

(Des J. Lukavský. Eng L. Jirka. Recess*)
1966 (31 Aug). *Military Manoeuvres.* P 12×11½.
1601 **476** 60 h. black and olive-yellow   . .   35   10

477 Moravian Silver Thaler   **478** Brno and
(reverse and obverse)   "Postmark"

(Des J. Liesler. Eng J. Schmidt (30 h., 60 h., 1 k. 60). Recess*.
Des J. Lukavský. Eng B. Housa (5 k.). Recess)
1966 (10 Sept). *Brno Stamp Exhibition. T* **477** *and similar designs and T* **478.** P 11½×12 (30 h.), 12×11½ (60 h., 1 k. 60) or 12 (5 k.).
1602   30 h. black and rosine   . .   30   10
1603   60 h. black and orange   . .   30   10
1604   1 k. 60, black and green   . .   80   25
MS1605   75×100 mm. 5 k. multicoloured   . .   2·40   2·40
Designs: *Horiz*—60 h. "Mercury"; 1 k. 60, Brno buildings and crest.

479 First Space Rendezvous

(Des J. Lukavský. Eng B. Housa (20 h., 30 h., 1 k. 20), J. Herčik (60 h., 80 h.), J. Herčik and L. Jirka (1 k.). Recess*)
1966 (26 Sept). *Space Research. T* **479** *and similar horiz designs.* P 11½×12.
1606   20 h. reddish violet and bluish green   . .   20   10
1607   30 h. blackish green and orange-red   . .   20   10
1608   60 h. indigo and bright mauve   . .   20   10
1609   80 h. purple and light blue   . .   20   10
1610   1 k. black and violet   20   20
1611   1 k. 20, rose-red and light blue   . .   1·90   50
1606/1611   *Set of 6* . .   . .   . .   2·50   95
Designs:—30 h. Satellite and "back" of Moon; 60 h. "Mariner 4" and first picture of Mars; 80 h. Satellite making "soft" landing on Moon; 1 k. Satellite, Laser beam and binary code; 1 k. 20, "Telstar", Earth and tracking station.

480 Eurasian Badger   **481** "Spring" (V. Hollar)

(Des J. Baláz. Litho Cartographic Institute, Bratislava)
1966 (28 Nov). *Game Animals. T* **480** *and similar designs. Multicoloured.* P 13½.
1612   30 h. Type **480**   20   10
1613   40 h. Red deer (*vert*)   . .   25   10
1614   60 h. Lynx   30   10
1615   80 h. Brown hare (inscr "europaens")   . .   40   20
           a. Inscr "europaeus"   . .   2·50   1·25
1616   1 k. Red fox   50   30
1617   1 k. 20, Brown bear (*vert*)   . .   50   40
1618   2 k. Wild boar   . .   . .   2·75   1·25
1612/1618   *Set of 7*   . .   . .   4·50   2·25
The 80 h. is incorrectly inscribed "europaens" (No. 1615) on 40 stamps out of each sheet of 50. No. 1615a occurs on all stamps of the fifth and tenth vertical rows.

(Eng J. Herčik (1623), J. Švengsbir (others). Recess)
1966 (8 Dec). *Art* (1st series). *T* **481** *and similar vert designs. Nos. 1620/3 multicoloured.* P 14.
1619   1 k. black (Type **481**)   . .   7·50   6·50
1620   1 k. "Mrs. F. Wussin" (J. Kupecký)   . .   3·00   2·50
1621   1 k. "Snowy Owl" (K. Purkyne)   . .   3·00   3·00
1622   1 k. "Bouquet" (V. Spalá)   . .   3·00   2·50
1623   1 k. "Recruit" (L. Fulla)   . .   35·00   27·00
1619/1623   *Set of 5* . .   . .   45·00   38·00
Issued in sheets of four stamps and two half stamp-sized labels, either bearing the artist's name in an ornamental frame (No. 1619) or blank (Nos. 1620/3).
See also Nos. 1669, 1699/1703, 1747, 1753, 1756, 1790/4, 1838, 1861/5, 1914/18, 1999/2003, 2067/71 2134/9, 2194/8, 2256/60, 2313/16, 2375/9, 2495/9, 2549/53, 2601/5, 2655/9, 2702/6, 2757/61, 2810/14, 2858/62, 2904/8, 2954/6, **MS**2976, 3000/2, 3044/7, 3077/81 and 3107/9.

482 "Carrier Pigeon"

(Des J. Kaiser. Eng J. Schmidt. Recess*)
1966 (17 Dec). *Stamp Day.* P 11½×12.
1624 **482** 1 k. ultramarine and yellow   . .   50   50

483 "Youth" (Fifth   **484** Distressed Family
Czech Youth Federation
Congress)

(Des F. Gross. Eng J. Herčík (1625), J. Mráček (1626). Recess*)

1967 (16 Jan). *Czech Congresses. T* **483** *and similar horiz designs. P* 11½.
1625 **483** 30 h. red and light blue 15 10
1626 – 30 h. carmine and light yellow .. 15 10
Design:—No. 1626, Rose and T.U. emblem (Sixth Trade Union Congress).

(Des F. Gross. Eng J. Schmidt. Recess*)

1967 (16 Jan). *"Peace in Vietnam". P* 11½.
1627 **484** 60 h. black and salmon-red .. 25 10

485 Jihlava **486** Black-tailed Godwit

(Des C. Bouda. Eng J. Mráček (30 h.), L. Jirka (40 h.). Des A. Bronovský. Eng B. Housa (1 k. 20). Des and eng B. Housa (1 k. 60), Recess)

1967 (13 Feb). *International Tourist Year. T* **485** *and similar horiz designs. P* 12×11½ (30 h., 40 h) or 11½ (*others*).
1628 30 h. maroon 15 10
1629 40 h. brown-red 15 10
1630 1 k. violet-blue 45 20
1631 1 k. 60, black .. .. .. 1·60 50
1628/1631 *Set of 4* .. .. .. 2·10 80
Designs: *As T* **485**—40 h. Brno. 76×30 *mm*—1 k. 20, Bratislava; 1 k. 60, Prague.

(Des O. Janeček. Litho Svoboda Ptg Wks, Prague)

1967 (20 Feb). *Water Birds. T* **486** *and similar multicoloured designs. P* 13½.
1632 30 h. Type **486** 30 10
1633 40 h. Common shoveler (*horiz*) .. 40 15
1634 60 h. Purple heron 40 10
1635 80 h. Penduline tit 85 30
1636 1 k. Avocet 85 30
1637 1 k. 40, Black stork .. .. 1·75 50
1638 1 k. 60, Tufted duck (*horiz*) .. 4·25 1·75
1632/1638 *Set of 7* .. .. 8·00 2·75

487 Sun and Satellite

(Des J. Lukavský. Eng L. Jirka (30 h., 1 k. 60), B. Housa (40 h., 1 k. 20), J. Herčík (60 h.), J. Schmidt (1 k.). Recess*)

1967 (24 Mar). *Space Research. T* **487** *and similar horiz designs. P* 11½.
1639 30 h. carmine and yellow .. 15 10
1640 40 h. ultramarine and drab-grey 15 10
1641 60 h. emerald-green and reddish violet 25 10
1642 1 k. deep blue and mauve .. 25 10
1643 1 k. 20, black and violet-blue .. 40 20
1644 1 k. 60, brown-lake and drab-grey 1·75 35
1639/1644 *Set of 6* .. .. 2·75 80
Designs:—40 h. Space vehicles in orbit; 60 h. "Man on the Moon" and orientation systems; 1 k. "Exploration of the planets"; 1 k. 20, Lunar satellites; 1 k. 60, Lunar observatory and landscape.

488 Gothic Art **489** Bicycle Wheels and Dove
(after painting by Theodoric)

(Des K. Vodák. Eng J. Schmidt (30, 60 h.), B. Housa (40 h.), L. Jirka (80 h., 1 k.), J. Herčík (1 k. 20, 3 k.). Recess)

1967 (10 Apr). *World Fair, Montreal. T* **488** *and similar horiz designs. Multicoloured. P* 14 *or* 11½ (3 k.).
1645 30 h. Type **488** 15 10
1646 40 h. Jena Codex-ancient manuscript "Burning of John Hus" .. 15 10
1647 60 h. Lead crystal glass .. 20 15
1648 80 h. "The Shepherdess and the Chimney Sweep" (Andersen's Fairy Tales), after painting by J. Trnka .. 30 15
1649 1 k. Atomic diagram ("Technical Progress") 35 30
1650 1 k. 20, Dolls by P. Rada ("Ceramics") 1·25 40
1645/1650 *Set of 6* .. .. 2·10 1·10
MS1651 95×75 mm. 3 k. Montreal skyline .. 2·40 1·90

(Des J. Fišer. Eng J. Mráček (1652/3), J. Schmidt (1654/5). Recess*)

1967 (17 Apr). *Sports Events of* 1967. *T* **489** *and similar designs. P* 12×11½ (*horiz*) *or* 11½×12 (*vert*).
1652 60 h. black and vermilion .. 20 10
1653 60 h. black and turquoise-blue .. 20 10
1654 60 h. black and new blue .. 20 10
1655 1 k. 60, black and violet .. 1·50 60
1652/1655 *Set of 4* .. .. 1·90 70
Designs: *Horiz*—No. 1652, *T* **489** (20th Warsaw-Berlin-Prague Cycle Race); 1654, Canoeist in kayak (Fifth World Canoeing Championships). *Vert*—1653, Basketball players (World Women's Basketball Championships); 1655 Canoeist (Tenth World Water-slalom Championships).

(Des and eng J. Herčík. Recess)

1967 (9 May). *Prague Castle* (third series). *Vert designs as T* **465**. *P* 11½.
1656 30 h. lake 20 10
1657 60 h. slate 45 15
MS1658 75×95 mm. 5 k. multicoloured .. 2·75 2·25
Designs: (*As T* **465**)—30 h. "Golden Street"; 60 h. St. Wenceslas' Hall; *Smaller* (30½×50 mm.)—5 k. "The Glory of Christ" (Bohemian 11th-century illuminated manuscript).

490 "PRAZSKE 1967" **491** Synagogue Curtain (detail) **492** Lidice Rose

(Des Z. Sklenář. Eng J. Mráček. Recess*)

1967 (10 May). *Prague Music Festival. P* 11½.
1659 **490** 60 h. deep reddish violet & blue-grn 25 10

(Des and eng J. Švengsbir (30 h., 60 h., 1 k.), Des K. Vodák. Eng J. Mráček (1 k. 20), J. Herčík (1 k. 40, 1 k. 60). Recess*)

1967 (22 May). *Jewish Culture. T* **491** *and similar vert designs. P* 11½×12.
1660 30 h. carmine-red and pale blue .. 20 10
1661 60 h. black and light emerald 25 10

1662	1 k. deep blue and light mauve	35	10
1663	1 k. 20, light brown-lake and brown	50	15
1664	1 k. 40, black and greenish yellow	50	15
1665	1 k. 60, bluish green and yellow	6·00	3·25
1660/1665	Set of 6	7·00	3·50

Designs:—60 h. Printers' imprint (1530); 1 k. Mikulov jug (1801); 1 k. 20, "Old-New" Synagogue, Prague (1268); 1 k. 40, Jewish memorial candelabra, Pinkas Synagogue (1536), (the memorial is for Czech victims of Nazi persecution); 1 k. 60 David Gans' tombstone (1613).

(Des K. Svolinský. Eng L. Jirka. Recess*)

1967 (9 June). *25th Anniv of Destruction of Lidice.* P 11½.
1666 **492** 30 h. black and carmine · · · · 20 10

493 "Architecture"   **494** Petr Bezruč

(Des J. Liesler. Eng J. Schmidt. Recess*)

1967 (10 June). *Ninth International Architects Union Congress, Prague.* P 11½×12.
1667 **493** 1 k. black and gold · · · · 40 15

(Des J. Šváb. Eng B. Housa. Recess*)

1967 (21 June). *Birth Centenary of Petr Bezruč (poet).* P 12×11½.
1668 **494** 60 h. black and brown-red · · 25 10

(Eng J. Švengsbír. Recess)

1967 (22 June). *Publicity for "Praga 68" Stamp Exhibition. Vert design as T 481. Multicoloured.* P 11½.
1669 2 k. "Henri Rousseau" (self-portrait) · · 2·00 1·25
Issued in sheets of four with a *se-tenant* label depicting the National Gallery, Prague.

495 Skalica

(Des V. Hložník. Eng J. Mráček (1670), J. Schmidt (1671). Des J. Novák. Eng J. Mráček (1672). Recess)

1967 (21 Aug). *Czech Towns. T 495 and similar horiz designs.* P 11½.
1670 **495** 30 h. deep violet-blue · · · · 15 10
1671 — 30 h. brown-lake (Prešov) · · 15 10
1672 — 30 h. blackish green (Příbram) · · 15 10

496 Thermal Fountain and Colonnade, Karlovy Vary

(Des J. Lukavský. Eng B. Housa. Recess*)

1967 (21 Aug). *Postal Employees Games.* P 11½×12.
1673 **496** 30 h. bluish violet and gold · · 25 10

497 Ondřejov Observatory   **498** *Miltonia*
and Universe   *spectabilis*

(Des J. Lukavský. Eng L. Jirka. Recess)

1967 (21 Aug). *13th International Astronomic Union Congress, Prague.* P 11½×12.
1674 **497** 60 h. silver, ultramarine & bright pur 1·40 25

(Des Ludmila Jiřincová. Litho Svoboda Ptg Wks, Prague)

1967 (30 Aug). *Botanical Garden Flowers. T 498 and similar vert designs. Multicoloured.* P 12½.
1675	20 h. Type **498**	25	10
1676	30 h. Cup and saucer plant (*Cobaea scandens*)	25	10
1677	40 h. *Lycaste deppei*	25	15
1678	60 h. *Glottiphyllum davisii*	40	10
1679	1 k. Painter's palette (*Anthurium andreanum*)	60	20
1680	1 k. 20, *Rhodocactus bleo*	60	35
1681	1 k. 40, *Dendrobium phalaenopsis*	2·00	65
1675/1681	Set of 7	4·00	1·50

499 Eurasian Red Squirrel   **500** Military Vehicles

(Des J. Baláž. Eng J. Goldschmied (30 h.—from drawing by B. Housa), B. Housa (60 h., 1 k. 20), J. Schmidt (1 k., 1 k. 40, 1 k. 60). Recess*)

1967 (25 Sept). *Fauna of Tatra National Park. T 499 and similar horiz designs.* P 12×11½.
1682	30 h. black, orange and pale yellow	35	10
1683	60 h. black and buff	35	10
1684	1 k. black and pale blue	40	15
1685	1 k. 20, black, yellow and pale green	60	15
1686	1 k. 40, black, yellow and pale pink	85	20
1687	1 k. 60, black, orange, pale greenish yellow and light orange	3·00	1·25
1682/1687	Set of 6	5·00	1·60

Designs:—60 h. Wild cat; 1 k. Stoat; 1 k. 20, Hazel dormouse; 1 k. 40, West European hedgehog; 1 k. 60, Pine marten.

(Des M. Ressel. Eng J. Schmidt. Recess)

1967 (6 Oct). *Army Day.* P 11½×12.
1688 **500** 30 h. bronze-green 35 10

501 Prague Castle
("PRAGA 62")

502 Cruiser *Aurora*

(Des J. Lukavský. Eng J. Herčík (60 h., 2, 5 k.), L. Jirka (others). Recess (5 k.) or recess* (others))

1967 (30 Oct). *AIR. "PRAGA 1968" International Stamp Exhibition (first issue). T 501 and similar vert designs. P 11½.*
1689 30 h. multicoloured 15 10
1690 60 h. multicoloured 25 10
1691 1 k. multicoloured 25 15
1692 1 k. 40, multicoloured 40 20
1693 1 k. 60, multicoloured 40 30
1694 2 k. multicoloured 65 25
1695 5 k. multicoloured .. .. 3·50 3·50
1689/1695 *Set of 7* .. .. 5·00 4·00

Designs: (as *T* 501)—Sites of previous international stamp exhibitions:—60 h. Selimiye Mosque, Edirne ("ISTANBUL 1963"); 1 k. Notre Dame, Paris ("PHILATEC 1964"); 1 k. 40, Belvedere Palace, Vienna ("WIPA 1965"); 1 k. 60, Capitol, Washington ("SIPEX 1965"); 2 k. Amsterdam ("AMPHILEX 1967"). *Larger* (40×55 mm.)—5 k. Prague ("PRAGA 1968")
Nos. 1689/94 were issued *se-tenant* with half stamp-size labels bearing the "Praga 1968" emblem and "WORLD STAMP EXHIBITION" in the language appropriate to the design. No. 1695 is printed in sheets of four stamps and a "label bearing an aircraft design and inscribed in Czech and Esperanto.
See also Nos. 1718/20, 1743/8, 1749/54, **MS**1755 and 1756.

(Des M. Romberg. Eng J. Herčík. Recess*)

1967 (7 Nov). *50th Anniv of October Revolution. T 502 and similar designs. P 12×11½ (30 h.) or 11½×12 (others).*
1696 30 h. carmine-red and black .. 10 10
1697 60 h. carmine-red and black .. 15 10
1698 1 k. carmine-red and black .. 15 10
Designs: *Vert*—60 h. Hammer and sickle emblems; 1 k. "Reaching hands".

(Eng J. Herčík (60 h., 1 k. 60), J. Švengsbír (80 h., 1 k. 20), B. Housa (1 k.). Recess)

1967 (13 Nov). *Art (2nd series). Vert designs as T 481. Multicoloured. P 11½.*
1699 60 h. "Conjurer with Cards" (F. Tichý) 25 25
1700 80 h. "Don Quixote" (C. Majernik) .. 25 25
1701 1 k. "Promenade in the Park" (N. Grund) 55 55
1702 1 k. 20, "Self-Portrait" (P. J. Brandl) 55 55
1703 1 k. 60, "Epitaph to Jan of Jeřeň" (Czech master) .. .. 4·25 4·25
1699/1703 *Set of 5* .. .. 5·25 5·25
All in National Gallery, Prague. Nos. 1699/703 are printed in sheets of four stamps and two blank labels.

503 Pres. Novotny

504 Letov L-13

(Des and eng B. Housa. Recess)

1967 (9 Dec). P 11½.
1704 **503** 2 k. deep bluish green .. 1·25 10
1705 3 k. brown .. .. 1·75 10

(Des J. Lukavský. Eng J. Herčík (30 h. to 1 k.), J. Herčík and J. Goldschmied (1 k. 60, 2 k.). Recess*)

1967 (11 Dec). *AIR. Czech Aircraft. T 504 and similar horiz designs. Multicoloured. P 12×11½.*
1706 30 h. Type **504** 15 10
1707 60 h. Letov L-40 Meta Sokol .. 20 10
1708 80 h. Letov L-200 Morava .. 20 10
1709 1 k. Letov Z-37 Cmelak crop sprayer .. 45 15
1710 1 k. 60, Zlin Z-526 Trener Master .. 55 20
1711 2 k. Aero L-29 Delfin jet trainer .. 2·25 65
1706/1711 *Set of 6* .. .. 3·50 1·10

505 Czech Stamps of 1920

506 "CESKOSLOVENSKO 1918–1968"

(Des K. Vodák. Eng L. Jirka. Recess*)

1967 (18 Dec). *Stamp Day.* P 11½.
1712 **505** 1 k. brown-lake and silver .. 1·50 1·40

(Des K. Svolinský. Eng L. Jirka. Recess)

1968 (28 Jan). *50th Anniv of Republic (first issue). P 11½.*
1713 **506** 30 h. red, blue and ultramarine .. 55 15
See Nos. 1780/2.

507 Skater and Stadium

508 Charles Bridge, Prague and Charles's Hydrogen Balloon

(Des Anna Podzemná. Eng J. Herčík (60 h., 2 k.), J. Mráček (1 k.), J. Schmidt (1 k. 60). Recess*)

1968 (29 Jan). *Winter Olympic Games, Grenoble. T 507 and similar horiz designs. P 11½.*
1714 60 h. black, greenish yellow and ochre 15 10
1715 1 k. olive-brown, bistre & light vio-bl 30 10

```
1716    1 k. 60, black, turquoise-green and lilac    55    15
1717    2 k. black, light blue and light yellow    1·50    60
1714/1717   Set of 4   ..    ..    ..    ..   2·25    75
```
Designs:—1 k. Bobsleigh run; 1 k. 60, Ski jump; 2 k. Ice hockey.

(Des J. Liesler. Eng J. Schmidt. Recess)

1968 (5 Feb). *AIR. "PRAGA 1968" International Stamp Exhibition (second issue).* T **508** *and similar vert designs. Multicoloured.* P 11½.

```
1718    60 h. Type 508 ..    ..    ..    ..    40    15
1719    1 k. Royal Summer-house, Belvedere,
        and William Henson's Aerial Steam
        Carriage ..    ..    ..    ..    65    25
1720    2 k. Prague Castle and airship ..    ..   1·25    65
```

513 "Radio" (45th anniv)   514 Athlete and Statuettes

(Des K. Vodák. Eng J. Goldschmied (No. 1730), J. Mráček (No. 1731). Recess*)

1968 (29 Apr). *Czech Radio and Television Anniversaries.* T **513** *and similar horiz design.* P 12×11½.

```
1730    30 h. black, carmine and ultramarine    ..    15    10
1731    30 h. black, carmine and ultramarine    ..    15    10
```
Designs:—No. 1730, T **513**; No. 1731, "Television" (15th anniv).

(Des J. Liesler. Eng B. Housa (30 h., 40 h.), J. Herčík (60 h., 2 k.), J. Schmidt (1 k.), J. Mráček (1 k. 60). Recess*)

1968 (30 Apr). *Olympic Games, Mexico.* T **514** *and similar vert designs. Multicoloured.* P 11½.

```
1732    30 h. Type 514    ..    ..    ..    ..    15    10
1733    40 h. Runner and seated figure (Quet-
        zalcoatl) ..    ..    ..    ..    20    10
1734    60 h. Netball and ornaments    ..    ..    25    10
1735    1 k. Altar and Olympic emblems    ..    35    15
1736    1 k. 60, Football and ornaments    ..    50    20
1737    2 k. Prague Castle and key    ..    ..   2·50    70
1732/1737   Set of 6 ..    ..    ..    ..   3·50   1·25
```

509 Industrial Scene   510 Battle Plan
and Red Sun

(Des J. Paukert. Eng L. Jirka. Recess*)

1968 (25 Feb). *20th Anniv of "Victorious February"* T **509** *and similar vert design.* P 11½×12.

```
1721    30 h. red and chalky blue    ..    ..    10    10
1722    60 h. red and chalky blue    ..    ..    15    10
```
Design:—60 h. Workers and banner.

(Des J. Lukavský. Eng J. Goldschmied. Recess*)

1968 (8 Mar). *25th Anniv of Sokolovo Battles.* P 11½.
```
1723    510    30 h. carm-red, new bl & bronze-grn    35    10
```

511 Human Rights   512 Liptovský Mikuláš (town)
Emblem   and Janko Král (writer)

(Des M. Hegar. Eng J. Schmidt. Recess)

1968 (8 Mar). *Human Rights Year.* P 11½.
```
1724    511    1 k. claret ..    ..    ..    ..    75    35
```

(Des V. Hložnik. Eng J. Herčík (1725). Des K. Svolinský. Eng L. Jirka (1726/7). Des M. Hegar. Eng J. Schmidt (1728). Des I. Strnad. Eng J. Herčík (1729). Recess (1725, 1728) or recess* (others))

1968 (25 Mar). *Various Commemorations.* T **512** *and similar designs.* P 11½.

```
1725    30 h. emerald ..    ..    ..    25    10
1726    30 h. deep blue and red-orange    ..    25    10
1727    30 h. carmine and gold    ..    ..    25    10
1728    30 h. brown-purple    ..    ..    25    10
1729    1 k. multicoloured    ..    ..    40    10
1725/1729   Set of 5 ..    ..    ..   1·25    30
```
Designs: *Horiz*—No. 1725 T **512**. *Vert*—1726, Allegorical figure of woman (150th anniv of Prague National Museum); 1727, Girl's head (centenary of Prague National Theatre); 1728, Karl Marx (150th anniv of birth); 1729, Diagrammatic skull (20th anniv of World Health Organization).

515 President Svoboda   516 "Business" (sculpture by O. Gutfreund)

(Des and eng J. Schmidt. Recess)

1968 (9 May)–**70**. P 12×11½.
```
1738    515    30 h. ultramarine ..    ..    10    10
1738a          50 h. blue-green (16.2.70)    ..    10    10
1739           60 h. brown-red    ..    ..    20    10
1739a          1 k. lake (16.2.70)    ..    ..    25    10
               b. Double impression    ..    ..
               c. Bright lake    ..    ..    25    10
               d. Dull mauve ..    ..    ..    25    10
1738/1739a  Set of 4 ..    ..    ..    55    20
```

(Des P. Sukdolák; eng L. Jirka (30 h.), J. Schmidt (60 h.). Des and eng L. Jirka (5 k.). Recess (5 k.) or recess* (others))

1968 (9 May). *Prague Castle (fourth series). Vert designs as* T **465.** P 11½.
```
1740    30 h. black, yellow, red and light green    25    10
1741    60 h. black, pale green and red    ..    25    10
MS1742 75×95 mm. 5 k. multicoloured    ..   3·00   3·00
```
Designs:—30 h. "Bretislav I" (from tomb in St. Vitus' Cathedral); 60 h. Knocker on door of St. Wenceslas' Chapel. *Smaller* (30½×51 *mm.*)—5 k. "St. Vitus" (detail from mosaic).

(Des and eng J. Švengsbír. Recess (2 k.) or recess* (others))

1968 (5 June). *"PRAGA 1968" International Stamp Exhibition (third issue). T 516 and similar vert designs. Multicoloured.* P 11½.

1743	30 h. Type **516**	20	10
1744	40 h. Broadcasting building, Prague	20	10
1745	60 h. Parliament building	20	15
1746	1 k. 40, "Prague" (Gobelin tapestry by Jan Bauch)	80	25
1747	2 k. "The Cabaret Artiste" (painting by F. Kupka)	2·25	2·25
1748	3 k. Presidential standard	80	45
1743/1748	Set of 6	4·00	3·00

Nos. 1743/6 and 1748 were each issued in sheets of 15 with vert *se-tenant* labels bearing the "Praga 1968" emblem and inscription. No. 1747 is larger (40×50 *mm.*) and was issued in sheets of four with one similarly inscribed horiz label.

(Des and eng J. Švengsbír. Recess (2 k.) or recess* (others))

1968 (21 June). *"PRAGA 1968" International Stamp Exhibition (fourth issue). Vert designs as T 516 and T 481 (2 k.). P 11½.*

1749	30 h. myrtle-grn, grnish yell & pale grey	20	10
1750	60 h. reddish vio, gold & pale yell-grn	20	10
1751	1 k. indigo, pink and pale blue	30	15
1752	1 k. 60, pink, gold, light bl & yell-olive	55	25
1753	2 k. multicoloured	1·50	1·50
1754	3 k. black, light blue, pink & grnish yell	1·60	40
1749/1754	Set of 6	4·00	2·25

Designs: As *T* **516**—30 h. St. George's Basilica, Prague Castle; 60 h. Renaissance fountain; 1 k. Dvořák's Museum; 1 k. 60, "Three Violins" insignia (18th-century house); 3 k. Prague emblem of 1475. As *T* **481**—2 k. "Josefina" (painting by Josef Mánes, National Gallery, Prague).

Nos. 1749/52 and 1754 are in sheets of 15 and 1753 in sheets of four as previous issue.

517 View of Prague

(Des and eng J. Švengsbír. Recess)

1968 (22 June). *"PRAGA 1968" (fifth issue—50th Anniv of Czechoslovak Stamps). Sheet 73×111½ mm. Imperf.*
MS1755 **517** 10 k. multicoloured .. .. 4·00 3·50
No. **MS**1755 was sold only at the Exhibition at 15 k. including entrance fee.

(Des and eng J. Švengsbír. Recess)

1968 (6 July). *"PRAGA 1968" (sixth issue—F.I.P. Day). Vert design as T 481. P 11½.*
1756 5 k. multicoloured .. .. .. 4·00 3·25
Design:—5 k. "Madonna of the Rosary" (detail from painting by Albrecht Dürer in National Gallery, Prague).
No. 1756 was issued in sheets of four with *se-tenant* label commemorating the F.I.P.

518 Horse-drawn Coach on Rails (140th Anniv of České Budějovice-Linz Railway)

519 Symbolic "S"

(Des F. Hudeček. Eng L. Jirka. Recess*)

1968 (6 Aug). *Railway Anniversaries. T 518 and similar horiz design. P 11½×11.*
1757 60 h. multicoloured 25 15
1758 1 k. multicoloured 80 25
Design:—1 k. Early steam locomotive *Johann Adolf* and modern electric locomotive (centenary of České Budějovice–Pilsen Railway).

(Des K. Svolinský. Eng L. Jirka. Recess*)

1968 (7 Aug). *Sixth International Slavonic Congress, Prague. P 11½.*
1759 **519** 30 h. carmine-red & deep ultram .. 50 10

520 Adrspach Rocks and Ammonite

(Des J. Lukavský. Eng B. Housa. Recess*)

1968 (8 Aug). *23rd International Geological Congress, Prague. T 520 and similar horiz designs. P 11½.*
1760 30 h. black and greenish yellow .. 20 10
1761 60 h. black and light mauve .. 20 10
1762 80 h. black, pink and lavender .. 30 10
1763 1 k. black and pale blue .. 40 10
1764 1 k. 60, black and pale olive-yellow .. 2·00 70
1760/1764 Set of 5 .. .. 2·75 90
Designs:—60 h. Basalt columns and fossilised frog; 80 h. Bohemian "Paradise" and agate; 1 k. Tatra landscape and shell; 1 k. 60, Barrandien (Bohemia) and limestone.

Two stamps, 30 and 60 h. values, were prepared for the 14th Czechoslovakian Communist Party Congress but were not issued.

521 M. J. Hurban and Standard-bearer

522 "Man and Child" (Jiri Beutler, aged 10)

(Des V. Hloznik. Eng J. Schmidt. Recess)

1968 (9 Sept). *120th Anniv of Slovak Insurrection and 25th Anniv of Slovak National Council. T 521 and similar horiz design. P 12×11½.*
1765 30 h. blue 15 10
1766 60 h. red 15 10
Design:—60 h. Partisans (120th Anniv of Slovak Insurrection).

(Eng L. Jirka (1 k.), J. Mráček (others). Recess*)

1968 (30 Sept). *30th Anniv of Munich Agreement. Drawings by children in Terezin concentration camp. T* **522** *and similar horiz designs. Multicoloured. P* 12×11½ (1 *k.*) or 12½×11½ (*others*).

1767	30 h.	Type **522**	15	10
1768	60 h.	"Butterflies" (Kitty Brunnerova, aged 11)	20	10
1769	1 k.	"The Window" (Jiri Schlessinger, aged 10)	30	10

The 1 k. is larger (40×22 *mm.*).

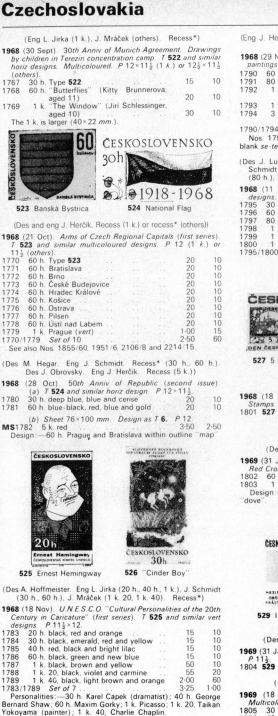

523 Banská Bystrica   **524** National Flag

(Des and eng J. Herčik. Recess (1 k.) or recess* (others))

1968 (21 Oct). *Arms of Czech Regional Capitals (first series). T* **523** *and similar multicoloured designs. P* 12 (1 *k.*) or 11½ (*others*).

1770	60 h.	Type **523**	20	10
1771	60 h.	Bratislava	20	10
1772	60 h.	Brno	20	10
1773	60 h.	České Budejovice	20	10
1774	60 h.	Hradec Králové	20	10
1775	60 h.	Košice	20	10
1776	60 h.	Ostrava	20	10
1777	60 h.	Pilsen	20	10
1778	60 h.	Ústi nad Labem	20	10
1779	1 k.	Prague (*vert*)	1·00	15
1770/1779		*Set of* 10	2·50	60

See also Nos. 1855/60, 1951/6, 2106/8 and 2214/15.

(Des M. Hegar. Eng J. Schmidt. Recess* (30 h., 60 h.). Des J. Obrovsky. Eng J. Herčik. Recess (5 k.))

1968 (28 Oct). *50th Anniv of Republic (second issue).*
(a) *T* **524** *and similar horiz design. P* 12×11½.

1780	30 h.	deep blue, blue and cerise	20	10
1781	60 h.	blue-black, red, blue and gold	20	10

(b) *Sheet* 76×100 *mm. Design as T* **6**. *P* 12.

MS1782	5 k.	red	3·50	2·50

Design:—60 h. Prague and Bratislava within outline "map".

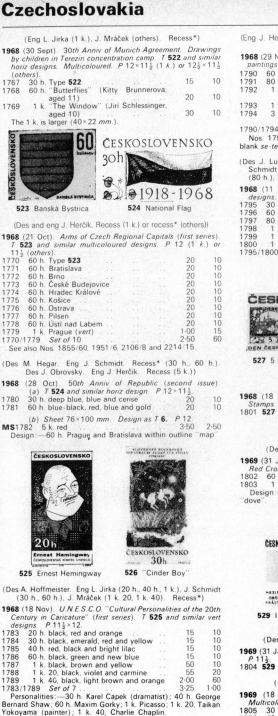

525 Ernest Hemingway   **526** "Cinder Boy"

(Des A. Hoffmeister. Eng L. Jirka (20 h., 40 h., 1 k.), J. Schmidt (30 h., 60 h.), J. Mráček (1 k. 20, 1 k. 40). Recess*)

1968 (18 Nov). *U.N.E.S.C.O. "Cultural Personalities of the 20th Century in Caricature" (first series). T* **525** *and similar vert designs. P* 11½×12.

1783	20 h.	black, red and orange	15	10
1784	30 h.	black, emerald, red and yellow	15	10
1785	40 h.	red, black and bright lilac	15	10
1786	60 h.	black, green and new blue	15	10
1787	1 k.	black, brown and yellow	50	10
1788	1 k. 20,	black, violet and carmine	55	20
1789	1 k. 40,	black, light brown and orange	2·00	60
1783/1789		*Set of* 7	3·25	1·00

Personalities:—30 h. Karel Capek (dramatist); 40 h. George Bernard Shaw; 60 h. Maxim Gorky; 1 k. Picasso; 1 k. 20, Taikan Yokoyama (painter); 1 k. 40, Charlie Chaplin.
See also Nos. 1829/34.

(Eng J. Herčik (60 h., 80 h.), B. Housa (1 k. 20), J. Švengsbír (1 k. 60), J. Schmidt (3 k.). Recess)

1968 (29 Nov). *Art (3rd series). Vert designs as T* **481**, *showing paintings in National Gallery, Prague. Multicoloured. P* 11½.

1790	60 h.	"Cleopatra. II" (J. Zrzavý)	50	40
1791	80 h.	"The Black Lake" (J. Preisler)	50	50
1792	1 k. 20,	"Giovanni Francisci as a Volunteer" (P. Bohuň)	1·50	70
1793	1 k. 60,	"Princess Hyacinth" (A Mucha)	1·00	70
1794	3 k.	"Madonna and Child" (altar detail, Master Paul of Levoča)	5·00	4·50
1790/1794		*Set of* 5	7·50	6·00

Nos. 1790/4 were each printed in sheets of four with two blank *se-tenant* labels.

(Des J. Lukavský, from book illustrations by L. Fulla. Eng J. Schmidt (30 h., 1 k. 20), B. Housa (60 h., 1 k. 80), J. Mráček (80 h.), L. Jirka (1 k.). Recess*)

1968 (11 Dec). *Slovak Fairy Tales. T* **526** *and similar vert designs. Multicoloured. P* 11½.

1795	30 h.	Type **526**	15	10
1796	60 h.	"The Proud Lady"	25	10
1797	80 h.	"The Knight who ruled the World"	30	10
1798	1 k.	"Good Day, Little Bench"	40	15
1799	1 k. 20,	"The Enchanted Castle"	45	15
1800	1 k. 80,	"The Miraculous Hunter"	2·10	55
1795/1800		*Set of* 6	3·25	95

527 5 h. and 10 h. Stamps of 1918   **528** Red Crosses forming Cross

(Des K. Vodák. Eng L. Jirka. Recess*)

1968 (18 Dec). *Stamp Day and 50th Anniv of First Czech Stamps. P* 11½×12.

1801	**527**	1 k. gold and royal blue	80	80

**FEDERAL SOCIALIST REPUBLIC
1 January 1969–20 April 1990**

(Des I. Strnad. Eng J. Goldschmied. Recess*)

1969 (31 Jan). *50th Anniv of Czech Red Cross and League of Red Cross Societies. T* **528** *and similar horiz design. P* 11½.

1802	60 h.	red, gold and deep sepia	25	10
1803	1 k.	red, ultramarine and black	45	15

Design:—1 k. Red Cross symbols within heart-shaped "dove".

529 I.L.O. Emblem   **530** Wheel-lock Pistol, *circa* 1580

(Des V. Kovářik. Eng J. Goldschmied. Recess*)

1969 (31 Jan). *50th Anniv of International Labour Organization. P* 11½.

1804	**529**	1 k. black and bluish grey	25	10

(Des V. Kovářik. Eng J. Herčik. Recess*)

1969 (18 Feb). *Early Pistols. Square designs as T* **530**. *Multicoloured. P* 11.

1805	30 h.	Type **530**	15	10
1806	40 h.	Italian horse-pistol, *c.* 1600	20	10

1807	60 h. Kubik wheel-lock carbine, c. 1720	20	10
1808	1 k. Flint-lock pistol, c. 1760	30	10
1809	1 k. 40, Lebeda duelling pistols, c. 1830	50	15
1810	1 k. 60, Derringer pistol, c. 1865	1·75	35
1805/1810	Set of 6	2·75	70

531 University Emblem and Symbols (50th Anniv of Brno University)

(Des J. Hadlač. Eng J. Herčík (No. 1811). Des V. Hložník, Eng J. Mráček (1812). Des C. Bouda. Eng J. Schmidt (1813). Des A. Brunovský. Eng J. Herčík (1814). Des A. Hollý. Eng J. Herčík (1815). Des E. Sedlák. Eng J. Schmidt (1816). Recess (No. 1812) or recess*)

1969 (24 Mar). *Anniversaries. T* **531** *and similar horiz designs. P* 11½.

1811	60 h. black, grey-blue and gold	20	10
1812	60 h. ultramarine	20	10
1813	60 h. red, gold, black and light blue	20	10
1814	60 h. black and red	20	10
1815	60 h. red, silver and light blue	20	10
1816	60 h. black and gold	20	10
1811/1816	Set of 6	1·10	30

Designs and Anniversaries:—No. 1811, T **531**; No. 1812, Bratislava Castle, open book and head of woman (50th Anniv of Comenius University, Bratislava); No. 1813, Harp and symbolic eagle (50th Anniv of Brno Conservatoire); No. 1814, Theatrical allegory (50th Anniv of Slovak National Theatre (1970)); No. 1815, Arms and floral emblems (50th Anniv of Slovak Republican Council); No. 1816, Grammar school and allegories of Learning (Centenary of Zniev Grammar School).

532 Veteran Cars of 1900–05

(Des F. Hudeček. Eng L. Jirka (30 h.), J. Schmidt (1 k. 60), J. Mráček (1 k. 80). Recess*)

1969 (25 Mar). *Motor Vehicles. T* **532** *and similar horiz designs. Multicoloured. P* 11½.

1817	30 h. Type **532**	40	10
1818	1 k. 60, Veteran cars of 1907	70	15
1819	1 k. 80, Prague buses of 1907 and 1967	1·75	70

533 "Peace" (after L. Guderna)

(Eng J. Herčík. Recess*)

1969 (21 Apr). *20th Anniv of Peace Movement. P* 11.
1820 **533** 1 k. 60, multicoloured ... 45 30
No. 1820 was issued in sheets of 15 stamps and 5 half stamp-size labels, depicting a kneeling woman setting free a dove, in black.

534 Engraving by H. Goltzius

(Eng B. Housa. Recess* (2 k. 40) or recess (others))

1969 (24 Apr). *Horses. Works of Art. T* **534** *and similar designs. P* 11½.

1821	30 h. sepia/*pale cream*	25	10
1822	80 h. slate-purple/*pale cream*	25	10
1823	1 k. 60, slate/*pale cream*	45	15
1824	1 k. 80, black/*pale cream*	45	25
1825	2 k. 40, multicoloured/*pale cream*	2·50	70
1821/1825	Set of 5	3·50	1·10

Designs: *Horiz*—80 h. Engraving by M. Merian. *Vert*—1 k. 60, Engraving by V. Hollar; 1 k. 80, Engraving by A. Dürer; 2 k. 40, Painting by J. E. Ridinger.

535 Dr. M. R. Štefánik as Civilian and Soldier

(Des J. Baláž. Eng J. Herčík. Recess)

1969 (4 May). *50th Death Anniv of General M. Štefánik. P* 11½.
1826 **535** 60 h. claret ... 40 10

536 "St. Wenceslas" (mural detail, Master of Litoměřice, 1511)   **537** "Music"

(Des and eng J. Schmidt (No. 1827), L. Jirka (No. 1828). Recess)

1969 (9 May). *Prague Castle (fifth series). T* **536** *and similar vert design. Multicoloured. P* 11½.

1827	3 k. Type **536**	2·25	1·40
1828	3 k. Coronation banner of the Czech Estates, 1723	2·25	1·40

Issued in sheets of four with two blank labels.
See also Nos. 1892/3, 1959/60, 2037/8, 2103/4, 2163/4, 2253/4, 2305/6, 2337/8, 2404/5, 2466/7, 2543/4, 2599/2600 and 2637/8.

(Des A. Hoffmeister. Eng J. Schmidt (30 h., 1 k., 1 k. 80). J. Herčík (40 h.), J. Mráček (60 h., 2 k.). Recess*)

1969 (17 June). *U.N.E.S.C.O. "Cultural Personalities of the 20th Century in Caricature" (second series). Vert designs similar to T* **525**. *P* 11½×12.

1829	30 h. black, red and new blue	10	10
1830	40 h. black, violet and light new blue	15	10
1831	60 h. black, red and light yellow	15	10

1832	1 k. multicoloured			30	10
1833	1 k. 80, black, bright blue & yell-orge			40	10
1834	2 k. black, light yellow and emerald			2·00	65
1829/1834	Set of 6			2·75	90

Personalities:—30 h. P. O. Hviezdoslav (poet); 40 h. G. K. Chesterton (writer); 60 h. V. Mayakovsky (poet); 1 k. Henri Matisse (painter); 1 k. 80, A. Hrdlička (anthropologist); 2 k. Franz Kafka (novelist).

(Eng J. Švengsbír. Recess (2 k. 40) or recess* (others))

1969 (14 July). *"Woman and Art". Paintings by Alfons Mucha. Vert designs as T 537 and similar to T 481 (2 k. 40). Multi-coloured. P 11½.*

1835	30 h. Type **537**			25	10
1836	60 h. "Painting"			30	10
1837	1 k. "Dance"			50	10
1838	2 k. 40, "Ruby and Amethyst" (40×51 mm)			2·50	1·25
1835/1838	Set of 4			3·25	1·25

No. 1838 was issued in sheets of four with two blank labels.

538 Astronaut, Moon and Aerial View of Manhattan

539 Soldier and Civilians

(Des J. Lukavský. Eng L. Jirka (60 h.), J. Schmidt (3 k.). Recess*)

1969 (21 July). *AIR. First Man on the Moon. T 538 and similar vert design. P 11½.*

1839	60 h. black, violet-blue, greenish yellow and silver			20	10
1840	3 k. black, new blue, yell-orge & silver			2·00	1·00

Design:—3 k. "Eagle" module and aerial view of J. F. Kennedy Airport, New York.

Nos. 1839/40 were each issued in sheets with *se-tenant* half stamp-size labels showing emblem and astronauts' names.

(Des V. Hložnik. Eng J. Herčík (No. 1841), J. Mráček (No. 1842). Recess*)

1969 (29 Aug). *25th Anniv of Slovak Rising and Battle of Dukla. T 539 and similar square design. P 11.*

1841	**539** 30 h. deep violet-blue & red/cream		15	10
1842	— 30 h. deep green and red/cream		15	10

Design:—No. 1842, General Svoboda and partisans.

540 Ganek

(Des J. Lukavský. Eng B. Housa (Nos. 1843/5), L. Jirka (Nos. 1846/8). Recess)

1969 (8 Sept). *20th Anniv of Tatra National Park. T 540 and other horiz designs. P 11 (Nos. 1843/5) or 11½ (others).*

1843	60 h. slate-purple			15	10
1844	60 h. deep blue			15	10
1845	60 h. grey-black			15	10
1846	1 k. 60, multicoloured			2·50	50
1847	1 k. 60, multicoloured			50	15
1848	1 k. 60, multicoloured			50	15
1843/1848	Set of 6			3·50	1·00

Designs: (As T 540)—No. 1844, Mala Valley; No. 1845, Bielovodska Valley. Smaller (40×23 mm.)—No. 1846, Velka valley and gentian; No. 1847, Mountain stream, Mala Valley and gentian; No. 1848, Krivan Peak and autumn crocus.

Nos. 1843/5 were each issued in sheets of 15 stamps, together with 5 se-tenant half stamp-size labels, showing Tatra flora.

541 Bronze Belt Fittings (8th-9th Century)

542 "Focal Point"—Tokyo

(Des J. Baláž. Eng J. Herčík (20 h., 1 k. 80, 2 k.), J. Schmidt (30 h.), J. Mráček (1 k.). Recess*)

1969 (30 Sept). *Archaeological Discoveries in Bohemia and Slovakia. T 541 and similar vert designs. Multicoloured. P 11½.*

1849	20 h. Type **541**		15	10
1850	30 h. Decoration showing masks (6th–8th century)		15	10
1851	1 k. Gold earrings (8th–9th century)		25	10
1852	1 k. 80, Metal crucifix (obverse and reverse) (9th-century)		50	20
1853	2 k. Gilt ornament with figure (9th-century)		2·25	45
1849/1853	Set of 5		3·00	80

(Des J. Liesler. Eng J. Schmidt. Recess)

1969 (1 Oct). *16th Universal Postal Union Congress, Tokyo. P 11½.*

1854	**542** 3 k. 20, red, yellow-orange, grn & blk		1·90	1·00

No. 1854 was issued in sheets of four.

(Des and eng J. Herčík. Recess*)

1969 (25 Oct). *Arms of Czech Regional Capitals (second series). Horiz designs similar to T 523. Multicoloured. P 11½.*

1855	50 h. Bardejov		20	10
1856	50 h. Hranice		20	10
1857	50 h. Kežmarok		20	10
1858	50 h. Krnov		20	10
1859	50 h. Litoměřice		20	10
1860	50 h. Manetin		20	10
1855/1860	Set of 6		1·10	45

(Eng J. Herčík (60 h.), J. Švengsbír (1 k.), L. Jirka (1 k. 60), J. Schmidt (1 k. 80), M. Ondráček (2 k. 20). Recess)

1969 (27 Nov). *Art (4th series). Vert designs similar to T 481. P 11½.*

1861	60 h. "Great Requiem" (F. Muzika)		70	45
1862	1 k. "Resurrection" (Master of Trebon)		70	45
1863	1 k. 60, "Crucifixion" (V. Hložnik)		70	45
1864	1 k. 80, "Girl with Doll" (J. Bencur)		70	65
1865	2 k. 20, "St. Jerome" (Master Theodoric)		2·75	2·50
1861/1865	Set of 5		5·00	4·00

Issued in sheets of four with blank se-tenant labels.

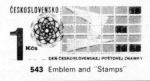

543 Emblem and "Stamps"

(Des J. Lukavský. Eng L. Jirka. Recess*)

1969 (18 Dec). *Stamp Day.* P 11½×12.
1866 **543** 1 k. maroon, gold and bright blue .. 80 80

548 "Autumn, 1955"   549 Lenin

544 Ski Jumping   545 J. A. Comenius
          (300th Death Anniv)

(Des J. Lukavský. Eng J. Goldschmied. Recess*)

(Des J. Šváb. Eng J. Schmidt (60 h., 2 k. 40), J. Mráček
          (1 k., 1 k. 80). Recess*)

1970 (6 Jan). *World Skiing Championships, High Tatras.*
T 544 and similar horiz designs. Multicoloured. P 11½.
1867   50 h. Type **544** 20 10
1868   60 h. Cross-country skiing 20 10
1869   1 k. Ski jumper taking-off 20 10
1870   1 k. 60, Woman skier .. .. 1·40 30
1867/1870   *Set of 4* .. .. .. 1·75 50

1970 (21 Apr). *Paintings by Josef Lada. Multicoloured designs
as T 548.* P 11½.
1884   60 h. Type **548** 20 10
1885   1 k. "The Magic Horse" (*vert*) .. 40 10
1886   1 k. 80, "The Water Demon" (*vert*) 45 15
1887   2 k. 40, "Children in Winter, 1943" .. 2·10 60
1884/1887 *Set of 4* .. .. .. 2·75 85

(Des and eng L. Jirka (30 h.). Des M. Hegar. Eng J. Herčik
          (60 h.). Recess*)

1970 (22 Apr). *Birth Centenary of Lenin. T 549 and similar.
vert design.* P 11½.
1888   30 h. brown-red and gold 10 10
1889   60 h. black and gold 15 10
Design:—60 h. Lenin (bareheaded).

(Des K. Svolinský. Eng L. Jirka. Recess)

1970 (17 Feb). *U.N.E.S.C.O. Anniversaries of World Figures.
T 545 and similar vert designs.* P 11½.
1871   40 h. black 15 10
1872   40 h. brownish grey 25 10
1873   40 h. bistre-brown 25 10
1874   40 h. carmine red 15 10
1875   40 h. carmine-red 15 10
1876   40 h. bistre-brown 15 10
1871/1876   *Set of 6* 90 30
Designs:—No. 1872, Beethoven (composer, birth bicent);
1873, Josef Mánes (artist, 150th birth anniv); 1874, Lenin (birth
centenary); 1875, Friedrich Engels (150th birth anniv); 1876,
Maximilian Hell (astronomer, 250th birth anniv).

550 Prague Panorama and Hand giving "V" Sign

(Des F. Gross. Eng J. Herčík. Recess*)

1970 (5 May). *25th Anniv of Prague Rising and Liberation of
Czechoslovakia. T 550 and similar horiz design.* P 11½×12.
1890   30 h. maroon, gold and blue .. 20 10
1891   30 h. myrtle-green, gold & orange-red 20 10
Design:—No. 1891, Soviet tank entering Prague.

(Des and eng J. Herčík (No. 1892), J. Schmidt (No. 1893).
          Recess)

1970 (7 May). *Prague Castle (sixth series). Art Treasures.
Vert design similar to T 536. Multicoloured.* P 11½.
1892   3 k. "Hermes and Athena" (painting, B.
          Spranger) .. .. 1·60 1·60
1893   3 k. "St. Vitus" (bust) .. .. 1·60 1·60
Issued in sheets of four with blank centre labels.

EXPO'70 OSAKA

546 Bells   547 Town Hall, Košice

(Des K. Vodák. Eng L. Jirka (50 h.), J. Mráček (80 h.), J. Schmidt
(1 k.), B. Housa (1 k. 60), J. Herčík (2, 3 k.). Recess* (50, 80 h.,
1 k.) or recess (others))

1970 (13 Mar). *World Fair, Osaka, Japan. "Expo '70". Horiz
designs similar to T 546. Multicoloured.* P 11½.
1877   50 h. Type **546** 15 10
1878   80 h. Heavy machinery 25 10
1879   1 k. Beehives (folk sculpture) .. 25 15
1880   1 k. 60, 'Angel and Saints" (17th-
          century icon) 50 40
1881   2 k. "Orlik Castle, 1787" (F. K. Wolf) 55 40
1882   3 k. "Fujiyama" (Hokusai) .. .. 3·25 1·00
1877/1882   *Set of 6* .. .. 4·50 1·90
Nos. 1880/2 are larger, 51×37 mm, and were issued in
sheets of four with two blank labels.

551 Compass and "World Capitals"

(Des J. Lukavský. Eng B. Housa. Recess*)

1970 (26 June). *25th Anniv of United Nations.* P 11.
1894   **551** 1 k. multicoloured 35 25
Issued in sheets of 15 stamps, together with 5 *se-tenant*
half stamp-size labels, showing U.N. emblem.

(Des A. Hollý. Eng J. Herčík. Recess*)

1970 (5 Apr). *25th Anniv of Kosice Reforms.* P 11.
1883   **547** 60 h. slate-blue, gold and orange-red 35 10

552 Thirty Years' War Cannon and "Baron Munchausen"

(Des V. Kovářik. Eng J. Herčík. Recess*)

1970 (31 Aug). *Historic Artillery. T* **552** *and similar horiz designs. Multicoloured. P* 11½.

1895	30 h. Type **552**	15	10
1896	60 h. Hussite bombard and St. Barbara	15	10
1897	1 k. 20, Austro-Prussian War field-gun and Hradec Kralove	45	10
1898	1 k. 80, Howitzer (1911) and Verne's *Colombiad*	50	25
1899	2 k. 40, Mountain-gun (1915) and "Good Soldier Schweik"	2·00	55
1895/1899	Set of 5	3·00	90

553 *Rudé Právo*

554 "Golden Sun", Bridge-tower, Prague

(Des J. Lukavský. Eng B. Housa. Recess*)

1970 (21 Sept). *50th Anniv of "Rudé Právo" (newspaper). P* 11½.

1900	**553** 60 h. red, drab and black	15	10

(Des J. Švengsbir. Eng J. Švengsbir, J. Herčík, B. Housa and M. Ondráček. Recess*)

1970 (23 Sept). *Ancient Buildings and House-signs from Prague, Brno and Bratislava. T* **554** *and similar vert designs. Multicoloured. P* 11½.

1901	40 h. Type **554**	15	10
1902	60 h. "Blue Lion" and Town Hall tower, Brno	25	10
1903	1 k. Gothic bolt and Town Hall tower, Bratislava	25	10
1904	1 k. 40, Coat-of-arms and Michael Gate, Bratislava	2·10	40
1905	1 k. "Moravian Eagle" and Town Hall gate, Brno	40	20
1906	1 k. 80, "Black Sun", "Green Frc" and bridge-tower, Prague	60	20
1901/1906	Set of 6	3·25	90

555 World Cup Emblem and Flags

556 "S.S.M." and Flags

(Des Anna Podzemná. Eng J. Herčík (20, 60 h., 1 k. 80), L. Jirka (40 h.), J. Schmidt (1 k.), J. Mráček (1 k. 20). Recess*)

1970 (29 Oct). *World Cup Football Championships, Mexico. T* **555** *and similar horiz designs. Multicoloured. P* 11½.

1907	20 h. Type **555**	10	10
1908	40 h. Two players and badges of Germany and Uruguay	15	10
1909	60 h. Two players and badges of England and Czechoslovakia	20	10
1910	1 k. Three players and badges of Rumania and Czechoslovakia	30	10
1911	1 k. 20, Three players and badges of Brazil and Italy	50	10
1912	1 k. 80, Two players and badges of Brazil and Czechoslovakia	2·00	40
1907/1912	Set of 6	3·00	70

(Des I. Strnad. Eng J. Herčík. Recess*)

1970 (9 Nov). *First Congress of Czechoslovak Socialist Youth Federation. P* 11½.

1913	**556** 30 h. multicoloured	40	10

(Eng B. Housa (1 k.), L. Jirka (1 k. 20), J. Švengsbír (1 k. 40), J. Schmidt (1 k. 80), J. Herčík (2 k. 40). Recess)

1970 (27 Nov). *Art* (5th series). *Vert designs similar to T* **481**. *Multicoloured. P* 11½.

1914	1 k. "Mother and Child" (M. Galanda)	25	25
1915	1 k. 20, "The Bridesmaid" (K. Svolinský)	50	50
1916	1 k. 40, "Walk by Night" (F. Hudeček)	50	50
1917	1 k. 80, "Bánská Bystrica Market" (D. Skutecký)	65	65
1918	2 k. 40, "Adoration of the Kings" (Vyšehrad Codex)	2·75	2·75
1914/1918	Set of 5	4·25	4·25

Issued in sheets of four with blank centre labels.

557 Dish Aerial

558 "Adam and Eve with Archangel Michael" (16th-century)

(Des J. Lukavský. Eng B. Housa (20 h., 1 k., 1k, 60), M. Ondráček (others). Recess*)

1970 (30 Nov). *"Intercosmos". Space Research Programme. T* **557** *and similar square designs. Multicoloured. P* 11.

1919	20 h. Type **557**	10	10
1920	40 h. Experimental satellite	15	10
1921	60 h. Meteorological satellite	20	10
1922	1 k. Astronaut ("medical research")	25	10
1923	1 k. 20, Solar research	30	10
1924	1 k. 60, Rocket on launch-pad	1·50	45
1919/1924	Set of 6	2·25	75

See also No. 1997.

(Des B. Housa. Eng J. Herčík (60 h.), L. Jirka (1 k.), J. Schmidt (2 k.), B. Housa (2 k. 80). Recess)

1970 (17 Dec). *Slovak Icons. Multicoloured designs on cream paper as T* **558**. *P* 11½.

1925	60 h. Type **558**	20	20
1926	1 k. "Mandylon" (16th-century) (horiz)	30	30
1927	2 k. "St. George slaying the Dragon" (18th-century) (horiz)	50	50
1928	2 k. 80, "St. Michael the Archangel" (18th-century)	2·25	2·25
1925/1928	Set of 4	3·00	3·00

Issued in sheets of four with blank centre labels.

559 Czech 5 h. Stamps of 1920

(Des M. Urbásek. Eng J. Schmidt. Recess*)

1970 (18 Dec). *Stamp Day.* P 11½.
1929 **559** 1 k. red, black and yellow-green .. 70 70

560 "Songs from the Walls" (frontispiece, K. Štika)

561 Šariš Church

(Des B. Housa. Eng J. Schmidt (40 h.), J. Herčík (50, 60 h.), L. Jirka (1 k.), J. Švengsbír (1 k. 60), B. Housa (2 k.). Recess (40, 60 h., 1 k.) or recess* (others))

1971 (28 Jan). *Czechoslovak Graphic Art* (1st series). *Vert designs as T* **560**. P 11½.
1930 40 h. blackish brown 15 10
1931 50 h. multicoloured 20 10
1932 60 h. deep grey 20 10
1933 1 k. deep slate 25 10
1934 1 k. 60, black and cream 45 10
1935 2 k. multicoloured .. .. 2·00 60
1930/1935 *Set of 6* .. .. .. 3·00 60
Designs:—50 h. "The Fruit Trader" (C. Bouda); 60 h. "Moon searching for Lilies-of-the-Valley" (J. Zrzavý); 1 k. "At the End of the Town" (K. Sokol); 1 k. 60, "Summer" (V. Hollar); 2 k. "Shepherd and Gamekeeper, Orava Castle" (P. Bohúň).
See also Nos. 2026/30, 2079/82, 2147/50 and 2202/5.

(Des J. Lukavský. Eng J. Mráček (1 k., 2 k. 40, 5 k. 40), J. Schmidt (1 k. 60, 2 k. 10 k.), B. Housa (3 k.), J. Goldschmied (50 h., 3 k. 60, 5, 20 k.), L. Jirka (6, 14 k.), M. Ondráček (9 k.). Recess*)

1971 (25 Feb)-**92**. *Regional Buildings. T* **561** *and similar designs.* P 12×11½ (1, 2, 5 k.), 11½×12 (3, 6, 9 k.) or 11½ (others).
1936 50 h. multicoloured (28.8.92) 10 10
1936a 1 k. black, rose-red and cobalt (22.6.71) 20 10
1937 1 k. 60, black, slate-violet & turq-grn .. 50 10
1938 2 k. multicoloured 60 10
1939 2 k. 40, multicoloured (22.6.71) .. 60 10
1940 3 k. multicoloured (28.8.72) .. 80 10
1941 3 k. 60, multicoloured .. .. 1·00 10
1942 5 k. multicoloured (14.6.72) .. 1·25 10
1943 5 k. 40, multicoloured (22.6.71) .. 1·25 10
1944 6 k. multicoloured (26.4.71) .. 1·75 10
1945 9 k. multicoloured (25.3.71) .. 2·50 10
1946 10 k. multicoloured (14.6.72) .. 2·40 10
1947 14 k. multicoloured (22.6.71) .. 3·25 10
1948 20 k. multicoloured (28.8.72) .. 5·00 15
1936/1948 *Set of 14* .. .. .. 19·00 85
Designs: *Vert* (19×22 *mm*)—1 k. Ornamental roofs, Horácko; 2 k. Bell-tower, Hronsek; 5 k. Watch-tower, Náchodsko. *Horiz* (as *T* **561**)—50 h., 3 k. 60, Church, Chrudimsko; 2 k. 40, House, Jičínsko; 5 k. 40, Southern Bohemia baroque house, Pošumaví; 10 k. Wooden houses, Liptov; 14 k. House and belfry, Valašsko; 20 k. Decorated house, Čičmany. (22×19 *mm*)—3 k. Half-timbered house, Mělnicko; 6 k. Cottages, Orava; 9 k. Cottage, Turnovsko.
The 1, 2 and 20 k. values were issued on phosphorescent paper in 1979, the 3 k. 60 in 1980, the 5 and 6 k. in 1986 and the 10 k. in 1987 (see note after No. 2384). The 50 h. exists on phosphorescent paper only.

562 "The Paris Commune" (allegory)

(Des J. Liesler. Eng L. Jirka. Recess*)

1971 (18 Mar). *U.N.E.S.C.O. World Anniversaries. T* **562** *and similar horiz design. Multicoloured.* P 11.
1949 1 k. Type **562** 30 15
1950 1 k. "World Fight against Racial Discrimination" (allegory) .. 30 15
Nos. 1949/50 were each issued in sheets of 15 stamps, together with 5 decorative half stamp-size labels *se-tenant*.

(Des and eng J. Herčík. Recess*)

1971 (26 Mar). *Arms of Czech Regional Capitals* (third series). *Horiz designs similar to T* **523**. *Multicoloured.* P 11½.
1951 60 h. Česká Třebová 20 10
1952 60 h. Karlovy Vary 20 10
1953 60 h. Levoča 20 10
1954 60 h. Trutnov 20 10
1955 60 h. Uherský Brod 20 10
1956 60 h. Zilina 20 10
1951/1956 *Set of 6* .. .. 1·10 40

563 Chorister

564 Lenin

(Des A. Brunovský. Eng J. Herčík (No. 1957). Des J. Lukavský. Eng B. Housa (No. 1958). Recess*)

1971 (27 Apr). *50th Anniversaries. T* **563** *and similar multicoloured design.* P 11½.
1957 30 h. Type **563** (Slovak Teachers' Choir) 15 10
1958 30 h. Edelweiss, ice-pick and mountain (Slovak Alpine Organization) (19×48 *mm*) 15 10

(Des and eng J. Švengsbír. Recess)

1971 (9 May). *Prague Castle* (seventh series). *Art Treasures. Vert designs similar to T* **536**. *Multicoloured.* P 11½.
1959 3 k. sepia, pale buff and black .. 1·75 1·75
1960 3 k. multicoloured .. .. 1·75 1·75
Designs:—No. 1959, "Music" (16th-century wallpainting); No. 1960, Head of 16th-century crozier.
Issued in sheets of four with two blank labels.

(Des I. Strnad. Eng M. Ondráček (30, 40 h.), J. Herčík (others). Recess*)

1971 (14 May). *50th Anniv of Czech Communist Party. T* **564** *and similar square designs. Multicoloured.* P 11.
1961 30 h. Type **564** 10 10
1962 40 h. Hammer and sickle emblems .. 10 10
1963 60 h. Clenched fists 15 10
1964 1 k. Emblem on pinnacle .. 20 10
1961/1964 *Set of 4* 50 25

565 "50" Star Emblem

Czechoslovakia

(Des J. Liesler. Eng M. Ondráček (30 h.), J. Schmidt (60 h.). Recess*)

1971 (24 May). *14th Czech Communist Party Congress. T* **565** *and similar multicoloured design.* P 11½.

1965	30 h. Type **565**	10	10
1966	60 h. Clenched fist, workers and emblems (*vert*)	15	10

566 Ring-necked Pheasant

(Des J. Baláž. Eng M. Ondráček (20 h., 2 k. 60), J. Schmidt (60, 80 h.), L. Jirka (1 k.), M. Mráček (2 k.). Recess*)

1971 (17 Aug). *World Hunting Exhibition, Budapest. T* **566** *and similar horiz designs. Multicoloured.* P 11½.

1967	20 h. Type **566**	30	10
1968	60 h. Trout	15	10
1969	80 h. Mouflon	20	10
1970	1 k. Chamois	20	10
1971	2 k. Red deer	45	15
1972	2 k. 60, Wild boar	2·10	45
1967/1972	Set of 6	3·25	90

567 Motorway Junction (diagram)

568 Diesel Locomotives

(Des V. Kovářík. Eng J. Goldschmied. Recess*)

1971 (2 Sept). *World Road Congress.* P 11½.

1973	**567** 1 k. multicoloured	25	10

Issued in sheets of 50 made up of 25 stamps and 25 stamp-size *se-tenant* labels which continue the diagram.

(Des F. Hudeček. Eng J. Mráček. Recess*)

1971 (2 Sept). *Centenary of C.K.D. Prague Locomotive Works.* P 11½×12.

1974	**568** 30 h. black, rose-red and pale turq-bl	20	10

569 Gymnasts

570 "Procession" (from *The Miraculous Bamboo Shoot* by K. Segawa)

(Des V. Kovářík. Eng J. Mráček. Recess*)

1971 (2 Sept). *50th Anniv of Proletarian Physical Federation.* P 12×11½.

1975	**569** 30 h. multicoloured	15	10

(Des J. Šváb. Eng M. Ondráček (60 h.), J. Herčik (others). Recess*)

1971 (10 Sept). *Biennial Exhibition of Book Illustrations for Children, Bratislava. T* **570** *and similar multicoloured designs.* P 11½.

1976	60 h. "Princess" (*Chinese Folk Tales, E. Bednářová*) (*vert*)	20	10
1977	1 k. "Tiger" (*Animal Fairy Tales, M. Hanák*) (*vert*)	20	10
1978	1 k. 60, Type **570**	50	20

571 Coltsfoot and Canisters

D **572** Stylized Plant

(Des J. Lukavský. Eng L. Jirka (30 h., 1 k. 80), B. Housa (60 h., 1 k. 20, 2 k. 40), M. Ondráček (1 k.). Recess*)

1971 (20 Sept). *International Pharmaceutical Congress, Prague. Medicinal Plants and Historic Pharmaceutical Utensils. T* **571** *and similar horiz designs. Multicoloured on yellow paper.* P 11½.

1979	30 h. Type **571**	10	10
1980	60 h. Dog rose and glass jars	15	10
1981	1 k. Yellow pheasant's-eye and hand scales	25	10
1982	1 k. 20 Common valerian, pestle and mortar	40	15
1983	1 k. 80, Chicory and crucibles	60	15
1984	2 k. 40, Henbane and grinder	2·10	55
1979/1984	Set of 6	3·25	95

(Des I. Strnad. Eng J. Mráček (80 h., 1 k. 20), J. Herčik (1, 2, 4, 6 k.), M. Ondráček (others). Recess*)

1971 (14 Nov)–72. *POSTAGE DUE. Type D* **572** *and similar horiz designs, showing various stylised flowers and plants.* P 11×11½.

D1985	10 h. light red & violet-blue (11.7.72)	10	10
D1986	20 h. light blue and violet (25.4.72)	10	10
D1987	30 h. magenta & bright green (25.4.72)	10	10
D1988	60 h. light green and purple (25.4.72)	15	10
D1989	80 h. ultramarine & red-orge (11.7.72)	20	10
D1990	1 k. lt emerald & carm-red (25.4.72)	25	10
D1991	1 k. 20, red-orange & emer (11.7.72)	30	10
D1992	2 k. red and light blue (11.7.72)	55	10
D1993	3 k. yellow and black (11.7.72)	85	10
D1994	4 k. violet-blue and brown (25.4.72)	1·10	15
D1995	5 k. 40, reddish lilac and scarlet	1·40	20
D1996	6 k. orange-yellow & carm (25.4.72)	1·60	25
D1985/1996	Set of 12	6·00	1·00

No. D1995 was issued on phosphorescent paper in 1983 (see note after No. 2384).

Since April 1985 postage due stamps have been used as normal postage stamps.

573 "Co-operation in Space"

(Des J. Lukavský. Eng M. Ondráček. Recess*)

1971 (15 Nov). *"Intersputnik" Day.* P 11.

1997	**573** 1 k. 20, multicoloured	35	10

574 "The Krompachy Revolt" (J. Nemčík)

(Des and eng J. Schmidt. Recess*)

1971 (28 Nov). *50th Anniversary of Krompachy Revolt. P* 11.
1998 574 60 h. multicoloured 35 10

(Eng J. Herčík (1 k., 1 k. 80), M. Ondráček (1 k. 20), J. Švengsbír
(1 k. 40), L. Jirka (2 k. 40). Recess)

1971 (29 Nov). *Art (6th series). Vert designs similar to T* **481**.
Multicoloured. P 11½.
1999 1 k. "Waiting" (I. Weiner-Kral) .. 25 25
2000 1 k. 20, "The Resurrection" (unknown
      14th-century artist) .. 40 40
2001 1 k. 40, "Woman with Jug" (M.
      Bazovský) 50 50
2002 1 k. 80, "Woman in National Costume"
      (J. Mánes) 65 65
2003 2 k. 40, "Festival of the Rosary" (Dürer) 3·25 3·25
1999/2003 *Set of 5* .. .. 4·50 4·50
Issued in sheets of four with blank centre labels.

575 Wooden Dolls
and Birds

576 Ancient Greek Runners

(Des J. Liesler. Eng L. Jirka (60 h.), J. Herčík (80 h., 1 k.),
J. Schmidt (1 k. 60, 2 k.), B. Housa (3 k.). Recess)

1971 (11 Dec)–**72**. *25th Anniversary of U.N.I.C.E.F. Czech and
Slovak Folk Art. T* **575** *and similar vert designs. Multicoloured.
P* 11½.
2004 60 h. Type **575** (frame and U.N.I.C.E.F.
      emblem in deep blue) .. 15 10
2005 60 h. Type **575** (frame and U.N.I.C.E.F.
      emblem in black) (1972) .. 3·00 1·50
2006 80 h. Decorated handle 20 10
2007 1 k. Horse and rider 30 15
2008 1 k. 60, Shepherd 45 20
2009 2 k. Easter eggs and rattle .. 65 25
2010 3 k. Folk hero .. .. 3·25 75
2004/2010 *Set of 7* .. .. 7·00 2·75

(Des V. Kovářik. Eng J. Herčík (30 h., 2 k. 60), J. Schmidt
(40 h.), J. Mráček (1 k. 60). Recess*)

1971 (16 Dec). *75th Anniversary of Czechoslovak Olympic
Committee, and 1972 Games at Sapporo and Munich.
Square designs as T* **576**. *Multicoloured. P* 11.
2011 30 h. Type **576** 10 10
2012 40 h. High jumper 10 10
2013 1 k. 60, Skiers 50 10
2014 2 k. 60, Discus-throwers, ancient and
      modern .. .. 1·75 70
2011/2014 *Set of 4* .. .. 2·25 80

577 Posthorns

(Des K. Vodák. Eng J. Goldschmied. Recess*)

1971 (17 Dec). *Stamp Day. P* 11.
2015 577 1 k. multicoloured 35 15

578 Figure Skating

579 Sentry

(Des I. Strnad. Eng J. Herčík (40 h.), M. Ondráček (50 h.),
L. Jirka (1 k.), J. Schmidt (1 k. 60). Recess*)

1972 (13 Jan). *Winter Olympic Games, Sapporo, Japan.
T* **578** *and similar vert designs. Multicoloured. P* 11½.
2016 40 h. Type **578** 10 10
2017 50 h. Skiing 15 10
2018 1 k. Ice hockey 50 10
2019 1 k. 60, Bobsleighing .. .. 1·50 40
2016/2019 *Set of 4* .. .. 2·00 60

(Des. J. Lukavský (Nos. 2020, 2022), I. Schurmann (others).
Eng B. Housa (No. 2020), L. Jirka (2022), M. Ondráček
(others). Recess*)

1972 (16 Feb). *30th Anniversaries. T* **579** *and similar designs.
P* 11½.
2020 30 h. black and chestnut .. 10 10
2021 30 h. black, red and orange-yellow .. 10 10
2022 60 h. multicoloured 20 10
2023 60 h. black, red and lemon .. 20 10
2020/2023 *Set of 4* 50 25

Anniversaries.*Horiz*—No. 2020, Child and barbed wire
(Terezin Concentration Camp); 2022, T **579** (Czechoslovak
Unit in Russian Army). *Vert*—2021, Widow and buildings
(Destruction of Ležáky); 2023, Hand and ruined building
(Destruction of Lidice).

580 Book Year Emblem

581 Steam and
Electric Locomotives

(Des Z. Sklenař. Eng M. Ondráček. Recess*)

1972 (17 Mar). *International Book Year. P* 12×11½.
2024 580 1 k. black and orange-red 30 10

(Des F. Hudeček. Eng J. Schmidt. Recess*)

1972 (17 Mar). *Centenary of Košice-Bohumin Railway.
P* 11½×12.
2025 581 30 h. multicoloured 30 10

(Des and eng J. Mráček (40 h., 1 k.), L. Jirka (50 h.), J. Herčík
(60 h.), M. Ondráček (1 k. 60). Recess (1 k. 60) or recess*
(others))

1972 (27 Mar). *Czechoslovak Graphic Art (2nd series). Vert
designs similar to T* **560**. *Multicoloured. P* 11½.
2026 40 h. "Pasture" (V. Sedláček) 10 10
2027 50 h. "Dressage" (F. Tichý) .. 15 10
2028 60 h. "Otakar Kubin" (V. Fiala) .. 20 15
2029 1 k. "The Three Kings" (E. Zmeták) .. 30 25
2030 1 k. 60, "Toilet" (L. Fulla) .. 1·75 1·10
2026/2030 *Set of 5* .. .. 2·25 2·10
No. 2030 was issued in sheets of four.

582 Cycling

583 Players in Tackle

586 Workers with Banners   **587** Wire Coil and Cockerel

(Des Anna Podzemná. Eng M. Ondráček (50 h., 1 k. 80), J. Herčík (others). Recess*)

1972 (7 Apr). *Olympic Games, Munich.* T **582** *and similar square designs. Multicoloured.* P 11.

2031	50 h. Type **582**	..	..	15	10
2032	1 k. 60, Diving	..	..	40	10
2033	1 k. 80, Kayak-canoeing	..	..	45	20
2034	2 k. Gymnastics	..	..	1·75	50
2031/2034	Set of 4	..	..	2·50	80

(Des V. Kovařík. Eng J. Mráček. Recess*)

1972 (7 Apr). *World and European Ice Hockey Championships, Prague.* T **583** *and similar square design. Multicoloured.* P 11.

2035	60 h. Type **583**	..	..	30	10
2036	1 k. Attacking goal	..	..	50	10

(Des and eng J. Švengsbír. Recess)

1972 (9 May). *Prague Castle* (8th series). *Roof Decorations. Vert designs similar to* T **536**. *Multicoloured.* P 11½.

2037	3 k. Bohemian Lion emblem (roof-boss), Royal Palace	..	..	1·50	75
2038	3 k. "Adam and Eve" (bracket), St. Vitus' Cathedral	..	..	2·75	2·50

Issued in sheets of four with two blank labels.

ČSSR MAJSTROM SVETA

(584 "Czechoslovakia – World Champions")   **585** František Bilek (sculptor: birth centenary)

1972 (22 May). *Czechoslovak Victory in Ice-hockey Championships. Nos.* 2035/6 *optd with* T **584**, *or similar Slovak inscr* (60 h.).

2039	**583** 60 h. multicoloured (B.)	..	..	5·00	5·00
2040	– 1 k. multicoloured	..	..	5·00	5·00

(Des A. Brunovský. Eng J. Herčík. Recess*)

1972 (14 June). *Cultural Anniversaries.* T **585** *and similar square portraits.* P 11.

2041	40 h. multicoloured	..	..	15	10
2042	40 h. multicoloured	..	..	15	10
2043	40 h. grey-green, yellow and blue	..	..	15	10
2044	40 h. multicoloured	..	..	15	10
2045	40 h. reddish violet, cobalt & yellow-green	..	..	15	10
2046	40 h. myrtle grn, blackish brn & red-orge	..	..	15	10
2041/2046	Set of 6	..	..	75	25

Designs:—No. 2041, Type **585**; No. 2042, Antonin Hudeček (painter: birth centenary); No. 2043, Janko Král (poet: 150th birth anniv); No. 2044, Ludmila Podjavorinská (writer: birth centenary); No. 2045, Andrej Sládkovič (painter: death centenary); No. 2046, Jan Preisler (painter: birth centenary).

1972 (14 June). *8th Trade Union Congress, Prague.* P 11½.

2047	**586** 30 h. bluish violet, red and lemon	..	15	10

(Des J. Baláž. Eng J. Mráček (20, 80 h.), J. Herčík (60 h.), J. Schmidt (others). Recess*)

1972 (29 Aug). *Slovak Wireworking.* T **587** *and similar horiz designs. Multicoloured.* P 11½.

2048	20 h. Type **587**	..	..	10	10
2049	60 h. Aeroplane and rosette	..	..	15	10
2050	80 h. Dragon and gilded ornament	..	20	10
2051	1 k. Locomotive and pendant	..	25	15
2052	2 k. 60, Owl and tray	..	..	1·75	60
2048/2052	Set of 5	..	..	2·25	80

588 *Jiskra* (freighter) at Basra

589 "Hussar" (ceramic tile)

(Des J. Lukavský. Eng M. Ondráček (1 k. 60), L. Jirka (others). Recess*)

1972 (27 Sept). *Czechoslovak Ocean-going Ships.* T **588** *and similar horiz designs. Multicoloured on pale blue paper.* P 11½. *(a) Size* 40×22 mm.

2053	50 h. Type **588**	..	..	25	10
2054	60 h. *Mir* (freighter)	..	..	35	10
2055	80 h. *Republika* (freighter)	..	40	10

(b) Size 49×30 mm

2056	1 k. *Košice* (freighter)	..	..	45	10
2057	1 k. 60, *Dukla* (freighter)	..	..	75	20
2058	2 k. *Kladno* (freighter)	..	..	2·75	60
2053/2058	Set of 6	..	..	4·50	1·10

(Des and eng B. Housa. Recess*)

1972 (24 Oct). "*Horsemanship*". *Ceramics and Glass.* T **589** *and similar vert designs. Multicoloured.* P 11½.

2059	30 h. Type **589**	..	..	10	10
2060	60 h. "Turkish Janissary" (enamel on glass)	..	15	10
2061	80 h. "St. Martin" (painting on glass)	..	25	10
2062	1 k. 60, "St. George" (enamel on glass)	..	50	10
2063	1 k. 80, "Nobleman's Guard, Bohemia" (enamel on glass)	..	60	15
2064	2 k. 20, "Cavalryman, *c* 1800" (ceramic tile)	..	2·25	50
2059/2064	Set of 6	..	..	3·50	95

590 Revolutionary and Red Flag

591 Warbler feeding young Cuckoo

(Des I. Schurmann. Eng M. Ondráček (30 h.). Des M. Hegar. Eng J. Mráček (60 h.). Recess*)

1972 (7 Nov). *55th Anniv of Russian October Revolution, and 50th Anniv of U.S.S.R. T* **590** *and similar horiz design. P* 11½.

2065	30 h. multicoloured	10	10
2066	60 h. carmine and gold	15	10

Design:—60 h. Soviet star emblem.

(Des and eng J. Schmidt (1 k.), J. Herčík (1 k. 20, 2 k. 40), B. Housa (1 k. 40), M. Ondráček (1 k. 80). Recess)

1972 (27 Nov). *Art (7th series). Vert designs similar to T* **481**. *P* 11½.

2067	1 k. multicoloured	70	55
2068	1 k. 20, multicoloured	75	60
2069	1 k. 40, black and pale cream	1·00	75
2070	1 k. 80, multicoloured	1·25	1·10
2071	2 k. 40, multicoloured	3·25	5·25
2067/2071	Set of 5	6·50	5·25

Designs:—1 k. "Nosegay" (M. Švabinský); 1 k. 20, "St. Ladislav fighting with a Nomad" (14th-century painter); 1 k. 40, "Lady with Fur Cap" (V. Hollar); 1 k. 80, "Midsummer Night's Dream" (J. Liesler); 2 k. 40, "Self-portrait" (P. Picasso). Issued in sheets of four with blank central labels.

(Des M. Hanák. Eng J. Schmidt (60 h., 2 k.), M. Ondráček (80 h.), J. Mráček (1, 3 k.), B. Housa (1 k. 60). Recess or recess* (Nos. 2072/4))

1972 (15 Dec). *Songbirds. T* **591** *and similar multicoloured designs. P* 11½. (*a*) *Vert designs,* 30×49 mm.

2072	60 h. Type **591**	40	10
2073	80 h. European cuckoo	50	10
2074	1 k. Magpie	50	10

(*b*) *Horiz designs,* 30×23 mm.

2075	1 k. 60, Bullfinch	70	20
2076	2 k. Goldfinch	1·40	45
2077	3 k. Song thrush	7·50	1·40
2072/2077	Set of 6	10·00	2·00

592 "Thoughts into Letters"

593 "Tennis Player"

(Des Eva Bednářová. Eng J. Herčík. Recess*)

1972 (18 Dec). *Stamp Day. P* 11½.

2078	**592** 1 k. black, gold and bright purple	45	45

(Des and eng M. Ondráček (60 h.), J. Herčík (others). Recess*)

1973 (25 Jan). *Czechoslovak Graphic Art (3rd series). Vert designs similar to T* **560**. *Multicoloured. P* 11½.

2079	30 h. "Flowers in the Window" (J. Grus)	10	10
2080	60 h. "Quest for Happiness" (J. Baláž)	15	10
2081	1 k. 60, "Balloon" (K. Lhoták)	45	20
2082	1 k. 80, "Woman with Viola" (R. Wiesner)	1·60	35
2079/2082	Set of 4	2·00	60

(Des I. Strnad (30 h., 1 k.), Anna Podzemná (60 h.). Eng J. Mráček (30 h.), J. Schmidt (60 h.), J. Herčík (1 k.). Recess*)

1973 (22 Feb). *Sports Events. T* **593** *and similar vert designs. Multicoloured. P* 11½.

2083	30 h. Type **593**	30	10
2084	60 h. Figure skating	15	10
2085	1 k. Spartakiad emblem	30	10

Events:—30 h. 80th anniv of lawn tennis in Czechoslovakia; 60 h. World Figure Skating Championships, Bratislava; 1 k. Third Warsaw Pact Armies Summer Spartakiad.

594 Red Star and Factory Buildings

595 Jan Nálepka and Antonin Sochor

(Des V. Kovařik. Eng J. Goldschmied (30 h.). Des O. Ĺupták. Eng J. Mráček (60 h.). Recess*)

1973 (23 Feb). *25th Anniv of "Victorious February", and People's Militia (60 h.). T* **594** *and similar horiz design. P* 11½.

2086	30 h. multicoloured	10	10
2087	60 h. deep violet-blue, rosine and gold	15	10

Design:—60 h. Militiaman and banners.

(Des V. Fiala and B. Housa. Eng J. Schmidt (30, 80 h., 1 k. 60), M. Ondráček (others). Recess*)

1973 (20 Mar). *Czechoslovak Martyrs during World War II. T* **595** *and similar horiz designs. P* 11½.

2088	30 h. black, orange-red and gold/cream	10	10
2089	40 h. black, orange-red and dull grn/cream	15	15
2090	60 h. black, orange-red and gold/cream	15	10
2091	80 h. black, orge-red and yell-ol/cream	15	10
2092	1 k. black, salmon and brt green/cream	20	10
2093	1 k. 60, black, orge-red and silver/cream	1·25	40
2088/2093	Set of 6	1·75	70

Designs:—40 h. Evžen Rošicky and Mirko Nešpor; 60 h. Vlado Clementis and Karol Šmidke; 80 h. Ján Osoha and Josef Molák; 1 k. Marie Kudeříková and Jožka Jaburková; 1 k. 60, Václav Sinkule and Eduard Urx.

596 Russian "Venera" Space-probe

597 Radio Aerial and Receiver

I

II

Two types of 3 k. 60:

I. With cross-hatching behind Komarov
II Horizontal lines only.

(Des J. Lukavský. Eng M. Ondráček (20, 40 h., 3 k. 60),
L. Jirka (others). Recess or recess* (20, 30, 40 h.))

1973 (12 Apr). *Cosmonautics' Day. T **596** and similar horiz
designs. Multicoloured. P 11½. (a) Size 40 × 23 mm.*

2094	20 h. Type **596**	..	10	10
2095	30 h. "Cosmos" satellite	.. ..	10	10
2096	40 h. "Lunokhod" on Moon	..	10	10

(b) Size 49 × 29 mm. Space Victims

2097	3 k. American astronauts Grissom, White and Chaffee	1·50	1·40
2098	3 k. 60, Russian cosmonaut Komarov, and crew of "Soyuz 11" (Type I)	1·60	1·50
	a. Type II	18·00	10·00
2099	5 k. Death of Yuri Gagarin (first cosmonaut)	5·00	4·50
2094/2099	*Set of 6 (cheapest)*	7·50	7·00

Nos. 2097/9 were each issued in sheets of four.

(Des F. Hudeček. Eng M. Ondráček (No. 2101), J. Herčík
(others). Recess*)

1973 (1 May). *Telecommunications Anniversaries T **597** and
similar horiz designs. Multicoloured. P 11½.*

2100	30 h. Type **597**	..	10	10
2101	30 h. T.V. colour chart..	..	10	10
2102	30 h. Map and telephone	..	10	10

Anniversaries:—No. 2100, 50th anniv of Czech broadcasting;
No. 2101, 20th anniv of Czechoslovak television service;
No. 2102, 20th anniv of nation-wide telephone system.

(Des and eng J. Švengsbír. Recess)

1973 (9 May). *Prague Castle (9th series). The Age of Charles IV.
Vert designs, similar to T **536**. Multicoloured. P 11½.*

2103	3 k. Gold seal of Charles IV	3·00	2·75
2104	3 k. "Imperial Legate" (rook) (from *The Game and Playe of Chesse* by William Caxton)	1·00	75

Each issued in sheets of four with two blank labels.

598 Czechoslovak Arms   **599** "Learning"

(Des J. Lukavský. Eng J. Schmidt. Recess*)

1973 (9 May). *25th Anniv of Constitution of 9th May. P 11½.*

2105	**598** 60 h. multicoloured	.. ..	20	10

(Des and eng J. Herčík. Recess*)

1973 (20 June). *Arms of Czech Regional Capitals. (4th series).
Horiz designs similar to T **523**. P 11½.*

2106	60 h. multicoloured (Mikulov)	15	10
2107	60 h. multicoloured (Smolenice)	15	10
2108	60 h. black and gold (Žlutice)..	15	10

(Des K. Svolinský. Eng J. Mráček. Recess*)

1973 (23 Aug). *400th Anniv of Olomouc University. P 11½.*

2109	**599** 30 h. multicoloured/*cream*	..	10	10

600 Tulip   **601** Irish Setter

(Des K. Svolinský. Eng J. Herčík (60 h., 1, 2 k.), L. Jirka
(others). Recess)

1973 (23 Aug). *Olomouc Flower Show. T **600** and similar
vert designs. Multicoloured. P 11½.*

2110	60 h. Type **600**	..	80	60
2111	1 k. Rose	..	50	40
2112	1 k. 60, Anthurium	..	45	15
2113	1 k. 80, Iris	..	50	20
2114	2 k. Chrysanthemum	..	2·75	2·75
2115	3 k. 60, Boat orchid	..	1·50	30
2110/2115	*Set of 6*	..	6·00	4·00

The 60 h., 1 k. and 2 k. are size 30 × 50 mm. and were issued
in sheets of four. The 1 k. 60, 1 k. 80 and 3 k. 60 designs are
smaller, 23 × 50 mm, and were issued in sheets of 10.

(Des J. Baláž. Eng J. Schmidt (20 h., 1 k. 60), M. Ondráček
(60 h.), J. Mráček (others). Recess*)

1973 (5 Sept). *50th Anniv of Czechoslovak Hunting Organization. T **601** and similar horiz designs, showing hunting dogs.
Multicoloured. P 11½.*

2116	20 h. Type **601**	..	10	10
2117	30 h. Czech whisker	..	10	10
2118	40 h. Bavarian mountain bloodhound ..		10	10
2119	60 h. German pointer	..	15	10
2120	1 k. Golden cocker spaniel	..	20	10
2121	1 k. 60, Dachshund	..	1·75	40
2116/2121	*Set of 6* ..	..	2·00	65

602 "St. John the Baptist"   **603** Congress Emblem
(M. Švabinský)

(Des and eng J. Schmidt. Recess or recess* (20, 60 h.))

1973 (17 Sept). *Birth Centenary of Max Švabinský (artist and
designer). T **602** and similar vert designs, showing his work.
P 11½.*

2122	20 h. black and pale green	..	10	10
2123	60 h. black and pale drab	..	20	10
2124	80 h. black	..	25	25
	a. Pair. Nos. 2124/5	..	50	50
2125	1 k. blackish green	..	25	25
2126	2 k. 60, multicoloured ..	..	2·25	2·25
2122/2126	*Set of 5* ..	..	2·75	2·75

Designs:—60 h. "August Noon"; 80 h. "Marriage of True
Minds"; 1 k. "Paradise Sonata 1"; 2 k. 60, "The Last Judgement"

(stained glass window).

Nos. 2124/5 were issued together in *se-tenant* vertical and horizontal pairs within sheets of four stamps. No. 2126 was issued in sheets of 4.

(Des I. Strnad. Eng M. Ondráček. Recess*)

1973 (15 Oct). *8th World Trade Union Congress, Varna, Bulgaria. P 11½.*
2127 **603** 1 k. multicoloured 15 10

604 Tupolev Tu-104A over Bitov Castle

606 "CSSR 1969–1974"

605 Mounted Postman

(Des J. Lukavský. Eng B. Housa (60 h.), M. Ondráček (1 k. 90), L. Jirka (others). Recess)

1973 (24 Oct). *50th Anniv of Czechoslovak Airlines. T* **604** *and similar horiz designs. Multicoloured. P 11½.*
2128 30 h. Type **604** 10 10
2129 60 h. Ilyushin Il-62 and Bezděz Castle .. 15 10
2130 1 k. 40, Tupolev Tu-134A and Orava Castle 40 10
2131 1 k. 90, Ilyushin Il-18 and Veveři Castle 55 20
2132 2 k. 40, Ilyushin Il-14P and Pernštejn Castle .. .. 3·75 80
2133 3 k. 60, Tupolev Tu-154 and Trenčín Castle 70 30
2128/2133 Set of 6 .. .. .. 5·00 1·25

(Des and eng L. Jirka (1 k.), M. Ondráček (1 k. 20), J. Schmidt (1 k. 80, 2 k. 40), J. Herčik (2 k., 3 k. 60). Recess)

1973 (27 Nov). *Art (8th series). Vert designs, similar to T* **481**. *P 11½.*
2134 1 k. multicoloured .. .. .. 2·50 2·50
2135 1 k. 20, multicoloured .. .. 2·50 2·50
2136 1 k. 80, black and buff 65 65
a. Sheet of four. Nos. 2136/9 .. 3·00
2137 2 k. multicoloured 75 75
2138 2 k. 40, multicoloured 90 90
2139 3 k. 60, multicoloured .. .. 1·00 1·00
2134/2139 Set of 6 .. .. .. 7·50 7·50
Designs:—1 k. "Boy from Martinique" (A. Pelc); 1 k. 20, "Fortitude" (M. Benka); 1 k. 80, Self-portrait (Rembrandt); 2 k. "Pierrot" (B. Kubišta); 2 k. 40, "Ilona Kubinyiová" (P. Bohun); 3 k. 60, "Madonna and Child" (unknown artist, c 1350).
Nos. 2134/5 each come in separate sheets of four with blank centre labels.
Nos. 2136/9 were issued *se-tenant* in sheets of four with inscribed central label.

(Des J. Liesler. Eng J. Herčik. Recess*)

1973 (18 Dec). *Stamp Day. P 11½.*
2140 **605** 1 k. multicoloured 25 15
No. 2140 was issued with two *se-tenant* half stamp-size labels, showing an early telephone and telegraph transmitter, one on each side of the stamp.

(Des M. Hegar. Eng M. Ondráček. Recess*)

1974 (1 Jan). *5th Anniv of Federal Constitution. P 11½×12.*
2141 **606** 30 h. red, bright blue and gold .. 10 10

607 Bedřich Smetana (composer) (150th birth anniv)

608 Council Building, Moscow

(Des A. Brunovský. Eng J. Herčik. Recess*)

1974 (4 Jan). *Celebrities' Birth Anniversaries. T* **607** *and similar vert designs. P 11½.*
2142 60 h. multicoloured 20 10
2143 60 h. multicoloured 20 10
2144 60 h. blackish brown, new blue and red 20 10
Designs:—No. 2142, T **607**; 2143, Josef Suk (composer) (birth centenary); 2144, Pablo Neruda (Chilean poet) (70th birth anniv).

(Des I. Strnad. Eng M. Ondráček. Recess*)

1974 (23 Jan). *25th Anniv of Communist Bloc Council of Mutual Economic Assistance. P 11½.*
2145 **608** 1 k. violet, red and gold .. 20 10

609 Exhibition Allegory

(Des J. Liesler. Eng J. Herčik. Recess*)

1974 (20 Feb). *"BRNO 74" National Stamp Exhibition (1st issue). P 11½.*
2146 **609** 3 k. 60, multicoloured 75 25
No. 2146 was issued in normal sheets of 25 stamps, and also in special sheets of 16 stamps *se-tenant* with 9 stamp-size labels depicting Brno, in six language versions.
See also Nos. 2171/2.

(Des and eng J. Herčik (60 h., 1 k. 60), M. Ondráček (1 k.), J. Mráček (1 k. 80). Recess*)

1974 (21 Feb). *Czechoslovak Graphic Art (4th series). Vert designs as T* **560**. *Multicoloured. P 11½.*
2147 60 h. "Tulips" (J. Brož) 20 10
2148 1 k. "Structures" (O. Dubay) .. 30 15
2149 1 k. 60, "Golden Sun, Glowing Day" (A. Zábranský) 55 20
2150 1 k. 80, "Artificial Flowers" (F. Gross) 1·40 35
2147/2150 Set of 4 .. .. .. 2·25 70

610 Oskar Beneš and Václav Procházka

(Des L. Sindelář. Eng J. Schmidt (30 h.), L. Jirka (40 h., 1 k. 60), M. Ondráček (60, 80 h.), J. Herčik (1 k.). Recess*)

1974 (21 Mar). *Czechoslovak Partisan Heroes. T 610 and similar horiz designs. Multicoloured. P 11½.*

2151	30 h. Type **610**	10	10
2152	40 h. Milos Uher and Anton Sedláček..	10	10
2153	60 h. Jan Háječek and Marie Sedláčkova	15	10
2154	80 h. Jan Sverma and Albin Grznár ..	20	10
2155	1 k. Jaroslav Neliba and Alois Hovorka	30	10
2156	1 k. 60, Ladislav Exnár and Ludovit Kukorelli	1·50	30
2151/2156	*Set of 6* ..	2·10	55

611 "Water—Source of Energy"   **612** "Telecommunications"

(Des J. Liesler. Eng J. Herčik (60 h., 1 k. 60), L. Jirka (1 k.), J. Mráček (1 k. 20), J. Schmidt (2 k.). Recess)

1974 (25 Apr). *International Hydrological Decade. T 611 and similar vert designs. Multicoloured. P 11½.*

2157	60 h. Type **611**	60	50
2158	1 k. "Water for Agriculture"	60	50
2159	1 k. 20, "Study of the Oceans"	60	50
2160	1 k. 60, Decade emblem	65	50
2161	2 k. "Keeping Water Pure"	2·40	2·40
2157/2161	*Set of 5* ..	4·25	4·00

Issued in sheets of four with two blank labels.

(Des I. Strnad. Eng J. Herčik. Recess*)

1974 (30 Apr). *Inauguration of Czechoslovak Satellite Telecommunications Earth Station. P 11½.*

2162	**612** 30 h. multicoloured	25	10

(Des and eng J. Švengsbir. Recess)

1974 (9 May). *Prague Castle (10th series). Vert designs similar to T 536. Multicoloured. P 11½.*

2163	3 k. "Golden Cockerel", 17th-century enamel locket	1·90	1·90
2164	3 k. Bohemian glass monstrance, 1840	1·90	1·90

Issued in sheets of four with two blank labels.

613 Sousaphone

614 "Child and Flowers" (book illustration)

(Des J. Baláž. Eng M. Ondráček (20 h.), J. Schmidt (30 h.), J. Mráček (40 h.), L. Jirka (1 k.), J. Herčík (1 k. 60). Recess*)

1974 (12 May). *Musical Instruments. T 613 and similar vert designs. Multicoloured. P 11½.*

2165	20 h. Type **613**	15	10
2166	30 h. Bagpipes	15	10
2167	40 h. Benka violin	20	10
2168	1 k. Sauer pyramid piano	30	15
2169	1 k. 60, Hulinský tenor quinton	1·25	40
2165/2169	*Set of 5* ..	1·75	60

(Des M. Hegar, after A. Zábranský. Eng J. Herčík. Recess*)

1974 (1 June). *25th Anniv of International Children's Day. P 11½.*

2170	**614** 60 h. multicoloured	15	10

615 "Stamp Collectors"

616 Slovak Partisan

(Des J. Liesler. Eng J. Schmidt (30 h.), M. Ondráček (6 k.). Recess*)

1974 (1 June). *"BRNO 74" National Stamp Exhibition (2nd issue). T 615 and similar horiz design. Multicoloured. P 11½.*

2171	30 h. Type **615**	10	10
2172	6 k. "Rocket Post"	2·40	1·10

Issued in sheets of 50 and also in sheets of 16 stamps and 14 stamp-size labels in two designs.

(Des I. Schurmann (No. 2173), E. Zmeták (others). Eng J. Mráček (No. 2173), J. Herčík (others). Recess*)

1974 (29 Aug). *Czechoslovak Anniversaries. T 616 and similar vert designs. Multicoloured. P 11½.*

2173	30 h. Type **616**	10	10
2174	30 h. Folk-dancer	10	10
2175	30 h. Actress holding masks	10	10

Events:—No. 2173, 30th anniv of Slovak Uprising; No. 2174, 25th anniv of Slovak SLUK Folk Song and Dance Ensemble; No. 2175, 25th anniv of Bratislava Assembly of Music and Dramatic Arts.

617 "Hero and Leander"

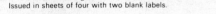

618 "Sentry on Guard", 1840

(Des and eng M. Ondráček. Recess)

1974 (25 Sept). *Bratislàva Tapestries. "Hero and Leander" (1st series). T 617 and similar vert design. Multicoloured. P 11½.*

2176	2 k. Type **617** ..	1·40	1·40
2177	2 k. 40, "Leander swimming the Hellespont"	1·75	1·75

Issued in sheets of four with two blank labels.
See also Nos. 2227/8 and 2281/2.

(Des and eng B. Housa. Recess* (30, 60 h., 1 k.) or recess (others))

1974 (26 Sept). *Old Shooting Targets. T* **618** *and similar vert designs. Multicoloured.* P 11½. (a) *Size* 30×50 mm.

2178	30 h. Type **618**		15	10
2179	60 h. "Pierrot and Owl", 1828		20	15
2180	1 k. "Diana awarding Marksman's Crown", 1832		30	15

(b) Size 41×51 mm.

2181	1 k. 60, "Still Life with Guitar", 1839		45	45
2182	2 k. 40, "Stag", 1834		50	50
2183	3 k. "Turk and Giraffe", 1831		3·50	3·50
2178/2183	*Set of 6*		4·50	4·25

Nos. 2181/3 were issued in sheets of four.

619 U.P.U. Monument and Postilion

(Des F. Hudeček. Eng J. Mráček (1 k., 1 k. 60), J. Herčík (others). Recess*)

1974 (9 Oct). *Centenary of Universal Postal Union. T* **619** *and similar horiz designs, showing forms of communication. Multicoloured.* P 11½.

2184	30 h. Type **619**		10	10
2185	40 h. Early mail coach		10	10
2186	60 h. Early railway carriage		25	10
2187	80 h. Modern mobile post office		25	10
2188	1 k. Ilyushin Il-14 mail plane		60	10
2189	1 k. 60, Dish aerial, earth station		1·40	40
2184/2189	*Set of 6*		2·40	70

620 Posthorn and Old Town Bridge Tower, Prague

621 Stylised Posthorn

(Des and eng J. Švengsbír (20, 40 h.). Des M. Urbásek. Eng M. Ondráček (30, 60 h.) Recess*)

1974 (31 Oct). *T* **620** *and similar vert designs connected with the postal service.* P 11½.

2190	20 h. multicoloured		10	10
2191	30 h. red-orange, cobalt and chocolate		10	10
2192	40 h. multicoloured		15	10
2193	60 h. red-orange, lemon and new blue		20	10
2190/2193	*Set of 4*		50	15

Designs:—30 h. P.T.T. emblem within letter; 40 h. Postilion; 60 h. P.T.T. emblem on dove's wing.

Nos. 2190/3 were issued on phosphorescent paper in 1978–79 (see note after No. 2384).

For 1 k. value as No. 2192, see No. 2900.

(Des and eng M. Ondráček (1 k., 1 k. 80), J. Herčík (1 k. 20), J. Švengsbír (1 k. 60), L. Jirka (2 k.). Recess)

1974 (27 Nov). *Art* (9th series). *Vert designs as T* **481**. *Multicoloured.* P 11½.

2194	1 k. "Self-portrait" (L. Kuba)		75	75
2195	1 k. 20, "František Ondříček" (V. Brožík)		75	75
2196	1 k. 60, "Pitcher with Flowers" (O. Kubin)		75	75
2197	1 k. 80, "Woman with Pitcher" (J. Alexy)		75	75
2198	2 k. 40, "Bacchanalia" (K. Škréta)		3·25	3·25
2194/2198	*Set of 5*		5·50	5·50

Issued in sheets of four.

(Des Z. Sklenář. Eng J. Mráček. Recess*)

1974 (18 Dec). *Stamp Day.* P 11½.

2199	**621**	1 k. multicoloured	25	15

622 Winged Emblem

623 "Woman"

(Des V. Kovařík. Photo)

1975 (22 Jan). *Coil stamps.* P 14.

2200	**622**	30 h. blue	10	10
2201		60 h. brown-red	15	15

(Des and eng B. Housa. Recess*)

1975 (26 Feb). *Czechoslovak Graphic Art* (5th series). *Engraved Hunting Scenes. Vert designs as T* **560**. P 11½.

2202	60 h. sepia and pale cream		25	10
2203	1 k. sepia and pale cream		35	20
2204	1 k. 60, sepia and pale green		50	25
2205	1 k. 80, sepia and pale brown		1·50	50
2202/2205	*Set of 4*		2·40	90

Designs:—60 h. "Still Life with Hare" (V. Hollar); 1 k. "The Lion and the Mouse" (V. Hollar); 1 k. 60, "Deer Hunt" (detail, P. Galle); 1 k. 80, "Grand Hunt" (detail, J. Callot).

(Des I. Schurmann. Eng J. Mráček. Recess*)

1975 (7 Mar). *International Women's Year.* P 11½.

2206	**623**	30 h. multicoloured	15	10

624 Village Family

625 "Little Queens" (Moravia)

(Des J. Baláž. Eng J. Herčík (60 h.), J. Schmidt (1 k.), L. Jirka (1 k. 20). Recess*)

1975 (25 Mar). 30*th Anniv of Razing of Fourteen Villages. T* **624** *and similar square designs. Multicoloured.* P 11.

2207	60 h. Type **624**		20	10
2208	1 k. Women and flames		25	10
2209	1 k. 20, Villagers and flowers		35	15

(Des K. Svolinský. Eng J. Schmidt (60 h., 1 k. 40), L. Jirka (1 k., 2 k.). Recess)

1975 (26 Mar). *Czechoslovak Folk Customs. T* **625** *and similar vert designs. Multicoloured.* P 11½.

2210	60 h. Type **625**		75	75
2211	1 k. Shrovetide parade, Slovakia		75	75
2212	1 k. 40, "Maid Dorothea" (play)		75	75
2213	2 k. "Morena" effigy, Slovakia		1·50	1·50
2210/2213	*Set of 4*		3·50	3·50

Each issued in sheets of four stamps and two half stamp-size labels bearing various motifs.

(Des and eng J. Herčík. Recess*)

1975 (17 Apr). *Arms of Czech Regional Capitals (5th series)
Horiz designs similar to T* **523** *P* 11½
2214	60 h. black, gold and vermilion		15	10
2215	60 h. multicoloured		15	10

Arms:—No. 2214, Nymburk; No. 2215, Znojmo.

626 Partisans at Barricade

(Des J. Brož (2216), A. Zábranský (2217), J. Adamcová (2218).
Eng J. Herčík. Recess (2217) or recess* (others))

1975 (9 May). *Czechoslovak Anniversaries T* **626** *and similar
horiz designs. P* 11.
2216	1 k. multicoloured		20	15
2217	1 k. sepia and pale cream		20	15
2218	1 k. multicoloured		20	15

Designs and Anniversaries:—No. 2216, Type **626** (30th anniv
of Czech Rising); No. 2217, Liberation celebrations (30th
anniv of Liberation by Soviet Army); No. 2218, Czech-Soviet
fraternity (5th anniv of Czech-Soviet Treaty).

627 Youth Exercises

(Des I. Strnad. Eng M. Ondráček. Recess*)

1975 (15 June). *National Spartacist Games T* **627** *and similar
horiz designs. P* 11½.
2219	30 h. purple, light blue and pink		10	10
2220	60 h. rose, lilac and yellow		15	10
2221	1 k. bluish violet, red and yellow		25	15

Designs:—60 h. Children's exercises; 1 k. Adult exercises.
Issued in sheets of thirty stamps with forty *se-tenant* labels,
19 × 23 mm, showing sports.

628 *Datnioides microlepis* and
Sea horse

629 "Pelicans"
(N. Charushin)

(Des J. Liesler. Eng L. Jirka (60 h.), J. Herčík (1 k., 1 k. 20),
J. Schmidt (1 k. 60), M. Ondráček (2 k.). Recess*)

1975 (27 June). *Aquarium Fishes. T* **628** *and similar horiz
designs. Multicoloured. P* 11½.
2222	60 h. Type **628**		15	10
2223	1 k. Siamese fighting fish and freshwater angel fish		30	10
2224	1 k. 20, Goldfish		50	15
2225	1 k. 60, Clown fish and butterfly fish		60	20
2226	2 k. Korean angel fish, purple moon angel fish and tang		2·75	55
2222/2226	*Set of 5*		4·00	90

(Des and eng M. Ondráček. Recess)

1975 (29 Aug). *Bratislava Tapestries. "Hero and Leander"
(2nd series). Vert designs as T* **617**. *Multicoloured. P* 11½.
2227	3 k. "Leander's Arrival"		1·00	90
2228	3 k. 60, "Hermione"		2·75	2·75

Issued in sheets of four.

(Des M. Hegar. Eng L. Jirka (60 h.), J. Mráček (80 h.),
J. Schmidt (others). Recess*)

1975 (5 Sept). *Biennial Exhibition of Book Illustrations for
Children, Bratislava. T* **629** *and similar vert designs.
Multicoloured. P* 11½.
2229	20 h. Type **629**		10	10
2230	30 h. "Sleeping Hero" (L. Schwarz)		10	10
2231	40 h. "Horseman" (V. Munteanu)		15	10
2232	60 h. "Peacock" (K. Ensikat)		20	10
2233	80 h. "The Stone King" (R. Dúbravec)		70	20
2229/2233	*Set of 5*		1·10	50

Issued in sheets of twenty-five stamps and fifteen *se-tenant*
stamp-size labels with multi-lingual inscriptions.

630 "CZ-150" Motor Cycle, 1951

(Des K. Lhoták. Eng L. Jirka (20 h.), J. Schmidt (40 h.),
J. Mráček (60 h.), M. Ondráček (1 k.), J. Herčík (1 k. 20,
1 k 80). Recess*)

1975 (29 Sept). *Czechoslovak Motor Cycles. T* **630** *and similar
horiz designs. Multicoloured. P* 11½.
2234	20 h. Type **630**		15	10
2235	40 h. Jawa "250", 1945		20	10
2236	60 h. Jawa "175", 1935		25	10
2237	1 k. Janatka "ITAR", 1921		30	15
2238	1 k. 20, Michl "Orion", 1903		50	20
2239	1 k. 80, Laurin and Klement, 1898		1·90	45
2234/2239	*Set of 6*		3·00	90

631 "Solar Radiation"   **632** Pres. Gustav Husák

(Des I. Strnad. Eng J. Mráček (30 h.), B. Housa (1 k.),
M. Ondráček (others). Recess (5 k.) or recess* (others))

1975 (30 Sept). *Co-operation in Space Research. T* **631** *and
similar designs. P* 11½.
2240	30 h. slate-violet, lemon and red		15	10
2241	60 h. carmine-red, lilac and yellow		20	10
2242	1 k. reddish purple, yellow & light blue		30	10
2243	2 k. multicoloured		70	20
2244	5 k. multicoloured		3·25	3·25
2240/2244	*Set of 5*		4·25	3·50

Designs: *Horiz* (40 × 23 *mm*)—60 h. *Aurora borealis*; 1 k.
Cosmic radiation measurement; 2 k. Copernicus and solar
radiation. *Vert* (40 × 50 *mm*)—5 k. "Apollo-Soyuz" space link.
No. 2244 was issued in sheets of four stamps with horiz label
depicting the constellations.

(Des and eng J. Herčík. Recess)

1975 (28 Oct). *P* 11½.
2245	**632** 30 h. ultramarine		10	10
2246	60 h. rose-red		20	10

Nos. 2245/6 were issued on phosphorescent paper in 1978.

633 Oil Refinery

(Des J. Lukavský. Eng A. Goldschmied (30 h.), M. Ondráček (60 h.), J. Mráček (1 k. 20), L. Jirka (others). Recess*)

1975 (28 Oct). *30th Anniv of Liberation. T **633** and similar horiz designs. Multicoloured. P 11½.*

2247	30 h. Type **633**		15	10
2248	60 h. Atomic power complex		15	10
2249	1 k. Underground Railway, Prague		25	10
2250	1 k. 20, Laying oil pipe-lines		40	15
2251	1 k. 40, Combine-harvesters and granary		35	20
2252	1 k. 60, Building construction		1·40	40
2247/2252	Set of 6		2·40	80

Nos. 2247/52 were issued in sheets with half stamp-size se-tenant labels.

(Des and eng J. Švengsbir. Recess)

1975 (29 Oct). *Prague Castle (11th series). Vert designs, similar to T **536**. Multicoloured. P 11½.*

2253	3 k. Late 9th-century gold earring		75	75
2254	3 k. 60, Leather Bohemian Crown case, 1347		2·40	2·40

Issued in sheets of four.

634 General Svoboda

636 František Halas (poet)

635 Posthorn Motif

(Des and eng L. Jirka. Recess)

1975 (25 Nov). *80th Birthday of General Ludvik Svoboda. Sheet 76 × 96 mm. P 11½.*

MS2255 **634**	10 k. multicoloured	12·50	12·50

No. **MS**2255 also exists imperforate.

HAVE YOU READ THE NOTES AT THE BEGINNING OF THIS CATALOGUE?

These often provide answers to the enquiries we receive.

(Des and eng J. Hercik (1 k., 1 k. 80), J. Mráček (1 k. 40), M. Ondráček (others). Recess)

1975 (27 Nov). *Art (10th series). Designs as T **481**. P 11½.*

2256	1 k. lake, stone and black		75	50
2257	1 k. 40, multicoloured		75	50
2258	1 k. 80, multicoloured		75	50
2259	2 k. 40, multicoloured		1·50	1·50
2260	3 k. 40, multicoloured		2·25	2·25
2256/2260	Set of 5		5·50	4·75

Paintings: *Vert*—1 k. "May" (Z. Sklenář); 1 k. 40, "Girl in National Costume" (E. Nevan); 2 k. 40, "Fire" (J. Čapek); 3 k. 40, "Prague, 1828" (V. Morstadt). *Horiz*—1 k. 80, "Liberation of Prague" (A. Cermáková).

Issued in sheets of four.

(Des I. Schurmann. Eng J. Mráček. Recess*)

1975 (18 Dec). *Stamp Day. P 11½.*

2261 **635**	1 k. multicoloured	30	15

(Des J. Lukavský (No. 2262), C. Bouda (2263), J. Baláž (2264), M. Hegar (2265), A. Brunovský (2266). Eng M. Ondráček (2262, 2264), J. Schmidt (2263), B. Housa (2265), J. Herčik (2266). Recess (No. 2264) or recess* (others))

1976 (25 Feb). *Celebrities' Anniversaries. T **636** and similar portraits. P 11½.*

2262	60 h. multicoloured		15	10
2263	60 h. multicoloured		15	10
2264	60 h. multicoloured		30	10
2265	60 h. chalky blue, scarlet and yellow		15	10
2266	60 h. multicoloured		15	10
2262/2266	Set of 5		80	40

Designs and Anniversaries: *Horiz*— No. 2262, Type **636** (75th birth anniv); No. 2266, Ivan Krasko (poet, birth centenary). *Vert*— No. 2263, Wilhelm Pieck (German statesman, birth centenary); No. 2264, František Lexa (Egyptologist, birth centenary); No. 2265, Jindřich Jindřich (ethnographer, birth centenary).

637 Ski Jumping   **639** Table Tennis Player

638 Throwing the Javelin

(Des J. Liesler. Eng J. Herčik (1 k. 40), M. Ondráček (1 k. 40), J. Mráček (1 k. 60). Recess)

1976 (22 Mar). *Winter Olympic Games, Innsbruck. T **637** and similar horiz designs. Multicoloured. P 11½.*

2267	1 k. Type **637**		20	10
2268	1 k. 40, Figure skating		30	15
2269	1 k. 60, Ice hockey		1·50	35

(Des I. Strnad. Eng J. Herčik. Recess*)

1976 (22 Mar). *Olympic Games, Montreal. T **638** and similar horiz designs. Multicoloured. P 11½.*

2270	2 k. Type **638**		40	25
2271	3 k. Relay-racing		65	35
2272	3 k. 60, Putting the shot		2·75	70

(Des J. Baláž. Eng M. Ondráček. Recess*)

1976 (22 Mar). *European Table Tennis Championships, Prague, and 50th Anniv of Organized Table Tennis in Czechoslovakia.* P 11½.

2273	**639**	1 k. multicoloured	40	20

640 Star Emblem and Workers

641 Microphone and Musical Instruments

(Des J. Adamcová (30 h.), I. Schurmann (60 h.). Eng J. Herčik. Recess*)

1976 (12 Apr). *15th Czechoslovak Communist Party Congress, Prague.* T **640** *and similar vert design. Multicoloured.* P 11½.

2274	30 h. Type **640**		10	10
2275	60 h. Furnaceman and monolith		15	10

(Des K. Svolinský (No. 2276), C. Bouda (2277), G. Štrba (2278), A. Strnadel (2279), I. Strnad (2280). Eng L. Jirka (2276), J. Schmidt (2277), J. Mráček (2278), M. Ondráček (2279/80). Recess*)

1976 (26 Apr). *Cultural Events and Anniversaries.* T **641** *and similar designs.* P 11½.

2276	20 h. multicoloured		10	10
2277	20 h. multicoloured		10	10
2278	20 h. multicoloured		10	10
2279	30 h. multicoloured		10	10
2280	30 h. bluish violet, rose & turquoise-blue		10	10
2276/2280	*Set of 5*		35	30

Designs: *Horiz*—No. 2276. Type **641** (50th anniv of Czechoslovak Radio Symphony Orchestra); No. 2278. Stage revellers (30th anniv of Nová Scéna Theatre, Bratislava); No. 2279. Folk dancers, Wallachia (International Folk Song and Dance Festival, Strážnice). *Vert*—No. 2277. Ballerina, violin and mask (30th anniv of Prague Academy of Music and Dramatic Art); No. 2280. Film "profile" (20th Film Festival, Karlovy Vary).

(Des and eng M. Ondráček. Recess)

1976 (9 May). *Bratislava Tapestries. "Hero and Leander"* (3rd series). *Vert designs as* T **617.** *Multicoloured.* P 11½.

2281	3 k. "Hero with Leander's body"		2·50	1·50
2282	3 k. 60. "Eros grieving"		1·25	90

Issued in sheets of four.

642 Hammer, Sickle and Red Flags   **643** Mánes Hall, Czechoslovak Artists' Union

(Des I. Schurmann (30 h.), M. Hegar (others). Eng M. Ondráček (30 h.), L. Jirka (60 h.), J. Herčik (6 k.). Recess*)

1976 (14 May). *55th Anniv of Czechoslovak Communist Party.* T **642** *and similar designs.* P 11½.

2283	30 h. chalky blue, gold and rosine		15	10
2284	60 h. multicoloured		20	10
MS2285	100 × 90 mm. 6 k. multicoloured		2·50	2·25

Designs: *Vert* (23 × 40 mm)—60 h. Hammer and sickle on flag. *Horiz* (50 × 30 mm)—6 k. Flag and commemorative inscription.

(Des J. Lukavský. Eng L. Jirka. Recess*)

1976 (23 June). *AIR. "PRAGA 78" International Stamp Exhibition* (1st issue). *Prague Architecture.* T **643** *and similar multicoloured designs.* P 11½.

2286	60 h. Type **643**		40	10
2287	1 k. 60, Congress Hall, Julius Fučík Park		45	15
2288	2 k. Powder Tower, Old Town (*vert*)		80	20
2289	2 k. 40, Charles Bridge and Old Bridge Tower		60	20
2290	4 k. Old Town Square and Town Hall (*vert*)		1·00	35
2291	6 k. Prague Castle and St. Vitus' Cathedral (*vert*)		4·50	1·00
2286/2291	*Set of 6*		7·00	1·75

See also Nos. 2313/16, 2326/30, 2339/42, 2349/52, 2358/62, 2389/93, 2407/12, 2413/18, 2420/3 and **MS**2424/5.

644 "Warship" (Frans Huys)

645 "UNESCO" Plant

(Des and eng B. Housa. Recess*)

1976 (21 July). *Ship Engravings.* T **644** *and similar vert designs.* P 11½.

2292	40 h. black, pale cream and light drab		25	10
2293	60 h. black, pale cream & brownish grey		25	10
2294	1 k. black, pale cream and light green		50	10
2295	2 k. black, pale cream and light blue		1·75	70
2292/2295	*Set of 4* ./		2·50	90

Designs:—60 h. "Dutch Merchantman" (V. Hollar); 1 k. "Ship at Anchor" (N. Zeeman); 2 k. "Galleon under Full Sail" (F. Chereau).

(Des Z. Sklenář. Eng J. Goldschmied. Recess)

1976 (30 July). *30th Anniv of United Nations Children's Fund.* P 11½.

2296	**645**	2 k. multicoloured	90	50

647 Merino Ram

646 "Protected Child"

648 "Stop Smoking"

(Des V. Hložnik. Eng J. Herčik. Recess)

1976 (30 July). *European Security and Co-operation Conference, Helsinki. Sheet 114×167 mm, containing two stamps as T* **646**. *P* 11½.
MS2297 6 k.×2, bright blue, yellow & scarlet   5·50   6·00

(Des E. Kotrba. Eng J. Schmidt (40 h.), M. Ondráček (others). Recess*)

1976 (28 Aug). *"Bountiful Earth" Agricultural Exhibition, České Budějovice. T* **647** *and similar horiz designs. Multicoloured. P* 11×12.
2298	30 h. Type **647**		10	10
2299	40 h. Bern-Haná cow		15	10
2300	1 k. 60, Kladruby stallion		45	15

(Des J. Liesler. Eng M. Ondráček. Recess)

1976 (7 Sept). *WHO Campaign against Smoking. P* 11½.
2301 **648** 2 k. multicoloured   1·25   45

ČESKOSLOVENSKO

649 Postal Code Emblem

650 "Guernica" (I. Weiner-Král)

(Des F. Hudeček. Photo)

1976 (7 Sept). *Coil stamps. Postal Code Campaign. T* **649** *and similar horiz design. P* 11½.
2302	30 h. emerald		10	10
2303	60 h. carmine-red (postal map)		15	10

(Des and eng J. Herčik. Recess*)

1976 (22 Oct). *40th Anniv of International Brigades in Spanish Civil War. P* 11½.
2304 **650** 5 k. multicoloured   1·40   50

(Des and eng J. Švengsbir. Recess)

1976 (22 Oct). *Prague Castle (12th series). Vert designs as T* **536**. *Multicoloured. P* 11½.
2305	3 k. "Prague Castle, 1572" (F. Hoogenberghe)		2·50	2·50
2306	3 k. 60, "Satyrs" (relief from Summerhouse balustrade)		90	90

Issued in sheets of four.

651 Common Zebra with Foal

(Des J. Baláž. Eng J. Mráček (10 h.), L. Jirka (20 h.), J. Schmidt (30 h., 3 k.), M. Ondráček (40 h.), J. Herčik (60 h.). Recess*)

1976 (3 Nov). *Dvůr Králové Wildlife Park. T* **651** *and similar multicoloured designs. P* 11½.
2307	10 h. Type **651**		15	10
2308	20 h. African elephant, calf and Cattle egret (vert)		60	10
2309	30 h. Cheetah		20	10
2310	40 h. Giraffe and calf (vert)		20	10
2311	60 h. Black rhinoceros		25	10
2312	3 k. Bongo with offspring		2·25	70
2307/2312	Set of 6		3·25	95

(Eng J. Mráček (1 k.), J. Schmidt (1 k. 40), J. Herčik (2 k.) M. Ondráček (3 k. 60). Recess)

1976 (27 Nov). *Art (11th series) and "Praga 1978" International Stamp Exhibition (2nd issue). Vert designs as T* **481**. *Multicoloured. P* 11½.
2313	1 k. "Flowers in Vase" (P. Matejka)	1·00	70
2314	1 k. 40, "Oleander Blossoms" (C. Bouda)	1·25	1·00
2315	2 k. "Flowers in Vase" (J. Brueghel)	2·25	1·60
2316	3 k. 60, "Tulips and Narcissi" (J. R. Bys)	1·10	65
2313/2316	Set of 4	5·00	3·50

Nos. 2313/16 were each issued in sheets of four stamps and two half stamp-size labels bearing the Exhibition emblem.

652 Postillion, Postal Emblem and Satellite

653 Ice Hockey

(Des V. Kovařík. Eng J. Herčik. Recess*)

1976 (18 Dec). *Stamp Day. P* 11½.
2317 **652** 1 k. indigo, magenta and gold   25   10

(Des I. Strnad. Eng J. Mráček (60 h.), L. Jirka (1 k.), J. Goldschmied (1 k. 60), J. Schmidt (2 k.). Recess*)

1977 (11 Feb). *Sixth Winter Spartakiad of Warsaw Pact Armies. T* **653** *and similar vert designs. Multicoloured. P* 11½.
2318	60 h. Type **653**		25	10
2319	1 k. Rifle shooting (Biathlon)		30	10
2320	1 k. 60, Ski jumping		2·00	60
2321	2 k. Slalom		55	20
2318/2321	Set of 4		2·75	90

654 Arms of Vranov

655 Window, Michna Palace

(Des and eng J. Herčik. Recess*)

1977 (20 Feb). *Arms of Czech Towns (1st series). T* **654** *and similar vert designs. Multicoloured. P* 11½.
2322	60 h. Type **654**		20	10
2323	60 h. Kralupy nad Vltavou		20	10
2324	60 h. Jičín		20	10
2325	60 h. Velašské Meziříčí		20	10
2322/2325	Set of 4		70	30

See also Nos. 2511/14 and 2612/15.

(Des Eva Smrčinová. Eng B. Housa. Recess*)

1977 (10 Mar). *"PRAGA 1978" International Stamp Exhibition (3rd issue). Historic Prague Windows. T* **655** *and similar vert designs. Multicoloured. P* 11½.
2326	20 h. Type **655**		10	10
2327	30 h. Michna Palace (different)		10	10
2328	40 h. Thun Palace		10	10
2329	60 h. Archbishop's Palace, Hradčany		15	10
2330	5 k. Church of St. Nicholas		3·25	75
2326/2330	Set of 5		3·25	85

656 Children crossing Road

657 Cyclists at Warsaw (starting point)

660 Coffee Pots

661 Mladá Boleslav Headdress

(Des V. Kovařík. Eng M. Ondráček. Recess*)

1977 (21 Apr). *25th Anniv of Police Aides Corps.* P 11½.
2331 **656** 60 h. multicoloured   25   10

(Des Anna Podzemná. Eng J. Herčík (30 h., 1 k. 40), J. Schmidt (others). Recess*)

1977 (7 May). *30th Peace Cycle Race. T* **657** *and similar square designs. Multicoloured.* P 11.
2332   30 h. Type **657**   15   10
2333   60 h. Cyclists at Berlin   20   10
2334   1 k. Cyclists at Prague (finishing point)   1·50   30
2335   1 k. 40, Cyclists and modern buildings   50   15
2332/2335   Set of 4   2·10   55

658 Congress Emblem

659 French Postal Rider, 19th Century

(Des M. Hegar. Eng L. Jirka. Recess*)

1977 (25 May). *Ninth Trade Unions Congress.* P 11½.
2336 **658** 30 h. gold, orange-vermilion and deep carmine   10   10

(Des and eng J. Švengsbir. Recess)

1977 (7 June). *Prague Castle (13th series). Vert designs as T* **536.** P 11½.
2337   3 k. multicoloured   1·25   1·25
2338   3 k. 60, dull green, gold and black   1·75   1·75
Designs:—3 k. Onyx cup, 1350 (St. Vitus Cathedral); 3 k. 60, Bronze horse, 1619 (A. de Vries).
Each issued in sheets of four with two blank labels.

(Des K. Toman. Eng L. Jirka (60 h.), M. Ondráček (3 k. 60), J. Herčík (others). Recess*)

1977 (8 June). *"PRAGA 1978" International Stamp Exhibition (4th issue). Postal Uniforms. T* **659** *and similar horiz designs. Multicoloured.* P 11½.
2339   60 h. Type **659**   15   10
2340   1 k. Austrian postal rider, 1838   25   10
2341   2 k. Austrian postal rider, c. 1770   50   20
2342   3 k. 60, German postal rider, 1700   3·00   90
2339/2342   Set of 4   3·50   1·10
Nos. 2339/42 were each issued in sheets of 50 and in sheets containing four stamps, four inscribed stamp-size labels and two blank labels.

(Des V. Kovarík. Eng J. Mráček (20, 30 h.), J. Schmidt (40, 60 h.), M. Ondráček (others). Recess*)

1977 (15 June). *Czechoslovak Porcelain. T* **660** *and similar vert designs.* P 11½.
2343   20 h. multicoloured   10   10
2344   30 h. multicoloured   10   10
2345   40 h. multicoloured   15   10
2346   60 h. multicoloured   20   10
2347   1 k. deep ultramarine, blue-green and reddish violet   25   10
2348   3 k. deep ultramarine, gold and rose-carmine   2·25   75
2343/2348   Set of 6   2·75   90
Designs:—30 h. Vase; 40 h. Amphora; 60 h. Jug, beaker, cup and saucer; 1 k. Plate and candlestick; 3 k. Coffee pot, cup and saucer.

(Des K. Svolinský. Eng J. Schmidt (1, 5 k.), L. Jirka (others). Recess)

1977 (31 Aug). *"PRAGA 1978" International Stamp Exhibition (5th issue). Regional Headdresses. T* **661** *and similar vert designs. Multicoloured.* P 11½.
2349   1 k. Type **661**   75   75
2350   1 k. 60, Važec   3·50   3·50
2351   3 k. 60, Závadka   75   75
2352   5 k. Bělkovice   1·25   1·25
2349/2352   Set of 4   5·75   5·75
Nos. 2349/52 were each issued both in sheets of 10 and in sheets of eight stamps and two labels bearing the Exhibition emblem.

662 V. Bombová's Illustrations of *Janko Gondashik* and the *Golden Lady*

663 Airships LZ-5 and *Graf Zeppelin*

(Des J. Šváb. Eng M. Ondráček (40 h.), L. Jirka (3 k.), J. Mráček (others). Recess*)

1977 (9 Sept). *Biennial Exhibition of Book Illustrations for Children, Bratislava. T* **662** *and similar horiz designs. Multicoloured.* P 12×11½.
2353   40 h. Type **662**   10   10
2354   60 h. G. Pavlishin's illustrations of *Tales of Amur* (D. Nagishkin)   15   10
2355   1 k. U. Löfgren's illustrations of *Almgist et Wiksel* (T. Gummian)   25   10
2356   2 k. N. Claveloux's illustrations of *Alice in Wonderland* and *Through the Looking Glass* (L. Carroll)   75   25
2357   3 k. J. Trnka's illustrations of *Eventyr* (H. C. Andersen)   3·00   65
2353/2357   Set of 5   3·75   1·10

(Des J. Liesler. Eng M. Ondráček (60 h.), J. Schmidt (1 k. 60),
J. Herčík (4 k. 40), L. Jirka (others). Recess*)

1977 (15 Sept). *AIR. "PRAGA 1978" International Stamp
Exhibition (6th issue). Early Aviation. T* **663** *and similar vert
designs. Multicoloured. P* 11½.

2358	60 h. Type **663**		15	10
2359	1 k. Clement Ader's monoplane *Eole,* Etrich Holubice and Dunne D-8		30	10
2360	1 k. 60, Jeffries and Blanchard's balloon, 1785		40	15
2361	2 k. Lilienthal biplane glider, 1896		50	20
2362	4 k. 40, Jan Kašpar's Blériot XI over Prague		3·50	90
2358/2362	*Set of* 5		4·25	1·25

Nos. 2358/62 were each issued in sheets of 30 stamps, 15
stamp-size labels bearing the Exhibition emblem and five blank
labels.

664 UNESCO Emblem,   **665** "Peace"
Violin and Doves

(Des J. Baláž. Eng M. Ondráček. Recess*)

1977 (28 Sept). *Congress of UNESCO International Music
Council. P* 11½.

2363	**664** 60 h. multicoloured		15	10

(Des K. Svolinský. Eng L. Jirka (60 h.), J. Schmidt (1 k. 60),
J. Mráček (2 k. 40). Recess*)

1977 (3 Oct). *European Co-operation for Peace. T* **665** *and
similar horiz designs. Multicoloured. P* 11½.

2364	60 h. Type **665**		15	10
2365	1 k. 60 "Co-operation"		40	20
2366	2 k. 40 "Social Progress"		1·25	40

Nos. 2364/6 were only issued in small sheets of two stamps.

666 Yuri Gagarin   **667** Revolutionaries   **668** "Wisdom"
and Cruiser *Aurora*

(Des I. Strnad. Eng M. Ondráček (20, 40 h.), L. Jirka (30 h.),
J. Mráček (1 k.), J. Schmidt (1 k. 60). Recess*)

1977 (4 Oct). *Space Research. T* **666** *and similar vert designs.
Multicoloured. P* 11½.

2367	20 h. S. P. Koroliov (space technician, launch of first satellite)		10	10
2368	30 h. Type **666** (first man in space)		10	10
2369	40 h. Aleksei Leonov (first space walker)		10	10
2370	1 k. Neil Armstrong (first man on the Moon)		25	10
2371	1 k. 60, "Salyut" and "Skylab" space stations		1·40	35
2367/2371	*Set of* 5		1·75	50

(Des J. Mikula. Eng J. Herčík. Recess*)

1977 (17 Nov). *60th Anniv of Russian Revolution and 55th
Anniv of USSR. T* **667** *and similar vert design. Multicoloured.
P* 11½.

2372	30 h. Type **667**		15	10
2373	30 h. Russian woman, Kremlin, rocket and USSR arms		15	10

(Des K. Svolinský. Eng L. Jirka. Recess*)

1977 (17 Nov). *25th Anniv of Czechoslovak Academy of
Sciences. P* 11½.

2374	**668** 3 k. multicoloured		70	25

(Des and eng M. Ondráček (2, 3 k.), L. Jirka (2 k. 40), B. Housa
(2 k. 60), J. Herčík (5 k.). Recess)

1977 (27 Nov). *Art (12th series). Vert designs as T* **481**. *P* 11½.

2375	2 k. multicoloured		75	75
2376	2 k. 40, multicoloured		3·25	3·25
2377	2 k. 60, pale yellow and black		2·50	2·50
2378	3 k. multicoloured		1·00	1·00
2379	5 k. multicoloured		1·00	1·00
2375/2379	*Set of* 5		7·50	7·50

Designs:—2 k. "Fear" (J. Mudroch); 2 k. 40, "Jan Francisci"
(P. M. Bohún); 2 k. 60, "Self portrait" (V. Hollar); 3 k. "Portrait
of a Girl" (L. Cranach); 5 k. "Cleopatra" (Rubens).

Each issued in sheets of four stamps and two blank labels.

669 "Bratislava, 1574"
(G. Hoefnagel)

(Des and eng M. Ondráček. Recess)

1977 (6 Dec). *Historic Bratislava (1st issue). T* **669** *and
similar horiz design. Multicoloured. P* 11½.

2380	3 k. Type **669**		2·25	2·25
2381	3 k. 60, Coat of arms, 1436		75	65

Each issued in sheets of four stamps and two blank labels.
See also Nos. 2402/3, 2500/1, 2545/6, 2582/3. 2642/3, 2698/9,
2736/7, 2793/4, 2842/3, 2898/9, 2952/3, 2997/8 and 3034/5.

670 Posthorn and Stamps   **671** Z. Nejedlý
(historian)

(Des J. Kaiser. Eng B. Housa. Recess*)

1977 (18 Dec). *Stamp Day. P* 11½.

2382	**670** 1 k. multicoloured		20	10

(Des V. Kovářik. Eng J. Schmidt (30 h.), J. Herčík (40 h.).
Recess*)

1978 (10 Feb). *Cultural Anniversaries. T* **671** *and similar vert
design. Multicoloured. P* 11½.

2383	30 h. Type **671** (birth centenary)		10	10
2384	40 h. Karl Marx (160th birth anniv)		10	10

PHOSPHORESCENT PAPER. From No. 2385 onwards many
issues are on phosphorescent paper; this reacts *yellow* under an
ultra-violet lamp. The non-phosphorescent paper used for other
issues reacts *white* under a UV lamp due to brighteners used in
the manufacture of the paper.

SPOLEČNÝ LET SSSR*ČSSR

(673)

672 Civilians greeting Armed Guards

(Des G. Strba. Eng J. Herčík (2385). Des J. Chudomel. Eng M. Ondráček (2386). Recess*)

1978 (25th Feb). 30*th Anniv of "Victorious February" and National Front. T* **672** *and similar horiz design. Multicoloured. Phosphorescent paper. P* 11½.

2385	1 k.	Type **672**		20	10
2386	1 k.	Intellectual, peasant woman and steel worker		20	10

Imperf miniature sheets containing four copies of No. 2385 were sold only at the "PRAGA 1978" stamp exhibition or by subscription.

1978 (2 Mar). *Soviet-Czechoslovak Space Flight. As T* **666** *but optd with T* **673.**

2387	**666**	30 h. brown-lake (B. and C.)		20	20
2388		3 k. 60, deep ultramarine (G. and C.)		5·00	5·00

674 Modern Coins **675** Tyre Marks and Ball **676** Hands supporting Globe

(Des D. Kállay. Eng M. Ondráček (20 h.), L. Jirka (40 h.), J. Mráček (5 k.), J. Herčík (others). Recess*)

1978 (14 Mar). 650*th Anniv of Kremnica Mint and "PRAGA 1978" International Stamp Exhibition (7th issue). T* **674** *and similar vert designs. Multicoloured. P* 11½.

2389	20 h.	Type **674**		10	10
2390	40 h.	Culture medal, 1972 (J. Kulich)		10	10
2391	1 k. 40,	Charles University Medal, 1948 (O. Španiel)		3·25	40
2392	3 k.	Ferdinand I medal, 1563 (L. Richter)		75	45
2393		Gold florin of Charles Robert, 1335	1·25	60
2389/2393		*Set of* 5		5·00	1·40

(Des V. Kovářik. Eng M. Ondráček. Recess*)

1978 (15 Mar). *Road Safety. P* 11½.

2394 **675** 60 h. multicoloured .. 20 10

No. 2394 exists on both ordinary and phosphorescent papers.

(Des M. Hegar. Eng J. Herčík. Recess*)

1978 (16 Apr). *Ninth World Federation of Trade Unions Congress, Prague. P* 11½.

2395 **676** 1 k. multicoloured 20 10

677 Putting the Shot **678** Ministry of Posts, Prague

(Des I. Rumanský. Eng J. Mráček (30 h.), J. Herčík (40 h.), M. Ondráček (60 h., 2 k.), J. Schmidt (others). Recess*)

1978 (26 Apr). *Sports Events. T* **677** *and similar designs. P* 11½.

2396	30 h. multicoloured			15	10
2397	40 h. multicoloured			15	10
2398	60 h. multicoloured			80	20
2399	1 k. multicoloured			40	10
2400	2 k. yellow, deep ultramarine and rose-carmine			60	25
2401	3 k. 60, multicoloured			2·40	75
2396/2401	*Set of* 6			4·00	1·25

Designs and events: *Horiz*—70th anniv of Bandy Hockey: 30 h. Three hockey players. World Ice Hockey Championships: 60 h. Tackle in front of goal; 2 k. Goalmouth scrimmage. *Vert*—European Athletics Championships, Prague: 40 h. Type **677**; 1 k. Pole vault; 3 k. 60, Running.

(Des and eng J. Mráček (3 k.), M. Ondráček (3k. 60). Recess)

1978 (9 May). *Historic Bratislava (2nd issue). Horiz designs as T* **669.** *P* 11½.

2402	3 k.	deep grey-green, bluish violet and bright scarlet		1·40	1·40
2403	3 k. 60,	multicoloured		2·40	2·40

Designs:—3 k. "Bratislava" (Orest Dubay); 3 k. 60, "Fishpond Square, Bratislava" (Imro Weiner-Král).

Each issued in sheets of four with two blank labels.

(Des and eng J. Švengsbir. Recess)

1978 (9 May). *Prague Castle (14th series). Vert designs as T* **536.** *P* 11½.

2404	3 k.	orange-yellow, black and yellowish green		80	80
2405	3 k. 60,	multicoloured		2·75	2·25

Designs:—3 k. Memorial to King Přemysl Otakar II, St. Vitus Cathedral; 3 k. 60, Portrait of King Charles IV (Jan Očko).

Each issued in sheets of four with two blank labels.

(Des J. Chudomel. Eng B. Housa. Recess*)

1978 (29 May). 14*th COMECON Meeting, Prague. P* 11½.

2406 **678** 60 h. multicoloured 15 10

679 Palacký Bridge **680** St. Peter and other Apostles

(Des and eng J. Švengsbír. Recess*)

1978 (30 May). "*PRAGA 1978*" *International Stamp Exhibition, Prague (8th issue). Prague Bridges. T* **679** *and similar horiz designs. Multicoloured. P* 11½.

2407	20 h. Type **679**	10	10
2408	40 h. Railway Bridge	35	10
2409	1 k. Bridge of 1 May	25	10
2410	2 k. Mánes Bridge	45	20
2411	3 k. Svatopluk Cech Bridge	55	40
2412	5 k. 40, Charles Bridge	4·50	1·25
2407/2412	*Set of 6*	5·50	1·75

(Des Anna Podzemná. Eng M. Ondráček. Recess (10 k.) or recess* (others))

1978 (20 June). "*PRAGA 1978*" *International Stamp Exhibition (9th issue). Prague Town Hall Astronomical Clock. T* **680** *and similar designs showing details of the clock. Multicoloured. P* 11½.

2413	40 h. Type **680**	15	10
2414	1 k. Astronomical clock face	20	15
2415	2 k. Centre of Mánes's calendar	35	20
2416	3 k. "September" (grape harvest)	3·25	1·10
2417	3 k. 60, Libra (sign of the Zodiac)	1·25	25
2413/2417	*Set of 5*	4·75	1·60
MS2418	89×125 mm. 10 k. Mánes's calendar (48×38 mm)	9·00	7·50

MS2418 also exists imperf.

681 Dancers   **682** Gottwald Bridge

(Des S. Greinerova. Eng M. Ondráček. Recess*)

1978 (7 July). *25th Vychodna Folklore Festival. Phosphorescent paper. P* 11×11½.

2419   **681**   30 h. multicoloured   10   10

(Des J. Chudomel. Eng B. Housa. Recess*)

1978 (8 Sept). "*PRAGA 1978*" *International Stamp Exhibition (10th issue). Modern Prague. T* **682** *and similar horiz designs. Multicoloured. Phosphorescent paper. P* 12×11½.

2420	60 h. Type **682**	40	10
2421	1 k. Powder Gate Tower and Kotva department store	25	10
2422	2 k. Ministry of Posts	50	20
2423	6 k. Prague Castle and flats	3·50	1·40
2420/2423	*Set of 4*	4·25	1·60

No. 2422 also exists on ordinary paper.

683 "Old Prague and Charles Bridge" (V. Morstadt)

(Des and eng M. Ondráček. Recess)

1978 (10 Sept). "*PRAGA 1978*" *International Stamp Exhibition (11th issue). Sheet* 96×74 *mm. P* 11½.

MS2424   **683**   20 k. multicoloured   12·00   12·00

ČESKOSLOVENSKO

684 Detail of "The Flaying of Marsyas" (Titian)   **685** Fair Buildings

(Des and eng J. Herčik. Recess)

1978 (12 Sept). "*PRAGA 1978*" *International Stamp Exhibition (12th issue). Sheet* 108×165 *mm containing T* **684** *and similar vert design showing detail of painting. Multicoloured. P* 11½.

MS2425   10 k. Type **684**; 10 k. King Midas   10·00 10·00

A sheet similar to No. **MS**2425 but with additional inscriptions commemorating FIP Day was sold on production of an entrance ticket at the Exhibition, or by subscription to include the price of entrance (*Price* £38 *un or used*).

(Des F. Hudeček. Eng L. Jirka. Recess*)

1978 (13 Sept). *20th International Engineering Fair, Brno. P* 11½.

2426   **685**   30 h. multicoloured   10   10

686 "Postal Newspaper Service" (25th anniv)   **687** Horses falling at Fence

(Des E. Smrčinová (2427), I. Schurmann (others). Eng M. Ondráček (2429), J. Herčik (others). Recess*)

1978 (21 Sept). *Press, Broadcasting and Television Days. T* **686** *and similar horiz designs. P* 11½.

2427	30 h. dull yellowish grn, steel bl & ornge	10	10
2428	30 h. multicoloured	10	10
2429	30 h. multicoloured	10	10

Designs:—No. 2428, Microphone, Newspapers, camera and Ministry of Information and Broadcasting; 2429, Television screen and Television Centre, Prague (25th anniv of Czechoslovak television).

(Des R. Kolář. Eng B. Housa (10, 40 h.), M. Ondráček (20, 30 h.), J. Schmidt (1 k. 40), J. Mráček (4 k. 40). Recess*)

1978 (6 Oct). *Pardubice Steeplechase. T* **687** *and similar horiz designs. Multicoloured. Phosphorescent paper. P* 11½.

2430	10 h. Type **687**	10	10
2431	20 h. Sulky racing	10	10
2432	30 h. Racing horses	15	10
2433	40 h. Passing winning post	15	10
2434	1 k. 60, Jumping a fence	40	20
2435	4 k. 40, Jockey leading winning horse	3·00	1·10
2430/2435	*Set of 6*	3·50	1·40

HAVE YOU READ THE NOTES AT THE BEGINNING OF THIS CATALOGUE?

These often provide answers to the enquiries we receive.

688 Woman holding Arms of Czechoslovakia

689 "Still Life with Flowers" (J. Bohdan)

(Des J. Hložník. Eng J. Herčík. Recess*)

1978 (28 Oct). 60th Anniv of Independence. P 11½.
2436 **688** 60 h. multicoloured 15 10

(Des M. Ondráček. Eng J. Schmidt (2 k. 40), M. Ondráček (3 k.), L. Jirka (3 k. 60). Recess)

1978 (27 Nov). 30th Anniv of Slovak National Gallery, Bratislava. T **689** and similar designs. Multicoloured. P 11½.
2437 2 k. 40, Type **689** 75 60
2438 3 k. "Dream in a Shepherd's Hut" (L. Fulla) (horiz) 75 75
2439 3 k. 60, "Apostle with Censer" (detail, Master of Spiš Chapter) .. 3·00 3·00
Each issued in sheets of four with two blank labels.

692 Council Building, Moscow

693 "Soyuz 28"

(Des O. Lupták (30 h.), J. Baláž (others). Eng J. Herčík. Recess*)

1979 (1 Jan). Anniversaries. T **692** and similar designs. Ordinary paper (1 k.) or phosphorescent paper (others). P 11½.
2446 30 h. sepia, dull yellowish green and dull orange 10 10
2447 60 h. multicoloured 15 10
2448 1 k. multicoloured 20 10
Designs: Horiz—30 h. Girl's head and ears of wheat (30th anniv of Unified Agricultural Co-operatives); 60 h. Czechoslovakians and doves (10th anniv of Czechoslovak Federation). Vert—1 k. Type **692** (30th anniv of Council of Economic Mutual Aid).

(Des V. Kovářik. Eng J. Mráček (30 h., 4 k.), M. Ondráček (60 h., 10 k.), L. Jirka (others). Recess*)

1979 First Anniv of Soviet-Czechoslovak Space Flight. T **693** and similar multicoloured designs. Ordinary paper (10 k.) or phosphorescent paper (others). P 11½.
2449 30 h. Type **693** 15 10
2450 60 h. A. Gubarev and V. Remek (vert) 15 10
2451 1 k. 60, J. Romanenko and G. Grechko 45 25
2452 2 k. "Salyut 6" space laboratory .. 2·50 50
2453 4 k. "Soyuz 28" touch down (vert) .. 90 50
2449/2453 Set of 5 .. .. .. 3·75 1·25
MS2454 75×95 mm. 10 k. Gubarev and Remek waving (38×54 mm) .. .. .. 5·50 5·50
No. **MS**2454 also exists imperf.
Nos. 2449 and 2451 also exist on ordinary paper.

690 Violinist and Bass Player (J. Könyveš)

691 Alfons Mucha and Design for 1918 Hradčany Stamp

(Des J. Baláž. Eng J. Mráček (1 k. 60), J. Herčík (others). Recess*)

1978 (5 Dec). Slovak Ceramics. T **690** and similar vert designs. Phosphorescent paper. P 11½.
2440 20 h. multicoloured 10 10
2441 30 h. greenish blue and violet 10 10
2442 40 h. multicoloured 10 10
2443 1 k. multicoloured 25 10
2444 1 k. 60, multicoloured .. .. 2·25 30
2440/2444 Set of 5 .. .. .. 2·50 45
Designs:—30 h. Horseman (J. Franko); 40 h. Man in kilt (M. Polaško); 1 k. Three girl singers (J. Bizmayer); 1 k. 60, Miner with axe (F. Kostka).

(Des V. Kovářik. Eng J. Herčík. Recess*)

1978 (18 Dec). Stamp Day. Phosphorescent paper. P 11½.
2445 **691** 1 k. multicoloured 20 15

694 Campanula alpina

695 Stylized Satellite

696 Arms of Vlachovo Březi

(Des K. Svolinský. Eng L. Jirka. Recess (3 k.) or recess* (others))

1979 (23 Mar). 25th Anniv of Mountain Rescue Service. T **694** and similar vert designs. Multicoloured. Ordinary paper (3 k.) or phosphorescent paper (others). P 11½.
2455 10 h. Type **694** 10 10
2456 20 h. Crocus scepusiensis 10 10
2457 30 h. Dianthus glacialis 10 10
2458 40 h. Alpine hawkweed (Hieracium alpinum) 15 10
2459 3 k. Delphinium oxysepalum .. .. 25·00 10·00
a. Perf 14 .. .. .. 1·75 80
2455/2459 Set of 5 (cheapest) .. .. 2·00 1·00
The 3 k. was issued in sheets of 10.

(Des I. Strnad (2460), A. Brunovský (2461), J. Schurmann (2462), J. Kaiser (2464), V. Hložník (others). Eng J. Herčík (2460), M. Ondráček (2461), L. Jirka (2464), J. Mráček (2465), J. Schmidt (others). Recess*)

1979 (2 Apr). *Anniversaries. T* **695** *and other horiz designs. Ordinary paper (Nos. 2462 and 2465) or phosphorescent paper (others). P* 11½.

2460	10 h. multicoloured	..	..	10	10
2461	20 h. multicoloured		..	10	10
2462	20 h. dp bl, yel-orge & pale new blue	..		10	10
2463	30 h. deep blue, gold & rose-carmine	..		10	10
2464	30 h. cerise, blue and black	..		10	10
2465	60 h. multicoloured	..	..	20	10
2460/2465	*Set of* 6 ..	..		55	30

Designs and events:—No. 2460, *T* **695** (30th anniv of telecommunications research). 46×19 *mm*—2461, Artist and model (30th anniv of Academy of Fine Arts, Bratislava); 2462, Student and technological equipment (40th anniv of Slovak Technical University, Bratislava); 2463, Musical instruments and Bratislava Castle (50th anniv of Radio Symphony Orchestra, Bratislava); 2464, Pioneer's scarf and IYC emblem (30th anniv of Young Pioneer Organization, and International Year of the Child); 2465, Adult and child with doves (30th anniv of Peace Movement).

(Des and eng J. Švengsbír (3 k.), L. Jirka (3 k. 60). Recess)

1979 (9 May). *Prague Castle* (15th series). *Vert designs as T* **536**. *Multicoloured. P* 11½.

2466	3 k. Burial crown of King Přemysl Otakar II	..	..	2·25	2·25
2467	3 k. 60, Portrait of Miss B. Reitmeyer (Karel Purkyne)	..	..	1·00	1·00

(Des J. Herčík. Eng J. Schmidt (30, 60 h.), J. Mráček (2 k.), J. Herčík (others). Recess*)

1979 (25 May). *Animals in Heraldry. T* **696** *and similar vert designs showing coats of arms from town charters. Multicoloured. P* 11½.

2468	30 h. Type **696**	..		10	10
2469	60 h. Jeseník (bear and eagle)		..	15	10
2470	1 k. 20, Vysoké Mýto (St. George and the dragon)	..		30	10
2471	1 k. 80, Martin (St. Martin on horseback)	..		1·75	50
2472	2 k. Žebrák (half bear, half lion)		..	40	15
2468/2472	*Set of* 5 ..	..	..	2·50	70

697 Healthy and Polluted Forests

698 Numeral and Printed Circuit

(Des J. Liesler. Eng J. Herčík (60 h.), J. Mráček (1 k. 80), M. Ondráček (3 k. 60), J. Schmidt (4 k.). Recess)

1979 (22 June). *Man and the Biosphere. T* **697** *and similar horiz designs. Multicoloured. Phosphorescent paper. P* 11½.

2473	60 h. Type **697**	..	..	15	15
2474	1 k. 80, Clear and polluted water	..		45	35
2475	3 k. 60, Healthy and polluted urban environment	..	..	3·25	1·00
2476	4 k. Healthy and polluted pasture		..	90	40
2473/2476	*Set of* 4 ..	..	..	4·25	1·75

(Des I. Strnad. Photo)

1979 (28 Aug)—**80**. *Coil stamps. T* **698** *and similar horiz designs. Phosphorescent paper. P* 11½.

2477	50 h. carmine-red (31.10.79)	..	..	20	10
2478	1 k. chocolate	..	..	25	10
2478a	2 k. green (15.1.80)	..		50	20
2478b	3 k. brown-purple (15.1.80)	..		80	30
2477/2478b	*Set of* 4 ..	..	..	1·60	60

Designs: Numeral and—50 h. Dish aerial; 2 k. Airplane; 3 k. Punched tape.

699 Industrial Complex   **700** Illustration by János Kass

(Des A. Brunovský. Eng M. Ondráček. Recess*)

1979 (29 Aug.) 35th *Anniv of Slovak Uprising. Phosphorescent paper. P* 11½.

2479	**699** 30 h. multicoloured		..	10	10

(Des V. Kovářík. Eng J. Schmidt (20 h.), M. Ondráček (40 h.), L. Jirka (60 h.), J. Herčík (1 k.), J. Mráček (3 k.). Recess*)

1979 (30 Aug). *International Year of the Child, and Biennial Exhibition of Book Illustrations for Children, Bratislava. T* **700** *and similar horiz designs showing illustrations by artists named. Multicoloured. Phosphorescent paper. P* 11½.

2480	20 h. Type **700**	..	..	10	10
2481	40 h. Rumen Skorčev	..		15	10
2482	60 h. Karel Svolinský	..		15	10
2483	1 k. Otto S. Svend		..	30	10
2484	3 k. Tatyana Mavrina		..	2·10	55
2480/2484	*Set of* 5 ..	..	..	2·50	75

Each issued in sheets of 35 stamps and 15 labels bearing another illustration by the same artist.

701 Modern Bicycles

702 Bracket Clock (Jan Kraus)

(Des K. Lhoták. Eng J. Mráček (3 k. 60), J. Herčík (others). Recess*)

1979 (14 Sept). *Historic Bicycles. T* **701** *and similar horiz designs. Multicoloured. Phosphorescent paper. P* 11½.

2485	20 h. Type **701**	..	..	15	10
2486	40 h. Bicycles, 1910	..		15	10
2487	60 h. "Ordinary" and tricycle, 1886	..		15	10
2488	1 k. "Bone-shakers", 1870	..		50	20
2489	3 k. 60, Drais cycles, 1820	..		2·75	75
2485/2489	*Set of* 5 ..	..	..	3·25	1·00

(Des and eng B. Housa. Recess*)

1979 (1 Oct). *Historic Clocks. T* **702** *and similar vert designs. Multicoloured. P* 11½.

2490	40 h. Type **702**	..	..	10	10
2491	60 h. Rococo clock	..		15	10
2492	80 h. Classicist clock	..		2·00	35
2493	1 k. Rococo porcelain clock (J. Kandler)	..		25	10
2494	k. Urn-shaped clock (Dufaud)	..		55	20
2490/2494	*Set of* 5 ..	..	..	2·75	75

No. 2490 was issued on phosphorescent paper in 1982.

(Des and eng M. Ondráček (1 k. 60, 3 k.), J. Mráček (2 k.),
J. Schmidt (3 k. 60), B. Housa (5 k.). Recess)

1979 (27 Nov). *Art* (13th series). *Vert designs as* T 481. *P* 11½.
2495	1 k. 60, multicoloured	..	45	35
2496	2 k. multicoloured	..	55	45
2497	3 k. multicoloured	..	80	70
2498	3 k. 60, multicoloured	..	4·75	4·75
2499	5 k. black and pale yellow	..	1·25	1·25
2495/2499	*Set of* 5	..	7·00	6·75

Designs:—1 k. 60, "Sunday by the River" (detail, Alois Moravec); 2 k. "Self-portrait" (Gustáv Mallý); 3 k. "Self-portrait" (Ilya Yefimovich Repin); 3 k. 60, "Horseback Rider" (Jan Bauch); 5 k. "Dancing Peasant Couple" (Albrecht Dürer).
Each issued in sheets of four with two blank labels.

(Des and eng M. Ondráček. Recess)

1979 (5 Dec). *Historic Bratislava* (3rd issue). *Horiz designs as* T 669. *Multicoloured.* P 11½.
2500	3 k. "Bratislava, 1787" (L. Janscha)	..	1·00	1·00
2501	3 k. 60, "Bratislava 1815" (after stone engraving by Wolf)	..	2·50	2·50

Each issued in sheets of four stamps and two blank labels.

703 Postmarks, Charles Bridge and Prague Castle

(Des J. Macha. Eng J. Herčík. Recess*)

1979 (18 Dec). *Stamp Day. Phosphorescent paper.* P 11½.
2502	**703** 1 k. multicoloured	..	25	10

704 Skiing   **705** Basketball

(Des I. Strnad. Eng M. Ondráček (3 k.), J. Herčík (others). Recess*)

1980 (29 Jan). *Winter Olympic Games, Lake Placid.* T **704** *and similar vert designs. Phosphorescent paper.* P 11½.
2503	1 k. multicoloured	..	25	10
2504	2 k. bright carmine, pink and indigo	..	1·75	40
2505	3 k. multicoloured	..	70	50

Designs:—2 k. Ice skating; 3 k. Four-man bobsleigh.

(Des I. Strnad. Eng J. Schmidt and M. Ondráček (40 h.), J. Mráček (1 k.), B. Housa (2 k.), M. Ondráček (3 k. 60). Recess*)

1980 (29 Jan). *Olympic Games, Moscow.* T **705** *and similar horiz designs. Multicoloured. Phosphorescent paper.* P 11½.
2506	40 h. Type **705**.	..	15	10
2507	1 k. Swimming	..	25	10
2508	2 k. Hurdling	..	2·25	45
2509	3 k. 60, Fencing	..	75	45
2506/2509	*Set of* 4	..	3·00	90

706 Marathon   **707** Bratislava Opera House and BakovaŽena as King Lear

(Des I. Rumansky. Eng J. Mráček. Recess*)

1980 (29 Jan). *50th International Peace Marathon, Košice. Phosphorescent paper.* P 11½.
2510	**706** 50 h. multicoloured	..	15	10

(Des and eng J. Herčík. Recess*)

1980 (20 Feb). *Arms of Czech Towns* (2nd series). *Vert designs as* T **654**. *Phosphorescent paper.* P 11½.
2511	50 h. greenish blue, black and gold	..	15	10
2512	50 h. black and silver	..	15	10
2513	50 h. multicoloured	..	15	10
2514	50 h. gold, black and dull new blue	..	15	10
2511/2514	*Set of* 4	..	55	30

Designs:—No. 2511, Bystřice nad Pernštejnem; 2512, Kunštát; 2513, Rožmitál pod Třemšínem; 2514, Zlatá Idka.

(Des V. Hložník. Eng J. Herčík. Recess*)

1980 (1 Mar). *60th Anniv of Slovak National Theatre, Bratislava. Phosphorescent paper.* P 11½.
2515	**707** 1 k. deep violet-blue, pale yellow and pale orange	..	20	10

708 Tragic Mask **709** Mouse in Space **710** Police Parade Banner

(Des K. Svolinský. Eng L. Jirka. Recess*)

1980 (1 Mar). *50th Anniv of Theatrical Review* Jiráskův Hronov. *Phosphorescent paper.* P 11½.
2516	**708** 50 h. multicoloured. .	..	15	10

(Des J. Levinovsky (10 k.), J. Fisher (others). Eng J. Mráček (50 h., 1 k.), J. Schmidt (1 k. 60, 4 k.), L. Jirka (5 k.), J. Herčík (10 k.). Recess (1 k. 60, 10 k.) or recess* (others))

1980 (12 Apr). *"Intercosmos" Space Programme.* T **709** *and similar designs. Ordinary paper* (1 k. 60, 10 k.) *or phosphorescent paper* (others). P 11½.
2517	50 h. dull new blue, black & brown-red	..	15	10
2518	1 k. multicoloured	..	30	10
2519	1 k. 60, violet, black & brt scarlet	..	3·25	60
2520	4 k. multicoloured	..	1·00	35
2521	5 k. greenish blue, black and purple	..	1·50	45
2517/2521	*Set of* 5	..	5·75	1·40
MS2522	75 ×94 mm. 10 k. multicoloured	..	5·00	5·00

Designs: *Vert*—1 k. Weather map and satellite; 1 k. 60, "Intersputnik" T.V. transmission; 4 k. Survey satellite and camera. *Horiz*—5 k. Czech-built satellite station; 10 k. "Intercosmos" emblem.
No. 2519 was issued in sheets of 10.
No. **MS**2522 also exists imperforate.

(Des V. Kovářík. Eng B. Housa. Recess*)

1980 (17 Apr). *35th Anniv of National Police Corps. Phosphorescent paper.* P 11½.
2523	**710** 50 h. gold, rosine and greenish blue	15	10

711 Lenin

712 Flag, Flowers and
Prague Buildings

715 *Gerbera jamesonii*

716 "Chod Girl"

(Des M. Hegar. Eng J. Herčík. Recess*)

1980 (22 Apr). 110th *Birth Anniv of Lenin and* 160th *Birth Anniv
of Engels. T* **711** *and similar vert design. Phosphorescent paper.
P* 11½.

| 2524 | 1 k. pale pinkish brown, reddish brown and pale grey-brown | 20 | 10 |
| 2525 | 1 k. deep brown & pale turquoise-green | 20 | 10 |

Design:—No. 2525, Engels.

(Des V. Kovářík. Eng J. Schmidt (2526), M. Ondráček (2527), J.
Herčík (2528/9). Recess*)

1980 (6 May).   *Anniversaries. T* **712** *and similar horiz designs.
Multicoloured. Phosphorescent paper. P* 11½.

2526	50 h. Type **712** (35th anniv of May uprising)	15	10
2527	1 k. Child writing "Mir" (peace) (35th anniv of liberation)	25	10
2528	1 k. Czech and Soviet arms (10th anniv of Czech–Soviet Treaty)	25	10
2529	1 k. Flowers, flags and dove (25th anniv of Warsaw Pact)	25	10
2526/2529	Set of 4	80	30

713 Gymnast

714 U.N. Emblem

(Des I. Schurmann. Eng M. Ondráček (50 h.), J. Herčík (1 k.).
Recess*)

1980 (3 June).   *National Spartakiad. T* **713** *and similar horiz
design. Phosphorescent paper. P* 11½.

| 2530 | 50 h. agate, rosine and greenish blue | 10 | 10 |
| 2531 | 1 k. multicoloured | 25 | 10 |

Design:—50 h. Opening parade of athletes.

(Des J. Liesler. Eng M. Ondráček. Recess)

1980 (3 June). 35th *Anniv of United Nations. Sheet*
109×165 *mm. P* 11½.

| MS2532 | **714** 4 k.×2, multicoloured | 3·75 | 3·75 |

MINIMUM PRICE

The minimum price quoted is 10p which represents a handling charge rather than a basis for valuing common stamps. For further notes about prices see introductory pages.

(Des D. Kallay (50 h., 1 k.), A. Brunovský (2, 4 k.). Eng L. Jirka
(50 h.), M. Ondráček (1 k.), J. Herčík (2 k.), B. Housa (4 k.).
Recess)

1980 (13 Aug). *Olomouc and Bratislava Flower Shows. T* **715** *and
similar vert designs. Multicoloured. Phosphorescent paper
(4 k.) or ordinary paper (others). P* 11½.

2533	50 h. Type **715**	15	15
2534	1 k. *Aechmea fasciata*	2·25	50
2535	2 k. Bird of paradise flower (*Strelitzia reginae*)	40	30
2536	4 k. Slipper orchid (*Paphiopedilum*)	85	60
2533/2536	Set of 4	3·25	1·40

Each issued in sheets of ten.

(Eng B. Housa (50 h., 2 k.), J. Mráček (1 k.), J. Schmidt (4 k.),
L. Jirka (5 k.). Recess*)

1980 (24 Sept).   *Graphic Cut-outs by Cornelia Nemečková.
T* **716** *and similar vert designs. Phosphorescent paper. P* 11½.

2537	50 h. multicoloured	15	10
2538	1 k. reddish purple, orange-brn & carm	25	10
2539	2 k. multicoloured	45	20
2540	4 k. multicoloured	3·50	90
2541	5 k. deep violet-blue, magenta & blue	1·10	50
2537/2541	Set of 5	5·00	1·60

Designs:—1 k. "Punch with his Dog"; 2 k. "Dandy (cat) with
Posy"; 4 k. Lion and Moon ("Evening Contemplation"); 5 k.
Dancer and piper ("Wallachian Dance").

717 Map of Czechoslovakia
and Family

718 Heads

(Des J. Jiskra. Eng B. Housa. Recess*)

1980 (24 Sept).   *National Census. Phosphorescent paper.
P* 11½.

| 2542 | **717** 1 k. multicoloured | 20 | 10 |

(Des and eng J. Švengsbír. Recess)

1980 (28 Oct).   *Prague Castle (16th series). Vert designs as
T* 536. *Multicoloured. P* 11½.

| 2543 | 3 k. Gateway of Old Palace | 2·25 | 2·25 |
| 2544 | 4 k. Armorial lion | 1·40 | 1·40 |

Each issued in sheets of four stamps and two blank labels.

(Des and eng M. Ondráček. Recess)

1980 (28 Oct).   *Historic Bratislava (4th issue). Horiz designs as
T* 669. *Multicoloured. P* 11½.

| 2545 | 3 k. "View across the Danube" (J. Eder) | 2·25 | 2·25 |
| 2546 | 4 k. "Old Royal Bridge" (J. A. Lántz) | 1·40 | 1·40 |

Each issued in sheets of four stamps and two blank labels.

(Des Z. Filip. Eng J. Mráček. Recess*)

1980 (9 Nov).   *Tenth Anniv of Socialist Youth Federation.
Phosphorescent paper. P* 11½.

| 2547 | **718** 50 h. deep ultramarine, orange & red | 15 | 10 |

1980 (18 Nov). *"Essen '80" International Stamp Exhibition. Sheet* 129 × 78 *mm containing No.* 2365 × 2 *optd* "DEN CSSR / 3. / MEZINARODNI VELETRH ZNAMEK / ESSEN '80 / TSCHECHOSLOWAKISCHER TAG" *and* "80 / 3. Internationale / Briefmarken-Messe / ESSEN / 1980" *with Exhibition emblems, in red.*
MS2548 1 k. 60 × 2, multicoloured .. .. 13·00 13·00

(Des and eng M. Ondráček (1, 2 k.), L. Jirka (3, 5 k.), J. Herčík (4 k.). Recess)

1980 (27 Nov). *Art* (14*th series). Designs as T* **481**. *P* 11½.
2549	1 k. buff, indigo and blackish brown ..	1·75	1·75
2550	2 k. multicoloured	2·75	2·75
2551	3 k. maroon, blackish brown and green	60	60
2552	4 k. multicoloured	1·00	1·00
2553	5 k. bottle green, buff and black	1·25	1·25
2549/2553	*Set of* 5	6·50	6·50

Designs: *Vert*—1 k. "Pavel Jozef Šafárik" (Jozef B. Klemens); 2 k. "Peasant Revolt" (mosaic, Anna Podzemná): 3 k. Bust of Saint from Lučivna Church; 5 k. "Labour" (sculpture, Jan Štursa). *Horiz*—4 k. "Waste Heaps" (Jan Zrzavý).
Each issued in sheets of four stamps and two blank labels.

719 Carrier Pigeon

(Des K. Svolinský. Eng L. Jirka. Recess*)

1980 (18 Dec). *Stamp Day. Phosphorescent paper. P* 11½.
2554 **719** 1 k. black, scarlet and cobalt .. 25 10

720 Five Year Plan Emblem   **721** Invalid and Half-bare Tree

(Des J. Kodejš. Eng M. Ondráček. Recess*)

1981 (1 Jan). *Seventh Five Year Plan. Phosphorescent paper. P* 11½.
2555 **720** 50 h. multicoloured .. 15 10

(Des R. Vanek. Eng B. Housa. Recess*)

1981 (24 Feb). *International Year of Disabled Persons. Phosphorescent paper. P* 11½.
2556 **721** 1 k. multicoloured .. 25 10

722 Landau, 1800   **723** Jan Šverma (partisan)

(Des K. Toman. Eng M. Ondráček (50 h., 5 k.), J. Herčík (1, 7 k.), B. Housa (3 k. 60). Recess*)

1981 (25 Feb). *Historic Coaches in Postal Museum. T* **722** *and similar horiz designs. Phosphorescent paper. P* 11½.
2557	50 h. pale greenish yellow, blk & scar	20	10
2558	1 k. pale greenish yellow, black & grn	30	10
2559	3 k. 60, pale green, blk & greenish bl	4·00	75
2560	5 k. stone, black and scarlet	1·25	55

2561	7 k. pale greenish yellow, black and greenish blue	1·75	75
2557/2561	*Set of* 5	7·00	2·00

Designs:—1 k. Mail coach 1830–44; 3 k. 60, Postal sleigh, 1840; 5 k. Mail coach and four horses, 1860; 7 k. Coupe- carriage, 1840.
See also No. **MS**2576.

(Des J. Baláž (2562/5), K. Svolinský (2566/9). Eng J. Herčík (2562, 2564), L. Jirka (2563, 2567, 2569), M. Ondráček (2565/6), B. Housa (2568). Recess*)

1981 (10 Mar). *Celebrities' Birth Anniversaries. T* **723** *and similar vert designs. Multicoloured. Phosphorescent paper. P* 11½.
2562	50 h. Type **723** (80th anniv) ..	20	10
2563	50 h. Mikuláš Schneider-Trnavsky (composer, centenary)	30	10
2564	50 h. Juraj Hronec (mathematician, centenary)	20	10
2565	50 h. Josef Hlávka (architect, 150th)	20	10
2566	1 k. Dmitri Shostakovich (composer, 75th)	50	15
2567	1 k. George Bernard Shaw (dramatist, 125th)	50	15
2568	1 k. Bernardo Bolzano (philosopher, bicentenary)	1·75	40
2569	1 k. Wolfgang Amadeus Mozart (composer, 225th) ..	1·00	30
2562/2569	*Set of* 8	4·25	1·25

724 Yuri Gagarin

(Des J. Baláž. Eng J. Herčík. Recess)

1981 (5 Apr). *20th Anniv of First Manned Space Flight. Sheet* 108 × 165 *mm. P* 11½.
MS2570 **724** 6 k. × 2, multicoloured .. 5·50 5·50

725 Party Member with Flag

(Des J. Adamcová (1 k.), Z. Filip (others). Eng J. Schmidt (50 h.), B. Housa (others). Recess*)

1981 (6 Apr). *60th Anniv of Czechoslovak Communist Party. T* **725** *and similar multicoloured designs. Phosphorescent paper. P* 11½.
2571	50 h. Type **725**	10	15
2572	1 k. Symbols of progress and hands holding flag	25	15
2573	4 k. Party member holding flag bearing symbols of industry (*vert*) ..	75	45

726 Hammer and Sickle

727 Fallow-plough

(Des V. Kovářík. Eng J. Herčík. Recess*)

1981 (6 Apr). *16th Czechoslovak Communist Party Congress. T* **726** *and similar horiz design. Multicoloured. Phosphorescent paper.* P 11½.

2574	50 h. Type **726**	10	10
2575	1 k. "XVI" and Prague buildings	20	10

(Des V. Kovářík. Des J. Herčík. Recess*)

1981 (10 May). *"WIPA 1981" International Stamp Exhibition, Vienna. Sheet 150 ×104 mm. Phosphorescent paper.* P 11½.

MS2576	No. 2561 ×4	23·00	23·00

(Des Z. Kočvar. Eng J. Mráček. Recess*)

1981 (14 May). *90th Anniv of Agricultural Museum. Phosphorescent paper.* P 11½.

2577	**727** 1 k. multicoloured	20	10

ČESKOSLOVENSKO Kčs 10

730 "Guernica"

(Des and eng J. Herčík. Recess)

1981 (2 July). *45th Anniv of International Brigades in Spain and Birth Centenary of Pablo Picasso (artist). Sheet 90 ×76 mm.* P 11½.

MS2584	**730** 10 k. multicoloured	4·50	4·50

731 Puppets

732 Map

(Des C. Nemečková. Eng L. Jirka. Recess*)

1981 (2 July). *30th National Festival of Amateur Puppetry Ensembles, Chrudim. Phosphorescent paper.* P 11½.

2585	**731** 2 k. multicoloured	40	20

(Des M. Strnadel. Eng M. Ondráček (40 h.), L. Jirka (50 h.). J. Mráček (1 k.). Recess*)

1981 (11 July). *National Defence. T* **732** *and similar multicoloured designs. Phosphorescent paper.* P 11½.

2586	40 h. Type **732** (Border Defence)	10	10
2587	50 h. Emblem of Civil Defence Organization (30th Anniv) (vert)	15	10
2588	1 k. Emblem of Svazarm (Organization for Co-operation with Army, 30th anniv) (28 ×23 mm)	20	10

728 Man, Woman and Dove

729 "Uran" (Tatra Mountains) and "Rudý Říjen" (Bohemia)

(Des W. Schlosser. Eng J. Herčík. Recess*)

1981 (1 June). *Elections to Representative Assemblies. Phosphorescent paper.* P 11½.

2578	**728** 50 h. scarlet-verm, stone & greenish bl	15	10

(Des W. Schlosser (2 k.), V. Kovářík (others). Eng J. Schmidt (80 h.), J. Mráček (1 k.), M. Ondráček (2 k.). Recess*)

1981 (10 June). *Achievements of Socialist Construction (1st series). T* **729** *and similar horiz designs. Multicoloured. Phosphorescent paper.* P 11½.

2579	80 h. Type **729** (Trade Union recreational facilities)	25	10
2580	1 k. Prague–Brno–Bratislava express-way	30	15
2581	2 k. Jaslovské Bohunice nuclear plant	50	20

See also Nos. 2644/6, 2695/7, 2753/**MS**2756 and 2800/2.

(Des and eng J. Mráček (3 k.), L. Jirka (4 k.). Recess)

1981 (10 June). *Historic Bratislava (5th issue). Horiz designs as T* **669**. *Multicoloured.* P 11½.

2582	3 k. "Bratislava, 1760" (G. B. Probst)	2·75	2·75
2583	4 k. "Grassalkovichov Palace, 1815" (C. Bschor)	70	70

Each issued in sheets of four stamps and two blank labels.

733 Edelweiss, Climbers and Lenin

734 Illustration by Albín Brunovský

(Des Z. Filip. Eng J. Schmidt. Recess*)

1981 (11 July). *25th International Youth Climb of Rysy Peaks. Phosphorescent paper.* P 11½.

2589	**733** 3 k. 60, multicoloured	80	35

(Des J. Svab. Eng J. Herčík (50 h.), B. Housa (1 k.), L. Jirka (2 k.), M. Ondráček (4 k.), J. Schmidt (10 k.). Recess*)

1981 (5 Sept). *Biennial Exhibition of Book Illustrations for Children, Bratislava. T* **734** *and similar horiz designs showing illustrations by artists named. Multicoloured. Phosphorescent paper.* P 11½.

2590	50 h. Type **734**	15	10
2591	1 k. Adolf Born	30	10
2592	2 k. Vive Tolli	60	30
2593	4 k. Etienne Delessert	90	55
2594	10 k. Suekichi Akaba	4·00	1·60
2590/2594	Set of 5	5·50	2·40

735 Gorilla Family

(Des R. Kolár. Eng L. Jirka (50 h.), B. Housa (1 k.), J. Mráček (7 k.).
Recess*)

1981 (28 Sept). 50th Anniv of Prague Zoo. T **735** and similar horiz
designs. Multicoloured. Phosphorescent paper. P 11½ × 12.
2595   50 h. Type **735**   30   10
2596   1 k. Lion family   35   15
2597   7 k. Przewalski's horses   ..   3·50   1·25

736 Skeletal Hand
removing Cigarette

(Des K. Svolinský. Eng B. Housa. Recess)

1981 (27 Oct). Anti-smoking Campaign. P 12.
2598 **736** 4 k. multicoloured   ..   2·00   80
No. 2598 was issued in sheets of eight stamps and two labels
showing an old man smoking.

(Des and eng J. Švengsbir. Recess)

1981 (28 Oct). Prague Castle (17th series). Vert designs as
T **536**. Multicoloured. P 12.
2599   3 k. Fragment of Pernštejn terracotta
      from Lobkovic Palace (16th cen-
      tury)   70   70
2600   4 k. St. Vitus's Cathedral (19th century
      engraving by J. Šembera and G.
      Döbler)   ..   ..   2·75   2·75
Each issued in sheets of four stamps and two blank labels.

(Des and eng B. Housa (1 k.), L. Jirka (2 k.), M. Ondráček (3, 4 k.),
J. Herčík (5 k.). Recess)

1981 (27 Nov). Art (15th series). Vert designs as T **481**. P 12.
2601   1 k. multicoloured   ..   ..   4·50   4·50
2602   2 k. blackish brown   60   60
2603   3 k. multicoloured   80   80
2604   4 k. multicoloured   ..   ..   1·25   1·25
2605   5 k. multicoloured   ..   ..   1·50   1·50
2601/2605   Set of 5   ..   ..   8·00   8·00
Designs:—1 k. "View of Prague from Petřín Hill" (Václav
Hollar); 2 k. Czech Academy of Arts and Sciences Medallion
(Otakar Španiel); 3 k. South Bohemian embroidery (Zdeněk
Sklenář); 4 k. "Peonies" (A. M. Gerasimov); 5 k. "Figure of a
Woman standing" (Picasso).
Each issued in sheets of four stamps and two blank labels.
In June 1982 No. 2605 was reissued in a sheetlet of four stamps
with centre gutter depicting "Philexfrance 82" and FIP emblems
and the Eiffel Tower.

737 Eduard Karel (engraver)

738 Lenin

(Des C. Bouda. Eng L. Jirka. Recess*)

1981 (18 Dec). Stamp Day. Phosphorescent paper. P 11½ × 12.
2606 **737** 1 k. pale yellow, dull vermilion & ind   20   15

(Des V. Kovářík. Eng J. Mráček. Recess)

1982 (18 Jan). 70th Anniv of Sixth Russian Workers' Party
Congress, Prague. P 12.
2607 **738** 2 k. scarlet-vermilion, gold & dp blue   55   25
MS2608 107 × 83 mm. No 2607 × 4   ..   6·50   6·50

739 Player kicking Ball   740 Hrob

(Des I. Strnad. Eng L. Jirka (1 k.), J. Schmidt (3 k. 60), J. Mráček
(4 k.). Recess*)

1982 (29 Jan). World Cup Football Championship, Spain. T **739**
and similar horiz designs. Multicoloured. Phosphorescent
paper. P 12 × 11½.
2609   1 k. Type **739**   20   15
2610   3 k. 60, Heading ball   70   40
2611   4 k. Saving goal   ..   ..   2·75   65

(Des and eng J. Herčík. Recess*)

1982 (10 Feb). Arms of Czech Towns (3rd series). T **740** and
similar vert designs. Multicoloured. Phosphorescent paper.
P 12 × 11½.
2612   50 h. Type **740**   15   10
2613   50 h. Mladá Boleslav   15   10
2614   50 h. Nové Město nad Metují   ..   15   10
2615   50 h. Trenčín   15   10
2612/2615   Set of 4   55   30
See also Nos. 2720/3, 2765/7, 2819/21 and 3017/20.

741 Conference   742 Workers and Mine
     Emblem

(Des M. Hegar. Eng J Herčík. Recess*)

1982 (10 Feb). Tenth World Federation of Trade Unions
Congress, Havana. Phosphorescent paper. P 11½.
2616 **741** 1 k. multicoloured   25   10

(Des J. Mikula. Eng J. Herčík. Recess*)

1982 (23 Mar). 50th Anniv of Great Strike at Most (coal miners'
and general strike). Phosphorescent paper. P 11½.
2617 **742** 1 k. multicoloured   25   10

743 Locomotives of 1922 and   744 Worker with Flag
     1982

(Des J. Bouda. Eng J. Herčík. Recess*)

1982 (23 Mar). *60th Anniv of International Railway Union. Phosphorescent paper.* P 12 × 11½.
2618. **743** 6 k. multicoloured .. .. .. 1·50 80

(Des Z. Filip. Eng L. Jirka. Recess*)

1982 (15 Apr). *Tenth Trade Unions Congress, Prague. Phosphorescent paper.* P 11½.
2619 **744** 1 k. multicoloured 25 15

745 Georgi Dimitrov

746 Girl with Flowers

(Des J. Baláž. Eng L. Jirka. Recess*)

1982 (1 May). *Birth Centenary of Georgi Dimitrov (Bulgarian statesman). Phosphorescent paper.* P 12 × 11½.
2620 **745** 50 h. multicoloured .. 15 10

(Des J. Kodejš. Eng J. Herčík. Recess)

1982 (18 May). *Tenth International Exhibition of Children's Art, Lidice. Sheet* 165 × 108 mm. P 12.
MS2621 **746** 2 k. × 6, multicoloured .. .. 14·00 14·00

747 "Euterpe" (Crispin de Passe)

748 Girl with Doves

(Des and eng B. Housa. Recess*)

1982 (18 May). *Engravings with a Music Theme.* T **747** *and similar vert designs. Phosphorescent paper.* P 11½ × 12.
2622 40 h. black, gold and brown-ochre .. 15 10
2623 50 h. black, gold and rosine .. 20 10
2624 1 k. black, gold and chestnut .. 30 15
2625 2 k. black, gold and blue .. 50 25
2626 3 k. black, gold and green .. .. 2·25 75
2622/2626 *Set of 5* .. .. .. 3·00 1·25
Designs:—50 h. "The Sanguine Man" (Jacob de Gheyn); 1 k. "The Crossing of the Red Sea" (Adriaen Collaert); 2 k. "Wandering Musicians" (Rembrandt); 3 k. "Beggar with Viol" (Jacques Callot).

(Des K. Svolinský. Eng B. Housa. Recess)

1982 (4 June). *Second Special Session of United Nations General Assembly on Disarmament, New York. Sheet* 165 × 108 mm. P 12.
MS2627 **748** 6 k. × 2 multicoloured .. .. 12·00 12·00

THE WORLD CENTRE FOR FINE STAMPS IS 399 STRAND

749 Child's Head, Rose and Barbed Wire (Lidice)

750 Memorial and Statue of Jan Žižka

(Des I. Schurmann. Eng M. Ondráček. Recess*)

1982 (4 June). *40th Anniv of Destruction of Lidice and Ležáky.* T **749** *and similar vert design. Multicoloured. Phosphorescent paper.* P 11½.
2628 1 k. Type **749** 25 15
2629 1 k. Hands and barbed wire (Ležáky) .. 25 15

(Des R. Vaněk. Eng L. Jirka. Recess*)

1982 (6 July). *50th Anniv of National Memorial, Prague. Phosphorescent paper.* P 12 × 11½.
2630 **750** 1 k. multicoloured 25 15

751 Satellite Orbits around Earth

(Des J. Liesler. Eng J. Herčík. Recess)

1982 (9 Aug). *Second United Nations Conference on Research and Peaceful Uses of Outer Space, Vienna. Sheet* 165 × 108 mm. P 12.
MS2631 **751** 5 k. × 2, multicoloured .. .. 11·00 11·00

752 Křivoklát Castle

(Des and eng J. Herčík. Recess*)

1982 (31 Aug). *Castles.* T **752** *and similar horiz designs. Multicoloured. Phosphorescent paper.* P 12 × 11½.
2632 50 h. Type **752** 20 10
2633 1 k. Interior and sculptures at Křivoklát Castle 35 15
2634 2 k. Nitra Castle 65 30
2635 3 k. Archeological finds from Nitra Castle 1·00 45
2632/2635 *Set of 4* .. .. .. 2·00 85
MS2636 105 × 125 mm. Nos. 2632/5 .. 3·00 3·00

(Des and eng L. Jirka (3 k.), M. Ondráček (4 k.). Recess)

1982 (28 Sept). *Prague Castle (18th series). Vert designs as* T **536**.
2637 3 k. blackish brown and blue-green .. 3·00 1·00
2638 4 k. multicoloured .. .. 1·60 1·25
Designs:—3 k. "St. George" (statue by George and Martin of Kluž, 1373); 4 k. Prince Vratislav I's tomb, St. George's Basilica.

753 Passenger Ferry *Kamzík* in Bratislava Harbour

(Des J. Baláž. Eng L. Jirka. Recess*)

1982 (29 Sept). *Danube Commission. T* **753** *and similar horiz design. Phosphorescent paper. Multicoloured. P* 11½ × 12.

2639	3 k. Type **753**	..	..	1·25	55
2640	3 k. 60, *TR 100* (tug) at Budapest	..	1·50	70

MS2641 Two sheets, each 127×127 mm. (a) No. 2639×4; (b) No. 2640×4 .. .. 20·00 20·00

(Des and eng M. Ondráček. Recess)

1982 (29 Sept). *Historic Bratislava* (6th issue). *Horiz designs as T* **669**. *P* 12.

2642	3 k. black and scarlet	..	..	2·40	75
2643	4 k. multicoloured	..	..	1·10	1·10

Designs:—3 k. "View of Bratislava with Steamer"; 4 k. "View of Bratislava with Bridge".

Each issued in sheets of four stamps and two blank labels.

754 Agriculture   **755** "Scientific Research"

(Des J. Kodejš. Eng J. Herčík (20 h.), M. Ondráček (others). Recess*)

1982 (28 Oct). *Achievements of Socialist Construction* (2nd series). *T* **754** *and similar horiz designs. Multicoloured. Phosphorescent paper. P* 12 × 11½.

2644	20 h. Type **754**	..	..	10	10
2645	1 k. Industry	..	..	35	10
2646	3 k. Science and technology	..	90	40

See also Nos. 2695/7, 2753/**MS**2756 and 2800/2.

(Des D. Kállay. Eng J. Mráček. Recess*)

1982 (29 Oct). *30th Anniv of Academy of Sciences. Phosphorescent paper. P* 11½.

2647	**755** 6 k. multicoloured	..	..	1·50	70

756 Couple with Flowers and Silhouette of Rider   **757** "Jaroslav Hašek" (writer) (Josef Malejovský)

(Des R. Kolář. Eng M. Ondráček. Recess*)

1982 (7 Nov). *65th Anniv of October Revolution and 60th Anniv of U.S.S.R. T* **756** *and similar horiz design. Multicoloured. Phosphorescent paper. P* 12 × 11½.

2648	50 h. Type **756**	..	..	15	10
2649	1 k. Cosmonauts and industrial complex	..	..	30	20

(Des J. Kodejš. Eng J. Herčík (1, 6 k.), M. Ondráček (2, 7 k.), L. Jirka (4 k. 40). Recess*)

1982 (26 Nov). *Sculptures. T* **757** *and similar vert designs. Multicoloured. Phosphorescent paper. P* 11½ × 12.

2650	1 k. Type **757**	..	..	30	10
2651	2 k. "Jan Zrzavý" (patriot) (Jan Simota)	55	20
2652	4 k. 40, "Leoš Janáček" (composer) (Miloš Axman)	..	1·10	50
2653	6 k. "Martin Kukučín" (patriot) (Ján Kulich)	..	..	1·50	70
2654	7 k. "Peaceful Work" (detail, Rudolf Pribiš)	..	..	4·00	1·50
2650/2654	*Set of* 5	..	..	6·75	2·75

(Des and eng M. Ondráček (2 k.), L. Jirka (4 k.), J. Herčík (others). Recess)

1982 (27 Nov). *Art* (16th series). *Vert designs as T* **481**. *Multicoloured. P* 12.

2655	1 k. "Revolution in Spain" (Josef Šíma)	1·60	30
2656	2 k. "Woman drying herself" (Rudolf Kremlička)	..	..	3·00	1·40
2657	3 k. "The Girl Bride" (Dezider Milly)	1·50	1·00
2658	4 k. "Oil Field Workers" (Ján Želibský)	1·50	1·60
2659	5 k. "The Birds' Lament" (Emil Filla)	1·75	1·75
2655/2659	*Set of* 5	..	..	8·50	5·50

Each issued in sheets of four stamps and two blank labels.

758 Jaroslav Goldschmied (engraver) and Engraving Tools   **759** President Husák

(Des and eng B. Housa. Recess*)

1982 (18 Dec). *Stamp Day. Phosphorescent paper. P* 11½ × 12.

2660	**758** 1 k. multicoloured	..	..	30	15

(Des R. Vaněk. Eng L. Jirka. Recess)

1983 (10 Jan). *70th Birthday of President Husák. Phosphorescent paper. P* 12 × 11½.

2661	**759** 50 h. deep blue	..	..	15	10

For 1 k. value see No. 2911.

760 Jaroslav Hašek (writer) (birth centenary)   **761** Armed Workers

(Des K. Svolinský (50 h., 1 k.), A. Brunovský (2, 5 k.). Eng M. Ondráček (50 h.), L. Jirka (1 k.), J. Herčík (others). Recess*)

1983 (24 Feb). *Celebrities' Anniversaries. T* **760** *and similar vert designs. Phosphorescent paper. P* 12 × 11½.

2662	50 h. blackish green, new blue and red	15	10
2663	1 k. purple-brown, new blue and red	30	10
2664	2 k. multicoloured	..	..	50	20
2665	5 k. black, new blue and red	..	1·50	55
2662/2665	*Set of* 4	..	..	2·00	85

Designs:—1 k. Julius Fučík (journalist) (80th birth and 40th

death annivs); 2 k. Martin Luther (church reformist) (500th birth anniv); 5 k. Johannes Brahms (composer) (150th brith anniv).

No. 2664 was also printed in special sheetlets of four stamps and four labels for "Nordposta '83" stamp exhibition, Hamburg (*price for sheetlet £13 un or used*).

(Des J. Chudomel. Eng J. Herčík. Recess*)

1983 (25 Feb). *Anniversaries. T **761** and similar horiz design. Multicoloured. Phosphorescent paper. P 11½.*
2666	50 h. Type **761** (35th anniv of "Victorious February")	15	10
2667	1 k. Family and agricultural and industrial landscapes (35th anniv of National Front)	25	15

762 Radio Waves and Broadcasting Emblem

763 Ski Flyer

(Des R. Vaněk. Eng B. Housa. Recess*)

1983 (16 Mar). *Communications. T **762** and similar horiz designs. Multicoloured. Phosphorescent paper. P 12 × 11½ (2 k.) or 11½ × 12 (others).*
2668	40 h. Type **762** (60th anniv of Czechoslovak broadcasting)	15	10
2669	1 k. Television emblem (30th anniv of Czechoslovak television)	25	10
2670	2 k. W.C.Y. emblem and "1983" (World Communications Year) (40×23 mm)	60	25
2671	3 k. 60, Envelopes, Aero A-10 airplane and mail vans (60th anniv of airmail and 75th anniv of mail transport by motor vehicles) (49×19 mm)	1·40	60
2668/2671	Set of 4	2·10	90

(Des K. Čapek. Eng L. Jirka. Recess*)

1983 (16 Mar). *Seventh World Ski Flying Championships, Harrochov. P 11½.*
2672	**763**	1 k. multicoloured	25	10

764 A. Gubarev and V. Remek

(Des V. Kovářik. Eng M. Ondráček. Recess)

1983 (12 Apr). *Fifth Anniv of Soviet–Czechoslovak Space Flight. Sheet 109×165 mm. P 12.*
MS2673	**764**	10 k.×2, multicoloured	14·00	14·00

HAVE YOU READ THE NOTES AT THE BEGINNING OF THIS CATALOGUE?

These often provide answers to the enquiries we receive.

765 Emperor moth (*Eudia pavonia*) and *Viola sudetica*

766 Ivan Stepanovich Konev

(Des J. Baláž. Eng M. Ondráček (50 h., 7 k.), V. Fajt (1 k., 3 k. 60), L. Jirka (2, 5 k.). Recess*)

1983 (28 Apr). *Nature Protection. T **765** and similar horiz designs. Multicoloured. Phosphorescent paper. P 12 × 11½.*
2674	50 h. Type **765**	25	15
2675	1 k. Water lilies (*Nymphaea candida*) and edible frog (*Rana esculenta*)	50	25
2676	2 k. Red crossbill (*Loxia curvirostra*) and cones	1·75	75
2677	3 k. 60, Grey herons (*Ardea cinerea*)	2·25	85
2678	5 k. *Gentiana asclepiadea* and lynx (*Lynx lynx*)	1·90	70
2679	7 k. Red deer (*Cervus elaphus*)	5·00	2·00
2674/2679	Set of 6	10·50	4·25

(Des D. Kállay. Eng L. Jirka. Recess*)

1983 (5 May). *Soviet Army Commanders. T **766** and similar vert designs. Multicoloured. Phosphorescent paper. P 11½.*
2680	50 h. Type **766**	15	10
2681	1 k. Andrei Ivanovich Yeremenko	25	15
2682	2 k. Rodion Yakovlevich Malinovsky	55	30

767 Dove

768 "Rudolf II" (Adrian de Vries)

(Des V. Kovářik. Eng B. Housa. Recess)

1983 (13 July). *World Peace and Life Congress, Prague. P 11½.*
2683	**767**	2 k. multicoloured	55	55
MS2684	108 × 83 mm. No. 2683×4		6·25	6·25

No. 2683 was issued in sheets of eight stamps.

(Des J. Solpera. Eng M. Ondráček. Recess)

1983 (25 Aug). *Prague Castle (19th series). T **768** and similar vert design. P 12.*
2685	4 k. multicoloured	1·40	90
2686	5 k. dull orange, deep violet-blue & rosine	90	90

Design:—5 k. Kinetic relief with timepiece by Rudolf Svoboda. Each issued in sheets of six stamps.
See also Nos. 2739/40.

769 Mounted Messenger (Oleg K. Zotov)

770 Ilyushin Il-62 and Globe

(Des J. Solpera. Eng V. Fajt (50 h., 4 k.), J. Mráček (1 k.), M. Ondráček (7 k.). Recess*)

1983 (9 Sept). *Ninth Biennial Exhibition of Book Illustration for Children. T* **769** *and similar horiz designs. Phosphorescent paper.* P 12 × 11½.

2687	50 h. multicoloured	15	10
2688	1 k. multicoloured	30	10
2689	4 k. multicoloured	1·10	45
2690	7 k. dull vermilion and black	2·00	90
2687/2690	Set of 4	3·25	1·40
MS2691	115×133 mm. Nos. 2687/90	7·00	5·00

Designs:—1 k. Boy looking from window at birds in tree (Zbigniew Rychlicki); 4 k. "Hansel and Gretel" (Lisbeth Zwerger); 7 k. Three young negroes (António P. Domingues).

(Des. I. Strnad. Eng V. Fajt (50 h.), M. Ondráček (1 k.), J. Mráček (4 k.). Recess*)

1983 (30 Sept). *World Communications Year and 60th Anniv of Czechoslovak Airlines. T* **770** *and similar designs. Phosphorescent paper.* P 11½.

2692	50 h. vermilion, slate-purple & salmon-pk	15	10
2693	1 k. slate-purple, vermilion & salmon-pk	30	10
2694	4 k. slate-purple, vermilion & salmon-pk	2·50	1·25

Designs: *Vert*—1 k. Ilyushin Il-62 and envelope. *Horiz*—4 k. Ilyushin Il-62 and Aero A-14 biplane.

(Des J. Kodejš. Eng M. Ondráček (50 h.) J. Herčík (1 k.), V. Fajt (3 k.). Recess*)

1983 (28 Oct). *Achievements of Socialist Construction (3rd series). Horiz designs as T* **754**. *Multicoloured. Phosphorescent paper.* P 12×11½.

2695	50 h. Surveyor	15	10
2696	1 k. Refinery	30	10
2697	3 k. Hospital and operating theatre	75	45

(Des and eng V. Fajt (3 k.), M. Ondráček (4 k.). Recess*)

1983 (28 Oct). *Historic Bratislava (7th series). Horiz designs as T* **669**. P 12.

2698	3 k. dp grey-green, brownish blk & verm	2·00	70
2699	4 k. multicoloured	1·75	70

Designs:—3 k. Sculptures by Viktor Tilgner; 4 k. "Mirbachov Palace" (Julius Schubert).

Each issued in sheets of four stamps and two blank labels.

771 National Theatre, Prague

772 "Soldier with Sword and Shield" (Hendrik Goltzius)

(Des M. Knobloch. Eng L. Jirka. Recess)

1983 (18 Nov). *Czechoslovak Theatre Year. T* **771** *and similar vert design. Phosphorescent paper.* P 11½.

2700	50 h. reddish brown	15	10
2701	2 k. bottle green	60	20

Design:—2 k. National Theatre and Tyl Theatre, Prague.

(Des J. Solpera. Eng M. Ondráček (3, 4 k.), L. Jirka (5 k.), J. Herčík (others). Recess)

1983 (18 Nov). *Art (17th series). Vert designs as T* **481** *showing works from the National Theatre, Prague.* P 12.

2702	1 k. multicoloured	1·75	1·75
2703	2 k. multicoloured	4·00	2·25
2704	3 k. blackish brown, pale stone & slate-bl	1·10	1·10
2705	4 k. multicoloured	1·40	1·75
2706	5 k. multicoloured	1·50	2·50
2702/2706	Set of 5	9·00	8·50

Designs:—1 k. "Žalov" (lunette detail, Mikoláš Aleš); 2 k. "Genius" (stage curtain detail, Vojtěch Hynais); 3 k. "Music" and

"Lyrics" (ceiling drawings, František Ženíšek); 4 k. "Prague" (detail from President's box, Václav Brožík); 5 k. "Hradcany Castle" (detail from President's box, Julius Mařák).

Each issued in sheets of four stamps and one double stamp-size label bearing various motifs.

(Des and eng B. Housa. Recess*)

1983 (2 Dec). *Period Costumes from Old Engravings. T* **772** *and similar vert designs. Multicoloured. Phosphorescent paper.* P 11½×12.

2707	40 h. Type **772**	15	10
2708	50 h. "Warrior with Sword and Lance" (Jacob de Gheyn)	15	10
2709	1 k. "Lady with Muff" (Jacques Callot)	30	10
2710	4 k. "Lady with Flower" (Vaclav Hollar)	1·10	40
2711	5 k. "Gentleman with Cane" (Antoine Watteau)	3·50	80
2707/2711	Set of 5	4·75	1·25

773 Karel Seizinger (stamp engraver)

(Des C. Bouda. Eng M. Ondráček. Recess*)

1983 (18 Dec). *Stamp Day. Phosphorescent paper.* P 11½×12.

2712	**773** 1 k. multicoloured	25	15

774 National Flag with Bratislava and Prague Castles

775 Council Emblem

(Des J. Hamza. Eng V. Fajt. Recess*)

1984 (1 Jan). *15th Anniv of Czechoslovak Federation. Phosphorescent paper.* P 11½.

2713	**774** 50 h. multicoloured	20	10

(Des J. Hamza. Eng J. Herčík. Recess*)

1984 (23 Jan). *35th Anniv of Council for Mutual Economic Aid. Phosphorescent paper.* P 11½.

2714	**775** 1 k. multicoloured	20	10

776 Cross-country Skiing

(Des Anna Podzemná. Eng V. Fajt. Recess*)

1984 (7 Feb). *Winter Olympic Games, Sarajevo. T* **776** *and similar horiz designs. Multicoloured. Phosphorescent paper.* P 12×11½.

2715	2 k. Type **776**	45	25
2716	3 k. Ice hockey	65	35
2717	5 k. Biathlon	1·40	60
MS2718	110×99 mm. No. 2716×4	5·50	5·50

777 Olympic Flag, Ancient Greek Athletes and Olympic Flame

778 "Soyuz" and Dish Aerials

781 Telecommunications Building

782 Dove, Globes and U.P.U. Emblem

(Des V. Kovařík. Eng J. Herčík. Recess*)

1984 (7 Feb). *90th Anniv of International Olympic Committee. Phosphorescent paper. P 11½ × 12.*

2719	**777**	7 k. multicoloured	..	1·60	60

(Des and eng J. Herčík. Recess*)

1984 (1 Mar). *Arms of Czech Towns (4th series). Vert designs as T **740**. Multicoloured. Phosphorescent paper. P 12 × 11½.*

2720	50 h. Turnov	..	..	20	10
2721	50 h. Kutná Hora	..	..	20	10
2722	1 k. Milevsko ..	..	..	30	10
2723	1 k. Martin	..	..	30	10
2720/2723	Set of 4	..	..	90	30

(Des J. Liesler. Eng V. Fajt (50 h., 1 k.), M. Ondráček (2, 4 k.), J. Herčík (5 k.). Recess*)

1984 (12 Apr). *"Interkosmos" International Space Flights. T **778** and similar vert designs. Multicoloured. Phosphorescent paper. P 11½ × 12.*

2724	50 h. Type **778**	..	20	10
2725	1 k. "Salyut"–"Soyuz" complex	..	35	15
2726	2 k. Cross-section of orbital station	..	50	25
2727	4 k. "Salyut" taking pictures of Earth's surface	..	1·00	60
2728	5 k. "Soyuz" returning to Earth	..	1·25	70
2724/2728	Set of 5	..	3·00	1·60

Nos. 2724/8 were each printed with a *se-tenant* stamp-sized label showing the "Interkosmos" emblem and flags of participating countries.

(Des J. Baláž. Eng V. Fajt. Recess*)

1984 (1 June). *Central Telecommunications Building, Bratislava. Phosphorescent paper. P 11½.*

2735	**781**	2 k. multicoloured	..	60	25

(Des and eng M. Ondráček. Recess)

1984 (1 June). *Historic Bratislava (8th series). Horiz designs as T **669**. Multicoloured. P 12 × 11½.*

2736	3 k. Arms of Vintners' Guild	1·50	80
2737	4 k. Painting of 1827 Shooting Festival	1·50	80

Each issued in sheets of four stamps and one double stamp-size blank label.

(Des J. Baláž. Eng M. Ondráček. Recess)

1984 (12 June). *110th Anniv of Universal Postal Union. Sheet 165 × 108 mm. P 12.*

MS2738	**782**	5 k. × 4, multicoloured	12·00	12·00

No. **MS**2738 was also issued with an additional inscription in blue commemorating the 19th U.P.U. Congress, Hamburg.

(Des. J. Solpera. Eng V. Fajt (3 k.), M. Ondráček (4 k.). Recess)

1984 (9 Aug). *Prague Castle (20th series). Vert designs as T **768**. Multicoloured. P 12.*

2739	3 k. Weather cock, St. Vitus's Cathedral	80	80
2740	4 k. King David playing psaltery (initial from Roudnice Book of Psalms) ..	1·25	1·25

Each issued in sheets of six stamps with decorative gutter.

779 Vendelín Opatrný

780 Musical Instruments

783 Jack of Spades (16th century)

784 Family and Industrial Complex

(Des D. Kállay. Eng L. Jirka (1 k.), V. Fajt (4 k.), J. Herčík (others). Recess*)

1984 (9 May). *Anti-fascist Heroes. T **779** and similar vert designs. Phosphorescent paper. P 11½.*

2729	50 h. black, rosine and new blue	..	20	10
2730	1 k. black, rosine and new blue	..	30	15
2731	2 k. black, rosine and new blue	..	55	25
2732	4 k. black, rosine and new blue	..	1·10	40
2729/2732	Set of 4	..	2·00	80

Designs:—1 k. Ladislav Novomeský; 2 k. Rudolf Jasiok; 4 k. Ján Nálepka.

(Des R. Vaněk. Eng V. Fajt (50 h.), L. Jirka (1 k.). Recess*)

1984 (11 May). *Music Year. T **780** and similar vert design. Phosphorescent paper. P 11½.*

2733	50 h. sepia, gold and blackish brown	..	20	10
2734	1 k. multicoloured	..	30	15

Design:—1 k. Organ pipes.

(Des and eng B. Housa. Recess*)

1984 (28 Aug). *Playing Cards. T **783** and similar vert designs. Multicoloured. Phosphorescent paper. P 11½ × 12.*

2741	50 h. Type **783**	..	25	10
2742	1 k. Queen of Spades (17th century)	..	40	10
2743	2 k. Nine of Hearts (18th century)	..	60	30
2744	3 k. Jack of Clubs (18th century)	..	1·00	50
2745	4 k. King of Hearts (19th century)	..	1·60	80
2741/2745	Set of 5	..	3·50	1·60

(Des J. Baláž. Eng M. Ondráček. Recess*)

1984 (29 Aug). *40th Anniv of Slovak Uprising. Phosphorescent paper. P 12 × 11½.*

2746	**784**	50 h. multicoloured	..	20	10

785 Soldiers with Banner

(Des I. Schurmann. Eng V. Fajt. Recess*)

1984 (8 Sept). *40th Anniv of Battle of Dukla Pass.*
Phosphorescent paper. P 11½ × 12.
2747 **785** 2 k. multicoloured 45 20

786 High Jumping

(Des R. Kolář. Eng M. Ondráček (1, 5 k.), V. Fajt (others). Recess*)

1984 (9 Sept). *Olympic Games, Los Angeles. T* **786** *and similar*
horiz designs. Multicoloured. Phosphorescent paper.
P 12 × 11½.
2748 1 k. Type **786** 30 15
2749 2 k. Cycling 60 30
2750 3 k. Rowing 80 60
2751 5 k. Weightlifting .. .. .. 1·50 75
2748/2751 *Set of* 4 .. .. .. 3·00 1·60
MS2752 107×95 mm. Nos. 2748/51 .. 3·75 3·75

(Des J. Kodejš. Eng V. Fajt (3 k.), M. Ondráček (others). Recess*)

1984 (28 Oct). *Achievements of Socialist Construction (4th*
series). Horiz designs as T **754**. *Multicoloured. Phosphorescent*
paper. P 12 × 11½.
2753 1 k. Telephone handset and letters
(Communications) 30 10
2754 2 k. Containers on railway trucks, and
barge (Transport) 60 30
2755 3 k. Map of Transgas pipeline .. 80 45
MS2756 157×105 mm. No. 2755×3 .. 3·75 3·00

(Eng J. Herčík (1 k.), M. Ondráček (2 k.), V. Fajt (3 k.), J. Mráček
(4 k.), L. Jirka (5 k.). Recess)

1984 (16 Nov). *Art (18th series). Horiz designs as T* **481**.
Multicoloured. P 12.
2757 1 k. "Milevský River" (Karel Stehlik) 1·50 70
2758 2 k. "Under the Trees" (Viktor Barvitius) 1·50 70
2759 3 k. "Landscape with Flowers" (Zolo
Palugyay) .. .. .. 1·50 70
2760 4 k. Illustration of king from Vyšehrad
Codex .. .. .. 1·50 70
2761 5 k. "Kokořín" (Antonín Mánes) .. 1·50 70
2757/2761 *Set of* 5 .. .. .. 6·75 3·25
Each issued in sheets of four stamps and two blank labels.

787 Dove and Head   **788** Zápotocký
of Girl

(Des I. Rumanský. Eng V. Fajt. Recess*)

1984 (17 Nov). *45th Anniv of International Students' Day.*
Phosphorescent paper. P 11½.
2762 **787** 1 k. multicoloured 20 15

(Des A. Brunovsky. Eng M. Ondráček. Recess*)

1984 (18 Dec). *Birth Centenary of Antonín Zápotocky*
(politician). Phosphorescent paper. P 11½.
2763 **788** 50 h. multicoloured 20 10

789 Bohumil Heinz (engraver) and   **790** "Art and
Hands engraving   Pleasure" (Jan
                                          Simota)

(Des and eng B. Housa. Recess*)

1984 (18 Dec). *Stamp Day. Phosphorescent paper. P 11½ × 12.*
2764 **789** 1 k. multicoloured 20 15

(Des and eng J. Herčík. Recess*)

1985 (5 Feb). *Arms of Czech Towns (5th series). Vert designs as*
T **740**. *Multicoloured. Phosphorescent paper. P 12 × 11½.*
2765 50 h. Kamýk nad Vltavou 20 10
2766 50 h. Havířov 20 10
2767 50 h. Trnava 20 10

(Des M. Hegar. Eng J. Herčík. Recess*)

1985 (6 Feb). *Centenary of Prague University of Applied Arts.*
Phosphorescent paper. P 11½ × 12.
2768 **790** 3 k. multicoloured 65 35

791 View of Trnava   **792** Helmet, Mail
                                 Shirt and Crossbow

(Des O. Lupták. Eng V. Fajt. Recess*)

1985 (6 Feb). *350th Anniv of Trnava University. Phosphorescent*
paper. P 11½ × 12.
2769 **791** 2 k. multicoloured 35 25

(Des V. Kovářík. Eng J. Herčík (1 k.), J. Mráček (others). Recess*)

1985 (7 Feb). *Exhibits from Military Museum. T* **792** *and similar*
multicoloured designs. Phosphorescent paper. P 12 × 11½ (2 k.)
or 11½ × 12 (others).
2770 50 h. Type **792** 15 10
2771 1 k. Cross and star of Za vítězství order 30 15
2772 2 k. Avia B-534 airplane and "Soyuz 28"
(horiz) .. .. .. 1·00 45

ALBUM LISTS

Write for our latest lists of albums
and accessories.
These will be sent free on request.

793 Lenin reading

794 U.N. Emblem and Stylized Dove

(Des A. Fuchs. Eng J. Herčík. Recess)

1985 (14 Mar). *115th Birth Anniv of Lenin. P 12.*
MS2773 **793** 2 k. × 6, multicoloured .. .. 5·00 2·75

(Des R. Vaněk. Eng M. Ondráček. Recess)

1985 (15 Mar). *40th Anniv of United Nations Organization and International Peace Year (1986). P 12.*
MS2774 **794** 6 k. × 4, multicoloured .. .. 12·00 12·00

795 State Arms and Crowd

796 State Arms and Soldiers with National Flag

(Des I. Shurmann. Eng J. Herčík. Recess*)

1985 (5 Apr). *40th Anniv of Košice Reforms. Phosphorescent paper. P 11½.*
2775 **795** 4 k. multicoloured 70 35

(Des V. Kovařík. Eng J. Mráček. Recess*)

1985 (5 Apr). *40th Anniv of National Security Forces. Phosphorescent paper. P 11½.*
2776 **796** 50 h. multicoloured 20 10

797 Automatic Optical Platform and Comet Trajectory

(Des R. Vaněk. Eng M. Ondráček. Recess*)

1985 (12 Apr). *Space Project "Vega" (research into Venus and Halley's Comet). Sheet 106×96 mm. Phosphorescent paper. P 12×11½.*
MS2777 **797** 5 k. × 2, multicoloured .. .. 8·00 8·00

798 Emblem and Ice Hockey Players

799 Pieces on Chessboard

(Des P. Mišek. Eng V. Fajt. Recess*)

1985 (13 Apr). *World and European Ice Hockey Championships, Prague. P 12×11½.*
2778 **798** 1 k. multicoloured 25 15

(Des Anna Podzemná. Eng V. Fajt. Recess*)

1985 (13 Apr). *80th Anniv of Czechoslovak Chess Organization. Phosphorescent paper. P 11½.*
2779 **799** 6 k. multicoloured .. .. 2·40 80

800 Freedom Fighters and Prague

(Des Z. Filip. Eng J. Mráček (2780/1), V. Fajt (2782/3). Recess*)

1985 (5 May). *Anniversaries. T 800 and similar horiz designs. Multicoloured. Phosphorescent paper. P 11½×12.*
2780 1 k. Type **800** (40th anniv of May uprising) 30 15
2781 1 k. Workers shaking hands, flag and industrial motifs (15th anniv of Czechoslovak–Soviet Treaty) 30 15
2782 1 k. Girl giving flowers to soldier, Prague Castle and tank (40th anniv of liberation) 30 15
2783 1 k. Soldiers and industrial motifs (30th anniv of Warsaw Pact) 30 15
2780/2783 Set of 4 .. .. .. 1·00 45

(801)

802 Tennis

1985 (31 May). *Czechoslovak Victory in Ice Hockey Championships. No. 2778 optd with T 801 in ultramarine.*
2784 **798** 1 k. multicoloured .. .. 5·50 5·50

(Des Z. Filip. Eng V. Fajt. Recess*)

1985 (3 June). *National Spartakiad. T 802 and similar horiz design. Multicoloured. Phosphorescent paper. P 11½ (50 h.) or 11½×12 (1 k.).*
2785 50 h. Type **802** 20 10
2786 1 k. Gymnasts performing with ribbons (48×19 mm) 30 15

803 Study for "Fire" and "Republic" (Josef Čapek)

(Des Z. Kočvar. Eng L. Jirka. Recess*)

1985 (4 June). *Anti-fascist Artists. T 803 and similar horiz designs. Multicoloured. Phosphorescent paper. P 12×11½.*
2787 50 h. Type **803** 15 10
2788 2 k. "Geneva Conference on Disarmament" and "Prophecy of Three Parrots" (František Bidlo) 45 25
2789 4 k. "Unknown Conscript" and "The almost peaceful Dove" (Antonín Pelc) 65 40

804 Girl holding Dove and
Olive Branch

(Des A. Fuchs. Eng M. Ondráček. Recess*)

1985 (1 July). *Tenth Anniv of European Security and Co-operation Conference, Helsinki. Sheet 107×135 mm. Phosphorescent paper. P 12 × 11½.*
MS2790 **804** 7 k. × 4, multicoloured .. 11·00 11·00
Similar imperforate sheets with "Finlandia 88" and "Praga '88" stamp exhibition emblems, showing a number at foot instead of the Helsinki Conference commemorative inscription, were included in the exhibition catalogues.

805 Moscow Buildings and Young People holding Doves   **806** Figures on Globe

(Des A. Fuchs. Eng J. Mráček. Recess*)

1985 (2 July). *12th World Youth and Students' Festival, Moscow. Phosphorescent paper. P 12 × 11½.*
2791 **805** 1 k. multicoloured .. 25 15

(Des V. Hájek. Eng L. Jirka. Recess*)

1985 (3 Sept). *40th Anniv of World Federation of Trade Unions. Phosphorescent paper. P 11½.*
2792 **806** 50 h. multicoloured .. 10 10

(Des and eng M. Ondráček. Recess)

1985 (4 Sept). *Historic Bratislava (9th series). Horiz designs as T 669. P 12.*
2793 3 k. brown-ochre, bronze green & lake-brn 70 70
2794 4 k. black, green and brown-red .. 1·00 1·00
Designs:—3 k. Tapestry (Elena Holéczyová); 4 k. Pottery.
Each issued in sheets of four stamps and two blank labels.

807 Rocking Horse (Květa Pacovská)   **808** Gateway to First Courtyard

(Des Z. Kočvar. Eng J. Herčík (1 k.), M. Ondráček (4 k.), L. Jirka (others). Recess*)

1985 (5 Sept). *Tenth Biennial Exhibition of Book Illustrations for Children, Bratislava. T 807 and similar vert designs. Phosphorescent paper. P 11½.*
2795 1 k. Type **807** 20 10
2796 2 k. Elves (Gennady Spirin) 35 15

2797 3 k. Girl, butterfly and flowers (Kaarina Kaila) .. 60 40
2798 4 k. Boy shaking hands with hedgehog (Erick Ingraham) 70 45
2795/2798 *Set of 4* .. .. .. 1·75 1·00
MS2799 95×128 mm. Nos. 2795/8 .. 5·50 5·50

(Des J. Kodejš. Eng J. Herčík (2 k.), V. Fajt (others). Recess*)

1985 (28 Oct). *Achievements of Socialist Construction (5th series). Horiz designs as T 754. Multicoloured. Phosphorescent paper. P 12×11½.*
2800 50 h. Mechanical excavator .. 10 10
2801 1 k. Train and map of Prague underground railway 40 20
2802 2 k. Modern textile spinning equipment 45 30

(Des and eng J. Herčík. Recess)

1985 (28 Oct). *Prague Castle (21st series). T 808 and similar vert design. P 12.*
2803 2 k. black, light blue and brown-red .. 50 50
2804 3 k. multicoloured 80 60
Design:—3 k. East side of castle
Each issued in sheets of six stamps with gutter showing engraving of the whole castle.

809 Jug (4th century)   **810** Bohdan Roule (engraver) and Engraving Plate

(Des and eng B. Housa. Recess*)

1985 (23 Nov). *Centenary of Prague Arts and Crafts Museum. Glassware. T 809 and similar vert designs. Multicoloured. Phosphorescent paper. P 11½×12.*
2805 50 h. Type **809** 10 10
2806 1 k. Venetian glass container (16th century) 20 10
2807 2 k. Bohemian glass with hunting scene (18th century) 40 25
2808 4 k. Bohemian vase (18th century) .. 75 40
2809 6 k. Bohemian vase (c. 1900) .. 1·40 75
2805/2809 *Set of 5* .. .. 2·50 1·40

(Eng J. Mráček (1 k.), M. Ondráček (2, 5 k.), V. Fajt (3, 4 k.). Recess)

1985 (25 Nov). *Art (19th series). Vert designs as T 481. Multicoloured. P 12.*
2810 1 k. "Young Woman in Blue Dress" (Jozef Ginovský) .. .. 1·75 90
2811 2 k. "Lenin on Charles Bridge" (Martin Sladký) .. .. 1·75 90
2812 3 k. "Avenue of Poplars" (Václav Rabas) .. 1·75 90
2813 4 k. "Beheading of St. Dorothea" (Hans Baldung Grien) .. 1·75 90
2814 5 k. "Jasper Schade van Westrum" (Frans Hals) .. .. 1·75 90
2810/2814 *Set of 5* .. .. 8·00 4·00
Each issued in sheets of four stamps and two blank labels.

(Des K. Vodák. Eng L. Jirka. Recess*)

1985 (18 Dec). *Stamp Day. Phosphorescent paper. P 11½×12.*
2815 **810** 1 k. multicoloured 30 15

811 Peace Dove with Olive Twig

(Des K. Svolinský. Eng V. Fajt. Recess*)

1986 (2 Jan). *International Peace Year. Phosphorescent paper.*
P 11½×12.
2816 **811** 1 k. multicoloured 25 15

812 Victory
Statue, Prague

813 Zlin Z-50LS Airplane,
Locomotive *Kladno* and
Rock Drawing of Chariot

(Des R. Vaněk. Eng L. Jirka. Recess*)

1986 (2 Jan). *90th Anniv of Czech Philharmonic Orchestra.
Phosphorescent paper.* P 11½.
2817 **812** 1 k. black, brown-ochre and blue-violet .25 15

(Des J. Fišer. Eng J. Herčík. Recess*)

1986 (23 Jan). *"Expo '86" International Transport and
Communications Exhibition, Vancouver. Phosphorescent paper.*
P 11½.
2818 **813** 4 k. multicoloured .. .. .. 1·25 35

(Des and eng J. Herčík. Recess*)

1986 (10 Feb). *Arms of Czech Towns (6th series). Vert designs
as T 740. Multicoloured. Phosphorescent paper.* P 12×11½.
2819 50 h. Vodňany 15 10
2820 50 h. Žamberk 15 10
2821 50 h. Myjava 15 10

814 Banner,
Industry and
Hammer and
Sickle

815 Couple, Banner and Star

(Des I. Schurmann. Eng J. Herčík. Recess*)

1986 (20 Mar). *17th Communist Party Congress, Prague. T 814
and similar vert design. Multicoloured. Phosphorescent paper.*
P 11½.
2822 50 h. Type **814** 10 10
2823 1 k. Buildings, hammer and sickle and
star 20 10
Nos. 2823 and 2825 with gold overprint "SOCFILEX '86 CSSR"
were only available cancelled and stuck to a souvenir card which
was inserted in the exhibition catalogue.

(Des I. Schurmann. Eng M. Ondráček. Recess*)

1986 (20 Mar). *65th Anniv of Czechoslovakian Communist Party.
T 815 and similar horiz design. Multicoloured. Phosphorescent
paper.* P 12×11½.
2824 50 h. Type **815** 10 10
2825 1 k. Workers, banner and hammer and
sickle 20 10
See note below No. 2823.

816 Map and Stylised Man

817 Emblem and
Crest on Film

(Des J. Hamza. Eng B. Housa. Recess*)

1986 (28 Mar). *National Front Election Programme. Phosphorescent paper.* P 12×11½.
2826 **816** 50 h. multicoloured 10 10

(Des Z. Kočvar. Eng M. Ondráček. Recess*)

1986 (3 Apr). *25th International Film Festival, Karlovy Vary.
Phosphorescent paper.* P 11½.
2827 **817** 1 k. multicoloured 25 10

818 Musical
Instruments

819 Ilyushin Il-86 and
Airspeed Envoy II

(Des J. Liesler. Eng J. Herčík. Recess*)

1986 (8 Apr). *40th Anniv of Prague Spring Music Festival.
Phosphorescent paper.* P 11½.
2828 **818** 1 k. multicoloured 25 10

(Des R. Vaněk. Eng M. Ondráček. Recess*)

1986 (25 Apr). *50th Anniv of Prague–Moscow Air Service.
Phosphorescent paper.* P 11½.
2829 **819** 50 h. multicoloured 25 10

820 Sports Pictograms

(Des V. Kovářík. Eng M. Ondráček. Recess*)

1986 (12 May). *90th Anniv of Czechoslovak Olympic
Committee. Phosphorescent paper.* P 11½×12.
2830 **820** 2 k. multicoloured 40 20

THE WORLD CENTRE FOR
FINE STAMPS IS 399 STRAND

821 Map and Goalkeeper

(Des P. Míšek. Eng L. Jirka. Recess*)

1986 (15 May). *World Cup Football Championship, Mexico. Phosphorescent paper. P 12×11½.*
2831 **821** 4 k. multicoloured 75 45

822 Globe, Net and Ball   **823** Emblems

(Des P. Míšek. Eng M. Činovský. Recess*)

1986 (19 May). *Women's World Volleyball Championship, Prague. Phosphorescent paper. P 12×11½.*
2832 **822** 1 k. multicoloured 30 15

(Des V. Kovářík. Eng J. Herčík. Recess)

1986 (3 June). *"Praga '88" Stamp Exhibition, Prague (1st issue) and 60th Anniv of International Philatelic Federation. Sheet 110×82 mm containing T **823** and two labels. P 12.*
MS2833 **823** 20 k. multicoloured .. .. 7·50 7·50
  No. **MS**2833 also exists completely imperf or imperf between stamp and labels from limited printings.
  See also Nos. 2880/4, 2900, **MS**2903, 2923/**MS**2927, 2929/**MS**2933, 2934/**MS**2938, 2940/**MS**2944, **MS**2945, **MS**2946, **MS**2947, **MS**2948 and **MS**2949.

824 Funeral   **825** Wooden
Pendant   Cock, Slovakia

(Des J. Solpera. Eng V. Fajt (2 k.), M. Ondráček (3 k.). Recess)

1986 (6 June). *Prague Castle (22nd series). T **824** and similar vert design. P 12.*
2834   2 k. multicoloured 55 45
2835   3 k. dull orange, blackish brown & ultram 65 55
  Design:—3 k. "Allegory of Blossoms" (sculpture, Jaroslav Horejc).
  Each issued in sheets of six stamps with decorative gutter.

(Des and eng B. Housa. Recess*)

1986 (1 Sept). *40th Anniv of United Nations Children's Fund. Toys. T **825** and similar vert designs. Multicoloured. Phosphorescent paper. P 11½.*
2836 10 h. Type **825** 10 10
2837 20 h. Wooden soldier on hobby horse, Bohemia 10 10
2838   1 k. Rag doll, Slovakia 15 10
2839   2 k. Doll 40 15
2840   3 k. Mechanical bus 55 20
2836/2840 *Set of 5* .. .. .. 1·10 50

826 Registration Label and
Mail Coach

(Des O. Pośmurný. Eng M. Ondráček. Recess*)

1986 (2 Sept). *Centenary of Registration Label. Phosphorescent paper. P 11½×12.*
2841 **826** 4 k. multicoloured 65 35

(Des I. Schurmann. Eng M. Ondráček. Recess)

1986 (11 Sept). *Historic Bratislava (10th series). Horiz designs as T **669**. P 12.*
2842   3 k. brownish black, brown-red & slate-bl 50 50
2843   4 k. black, brown-red and green 65 65
  Designs:—3 k. Sigismund Gate, Bratislava Castle; 4 k. "St. Margaret with Lamb" (relief from castle).
  Each issued in sheets of four stamps.

827 Eagle Owl
(*Bubo bubo*)

(Des Hana Čápová and Z. Kočvar. Eng J. Herčík (50 h., 5 k.), M. Ondráček (2, 3 k.), V. Fajt (4 k.). Recess*)

1986 (18 Sept). *Owls. T **827** and similar horiz designs. Multicoloured. Phosphorescent paper. P 11½.*
2844 50 h. Type **827** 25 10
2845   2 k. Long-eared owl (*Asio otus*) .. 60 30
2846   3 k. Tawny owl (*Strix aluco*) .. 90 40
2847   4 k. Barn owl (*Tyto alba*) .. 1·10 50
2848   5 k. Short-eared owl (*Asio flammeus*) 2·10 60
2844/2848 *Set of 5* .. .. .. 4·50 1·75

828 Curtain of D 37 Theatre
(Vladimír Sychra)

(Des J. Solpera. Eng V. Fajt. Recess)

1986 (1 Oct). *50th Anniv of Formation of International Brigades in Spain. Sheet 165×108 mm. P 12.*
MS2849 **828** 5 k. ×2, multicoloured .. .. 5·50 5·50

829 Type "Kt 8" Articulated
Tram and 1920s' Prague Tram

(Des and eng J. Bouda. Recess*)

1986 (6 Oct). *Rail Vehicles. T* **829** *and similar horiz designs. Multicoloured. Phosphorescent paper. P* 12×11½.
2850	50 h. Type **829** ..			15	10
2851	1 k. Series "E 458.1" electric shunting engine and 1882–1913 steam locomotive			25	15
2852	3 k. Series "T 466.2" diesel and 1900–24 steam locomotives			70	40
2853	5 k. Series "M 152.0" railcar and 1930–35 railbus			1·50	1·00
2850/2853	*Set of 4* ..			2·25	1·00

830 "The Circus Rider"
(Jan Bauch)

(Des O. Pošmurný. Eng M. Ondráček (1, 3 k.), V. Fajt (2, 6 k.). Recess)

1986 (13 Oct). *Circus and Variety Acts on Paintings. T* **830** *and similar vert designs. Multicoloured. P 12.*
2854	1 k. Type **830** ..			35	35
2855	2 k. "The Ventriloquist" (František Tichý)			70	70
2856	3 k. "In the Circus" (Vincent Hložník)	..		80	80
2857	6 k. "Clown" (Karel Svolinský)	..		1·90	1·90
2854/2857	*Set of 4* ..			3·50	3·50

Each issued in sheets of four stamps.

(Eng B. Housa (1 k.), V. Fajt (2 k.), M. Ondráček (3, 4 k.), J. Herčík (5 k.). Recess)

1986 (3 Nov). *Art* (20th series). *Vert designs as T* **481**. *Multicoloured. P 12.*
2858	1 k. "The Czech Lion, May 1918" (Vratislav H. Brunner) (cross-hatched background)			40	40
	a. Background of diagonal lines	..		3·25	3·25
2859	2 k. "Boy with Mandolin" (Jozef Šturdík)			70	70
2860	3 k. "The Metra Building" (František Gross)			80	80
2861	4 k. "Maria Maximiliana of Sternberk" (Karel Škréta)	..		1·10	1·10
2862	5 k. "Adam and Eve" (Lucas Cranach)	..		1·75	1·75
2858/2862	*Set of 5* ..			4·25	4·25

Each issued in sheets of four stamps.

831 Brunner and Stamps of 1920

(Des K. Svolinský. Eng J. Herčík. Recess*)

1986 (1 Dec). *Stamp Day. Birth Centenary of Vratislav Hugo Brunner* (stamp designer). *Phosphorescent paper. P* 11½×12.
2863 **831** 1 k. multicoloured 25 15

832 Bicyclists **833** Pins and Ball

(Des Radana Hamsíková. Eng J. Herčík. Recess*)

1987 (20 Jan). *World Cross-country Cycling Championships, Mladá Boleslav. Phosphorescent paper. P* 12×11½.
2864 **832** 6 k. multicoloured 90 50

(Des V. Hájek. Eng J. Herčík. Recess*)

1987 (22 Jan). *50th Anniv of Czechoslovakian Bowling Federation. Phosphorescent paper. P* 11½.
2865 **833** 2 k. multicoloured 40 20

834 Gold Stars of Heroes of
C.S.S.R. and of Socialist
Labour

(Des V. Kovářik. Eng J. Mráček (50 h.), B. Housa (2, 3 k.), M. Ondráček (4 k.), J. Bouda (5 k.). Recess*)

1987 (4 Feb). *State Orders and Medals. T* **834** *and similar horiz designs. Phosphorescent paper. P* 12×11½.
2866	50 h. red, black and gold		..	10	10
2867	2 k. multicoloured	..		30	20
2868	3 k. multicoloured	..		50	35
2869	4 k. multicoloured	..		65	50
2870	5 k. multicoloured	..		80	50
2866/2870	*Set of 5*	..		2·10	1·50

Designs:—2 k. Order of Klement Gottwald; 3 k. Order of the Republic; 4 k. Order of Victorious February; 5 k. Order of Labour.

835 Poplar admiral
(*Limenitis populi*)

Czechoslovakia 1987

(Des K. Štanclová. Eng J. Herčík (1, 4 k.), V. Fajt (2, 3 k.). Recess*)

1987 (4 Mar). *Butterflies. T **835** and similar horiz designs. Multicoloured. Phosphorescent paper. P 12×11½.*

2871	1 k.	Type **835**	..	..	25	10
2872	2 k.	Eyed hawk moth (*Smerinthus ocellatus*)		..	55	25
2873	3 k.	Large tiger moth (*Pericallia matronula*)			95	40
2874	4 k.	Viennese emperor moth (*Saturnia pyri*)		..	1·25	50
2871/2874	*Set of 4*	..	..	..	2·75	1·10

836 Emblem   **837** Emblem

(Des V. Hájek. Eng M. Ondráček. Recess*)

1987 (6 Apr). *Nuclear Power Industry. Phosphorescent paper. P 12×11½.*

2875	**836**	5 k. multicoloured	..	..	75	45

(Des V. Hájek. Eng M. Ondráček. Recess*)

1987 (7 Apr). *11th Trade Unions Congress, Prague. Phosphorescent paper. P 11½.*

2876	**837**	1 k. multicoloured	..	..	15	10

838 Aleksei Gubarov and Vladimír Remek   **839** Stained Glass Window, St. Vitus's Cathedral (František Sequens)

(Des J. Baláž. Eng M. Ondráček. Recess)

1987 (12 Apr). *20th Anniv of "Interkosmos" Space Programme. Sheet 165×104 mm. P 12.*

MS2877	**838**	10 k.×2, multicoloured	..	5·50	5·50

See also Nos. **MS**2903 and **MS**2940.

(Des J. Solpera. Eng L. Jirka and M. Ondráček (2 k.), J. Herčík (3 k.). Recess)

1987 (9 May). *Prague Castle (23rd series). T **839** and similar vert design. Multicoloured. P 12.*

2878	2 k.	Type **839**	..	..	40	35
2879	3 k.	Arms (mural), New Land Rolls Hall, Old Royal Palace			70	50

Each issued in sheets of six stamps with decorative gutter.
See also Nos. 2950/1 and 2977/8.

MINIMUM PRICE

The minimum price quoted is 10p which represents a handling charge rather than a basis for valuing common stamps. For further notes about prices see introductory pages.

840 Telephone, 1894   **841** "When the Fighting Ended" (Pavel Simon)

(Des and eng B. Housa. Recess*)

1987 (12 May). *"Praga '88" International Stamp Exhibition (2nd issue). T **840** and similar horiz designs. Multicoloured. Phosphorescent paper. P 12×11½.*

2880	3 k.	Type **840**	..	..	70	35
2881	3 k.	Mail van, 1924	..	..	70	35
2882	4 k.	Tank locomotive *Archduke Charles*, 1907			95	35
2883	4 k.	Prague tram, 1900	..	..	95	35
2884	5 k.	Steam roller, 1936	..		1·10	60
2880/2884	*Set of 5*	..	..	..	4·00	2·10

Nos. 2880/4 were each issued in sheets of eight stamps and two double stamp-size labels; Nos. 2881/2 were also each issued in sheets of four stamps with decorative gutter.

(Des R. Vaněk. Eng J. Bouda (2885), J. Herčík (2886). Recess*)

1987 (10 June). *45th Anniv of Destruction of Lidice and Ležáky. T **841** and similar vert design. Multicoloured. Phosphorescent paper. P 11½.*

2885	1 k.	Type **841**	..	..	15	10
2886	1 k.	"The End of the Game" (Ludmila Jiřincová)		..	15	10

842 Prague Town Hall Clock and Theory of Functions Diagram   **843** Chickens in Kitchen (Asun Balzola)

(Des J. Hamza. Eng J. Mráček (2887), M. Ondráček (2888), B. Housa and M. Ondráček (2889). Recess*)

1987 (6 July). *125th Anniv of Union of Czechoslovakian Mathematicians and Physicists. T **842** and similar horiz designs. Multicoloured. Phosphorescent paper. P 11½×12.*

2887	50 h.	Type **842**	..		10	10
2888	50 h.	J. M. Petzval, Č. Strouhal and V. Jarnik		..	10	10
2889	50 h.	Trajectory of Brownian motion and earth fold diagram			10	10

(Des Z. Kočvar. Eng J. Mráček (50 h.), B. Housa (1 k.), M. Činovský (2 k.), J. Bouda (4 k.). Recess*)

1987 (3 Sept). *11th Biennial Exhibition of Book Illustrations for Children, Bratislava. T **843** and similar vert designs showing illustrations by artists named. Multicoloured. P 11½.*

2890	50 h.	Type **843**	..		40	15
2891	1 k.	Cranes with egg at railway points (Frédéric Clément)			30	10
2892	2 k.	Birds on nest (Elżbieta Gaudasińska)			40	25
2893	4 k.	Couple looking over rooftops (Marija Lucija Stupica)			70	40
2890/2893	*Set of 4*	..			1·60	80
MS2894	97×130 mm. No. 2892×2 plus label				1·00	1·00

Czechoslovakia

844 Barbed Wire,
Flames and Menorah

845 "OSS" and
Communications
Equipment

(Des J. Kodejš. Eng. V. Fajt. Recess*)

1987 (23 Sept). *40th Anniv of Terezín Memorial. Phosphorescent paper. P 11½.*
2895 **844** 50 h. multicoloured 10 10

(Des V. Kovářík. Eng J. Mráček. Recess*)

1987 (23 Sept). *30th Anniv of Organization of Socialist Countries' Postal Administrations. Phosphorescent paper. P 11½.*
2896 **845** 4 k. multicoloured 65 35

846 Purkyně and
Microtome

847 Detail of Projecting Window
by Výzdoby

(Des J. Mikula. Eng J. Herčík. Recess*)

1987 (30 Sept). *Birth Bicentenary of Jan Evangelista Purkyně (physiologist). Phosphorescent paper. P 11½.*
2897 **846** 7 k. multicoloured .. .. .. 1·10 65

(Des I. Schurmann; eng M. Ondráček (3 k.). Des M. Ondráček; eng M. Činovský (4 k.). Recess)

1987 (1 Oct). *Historic Bratislava* (11th series). *T* **847** *and similar horiz design. P* 12.
2898 3 k. buff, black and slate-blue 50 50
2899 4 k. black and lake-brown 75 75
Design:—4 k. "View of Bratislava" (engraving, Hans Mayer).
Each issued in sheets of four stamps with gutter showing detail of Mayer's engraving.
See also Nos. 2952/3, 2997/8 and 3034/5.

848 Postilion

849 Symbols of Industry, Lenin
and Red Flag

(Des and eng J. Švengsbir. Recess*)

1987 (1 Nov). *"Praga '88" International Stamp Exhibition (3rd issue). Phosphorescent paper. P* 12×11½.
2900 **848** 1 k. multicoloured 20 10
No. 2900 was issued with *se-tenant* label bearing the Exhibition emblem. The design of the stamp is the same as No. 2192.

(Des J. Lidral; eng J. Herčík (2901). Des P. Míšek; eng V. Fajt (2902). Recess*)

1987 (6 Nov). *70th Anniv of Russian Revolution (2901) and 65th Anniv of U.S.S.R (2902). T* **849** *and similar horiz design. Multicoloured. Phosphorescent paper. P* 12×11½.
2901 50 h. Type **849** 10 10
2902 50 h. Hammmer and sickle 10 10

(Des I. Baláž. Eng M. Ondráček. Recess*)

1987 (15 Nov). *"Praga '88" International Stamp Exhibition (4th issue). Sheet* 101×100 *mm. Phosphorescent paper. Imperf.*
MS2903 **838** 10 k.×4, multicoloured .. .. 12·00 12·00
No. **MS**2903 has the "Praga '88" emblem at the top. For sheet with inscription at top see No. **MS**2940.

(Eng M. Ondráček (1 k.), J. Herčík (2, 3 k.), J. Bouda (4 k.), V. Fajt (5 k.). Recess)

1987 (18 Nov). *Art* (21st series). *Vert designs as T* **481**. *P* 12.
2904 1 k. multicoloured 25 25
2905 2 k. multicoloured 60 60
2906 3 k. multicoloured 80 80
2907 4 k. black, blue and red .. .. 1·00 1·00
2908 5 k. multicoloured .. .. .. 1·40 1·40
2904/2908 *Set of* 5 .. .. 3·75 3·75
Designs:—1 k. "Enclosure of Dreams" (Kamil Lhoták); 2 k. "Tulips" (Ester Šimerová-Martinčeková); 3 k. "Bohemian Landscape" (triptych, Josef Lada); 4 k. "Accordion Player" (Josef Čapek); 5 k. "Self-portrait" (Jiří Trnka).
Each issued in sheets of four stamps.

850 Obrovský and Detail of 1919
Stamp

(Des R. Vaněk. Eng M. Ondráček. Recess*)

1987 (18 Dec). *Stamp Day. 105th Birth Anniv of Jakub Obrovský (designer). Phosphorescent paper. P* 11½×12.
2909 **850** 1 k. multicoloured 15 10
No. 2909 was issued both in sheets of 35 and in sheetlets of four stamps and 12 labels (four blank).

851 "Czechoslovakia", Linden
Tree and Arms

(Des V. Hložník. Eng M. Ondráček. Recess*)

1988 (1 Jan). *70th Anniv of Czechoslovakia. Phosphorescent paper. P* 12×11½.
2910 **851** 1 k. multicoloured 15 10

(Des L. Jirka. Eng R. Vaněk. Recess*)

1988 (10 Jan). *75th Birthday of President Husák. Phosphorescent paper. P* 12×11½.
2911 **759** 1 k. lake-brown and bright crimson .. 15 10

852 Ski Jumping and Ice Hockey

(Des J. Lidral. Eng V. Fajt. Recess*)

1988 (1 Feb). *Olympic Games, Calgary and Seoul. T* **852** *and similar horiz designs. Multicoloured. Phosphorescent paper. P* 11½×12.
2912 50 h. Type **852** 10 10
2913 1 k. Basketball and football 15 10
2914 6 k. Throwing the discus and weightlifting 75 40
Nos. 2912/14 also exist in numbered sheetlets, each containing a vertical pair imperforate between, from a limited printing.

853 Red Flags and Klement Gottwald Monument, Pečky

854 Laurin and Klement Car, 1914

856 Woman with Linden Leaves as Hair and Open Book

857 Strahov Monastery

(Des O. Pošmurný; eng B. Housa (50 h.). Des M. Stretti; eng S. Jindra (60 h.). Recess (60 h.) or recess* (others))

1988 (25 Feb). 40th Anniversaries of "Victorious February" (2915) and National Front (2916). T **853** and similar horiz design. Multicoloured. Phosphorescent paper. P 11½.

2915	50 h. Type **853** ..	..	..	10	10
2916	50 h. Couple and detail of "Czech Constitution, 1961" (Vincent Hložnik)	..	10	10
MS2917	87×99 mm. 50 h.×2, multicoloured (Type **853**); 60 h.×2, sepia (Type **246**). Perf or imperf	..	2·40	2·40

On the perforate version of No. **MS**2917 only the two 50 h. stamps are perforated.

No. **MS**2917 was sold at "Praga '88" Stamp Exhibition together with the entrance ticket.

(Des K. Lhoták. Eng J. Herčík. Recess*)

1988 (1 Mar). Historic Motor Cars. T **854** and similar horiz designs. Multicoloured. Phosphorescent paper. P 12×11½.

2918	50 h. Type **854**	..	..	10	10
2919	1 k. Tatra "NW" type B, 1902	..	15	10
2920	2 k. Tatra "NW" type E, 1905	..	30	15
2921	3 k. Tatra "12 Normandie", 1929	..	45	20
	a. Booklet pane. Nos. 2921×2, 2922×3 plus label ..		3·25	
2922	4 k. "Meteor", 1899	..	..	60	35
2918/2922	Set of 5	..	..	1·40	70

855 Prague Post Office and Velka Javorina T.V. Transmitter

(Des K. Toman. Eng M. Ondráček. Recess*)

1988 (10 Mar). "Praga '88" International Stamp Exhibition (5th issue) and 70th Anniv of Postal Museum. T **855** and similar horiz designs. Multicoloured. Phosphorescent paper. P 12×11½.

2923	50 h. Type **855**	..	..	10	10
2924	1 k. Mladá Boleslav telecommunications centre and Carmelite Street post office, Prague	..	30	10
2925	2 k. Prague 1 and Bratislava 56 post offices	..	..	40	20
2926	4 k. Malta Square, Prague, and Prachatice post offices	..	80	40
2923/2926	Set of 4	..	..	1·40	70
MS2927	108×80 mm. Nos. 2924/5, each×2 ..		3·00	3·00

The four stamps in No. **MS**2927 are arranged in a chessboard design, the upper pair perforated along the bottom edge only and the lower pair fully perforated.

(Des A. Brunovský. Eng M. Činovský. Recess*)

1988 (29 Mar). 125th Anniv of Slovak Cultural Society. Phosphorescent paper. P 11½.

2928	**856** 50 h. multicoloured ..	..	..	10	10

(Des J. Liesler. Eng J. Herčík. Recess*)

1988 (12 May). "Praga '88" International Stamp Exhibition (6th issue). National Literature Memorial, Strahov Monastery. T **857** and similar horiz designs. Multicoloured. Phosphorescent paper. P 11½.

2929	1 k. Type **857**	..	..	15	10
2930	2 k. Open book and celestial globe	..	35	15
2931	5 k. Illuminated initial "B", scrolls and decorative binding	..	..	80	45
2932	7 k. Astrological signs, Strahov, illuminated book and globe	..	..	1·25	95
2929/2932	Set of 4	..	..	2·25	1·50
MS2933	125×79 mm. Nos. 2929/32. Imperf ..		3·00	3·00

Nos. 2929/32 were each issued both in sheets of 30 stamps and in sheetlets of four stamps of one value with decorative gutter.

858 Waldstein Garden Fountain

(Des R. Vaněk. Eng V. Fajt. Recess*)

1988 (1 June). "Praga '88" International Stamp Exhibition (7th issue). Prague Fountains. T **858** and similar horiz designs. Multicoloured. Phosphorescent paper. P 11½×12.

2934	1 k. blue-black, rose-lilac & greenish blue	15	10
2935	2 k. multicoloured	..	..	35	15
2936	3 k. blue-black, yellow-orange & rose-lilac	55	25
2937	4 k. blue-black, yellow-orange & lt green	65	40
2934/2937	Set of 4	..	..	1·50	80
MS2938	79×125 mm. Nos. 2934/7 ..	..	2·50	2·50

Designs:—2 k. Old town square; 3 k. Charles University; 4 k. Courtyard, Prague Castle.

859 Washington Capitol and Moscow Kremlin

(Des A. Fuchs. Eng V. Fajt. Recess*)

1988 (1 June). Soviet–American Strategic Arms Limitation Talks, Moscow. Sheet 110×106 mm. Phosphorescent paper. P 12×11½.

MS2939	**859** 4 k. multicoloured ..	..	1·10	1·10

No. **MS**2939 also exists imperforate from a limited printing.

1988 (15 June). *"Praga '88" (8th issue). Thematic Philately Day. As No.* **MS**2903 *but inscr* "DEN NÁMĚTOVE FILATELIE" *at top.*
MS2940 **838** 10 k.×4, multicoloured   ..   6·00   6·00

860 Trade Unions Central   **861** Alfons
Recreation Centre   Mucha (designer
                     of first stamps)

(Des Radana Hamsíková. Eng M. Ondráček. Recess*)

1988 (1 July). *"Praga '88" International Stamp Exhibition (9th issue). Present-day Prague. T* **860** *and similar horiz designs. Multicoloured. Phosphorescent paper. P* 12×11½.
2941   50 h. Type **860**   10   10
2942   1 k. Koospol foreign trade company   ..   20   10
2943   2 k. Motol teaching hospital   ..   35   15
2944   4 k. Palace of Culture   65   40
2941/2944   *Set of* 4   ..   ..   1·10   55
MS2945   Two sheets, each 148×96 mm. Imperf.
(a) Nos. 2941×2 and 2944×2; (b) Nos. 2942/3,
each×2   ..   ..   ..   1·60   1·60

(Des R. Klimovič. Eng V. Fajt. Recess)

1988 (18 Aug). *"Praga '88" International Stamp Exhibition (10th issue). 70th Anniv of First Czechoslovak Stamps. Sheet* 82×96 mm. P 12.
MS2946 **861** 5 k.×2, multicoloured   ..   ..   1·75   1·75

862 "Turin, Monte Superga"
(detail, Josef Navrátil)

(Des and eng M. Ondráček. Recess)

1988 (19 Aug). *"Praga '88" International Stamp Exhibition (11th issue). Postal Museum. Sheet* 108×165 mm. P 12.
MS2947 **862** 5 k.×2, multicoloured   ..   ..   1·90   1·90

SET PRICES

Set prices are given for many issues generally those containing four stamps or more. Definitive sets include one of each value or major colour change but do not cover different perforations, die types or minor shades. Where a choice is possible the catalogue set prices are based on the cheapest versions of the stamps included in the listings.

863 Ariadne

(Des and eng V. Fajt. Recess)

1988 (26 Aug). *"Praga '88" (12th issue). Prague National Gallery. Sheet* 108×165 mm *containing T* **863** *and similar vert design showing details of "Bacchus and Ariadne" by Sebastian Ricci. Multicoloured. P* 12.
MS2948   10 k. Type **863**; 10 k. Bacchus   2·75   2·75
No. **MS**2948 is inscribed at the top with the "Praga '88" emblem only. Sheets with an additional inscription at the top commemorating F.I.P. Day come from a limited printing.

864 King George

(Des and eng J. Švengsbír. Recess*)

1988 (26 Aug). *"Praga '88" International Stamp Exhibition (13th issue). King George of Poděbrady's Religious Peace Plans. Sheet* 106×133 mm. *Phosphorescent paper. Imperf.*
MS2949 **864** 1 k. 60×4, black and bistre-yellow   5·00   5·00
The design of the stamp is the same as No. 1415.

(Des J. Solpera. Eng V. Fajt (2 k.), M. Ondráček (3 k.). Recess)

1988 (28 Sept). *Prague Castle (24th series). Vert designs as T* **839**. *Multicoloured. Phosphorescent paper. P* 12.
2950   2 k. 17th-century pottery jug   ..   30   30
2951   3 k. "St. Catherine" (Paolo Veronese)   ..   45   45
Each issued in sheets of six stamps.

(Des and eng M. Činovský. Eng M. Ondráček. Recess)

1988 (19 Oct). *Historic Bratislava (12th series). Horiz designs as T* **847**. *Multicoloured. P* 12.
2952   3 k. Hlavne square (detail of print by R.
        Alt-Sandman)   40   40
2953   4 k. Ferdinand House   50   50
Each issued in sheets of four stamps.

(Eng M. Činovský (2 k.), B. Housa (6 k.), M. Ondráček (7 k.). Recess)

1988 (17 Nov). *Art (22nd series). Vert designs as T* **481**. *Phosphorescent paper. P* 12.
2954   2 k. multicoloured   40   40
2955   6 k. ochre, black and greenish blue   ..   1·00   1·00
2956   7 k. multicoloured   ..   ..   1·40   1·40
Designs:—2 k. "Field Workers carrying Sacks" (Martin Benka);
6 k. "Woman watching Bird" (Vojtěch Preissig); 7 k. "Leopard attacking Horseman" (Eugène Delacroix).
Each issued in sheets of four stamps.

Czechoslovakia

865 Benda and Drawings   **866** Emblem

(Des I. Schurmann. Eng M. Činovský. Recess*)

1988 (18 Dec). *Stamp Day. 106th Birth Anniv of Jaroslav Benda (stamp designer). Phosphorescent paper.* P 11½×12.
2957 **865** 1 k. multicoloured 15 10

(Des I. Trulíková and R. Vaněk. Eng M. Ondráček. Recess*)

1989 (1 Jan). *20th Anniv of Czechoslovak Federal Socialist Republic. Phosphorescent paper.* P 12×11½.
2958 **866** 50 h. multicoloured 10 10

867 Globe and Truck   **868** Taras G. Shevchenko

(Des P. Míšek. Eng V. Fajt (50 h., 4 k.), M. Ondráček (others). Recess*)

1989 (2 Jan). *Paris–Dakar Rally.* T **867** *and similar horiz designs. Multicoloured. Phosphorescent paper.* P 12×11½.
2959 50 h. Type **867** 10 10
2960 1 k. Globe and view of desert on truck
    side 15 10
2961 2 k. Globe and truck (*different*) .. 30 15
2962 4 k. Route map, turban and truck .. 50 30
2959/2962 *Set of 4* 95 55

(Des I. Schurmann (2963/4), A. Brunovský (2965), R. Klimovič (2966), P. Hrach (2967/8). Eng M. Ondráček (2963/4), M. Činovský (2965), V. Fajt (2966), B. Housa (2967/8). Recess*)

1989 (9 Mar). *Birth Anniversaries.* T **868** *and similar vert designs. Phosphorescent paper.* P 12×11½.
2963 50 h. multicoloured 10 10
2964 50 h. multicoloured 10 10
2965 50 h. deep brown and emerald .. 10 10
2966 50 h. sepia and light green .. 10 10
2967 50 h. greenish black, chestnut & lake-brn 10 10
2968 50 h. multicoloured 10 10
2963/2968 *Set of 6* 50 20
Designs:—No. 2963, Type **868** (Ukrainian poet and painter, 175th anniv); 2964, Modest Petrovich Musorgsky (composer, 150th anniv); 2965, Jan Botto (poet, 160th anniv); 2966, Jawaharlal Nehru (Indian statesman, centenary); 2967, Jean Cocteau (writer and painter, centenary); 2968, Charlie Chaplin (actor, centenary).

869 *Republika* (freighter)   **870** Dove and Pioneers

(Des V. Hájek. Eng M. Ondráček (50 h., 3, 5 k.), V. Fajt (others). Recess*)

1989 (27 Mar). *Shipping.* T **869** *and similar horiz designs. Phosphorescent paper.* P 12×11½.
2969 50 h. dp violet-blue, brt scarlet & new blue 10 10
2970 1 k. multicoloured 15 10
2971 2 k. multicoloured 30 15
2972 3 k. dp violet-blue, brt scarlet & new blue 50 20
2973 4 k. multicoloured 65 40
2974 5 k. multicoloured 75 45
2969/2974 *Set of 6* .. .. .. 2·25 1·25
Designs:—1 k. *Pionýr* (trawler); 2 k. *Brno* (tanker); 3 k. *Třinec* (container ship); 4 k. *Orlík* (container ship); 5 k. *Vltava* (tanker) and communications equipment.

(Des J. Chadima. Eng B. Housa. Recess*)

1989 (20 Apr). *40th Anniv of Young Pioneer Organization. Phosphorescent paper.* P 11½.
2975 **870** 50 h. multicoloured 10 10

(Eng M. Ondráček. Recess)

1989 (21 Apr). *Art (23rd series). Sheet* 110×166 mm *containing vert designs as* T **481** *showing details of "Festival of Rose Garlands" by Albrecht Dürer.* P 12.
MS2976 10 k.×2, multicoloured .. .. 2·50 2·50

(Des J. Solpera. Eng M. Ondráček and L. Jirka (2 k.), V. Fajt (3 k.). Recess)

1989 (9 May). *Prague Castle (25th series). Vert designs as* T **839**. P 12.
2977 2 k. reddish brown, yellow-ochre & scarlet 20 20
2978 3 k. multicoloured 35 35
Designs:—2 k. King Karel of Bohemia (relief by Alexander Colin from Archduke Ferdinand I's mausoleum); 3 k. "Self-portrait" (V. V. Reiner).
Each issued in sheets of six stamps.

871 Bastille, Crowd and Flag

(Des I. Schurmann. Eng J. Herčík. Recess)

1989 (1 July). *Bicentenary of French Revolution. Sheet* 73×98mm. P 12.
MS2979 **871** 5 k. black, brt scarlet & dull ultram 60 60

872 White-tailed Sea Eagle (*Haliaeetus albicilla*)

(Des Radana Hamsíková. Eng B. Housa. Recess*)

1989 (17 July). *Endangered Species. Phosphorescent paper.* P 12×11½.
2980 **872** 1 k. multicoloured 30 15

873 Fire-bellied Toads
(*Bombina bombina*)

874 Dancers

(Des Radana Hamsíková. Eng M. Srb (2 k.), B. Housa (3 k.),
B. Šneider (4 k.), M. Ondráček (5 k.). Recess*)

1989 (18 July). *Endangered Amphibians.* T **873** and similar horiz
designs. Multicoloured. Phosphorescent paper. P 11½×12.

2981	2 k.	Type **873**		30	15
2982	3 k.	Yellow-bellied toad (*Bombina variegata*)		45	20
2983	4 k.	Alpine newts (*Triturus alpestris*)		60	35
2984	5 k.	Carpathian newts (*Triturus montandoni*)		70	40
2981/2984		*Set of 4*		1·90	1·10

(Des S. Greinerová. Eng M. Ondráček. Recess*)

1989 (29 Aug). *40th Anniv of Slovak Folk Art Collective.*
Phosphorescent paper. P 12×11½.

2985 **874** 50 h. multicoloured ..   10   10

875 Horsemen and Mountains

876 "Going Fishing" (Hannu Taina)

(Des J. Pavlíčková. Eng M. Ondráček. Recess*)

1989 (29 Aug). *45th Anniv of Slovak Rising.* Phosphorescent
paper. P 11½×12.

2986 **875** 1 k. multicoloured ..   15   10

(Des J. Solpera. Eng B. Housa (50 h., 4 k.), M. Činovský (1, 2 k.).
Recess*)

1989 (4 Sept). *12th Biennial Exhibition of Book Illustrations for
Children.* T **876** and similar vert designs. Multicoloured.
Phosphorescent paper. P 11½.

2987	50 h.	Type **876**		10	10
2988	1 k.	"Donkey Rider" (Aleksandur Aleksov)		15	10
2989	2 k.	"Animal Dreams" (Jurgen Spohn)		30	15
2990	4 k.	"Scarecrow" (Róbert Brun)		55	35
2987/2990		*Set of 4*		1·00	55
MS2991		100×143 mm. No. 2990×2		90	90

877 *Nolanea verna*

878 Jan Opletal (Nazi victim)

(Des J. Saska. Eng M. Ondráček (50 h., 5 k.), V. Fajt (others).
Recess)

1989 (5 Sept). *Poisonous Fungi.* T **877** and similar vert designs.
P 12.

2992	50 h. orange-brown, blackish brn & dp grn		10	10
2993	1 k. multicoloured		15	10
2994	2 k. olive-green and sepia		30	15
2995	3 k. blackish brn, orge-yell & Indian red		45	25
2996	5 k. multicoloured		70	45
2992/2996	*Set of 5*		1·50	95

Designs:—1 k. Death cap (*Amanita phalloides*); 2 k. Destroying
angel (*Amanita virosa*); 3 k. *Cortinarius orellanus* ; 5 k. *Galerina
marginata*.
Each issued in sheets of ten stamps.

(Des I. Schurmann. Eng M. Činovský. Recess)

1989 (16 Oct). *Historic Bratislava (13th series). Horiz designs as*
T **847**. P 12.

2997	3 k. multicoloured		30	30
2998	4 k. black, dull vermilion & yellowish grn		45	45

Designs:—3 k. Devin Fortress and flower; 4 k. Devin Fortress
and pitcher.
Each issued in sheets of four stamps.

(Des and eng J. Herčík. Recess*)

1989 (10 Nov). *50th Anniv of International Students Day.*
Phosphorescent paper. P 12×11½.

2999 **878** 1 k. multicoloured ..   15   10

(Eng M. Činovský (2 k.), V. Fajt (4 k.), J. Herčík (5 k.). Recess)

1989 (27 Nov). *Art (24th series). Multicoloured designs as* T **481**.
P 12.

3000	2 k. "Nirvana" (Anton Jasusch)		25	25
3001	4 k. "Dusk in the Town" (Jakub Schikaneder) (*horiz*)		50	50
3002	5 k. "Bakers" (Pravoslav Kotík) (*horiz*)		60	60

Each issued in sheets of four stamps.

879 Peregrine Falcon Stamp, Pens and Bouda

880 Practising Alphabet

(Des and eng J. Bouda. Recess*)

1989 (18 Dec). *Stamp Day. Fifth Death Anniv of Cyril Bouda
(stamp designer).* Phosphorescent paper. P 11½×12.

3003 **879** 1 k. brown, pale yellow & bright scarlet   30   15

(Des R. Vaněk. Eng V. Fajt. Recess*)

1990 (8 Jan). *International Literacy Year.* Phosphorescent paper.
P 11½×12.

3004 **880** 1 k. multicoloured ..   15   10

No. 3004 was issued with se-tenant inscribed label.

881 Tomáš Masaryk (first President)

882 Pres. Vaclav Havel

(Des A. Brunovský. Eng M. Činovský (1, 2 k.), J. Herčík (10 k.),
M. Ondráček (others). Recess*)

1990 (9 Jan). *Birth Anniversaries.* T **881** and similar horiz
designs. Multicoloured. Phosphorescent paper. P 11½.

3005	50 h. Type **881** (140th anniv)		10	10
3006	50 h. Karel Čapek (writer, centenary)		10	10

3007	1 k.	Vladimir Ilyich Lenin (120th anniv)	15	10
3008	2 k.	Émile Zola (novelist, 150th anniv) ..	30	15
3009	3 k.	Jaroslav Heyrovský (chemist, centenary)	35	20
3010	10 k.	Bohuslav Martinů (composer, centenary)	1·25	85
3005/3010		Set of 6 ..	2·00	1·10

(Des and eng M. Ondráček. Recess*)

1990 (9 Jan). *Phosphorescent paper. P 12×11½.*
3011 **882** 50 h. dp ultramarine, new bl & rosine   10   10

883 Players   **884** Snapdragon *(Antirrhinum majus)*   **885** Pope John Paul II

(Des Radana Hamsíková. Eng V. Fajt. Recess*)

1990 (1 Feb). *Men's World Handball Championship. Phosphorescent paper. P 11½.*
3012 **883** 50 h. multicoloured ..   10   10

(Des J. Saska. Eng M. Ondráček (50 h. 5 k.), V. Fajt (others). Recess (5 k.) or recess* (others))

1990 (1 Mar). *Flowers. T* **884** *and similar vert designs. Multicoloured. Phosphorescent paper (50 h. to 3 k.). P 11½.*
3013	50 h. Type **884** ..	10	10
3014	1 k. *Zinnia elegans*	15	10
3015	3 k. Tiger flower (*Tigridia pavonia*)	35	20
3016	5 k. Madonna lily (*Lilium candidum*)	60	50
3013/3016	Set of 4 ..	1·00	70

No. 3016 was issued in sheets of ten stamps.

(Des and eng J. Herčík. Recess*)

1990 (28 Mar). *Arms of Czech Towns (7th series). Vert designs as T* **740**. *Multicoloured. Phosphorescent paper. P 12×11½.*
3017	50 h. Bytča	10	10
3018	50 h. Poděbrady	10	10
3019	50 h. Soběslav ..	10	10
3020	50 h. Prostějov ..	10	10
3017/3020	Set of 4 ..	20	15

(Des R. Klimovič. Eng M. Ondráček. Recess*)

1990 (16 Apr). *Papal Visit. Phosphorescent paper. P 11½×12.*
3021 **885** 1 k. purple-brown, yell-ochre & rosine   15   10

CZECH AND SLOVAK FEDERATIVE REPUBLIC
20 April 1990–31 December 1992

886 Woman holding Flags   **887** Twopenny Blue

(Des Z. Filip. Eng V. Fajt. Recess*)

1990 (5 May). *45th Anniv of Liberation. Phosphorescent paper. P 11½.*
3022 **886** 1 k. multicoloured ..   15   10

(Des and eng B. Housa. Recess)

1990 (6 May). *150th Anniv of Penny Black. Sheet 102×94 mm. P 12.*
MS3023 **887** 7 k. multicoloured   80   80

888 Footballers   **889** Victory Signs

(Des R. Kolář. Eng M. Srb. Recess*)

1990 (8 May). *World Cup Football Championship, Italy. Phosphorescent paper. P 11½.*
3024 **888** 1 k. multicoloured ..   15   10

(Des R. Vaněk. Eng V. Fajt. Recess*)

1990 (1 June). *Free General Election. Phosphorescent paper. P 11½.*
3025 **889** 1 k. multicoloured ..   15   10

(Des J. Solpera. Eng V. Fajt. Recess)

1990 (6 June). *Prague Castle (26th series). Vert designs as T* **824**. *P 12.*
3026	2 k. multicoloured ..	20	20
3027	3 k. emerald, blackish green and scarlet	35	35

Designs:—2 k. Jewelled glove (from reliquary of St. George);
3 k. Seal of King Přemysl Otakar II of Bohemia.
Each issued in sheets of six stamps.

890 Map of Europe and Branch

(Des B. Votruba. Eng M. Srb. Recess*)

1990 (21 June). *15th Anniv of European Security and Co-operation Conference, Helsinki. Phosphorescent paper. P 12×11½.*
3028 **890** 7 k. multicoloured ..   80   50

891 Milada Horáková

(Des O. Pošmurný. Eng M. Ondráček. Recess*)

1990 (27 June). *40th Anniv of Execution of Milada Horáková. Phosphorescent paper. P 12×11½.*
3029 **891** 1 k. multicoloured ..   15   10

892 Poodles

(Des Hana Čápová. Eng M. Ondráček. Recess*)

1990 (2 July). *"Inter Canis" Dog Show, Brno. T* **892** *and similar horiz designs. Multicoloured. Phosphorescent paper. P* 12×11½.
3030	50 h. Type **892** ..			10	10
3031	1 k. Afghan hound, Irish wolfhound and greyhound		15	10
3032	4 k. Czech terrier, bloodhound and Hanoverian bearhound		50	35
3033	7 k. Cavalier King Charles, cocker and American cocker spaniels		80	60
3030/3033	Set of 4 ..	..	..	1·40	95

(Eng M. Činovský. Recess)

1990 (21 July–Sept). *Historic Bratislava* (14*th series). Horiz designs as T* **847**. *P* 12.
3034	3 k. black and crimson (29.9)	..	..	35	35
3035	4 k. multicoloured	..	..	50	50

Designs:—3 k. "Coin"; 4 k. "M. R. Štefánik" (J. Mudroch).
Each issued in sheets of four stamps.

893 Horses jumping

(Des R. Kolář. Eng M. Ondráček. Recess*)

1990 (7 Sept). *Centenary of Pardubice Steeplechase. T* **893** *and similar horiz design. Multicoloured. Phosphorescent paper. P* 12×11½.
3036	50 h. Type **893** ..	..	..	10	10
3037	4 k. Horses galloping	..	..	45	35

894 Alpine Marmot
(*Marmota marmota*)

(Des I. Schurmann. Eng V. Fajt. Recess*)

1990 (1 Oct). *Mammals. T* **894** *and similar horiz designs. Multicoloured. Phosphorescent paper. P* 12×11½.
3038	50 h. Type **894** ..	..	..	10	10
3039	1 k. European wild cat (*Felis silvestris*)	..	10	10
3040	4 k. Eurasian beaver (*Castor fiber*)	..	40	35
3041	5 k. Common long-eared bat (*Plecotus auritus*)	..	50	40
3038/3041	Set of 4 ..	..	..	1·00	80

895 European Flag **896** Snow-covered Church

(Des V. Kovářik. Eng J. Herčík. Recess*)

1990 (15 Oct). *Helsinki Pact Civic Gathering, Prague. Phosphorescent paper. P* 12×11½.
3042	**895** 3 k. blue, greenish yellow and gold ..	30	20

(Des V. Kompánek and R. Vaněk. Eng M. Činovský. Recess*)

1990 (15 Nov). *Christmas. Phosphorescent paper. P* 11½×12.
3043	**896** 50 h. multicoloured	..	10	10

(Des and eng B. Housa (2 k.), J. Herčík (3 k.), M. Ondráček (4 k.), V. Fajt (5 k.). Recess)

1990 (27 Nov). *Art* (25*th series). Multicoloured designs as T* **481**. *P* 12.
3044	2 k. multicoloured	..	..	20	20
3045	3 k. black, cinnamon and blue	..	30	30
3046	4 k. multicoloured	..	..	40	40
3047	5 k. multicoloured	..	..	50	50
3044/3047	Set of 4 ..	..	..	1·25	1·25

Designs: *Horiz*—2 k. "Krucemburk" (Jan Zrzavý). *Vert*—3 k. "St. Agnes" (detail of sculpture, Josef Václav Myslbek); 4 k. "Slovene in his Homeland" (detail, Alfons Mucha); 5 k. "St. John the Baptist" (detail of sculpture, Auguste Rodin).
Each issued in sheets of four stamps.

897 Karel Svolinský (stamp designer) and "Czechoslovakia" **898** Judo Throw

(Des O. Kulhánek. Eng M. Ondráček. Recess*)

1990 (18 Dec). *Stamp Day. Phosphorescent paper. P* 11½×12.
3048	**897** 1 k. dp reddish pur, lavender & ultram	10	10

(Des Z. Filip. Eng V. Fajt. Recess*)

1991 (10 Jan). *European Judo Championships, Prague. Phosphorescent paper. P* 11½.
3049	**898** 1 k. multicoloured ..	..	10	10

899 Svojsík **900** Jan Hus preaching **901** Alois Senefelder

(Des and eng M. Ondráček. Recess*)

1991 (10 Jan). *80th Anniv of Czechoslovak Scout Movement and 115th Birth Anniv of A. B. Svojsík* (founder). *Phosphorescent paper. P* 11½.
3050	**899** 3 k. multicoloured ..	..	30	20

(Des F. Kraus (5 k.), P. Sivko (others). Eng M. Srb (50 h.), B. Šneider (others). Recess*)

1991 (4 Feb). *Anniversaries. T* **900** *and other horiz designs. Phosphorescent paper.* P 11½×12 (5 k.) *or* 12×11½ (*others*).
3051	50 h. sepia, stone and vermilion			10	10
3052	1 k. multicoloured	..	..	10	10
3053	5 k. multicoloured	..	..	50	40

Designs and events:—50 h. Type **900** (600th anniv of Bethlehem Chapel, Prague). 40×23 *mm*—1 k. Estates Theatre, Prague (re-opening) and Mozart (death bicentenary). 49×19 *mm*—5 k. Paddle-steamer *Bohemia* (150th anniv of boat excursions in Bohemia).

(Des I. Schurmann. Eng M. Ondráček. Recess*)

1991 (18 Feb). *Birth Anniversaries. T* **901** *and similar vert designs. Phosphorescent paper.* P 12×11½.
3054	1 k. deep green, brown-ochre & vermilion	10	10
3055	1 k. greenish black, yellowish grn & verm	10	10
3056	1 k. dp ultramarine, dp magenta & scarlet	10	10
3057	1 k. deep violet, new blue and vermilion	10	10
3058	1 k. deep brown, dull orange & vermilion	10	10
3054/3058	*Set of 5* ..	35	25

Designs:—No. 3054, Type **901** (inventor of lithography, 220th anniv); 3055, Andrej Kmet (naturalist, 150th anniv); 3056, Jan Masaryk (politician, 105th anniv); 3057, Jaroslav Seifert (composer, 90th anniv); 3058, Antonin Dvořák (composer, 150th anniv).

Nos. 3054/8 were each issued with *se-tenant* label bearing the subject's signature and a motif.

902 "Magion II" Satellite and Earth

903 Exhibition Pavilion, 1891

(Des J. Fišer. Eng V. Fajt. Recess*)

1991 (6 May). *Europa. Europe in Space. Phosphorescent paper.* P 11½×12.
3059	**902** 6 k. blue, black and bright scarlet	..	60	45

(Des O. Kulhánek. Eng M. Ondráček. Recess*)

1991 (10 May). *Centenary of International Exhibition, Prague. Phosphorescent paper.* P 11½×12.
3060	**903** 1 k. steel bl, brownish grey & dp mve	10	10

904 Chinstrap Penguins, Map and State Flag

905 Blatná Castle

(Des I. Schurmann. Eng M. Ondráček. Recess*)

1991 (20 May). *30th Anniv of Antarctic Treaty. Phosphorescent paper.* P 12×11½.
3061	**904** 8 k. multicoloured	..	75	55

(Des A. Fuchs. Eng V. Fajt. Recess*)

1991 (3 June). *Castles. T* **905** *and similar vert designs. Multicoloured. Phosphorescent paper.* P 11½.
3062	50 h. Type **905** ..	..	10	10
3063	1 k. Bouzov	..	10	10
3064	3 k. Kežmarok	..	30	20

906 Jan Palach   **907** Říp   **908** "The Frog King" (Binette Schroeder)

(Des I. Strnad. Eng K. Pavel. Recess)

1991 (9 Aug). *Jan Palach Scholarship. Phosphorescent paper.* P 12×11½.
3065	**906** 4 k. black	..	30	25

No. 3065 was issued with *se-tenant* label showing emblem.

(Des J. Saska; eng V. Fajt (3066). Des K. Ondreička; eng M. Činovský (3067). Recess)

1991 (28 Aug). *Beauty Spots. T* **907** *and similar horiz design.* P 11½×12.
3066	4 k. brt scarlet, new blue & greenish yell	30	25
3067	4 k. blackish purple, bronze green & black	30	25

Design:—No. 3067, Kriváň.

(Des O. Pošmurný. Eng M. Srb. Recess*)

1991 (2 Sept). *13th Biennial Exhibition of Book Illustrations for Children. T* **908** *and similar vert design. Multicoloured. Phosphorescent paper.* P 11½.
3068	1 k. Type **908** ..	..	10	10
3069	2 k. "Pinocchio" (Stasys Eidrigevičius)	..	20	15

909 Hlinka   **910** "Prague Jesus Child" (Maria-Victoria Church)

(Des J. Baláž. Eng M. Činovský. Recess)

1991 (27 Sept). *53rd Death Anniv of Father Andrej Hlinka* (*Slovak nationalist*). *Phosphorescent paper.* P 11½.
3070	**909** 10 k. blue-black	..	..	1·00	75

(Des and eng V. Fajt (3071), J. Herčík (3072). Recess)

1991 (30 Sept). *Prague and Bratislava. T* **910** *and similar vert design. Multicoloured.* P 11½.
3071	3 k. Type **910** ..	..	25	25
3072	3 k. St. Elisabeth's Church, Bratislava	..	25	25

Each issued in sheets of eight stamps.

911 Gagea
bohemica

912 Boys in
Costume

(Des and eng B. Housa. Recess*)

1991 (3 Nov). *Nature Protection. Flowers. T* **911** *and similar vert designs. Multicoloured. Phosphorescent paper. P* 12×11½.

3073	1 k. Type **911**	..	..	10	10
3074	2 k. Aster alpinus	..	..	20	15
3075	5 k. Fritillaria meleagris	..	..	50	40
3076	11 k. Daphne cneorum	..	..	1·00	75
3073/3076	Set of 4	..	..	1·60	1·25

(Des and eng B. Šneider (3077), B. Housa (3078), M. Ondráček (3079), V. Fajt (3080), J. Herčík (3081). Recess)

1991 (3 Nov). *Art (26th series). Vert designs as T* **481**. *Multicoloured. P* 12.

3077	2 k. "Family at Home" (Max Ernst)	..	20	20
3078	3 k. "Milenci" (Auguste Renoir)	..	30	30
3079	4 k. "Christ" (El Greco)	..	40	40
3080	5 k. "Coincidence" (Ladislav Guderna)	..	50	50
3081	7 k. "Two Japanese Women" (Utamaro)		70	70
3077/3081	Set of 5	..	1·90	1·90

Each issued in sheets of four stamps with gutter.

(Des A. Strnadel and V. Kovářik. Eng J. Herčík, Recess*)

1991 (11 Nov). *Christmas. Phosphorescent paper. P* 12×11½.
3082 **912** 50 h. multicoloured   10   10

913 Martin Benka (stamp designer)
and Slovakian 1939 Stamp

914 Biathlon

(Des and eng M. Činovský. Recess*)

1991 (18 Dec). *Stamp Day. Phosphorescent paper. P* 11½×12.
3083 **913** 2 k. Venetian red, black and salmon   20   15

(Des R. Jančovič. Eng V. Fajt. Recess*)

1992 (6 Jan). *Winter Olympic Games, Albertville. Phosphorescent paper. P* 11½.
3084 **914** 1 k. multicoloured   10   10

915 Comenius

916 Player

(Des K. Beneš. Eng J. Herčík. Recess)

1992 (5 Mar). *400th Birth Anniv of Jan Komenský (Comenius) (educationist). Sheet 63×76 mm. P* 11½.
MS3085 **915** 10 k. multicoloured ..   ..   1·00   1·00

(Des V. Kovářik. Eng K. Pavel. Recess*)

1992 (31 Mar). *World Ice Hockey Championship, Prague and Bratislava. Phosphorescent paper. P* 11½.
3086 **916** 3 k. multicoloured   25   20

917 Traffic Lights

918 Tower, Seville
Cathedral

(Des J. Fišer. Eng M. Srb. Recess*)

1992 (2 Apr). *Road Safety Campaign. Phosphorescent paper. P* 12×11½.
3087 **917** 2 k. multicoloured ..   20   15

(Des V. Kučera. Eng M. Ondráček. Recess*)

1992 (2 Apr). *"Expo '92" World's Fair, Seville. Phosphorescent paper. P* 11½.
3088 **918** 4 k. multicoloured ..   30   25

919 Amerindian, Santa Maria
and Columbus

(Des A. Born. Eng B. Housa. Recess)

1992 (5 May). *Europa. 500th Anniv of Discovery of America by Columbus. P* 11½×12.
3089 **919** 22 k. multicoloured ..   ..   1·50   1·10
Issued in sheets of eight stamps with decorative gutter.

920 J. Kubiš and J. Gabčík

921 Tennis
Player

(Des K. Ondreička. Eng B. Šneider (1, 2 k.), M. Ondráček (3, 6 k.). Recess*)

1992 (21 May). *Free Czechoslovak Forces in World War II. T* **920** *and similar horiz designs. Multicoloured. Phosphorescent paper. P* 12×11½.

3090	1 k. Type **920** (50th anniv of assassination of Reinhard Heydrich)	10	10
3091	2 k. Supermarine Spitfires (air battles over England, 1939–45) ..	20	15
3092	3 k. Barbed wire and soldier (Tobruk, 1941)	25	20
3093	6 k. Soldiers (Dunkirk, 1944–45)	50	40
3090/3093	Set of 4	90	75

(Des R. Jančovič. Eng V. Fajt. Recess*)

1992 (21 May). *Olympic Games, Barcelona. Phosphorescent paper.* P 11½.
3094 **921** 2 k. multicoloured 20 15

922 Nurses' Hats and Red Cross

923 Player

(Des K. Felix. Eng M. Činovský. Recess*)

1992 (10 June). *Red Cross. Phosphorescent paper.* P 11½.
3095 **922** 2 k. multicoloured 20 15

(Des I. Rumanský. Eng V. Fajt. Recess*)

1992 (30 June). *European Junior Table Tennis Championships, Topolčany. Phosphorescent paper.* P 11½.
3096 **923** 1 k. multicoloured 10 10

924 Crawling Cockchafer (*Polyphylla fullo*)

925 Troja Castle

(Des P. Johanis. Eng M. Ondráček. Recess*)

1992 (15 July). *Beetles. T* **924** *and similar horiz designs. Multicoloured. Phosphorescent paper.* P 11½.
3097 1 k. Type **924** 10 10
3098 2 k. *Ergates faber* 20 15
3099 3 k. *Meloe violaceus* 25 20
3100 4 k. *Dytiscus latissimus* 30 25
3097/3100 *Set of 4* 75 60

(Des and eng M. Ondráček (6 k.), M. Činovský (7 k.), K. Pavel (8 k.). Recess)

1992 (22 July). *T* **925** *and similar designs.* P 11½.
3101 6 k. multicoloured 50 40
3102 7 k. black and brown-lilac 60 45
3103 8 k. multicoloured 70 55
Designs: *Vert*—7 k. "St. Martin" (sculpture, G. R. Donner), Bratislava Cathedral. *Horiz*—8 k. Lednice Castle.
Each issued in sheets of eight stamps.

PUZZLED ?

Then you need
PHILATELIC TERMS ILLUSTRATED
to tell you all you need to know about printing methods, papers, errors, varieties, watermarks, perforations, etc. 192 pages, some in full colour, soft cover. Third Edition.

926 Double Head and Posthorns

927 Anton Bernolak and Georgius Fandly

(Des I. Strnad. Eng B. Housa. Recess*)

1992 (28 Aug). *Post Bank. Phosphorescent paper.* P 11½×12.
3104 **926** 20 k. multicoloured .. .. 1·50 1·00

(Des J. Baláž. Eng M. Činovský. Recess*)

1992 (6 Oct). *Bicentenary of Slovak Education Association. Phosphorescent paper.* P 12×11½.
3105 **927** 5 k. multicoloured 40 30

928 Český Krumlov

929 Organ

(Des and eng J. Herčík. Recess*)

1992 (19 Oct). *Phosphorescent paper.* P 11½×12.
3106 **928** 3 k. deep brown and vermilion .. 25 20

(Des and eng J. Herčík (6 k.), B. Housa (others). Recess)

1992 (2 Nov). *Art (27th series). Designs as T* **481**. P 12.
3107 6 k. black and red-brown 50 40
3108 7 k. multicoloured 60 45
3109 8 k. multicoloured 70 55
Designs: *Vert*—6 k. "The Old Raftsman" (Koloman Sokol); 8 k. "Abandonned" (Toyen). *Horiz*—7 k. "Still Life with Grapes" (Georges Braque).
Each issued in sheets of four stamps.

(Des K. Franta. Eng B. Housa. Recess*)

1992 (9 Nov). *Christmas. Phosphorescent paper.* P 12×11½.
3110 **929** 2 k. multicoloured 20 15

930 Jindra Schmidt (engraver)

(Des and eng B. Housa. Recess*)

1992 (18 Dec). *Stamp Day. Phosphorescent paper.* P 11½×12.
3111 **930** 2 k. multicoloured 20 15

The Federation was dissolved on 31 December 1992, the constituent republics becoming the separate independent states of Czech Republic and Slovakia.

CZECHOSLOVAK ARMY IN SIBERIA

MILITARY POST

During the War of 1914–18 many Czech and Slovak soldiers in the Austro-Hungarian armies surrendered to the Russian Army. After the war 70,000 of these formed an army in Siberia and fought the Bolshevists. They issued stamps for their own postal service and these were also sold to the public on the Siberian Railway.

4   Lion of Bohemia   **2**

(5)

(Des Rybák and Rössler-Orovsky. Printed K. Kolman, Prague)

1919. *Lion and inscription embossed. Percé en arc.*
7   **4**   (25 k.) carmine and blue ..   1·25
   There are two types of Nos. 7/8, differing in the hilt of the sabre at left and the lance-point at right (*same price either type*).

1920. *No. 7 optd "1920" in Irkutsk.*
8   **4**   (25 k.) carmine and blue .. ..   5·00

1920. *No. 8 surch as T* **5,** *in green.*

9	**4**	2	(k.) carmine and blue	18·00
10		3	(k.) carmine and blue	18·00
11		5	(k.) carmine and blue	18·00
12		10	(k.) carmine and blue	18·00
13		15	(k.) carmine and blue	18·00
14		25	(k.) carmine and blue	18·00
15		35	(k.) carmine and blue	18·00
16		50	(k.) carmine and blue	18·00
17		1	r. carmine and blue	18·00

   This surcharge is also known inverted on all values, and also normal on stamps without the "1920" overprint.

1   Church in   **2**   Armoured   **3**   Sentry
   Irkutsk   Train *Orlík*

(Des K. Čila, J. Malý and J. Svec. Litho Makušin and Posochin, Irkutsk)

1919–20. *Crackled yellow gum.* (a) *Imperf* (12.19).

1	**1**	25 k. scarlet	..	..	8·75	12·50
2	**2**	50 k. yellow-green	..	..	8·75	12·50
3	**3**	1 r. red-brown	..	..	20·00	25·00

(b) *P* 11½ (1.20)

4	**1**	25 k. scarlet	..	..	8·25	8·25
5	**2**	50 k. yellow-green	..	..	8·25	8·25
6	**3**	1 r. red-brown	..	..	19·00	19·00

   Stamps from the margins of sheets perf 11½ are imperf on one or two sides.
   Imperf stamps without gum are from remainders sent to Prague from Siberia. Stamps also exist perf 13½; those with Irkutsk gum are very scarce, those with smooth shiny gum are from imperf remainders perforated and gummed in Prague (*price* £1·50 set of 3).

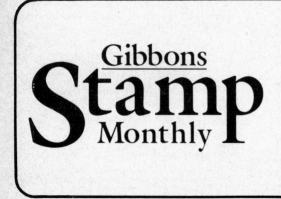

East Silesia

(TESCHEN)

100 Haleru=1 Krone
100 Fenni=1 Korona

East Silesia (Silésie Orientale), the area round Teschen, in the former Austrian Empire, was in dispute between the Czechs and the Poles in 1919. Although the Allies decided on a plebiscite it was never held owing to disorders and the Council of Ambassadors divided the area between Czechoslovakia and Poland on 28 July 1920.

A. CZECHOSLOVAKIAN ISSUES

SO

S O

SO

SO 19 20 1920

1920 **19** **20** 1920

(1) (E **2**) (D **3**)

1920 (13 Feb). *T* **2** to **5** of Czechoslovakia optd with *T* **1**.

(a) Imperf

1	3	1 h. chocolate		25	25
2	2	3 h. reddish purple		10	10
3	4	5 h. blue-green		25·00	23·00
4		10 h. yellow-green		£550	£250
5		15 h. vermilion		12·50	7·50
6	2	20 h. turquoise-green		10	10
7	4	20 h. carmine		£650	£300
8		25 h. purple		75	75
9	2	30 h. olive-bistre (R.)		15	15
10		40 h. brown-orange		15	15
11	3	50 h. purple		40	40
12	4	50 h. blue		1·10	1·10
13	5	60 h. yellow-orange (B.)		45	45
14	4	75 h. grey-green (R.)		30	30
15	5	80 h. yellow-olive (R.)		40	40
16	2	100 h. red-brown		50	50
17	4	120 h. slate-black (R.)		1·10	1·10
18	2	200 h. bright blue (R.)		1·10	1·10
19	5	300 h. dull green (R.)		1·60	1·60
20	2	400 h. violet (R.)		1·40	1·40
21	4	500 h. lake-brown (B.)		3·75	3·00
		a. Black opt		7·50	6·25
22	5	1000 h. purple (B.)		10·00	6·00
		a. Black opt		£130	90·00

(b) P 13½

23	3	1 h. chocolate		10	10
24	4	5 h. blue-green		15	15
25		10 h. yellow-green		20	20
26		15 h. rose-red		10	10
27		20 h. carmine		20	20
28		25 h. purple		20	20
29	5	60 h. yellow-orange (B.)		£225	£250
30	2	200 h. bright blue (R.)		2·25	2·25

(c) P 11½

31	4	5 h. blue-green		30	30
32		10 h. yellow-green		10·00	5·00
33		15 h. rose-red		8·75	6·25
34		25 h. purple		23·00	22·00
35		30 h. mauve (B.)		25	25
36	5	60 h. yellow-orange (B.)		30	30

(d) P 13½×11½

37	4	15 h. rose-red		1·50	1·50
38		25 h. purple		12·50	12·50

The 500 and 1000 h., with portrait of President Masaryk, were prepared for use but not issued to the public.

1920 (13 Feb). *NEWSPAPER EXPRESS. Type E* **4** *of Czechoslovakia optd with Type E* **2**, *in blue.*

E39	E **4**	2 h. purple/yellow		10	10
		a. Black opt		75	50
E40		5 h. green/yellow		10	10
		a. Black opt		3·75	3·25

1920 (13 Feb). *NEWSPAPER. Type N* **4** *of Czechoslovakia optd with T* **1**.

N41	N **4**	2 h. green		30	30
N42		6 h. red		10	10
N43		10 h. lilac		20	20
N44		20 h. blue		25	25
N45		30 h. brown		25	25
N41/45		*Set of 5*		1·00	1·00

1920 (13 Feb). *POSTAGE DUE. Type D* **4** *of Czechoslovakia optd with Type D* **3**.

D46	D **4**	5 h. olive-bistre (B.)		10	10
		a. Black opt		35·00	32·00
D47		10 h. olive-bistre (B.)		15	10
D48		15 h. olive-bistre (B.)		15	10
D49		20 h. olive-bistre (B.)		25	15
D50		25 h. olive-bistre (B.)		25	20
D51		30 h. olive-bistre (B.)		25	20
D52		40 h. olive-bistre (B.)		40	30
D53		50 h. olive-bistre (B.)		40	30
D54		100 h. deep brown (R.)		75	55
D55		500 h. green (R.)		3·00	2·25
D56		1000 h. violet (R.)		6·00	6·00
D46/56		*Set of 11*		10·50	9·00

A variety with larger "2" in "1920" may be found on all values of the above series.

B. POLISH ISSUE

S. O.
1920.

S. O. 1920.

(2) **(3)**

1920 (15 Apr). *Stamps of Poland, optd with T* **2** *or* **3**. *P 10, 11½ or compound.*

(a) With T **2**
A. Opt 9¼–9½ mm. high. B. Opt 8½ mm. high

			A		B	
57	**15**	5 f. green	10	10	15	15
58		10 f. chocolate	10	10	15	15
59		15 f. red	10	10	25	25
60	**16**	25 f. olive	10	10	10	10
61		50 f. blue-green	10	10	30	30

(b) With T **3**
Distance between stops after "S" and "O": A. 6 mm. B. 5¼ mm.

			A		B	
62	**17**	1 k. deep green	10	10	30	30
63		1 k. 50, brown	10	10	45	40
64		2 k. deep blue	10	10	25	25
65	**18**	2 k. 50, deep purple	10	10	45	45
66	**19**	5 k. grey-blue	15	15	45	45
57/66		*Set of 10*	75	75	2·50	2·50

The "fenigow" stamps were overprinted for the low values, owing to a shortage of the same types with value in "halerzy".

Stamps issued during the plebiscite in Upper Silesia, 1920–22, are listed in Part 7 (*Germany*) of this catalogue.

Bohemia and Moravia

100 Haleru=1 Koruna

GERMAN PROTECTORATE

16 March 1939 to 8 May 1945

After Slovakia declared its independence on 14 March 1939, the President of Czechoslovakia was induced to agree to a German protectorate over Bohemia and Moravia, the Czech areas of the country.

PRINTERS. All stamps and overprints were produced by the Czech Graphic Union, Prague.

BÖHMEN u. MÄHREN

ČECHY a MORAVA
(1)

1939 (15 July). *Stamps of Czechoslovakia variously optd as T* **1**.

1	**34**	5 h. deep ultramarine		10	20
2	–	10 h. brown		10	20
3	–	20 h. vermilion		15	20
4	–	25 h. blue-green		10	20
5	–	30 h. purple		10	20
6	**59**	40 h. blue		2·25	4·25
7	**77**	50 h. blue-green		10	20
8	**60***a*	60 h. violet		2·25	4·00
9	**61**	1 k. claret		85	1·10
10	–	1 k. claret (No. 395)		35	55
11	–	1 k. 20, purple (No. 354)		3·50	4·00
12	**64**	1 k. 50, carmine		2·40	4·25
13	–	1 k. 60, olive-green (No. 355*a*)		2·40	4·25
		a. Error: "MAHNEN"		22·00	28·00
14	–	2 k. green (No. 356)		1·25	1·50
15	–	2 k. 50, blue (No. 357)		3·00	3·75
16	–	3 k. chocolate (No. 358)		3·00	3·75
17	**65**	4 k. violet		3·25	5·50
18	–	5 k. grey-green (No. 361)		3·25	6·50
19	–	10 k. blue (No. 362)		4·00	9·00
1/19		*Set of* 19		30·00	48·00

Overprint sizes:—Nos. 1/6, 17½×16 mm; No. 7, 23×13½ mm; Nos. 8/10, 18×15½ mm; Nos. 11/16, 19½×18 mm; Nos. 17 and 19, 28½×18 mm; No. 18, 23½×23½ mm.

2 Linden Leaves and Buds

3 Karluv Tyn Castle

4 Brno Cathedral

5 Zlin

(Des K. Vik. Eng K. Seizinger (40, 60 h., 2 k., 2 k. 50). Des and eng B. Heinz (50 h.). Des J. C. Voudrous. Eng B. Heinz (1 k., 1 k. 20, 1 k. 50, 3, 5, 10, 20 k.). Des V. Silovsky. Eng B. Heinz (4 k.). T **2** photo, others recess).

1939–40. *T* **2** *and views as T* **3** *to* **5**. *P* 14 (*T* **2**) *or* 12½ (*others*).

20	**2**	5 h. blue (30.8.39)		10	10
21	–	10 h. sepia (30.8.39)		10	10
22	–	20 h. scarlet (30.8.39)		10	10
23	–	25 h. blue-green (30.8.39)		10	10
24	**2**	30 h. purple (30.8.39)		10	10
25	–	40 h. blue (29.7.39)		10	10
26	**3**	50 h. green (29.7.39)		10	10
27	–	60 h. violet (29.7.39)		10	10
28	–	1 k. claret (29.7.39)		10	10
29	**4**	1 k. 20, purple (29.7.39)		15	25
30	–	1 k. 50, carmine (29.7.39)		10	10
31	–	2 k. green (29.7.39)		10	10
32	–	2 k. 50, blue (29.7.39)		10	10
33	**5**	3 k. mauve (4.11.40)		10	10
34	–	4 k. slate (4.11.40)		10	10
35	–	5 k. green (30.8.39)		25	25
36	–	10 k. ultramarine (30.8.39)		15	50
37	–	20 k. brown (30.8.39)		60	1·00
20/37		*Set of* 18		2·00	2·75

Designs: As T **3**—40 h. Svikov Castle; 60 h. St. Barbara's Church, Kutna Hora; 1 k. St. Vitus's Cathedral, Prague. As T **4**—2 k. and 2 k. 50, Olomouc. As T **5**—4 k. Iron works, Moravska-Ostrava; 5 k., 10 k. and 20 k. Karlsburg, Prague.

Nos. 29/37 were each issued in sheets of 100 stamps and 12 blank labels.

N **6** Dove   D **6**   P **6**

(Des J. Benda. Typo)

1939 (25 Aug). *NEWSPAPER. Imperf.*

N38	N **6**	2 h. yellow-brown		10	15
N39	–	5 h. pale blue		10	15
N40	–	7 h. orange-vermilion		10	15
N41	–	9 h. emerald-green		10	15
N42	–	10 h. brown-lake		10	15
N43	–	12 h. bright ultramarine		10	15
N44	–	20 h. deep green		10	15
N45	–	50 h. red-brown		15	20
N46	–	1 k. grey-olive		15	20
N38/46		*Set of* 9		60	1·25

These stamps exist perforated privately.

(Des A. Erhardt. Typo)

1939 (1 Dec)—**40**. *POSTAGE DUE. P* 14.

D38	D **6**	5 h. lake		10	10
D39	–	10 h. lake		10	10
D40	–	20 h. lake		10	10
D41	–	30 h. lake		10	10
D42	–	40 h. lake		10	10
D43	–	50 h. lake		10	10
D44	–	60 h. lake		10	10
D45	–	80 h. lake (10.6.40)		10	10
D46	–	1 k. ultramarine		10	20
D47	–	1 k. 20, ultramarine (10.6.40)		15	20
D48	–	2 k. ultramarine		35	60
D49	–	5 k. ultramarine		40	70
D50	–	10 k. ultramarine		65	1·10
D51	–	20 k. ultramarine		1·75	2·75
D38/51		*Set of* 14		3·75	5·75

(Des A. Erhardt. Photo)

1939–40. *PERSONAL DELIVERY. P* 13½.

P38	P **6**	50 h. blue (1940)		40	80
		a. Tête-bêche (pair)		2·25	5·00
P39	–	50 h. carmine		60	1·10
		a. Tête-bêche (pair)		2·40	6·25

No. P38 was for the prepayment of the Personal Delivery charge and No. P39 was used when the charge was collected on receipt of the letter.

(Des A. Schaumann. Eng I. Goldschmied (Nos. 41/3))

1940–41. *Colour changed and new values.*

(a) T **2**. *Photo.* P 14

38	30 h. yellow-brown (1.6.41)			10	10
39	40 h. orange (3.40)			10	10
40	50 h. slate-green (20.12.40)			10	10

(b) As T **2** but redrawn (*Leaves and Flowers*). *Recess.* P 12½ (28.7.41)

41	60 h. violet			10	10
42	80 h. red-orange			10	10
43	1 k. brown			10	10
38/43	Set of 6			35	35

(Des K. Vik (50 h., 1 k. 50), V. Silovský (80 h., 3, 6, 10 k.), J. C. Vondrouš (others). Eng I. Goldschmied (2, 6, 8 k.), K. Seizinger (1 k. 50), B. Heinz (others). Recess)

1940–41. *Various views, as 1939–40.* P 12½.

(a) 19 × 24 mm.

44	50 h. blue-green (31.3.40)			10	10
45	1 k. blue (29.6.40)			10	20
46	1 k. 20, violet-brown (Brno) (10.6.40)			20	15
47	1 k. 20, carmine (Prague) (1941)			10	10
48	1 k. 50, lilac-rose (1941)			10	10
49	2 k. grey-green (20.12.40)			10	10
50	2 k. light blue (1941)			10	15
51	2 k. 50, ultramarine (1941)			10	15
52	3 k. olive (1941)			10	15

(b) 30 × 24 mm.

53	5 k. blue-green (20.11.40)			15	10
54	6 k. lilac-brown (20.11.40)			15	20
55	8 k. slate-green (31.12.40)			15	20
56	10 k. blue (20.11.40)			20	20
57	20 k. chocolate-brown (1.10.40)			45	90
44/57	Set of 14			1·75	2·40

Designs:—50 h. Neuhaus Castle; 80 h., 3 k. Pernstyn Castle; 1 k. 20 (violet-brown) and 2 k. 50, Brno Cathedral (as T **4**, but reduced); 1 k. 20 (carmine) St. Vitus's Cathedral, Prague; 1 k. 50, St. Barbara's Church, Kutna Hora; 2 k. (2) Pardubitz Castle; 5 k. Bridge at Beching; 6 k. Samson Fountain, Budweis; 8 k. Kremsier; 10 k. Wallenstein Palace, Prague; 20 k. Karlsburg, Prague.

Nos. 53/57 were each issued in sheets of 100 stamps and 12 blank labels.

6 Red Cross Nurse and Wounded Soldier   (N **7**)   O **7** Numeral and Laurel Wreath

(Des Max Geyer. Photo)

1940 (29 June). *Red Cross Relief Fund.* P 13½.

58	**6**	60 h. + 40 h. indigo		40	50
59		1 k. 20 + 80 h. plum		45	55

Nos. 58/9 were issued in sheets of 50, se-tenant with 50 stamp-size labels, showing emblem.

1940. NEWSPAPER. *For Bulk Postings. No.* N42 *optd with Type* N **7**.

N60	N **6**	10 h. brown-lake		50	1·00

(Des A. Erhardt. Typo)

1941 (1 Jan). OFFICIAL. P 14.

O60	O **7**	30 h. yellow-brown		10	10
O61		40 h. slate-blue		10	10
O62		50 h. emerald-green		10	10
O63		60 h. deep green		10	10
O64		80 h. vermilion		40	15
O65		1 k. brown		15	10
O66		1 k. 20, carmine		15	10
O67		1 k. 50, maroon		30	15
O68		2 k. light blue		30	30
O69		3 k. olive-green		30	10
O70		4 k. bright purple		40	45
O71		5 k. yellow		1·00	70
O60/71		Set of 12		3·00	2·00

7 Patient in Hospital   **8** Anton Dvořák

1941 (20 Apr). *Red Cross Relief Fund. Photo.* P 13½.

60	**7**	60 h. + 40 h. indigo		20	25
61		1 k. 20 + 80 h. plum		20	30

Issued with se-tenant labels as Nos. 58/9.

(Des J. Sejpka. Eng J. Goldschmied. Recess)

1941 (25 Aug). *Birth Centenary of Dvorak (composer).* P 12½.

62	**8**	60 h. grey-violet		15	15
63		1 k. 20, sepia		20	20

Issued with se-tenant labels as Nos. 58/9.

9 Harvesting   **10** Blast furnace, Pilsen

(Des J. Sejpka (T **9**), V. Silovsky (T **10**). Photo)

1941 (7 Sept). *Prague Fair.* P 13½.

64	**9**	30 h. red-brown		10	10
65		60 h. green		10	10
66	**10**	1 k. 20, plum		10	15
67		2 k. 50, blue		15	25
64/67		Set of 4		35	50

11 "Ständetheater", Prague   **12** Mozart   **(13)**

15. III. 1939

15.III.1942

(Des M. Geyer (T **11**), A. Langenberger (T **12**). Photo)

1941 (26 Oct). *150th Death Anniv of Mozart.* P 13½.

68	**11**	30 h. + 30 h. brown		10	10
69		60 h. + 60 h. green		10	10
70	**12**	1 k. 20 + 1 k. 20, scarlet		15	25
71		2 k. 50 + 2 k. 50, blue		15	30
68/71		Set of 4		35	60

Each issued with se-tenant labels, depicting bars of music (Nos. 68/9) or a piano (70/1).

1942 (15 Mar). *Third Anniv of German Occupation. Nos.* 47 *and* 51 *optd with* T **13**.

72		1 k. 20, carmine (B.)		20	40
73		2 k. 50, ultramarine (R.)		30	45

14 Adolf Hitler   **15**   **16** Nurse and Patient

(Des J. Sejpka. Eng J. Goldschmied. Recess)

1942 (20 Apr). *Hitler's 53rd Birthday.* P 12½.

74	**14**	30 h. + 20 h. brown	..	..	10	10
75		60 h. + 40 h. green	..	..	10	10
76		1 k. 20 + 80 h. maroon	..	..	10	10
77		2 k. 50 + 1 k. 50, blue	..	..	10	25
74/77		*Set of 4*			25	50

Each issued in sheets of 100 stamps and 12 blank labels.

(Des J. Sejpka. Eng J. Goldschmied (Nos. 84/99))

1942. As T **15** (*various sizes*).

(a) Photo. 17½ × 21½ *mm.* P 14 (1 July)

78	10 h. black	..	10	10
79	30 h. brown	..	10	10
80	40 h. indigo	..	10	10
81	50 h. blackish green	..	10	10
82	60 h. violet	..	10	10
83	80 h. orange-red	..	10	10

(b) Recess. 18½ × 21 *mm.* P 12½ (1 July)

84	1 k. chocolate	..	10	10
85	1 k. 20, carmine	..	10	10
86	1 k. 50, claret	..	10	10
87	1 k. 60, blue-green	..	10	15
88	2 k. light blue	..	10	10
89	2 k. 40, chestnut	..	10	10

(c) Recess. 19 × 24 *mm.* P 12½ (22 July)

90	2 k. 50, ultramarine	..	10	10
91	3 k. olive-green	..	10	10
92	4 k. purple	..	10	10
93	5 k. green	..	10	10
94	6 k. purple-brown	..	10	10
95	8 k. indigo	..	10	10

(d) Recess. 24 × 30 *mm.* P 12½ (22 July)

96	10 k. grey-green	..	10	50
97	20 k. slate-violet	..	15	75
98	30 k. scarlet	..	20	80
99	50 k. blue	..	70	2·00
78/99	*Set of 22*		2·50	5·50

Nos. 96/9 were each issued in sheets of 100 stamps and 12 blank labels.

(Des M. Geyer. Photo)

1942 (4 Sept). *Red Cross Relief Fund.* P 13½.

100	**16**	60 h. + 40 h. blue	..	10	10
101		1 k. 20 + 80 h. claret	..	10	10

17 Mounted Postman   **18** Peter Parler   N **19** Dove

(Des A. Erhardt. Photo)

1943 (10 Jan). *Stamp Day.* P 13½.

102	**17**	60 h. purple	..	10	10

(Des A. Langenberger. Photo)

1943 (29 Jan). *Winter Relief Fund.* As T **18** (*busts*). P 13½.

103	60 h. + 40 h. violet	..	10	10
104	1 k. 20 + 80 h. carmine	..	10	10
105	2 k. 50 + 1 k. 50, blue	..	10	15

Designs:—60 h. Charles IV; 2 k. 50, King John of Luxembourg.

(Des J. Benda. Typo)

1943 (15 Feb). *NEWSPAPER. Imperf.*

N106	N **19**	2 h. yellow-brown	..	10	10
N107		5 h. pale lilac	..	10	10
N108		7 h. orange-vermilion	..	10	10
N109		9 h. emerald-green	..	10	10
N110		10 h. brown-lake	..	10	10
N111		12 h. bright ultramarine	..	10	10
N112		20 h. deep green	..	10	10
N113		50 h. red-brown	..	10	10
N114		1 k. grey-olive	..	10	20
N106/114		*Set of 9*	..	35	65

O **19** Eagle and Numeral   **19** Adolf Hitler

(Des A. Erhardt. Typo)

1943 (15 Feb). *OFFICIAL.* P 14.

O106	O **19**	30 h. yellow-brown		10	10
O107		40 h. slate-blue		10	10
O108		50 h. grey-green	..	10	10
O109		60 h. violet		10	10
O110		80 h. vermilion		10	10
O111		1 k. purple-brown	..	10	10
O112		1 k. 20, carmine	..	10	10
O113		1 k. 50, red-brown	..	10	10
O114		2 k. light blue		10	15
O115		3 k. olive-green	..	10	15
O116		4 k. bright purple	..	10	15
O117		5 k. blue-green	..	15	40
O106/117		*Set of 12*		70	1·40

(Des and eng J. Schmidt. Recess)

1943 (20 Apr). *Hitler's 54th Birthday.* P 12½.

106	**19**	60 h. + 1 k. 40, violet	..	10	15
107		1 k. 20 + 3 k. 80, carmine	..	15	20

Each issued in sheets of 100 stamps and 12 blank labels.

20 Scene from   **21** Richard   **22** Reinhard
The Mastersingers   Wagner   Heydrich
of Nuremberg

(Des A. Langenberg (1 k. 20), A. Erhardt (others). Photo)

1943 (22 May). *130th Birth Anniv of Richard Wagner.* T **20**, **21**, *and similar type.* P 13½.

108	**20**	60 h. violet	..	10	10
109	**21**	1 k. 20, carmine	..	10	10
110	—	2 k. 50, ultramarine	..	10	15

Design:—2 k. 50, Blacksmith scene from *Siegfried*.

(Des F. Rotter. Photo)

1943 (28 May). *1st Death Anniv of Reinhard Heydrich (German Governor).* P 13½.

111	**22**	60 h. + 4 k. 40, black	..	15	30

23 Arms of Bohemia   **24** National   **25** Arms of Bohemia
and Moravia and   Costumes   and Moravia
Red Cross

(Des A. Erhardt. Photo)

1943 (16 Sept). *Red Cross Relief Fund.* P 13½.

112	**23**	1 k. 20 + 8 k. 80, black and carmine	..	10	15

(Des A. Erhardt. Photo)

1944 (15 Mar). *5th Anniv of German Occupation.* P 13½.
113 **24** 1 k. 20+3 k. 80, carmine 10 10
114 **25** 4 k. 20+10 k. 80, brown 10 10
115 **24** 10 k.+20 k. blue 10 15

(Des and eng J. Schmidt. Recess)

1944 (21 Nov). P 12½.
120 **28** 1 k. 50, brown-purple 10 15
121 2 k. 50, slate-violet 10 20
Each issued in sheets of 100 stamps and 12 blank labels.

26 Adolf Hitler   **27** Smetana   **28** St. Vitus's Cathedral, Prague

29 Adolf Hitler

(Des A. Erhardt. Photo)

1944 (20 Apr). *Hitler's 55th Birthday.* P 13½.
116 **26** 60 h.+1 k. 40, brown 10 10
117 1 k. 20+3 k. 80, green 10 15

(Des J. Schmidt after photograph by H. Hoffmann. Eng J. Goldschmied. Recess)

1944. P 12½.
122 **29** 4 k. 20, blue-green 10 30

(Des J. Sejpka. Eng J. Goldschmied. Recess)

1944 (12 May). *60th Death Anniv of Bedřich Smetana (composer).* P 12½.
118 **27** 60 h.+1 k. 40, grey-green 10 10
119 1 k. 20+3 k. 80, claret 10 15
Each issued in sheets of 100 stamps and 12 blank labels.

Bohemia and Moravia were freed from German rule during April and early May, 1945, and the Sudeten German inhabitants were then deported to Germany. Issues of stamps for Czechoslovakia were resumed.

Czech Republic

100 Haleru = 1 Koruna

The Czech and Slovak Federative Republic (Czechoslovakia) was dissolved on 31 December 1992, the two constituent republics becoming independent. The Czech Republic consists of Bohemia and Moravia and the area of Silesia which formed part of Czechoslovakia from 1920.

Stamps of Czechoslovakia remained valid in the Czech Republic until 30 September 1993.

PRINTERS AND PRINTING PROCESS. All stamps were printed by the Post Office Ptg Wks, Prague, *unless otherwise indicated.* Recess* = Printed by a combination of recess-printing and photogravure.

PHOSPHORESCENT PAPER. Many issues are on phosphorescent paper; this reacts *yellow* under an ultra-violet lamp. The non-phosphorescent paper used for other issues reacts *white* under a UV lamp due to brighteners used in the manufacture of the paper.

1 State Arms   **2** Skater's Boots and Tulip

(Des and eng J. Herčík. Recess*)

1993 (20 Jan). *Phosphorescent paper.* P 11½.
1 **1** 3 k. multicoloured   15   10

(Des I. Strnad. Eng M. Ondráček. Recess*)

1993 (17 Feb). *Ice Skating Championships, Prague. Phosphorescent paper.* P 11½.
2 **2** 2 k. multicoloured   10   10

3 Pres. Vaclav Havel   **4** St. John and Charles Bridge, Prague

(Des and eng M. Ondráček. Recess*)

1993 (2 Mar). *Phosphorescent paper.* P 12×11½.
3 **3** 2 k. dull purple, bright blue and deep mauve   10   10

(Des J. Riess. Eng J. Herčík. Recess*)

1993 (11 Mar). *600th Death Anniv of St. John of Nepomuk (patron saint of Bohemia). Phosphorescent paper.* P 12×11½.
4 **4** 8 k. multicoloured   60   50

HAVE YOU READ THE NOTES AT THE BEGINNING OF THIS CATALOGUE?

These often provide answers to the enquiries we receive.

5 "Hladový Svatý I" (Mikuláš Medek)   **6** Church of Sacred Heart, Prague

(Des and eng V. Fajt. Recess)

1993 (11 Mar). *Europa. Contemporary Art.* P 11½.
5 **5** 14 k. multicoloured   ..   ..   ..   1·40   1·40
Issued in sheets of four stamps.

(Des and eng K. Pavel. Recess)

1993 (30 Mar). P 11½.
6 **6** 5 k. multicoloured   40   40
Issued in sheets of eight stamps.

7 Břevnov Monastery   **8** Weightlifter

(Des and eng K. Pavel. Recess*)

1993 (14 Apr). *U.N.E.S.C.O. World Heritage Site. Millenary of Brevnov Monastery, Prague. Phosphorescent paper.* P 12×11½.
7 **7** 4 k. multicoloured   30   15

(Des I. Strnad. Eng M. Ondráček. Recess*)

1993 (12 May). *Junior Weightlifting Championships, Cheb. Phosphorescent paper.* P 11½.
8 **8** 6 k. multicoloured   40   25

9 Town Hall Tower and Cathedral of St. Peter and St. Paul   **10** Sts. Cyril and Methodius

(Des J. Fišer. Eng V. Fajt. Recess)

1993 (16 June). *750th Anniv of Brno.* P 11½.
9 **9** 8 k. multicoloured   60   35
Issued in sheets of eight stamps.

(Des I. Benca. Eng M. Srb. Recess*)

1993 (22 June). *1130th Anniv of Arrival of Sts. Cyril and Methodius in Moravia. Phosphorescent paper.* P 12×11½.
10 **10** 8 k. multicoloured 60 35

11 State Arms   **12** České Budějovice

(Des and eng B. Housa. Recess)

1993 (22 June). *Sheet 76×90 mm.* P 11½.
MS11 **11** 8 k.×2, multicoloured .. .. 1·00 1·00

(Des J. Bouda; eng B. Šneider (Nos. 15, 20). Des and eng J. Herčík (14), J. Bouda (others). Recess*)

1993 (1 July)–**94**. *Towns.* T **12** *and similar designs. Phosphorescent paper.* P 11½×12 (No. 14) or 12×11½ (others).
12	1 k. purple-brown and orange-red		10	10
13	2 k. crimson and blue	..	10	10
14	3 k. slate-blue and bright carmine	..	15	10
15	3 k. blue and vermilion (30.3.94)	..	15	10
16	5 k. blue-green and chestnut	..	25	20
20	8 k. deep violet and orange-yellow		40	30
21	10 k. blackish green and scarlet	..	55	35
23	20 k. rose-red and dull ultramarine	..	1·10	70
26	50 k. chestnut and green ..	..	2·50	1·60
12/26	Set of 9	..	4·75	3·25

Designs: *Vert*—2 k. Ústi nad Labem; 3 k. (15) Brno; 5 k. Pilsen; 8 k. Olomouc; 10 k. Hradec Králové; 20 k. Prague; 50 k. Opava. *Horiz*—3 k. (14) Český Krumlov (U.N.E.S.C.O. World Heritage Site).

Numbers have been left for additions to this series.

13 Rower   **14** August Sedláček (historian, 150th anniv)

(Des I. Strnad. Eng M. Ondráček. Recess*)

1993 (18 Aug). *World Rowing Championships, Račice. Phosphorescent paper.* P 11½.
27 **13** 3 k. multicoloured 15 10

(Des J. Baláž. Eng M. Činovský. Recess*)

1993 (26 Aug). *Birth Anniversaries.* T **14** *and similar vert design. Phosphorescent paper.* P 12×11½.
28 2 k. buff, indigo and green .. 10 10
29 3 k. buff, blue-violet and reddish violet .. 15 10
Design:—3 k. Eduard Čech (mathematician, centenary).

15 Pedunculate Oak (*Quercus robur*)   **16** "Composition" (Joan Miró)

(Des K. Ševellová. Eng M. Ondráček. Recess*)

1993 (26 Oct). *Trees.* T **15** *and similar vert designs. Multicoloured. Phosphorescent paper.* P 11½.
30 5 k. Type **15** 25 20
31 7 k. Hornbeam (*Carpinus betulus*) .. 35 25
32 9 k. Scots pine (*Pinus silvestris*) .. 50 35

(Des and eng B. Šneider (11 k.), M. Ondráček (14 k.). Recess)

1993 (8 Nov). *Art.* T **16** *and similar horiz design. Multicoloured.* P 12.
33 11 k. Type **16** 75 75
34 14 k. "Green Corn Field with Cypress" (Vincent van Gogh) 95 95
Each issued in sheets of four stamps.

17 St. Nicholas   **18** "Strahov Madonna"

(Des A. Born. Eng M. Srb. Recess*)

1993 (8 Nov). *Christmas. Phosphorescent paper.* P 11½×12.
35 **17** 2 k. multicoloured 10 10

(Des and eng B. Housa. Recess)

1993 (15 Dec). *Christmas.* P 12.
36 **18** 9 k. multicoloured 60 60
Issued in sheets of four stamps.

19 "Family" (C. Littasy-Rollier)   **20** Kubelík

(Des A. Fuchs. Eng V. Fajt. Recess*)

1994 (19 Jan). *International Year of the Family. Phosphorescent paper.* P 11½.
37 **19** 2 k. multicoloured 10 10

(Des K. Demel. Eng M. Srb. Recess*)

1994 (19 Jan). *54th Death Anniv of Jan Kubelík (composer and violinist). Phosphorescent paper.* P 11½.
38 **20** 3 k. greenish yellow and black 15 10

21 Voltaire (writer, 300th anniv)   **22** Athletes

(Des O. Kulhánek. Eng M. Ondráček. Recess*)

1994 (2 Feb). *Birth Anniversaries. T* **21** *and similar horiz design. Phosphorescent paper.* P 12×11½.
39 2 k. maroon, brownish grey and mauve .. 10 10
40 6 k. blue-black, slate-blue and blue-green .. 30 20
Design:—6 k. Georg Agricola (mineralogist, 500th anniv).

(Des R. Kolář. Eng M. Ondráček. Recess*)

1994 (2 Feb). *Winter Olympic Games, Lillehammer, Norway. Phosphorescent paper.* P 11½.
41 **22** 5 k. multicoloured 25 20

23 Marco Polo and   **24** Beneš
Fantasy Animal

(Des A. Born. Eng M. Ondráček. Recess)

1994 (4 May). *Europa. Discoveries. Marco Polo's Journeys to the Orient. T* **23** *and similar vert design. Multicoloured.* P 11½.
42 14 k. Type **23** 75 75
 a. Pair. Nos. 42/3 .. .. .. 1·50
43 14 k. Marco Polo and woman on fantasy animals 75 75
Nos. 42/3 were issued together in *se-tenant* pairs within sheets of four stamps.

(Des and eng V. Fajt. Recess*)

1994 (18 May). *110th Birth Anniv of Edvard Beneš (President of Czechoslovakia 1935–38 and 1945–48). Phosphorescent paper.* P 11½.
44 **24** 5 k. deep violet and bright purple .. 25 20

GIBBONS STAMP MONTHLY

—finest and most informative magazine for all collectors. Obtainable from your newsagent or by postal subscription—details on request.

25 Cubist Flats by Josef   **26** Crayon
Chochol, Prague   Figures

(Des P. Hrach; eng V. Fajt (8 k.). Des Z. Ziegler; eng B. Šneider (9 k.). Recess)

1994 (18 May). *U.N.E.S.C.O. World Heritage Sites. T* **25** *and horiz design similar to T* **6**. *Multicoloured.* P 11½.
45 8 k. Market place, Telč 40 40
46 9 k. Type **25** 50 50
Each issued in sheets of eight stamps.

(Des K. Pacovská. Eng V. Fajt. Recess*)

1994 (1 June). *For Children. Phosphorescent paper.* P 11½.
47 **26** 2 k. multicoloured 10 10

27 *Stegosaurus ungulatus*   **28** Statue of Liberty
holding Football

(Des O. Pošmurný. Litho)

1994 (1 June). *Prehistoric Animals. T* **27** *and similar multi-coloured designs. Phosphorescent paper.* P 11½×12 (5 k.) or 12×11½ (others).
48 2 k. Type **27** 10 10
49 3 k. *Apatosaurus excelsus* .. 15 10
50 5 k. *Tarbosaurus bataar* (vert) .. 25 15

(Des I. Strnad. Eng J. Herčík. Recess*)

1994 (1 June). *World Cup Football Championship, U.S.A. Phosphorescent paper.* P 11½.
51 **28** 8 k. multicoloured 35 35

29 Flag of   **30** Olympic Flag
Prague Section   and Flame

(Des Z. Ziegler. Eng M. Ondráček. Recess*)

1994 (15 June). *12th Sokol (sports organization) Congress, Prague. Phosphorescent paper.* P 11½×12.
52 **29** 2 k. multicoloured 10 10

(Des J. Fišer. Eng M. Srb. Recess*)

1994 (15 June). *Centenary of International Olympic Committee. Phosphorescent paper. P 11½×12.*
53 **30** 7 k. multicoloured 30 20

(Des V. Kovářík. Eng K. Pavel. Recess)

1994 (3 Aug). *120th Anniv of Universal Postal Union. P 11½×12.*
54 **31** 11 k. multicoloured 50 50
Issued in sheets of eight stamps.

31 Stylized Carrier Pigeons

Slovakia

100 Haleru=1 Koruna

A. REPUBLIC OF SLOVAKIA
1939–1945

On 6 October 1938, Slovakia was given the autonomy which her leaders had demanded for years. On 10 March 1939, Mgr. Josef Tiso, the Slovak premier, was deposed by Prague for separatist intrigue; with the support of Hitler, Slovakia declared its independence on 14 March, and placed itself under German protection.

No. 362 of Czechoslovakia overprinted "Otvorenle slovenského snemu" and date "18.1.1939" and surcharged "300 h." which was formerly listed as No. 1 of Slovakia is now listed as No. 393b of Czechoslovakia.

Slovenský štát
1939
(2)

1939 (From 21 Mar). *Stamps of Czechoslovakia optd with T* **2.**

Optd horizontally

2	**34**	5 h. deep blue (R.)	..	..	55	70
3		10 h. bistre-brown (R.)		..	10	15
4		20 h. vermilion (B.)		..	10	10
5		25 h. deep blue-green (R.)		..	1·00	1·25
6		30 h. deep claret (B.)		..	10	10
7	**59**	40 h. blue (R.)		..	10	15
8	**60a**	50 h. green (R.)		..	10	10
9	**66**	50 h. green (R.)		..	10	10
10	**60a**	60 h. violet (No. 347) (R.)		..	10	10
11		60 h. blue (No. 391) (R.) (30.3)			6·50	7·50
12	**61**	1 k. claret (B.)		..	10	10

Optd diagonally

13	–	1 k. 20, purple (No. 354) (B.)		..	20	30
14	**64**	1 k. 50, carmine (B.)			20	30
15	–	1 k. 60, olive-green (No. 355a) (B.)			1·75	2·00
16	–	2 k. green (No. 356) (R.)			1·75	2·00
17	–	2 k. 50, blue (No. 357) (R.)			35	45
18	–	3 k. chocolate (No. 358) (R.)			40	60
19	–	3 k. 50, violet (No. 359) (R.)			18·00	20·00
		a. Blue opt			22·00	25·00
20	**65**	4 k. violet (R.)			8·00	10·00
21	–	5 k. grey-green (No. 361) (R.)			10·00	12·00
22	–	10 k. blue (No. 362) (R.)			75·00	85·00
2/22		*Set of 21*			£110	£130

(3)　　　　(N 4)

1939 (Apr). *As T* **4,** *but inscr* "CESKO-SLOVENSKO SLOV-ENSKA POSTA", *optd with T* **3.** *P* 12½.

23	50 h. green (R.)		..	1·25	50
	a. Perf 10½			1·25	75
	b. Perf compound of 10½ and 12½		2·75	2·25
24	1 k. carmine (B.)		..	1·00	50
	a. Perf 10½			85·00	£120
	b. Perf compound of 10½ and 12½		5·50	5·00

1939 (Apr). *NEWSPAPER. Nos.* N364/72 *of Czechoslovakia optd with Type N* **4.**

N25	**N 67**	2 h. yellow-brown (B.)		25	25
N26		5 h. pale blue (R.)		25	25
N27		7 h. orange-vermilion (B.)		25	25
N28		9 h. emerald-green (R.)		25	25
N29		10 h. brown-lake (B.)		25	25
N30		12 h. bright ultramarine (R.)		25	25
N31		20 h. deep green (R.)		60	75
N32		50 h. red-brown (B.)		1·90	2·00
N33		1 k. grey-olive (R.)		7·00	7·50
N25/33		*Set of 9*		10·00	10·50

PRINTING PROCESS. All the following postage stamps were printed in photogravure unless otherwise stated.

4 Father Hlinka　　　**5**

(Photo "Slovenska Grafia" Ptg Wks, Bratislava)

1939 (Apr)–**42.** *P* 12½.

(a) No wmk (April–June 1939)

25	**4**	5 h. ultramarine		40	40
26		10 h. olive-green		65	55
		a. Perf 10½		16·00	13·00
		b. Perf compound of 10½ and 12½	18·00	8·75
27		20 h. orange-red		65	55
		a. Imperf		50	65
28		30 h. violet		65	55
		a. Perf 10½		12·00	12·00
		b. Perf compound of 10½ and 12½	4·50	4·50
		c. Imperf		75	75
29		50 h. green (5.6.39)		65	55
30		1 k. carmine		75	55
31	–	2 k. 50, blue		75	25
		a. Perf compound of 10½ and 12½	18·00	7·50
32	–	3 k. sepia		2·00	50
		a. Perf 10½		1·75	75
		b. Perf compound of 10½ and 12½	1·75	75

(b) W **5** (1940–42)

33	**4**	1 k. carmine		65	45
34	–	2 k. 50, blue		75	65
		a. Perf 10½		50	65
35	–	3 k. sepia		1·00	75
		a. Perf 10½		1·10	75
25/35		*Set of 11* (*cheapest*)		7·50	5·00

The portrait of the 2 k. 50 and 3 k. values is smaller and the frame is beaded.

For 1 k. 30 value, see No. 81.

6 Gen. M. R. Štefánik　　**N 7**
and his Grave

The following stamps as Type **6.** perf 12½. were prepared in May 1939 to commemorate the twentieth anniversary of the death of General Štefánik, but were not issued:—

40 h. green
60 h. blackish olive
1 k. deep violet
2 k. brown and deep blue (*larger, 30 × 24 mm.*).

Price per set, un. £3

1939 (15 June). *NEWSPAPER. Typo. No wmk. Imperf.*

N40	**N 7**	2 h. yellow-brown		20	15
N41		5 h. blue		60	30
N42		7 h. orange-vermilion		20	20
N43		9 h. emerald-green		20	20
N44		10 h. brown-lake		1·10	65
N45		12 h. bright ultramarine		20	20
N46		20 h. deep green		1·00	65
N47		50 h. red-brown		1·25	75
N48		1 k. grey-olive		1·00	75
N40/48		*Set of 9*		5·25	3·50

See also Nos. N65/73.

7 Krivan   **8** Chamois   **9** Mgr. Tiso

10 Weaving   **11** Sawyer   **12** Presidential Palace, Bratislava

(Des J. Votruba (Nos. 40/46). Benka (Nos. 47/50))

1939 (Sept)**—42.** *T* **7** *to* **12** *and similar types. Nos.* 40/44 17½×21 *mm.* **W 5.** *P* 10 *or* 12½

40	–	5 h. olive-green (1.8.40)		15	15
41	**7**	10 h. chocolate (1.8.40)		10	10
42	–	20 h. blue-grey (1.8.40)		10	10
43	**8**	25 h. sepia (1.8.40)		40	15
44	–	30 h. chestnut (1.8.40)		20	15
45	**9**	50 h. dull olive-green (6.10.39)		40	25
46		70 h. red-brown (1942)		25	15
47	**10**	2 k. green (9.39)		4·50	40
48	**11**	4 k. red-brown (6.10.39)		1·00	60
49	–	5 k. red (6.10.39)		90	25
50	**12**	10 k. blue (14.3.40)		75	55
40/50		*Set of* 11		7·75	2·50

Designs:—As T **7**, 5 h. Zelené Pleso; 20 h. Kvety Satier (Edelweiss); 30 h. Javorina. As T **11**, 5 k. Woman filling ewer at spring.
See also Nos. 101/5 and 125/9.

D 13   **13** Rev. J. Murgas and Wireless Masts

1939–40. *POSTAGE DUE. P* 12½
A. *No wmk* (9.39). B. **W 5** (1940)

					A		B	
D51	D **13**	5 h. blue			25	40	50	45
D52		10 h. blue			25	40	25	20
D53		20 h. blue			25	60	40	20
D54		30 h. blue			1·00	65	5·00	4·00
D55		40 h. blue			1·00	90	50	40
D56		50 h. blue			1·25	75	65	75
D57		60 h. blue			1·00	75	75	75
D58		1 k. scarlet			11·50	8·50	1·25	85
D59		2 k. scarlet			11·50	2·50	7·50	6·50
D60		5 k. scarlet			3·75	2·50	2·00	1·90
D61		10 k. scarlet			30·00	8·00	2·50	2·40
D62		20 k. scarlet			12·50	9·00	†	
D51/62A		*Set of* 12			65·00	30·00	†	
D51/61B		*Set of* 11			†		19·00	16·00

1939–41. 10*th Death Anniv of Rev. J. Murgas. P* 12½

(a) No wmk (Sept 1939)

51	**13**	60 h. bright violet		25	25
52		1 k. 20, slate		50	15

(b) **W 5** (1941)

53	**13**	60 h. bright violet		20	15

1939. (6 Nov). *Child Welfare. As No.* 45, *but larger portrait of Dr. Tiso inscr* "+2.50 DETOM" (24×30 *mm.*)

54		2 k. 50+2 k. 50, blue		2·25	2·50

14 Heinkel   **15** Heinkel   **16** Eagle and
He 111C over   He 116A over   Aero A-204
Lake Csorba   Tatra Mountains

(Des J. C. Vondrous (T **14**/**15**) and J. Vlček (T **16**))

1939–44. *AIR. P* 12½. *(a) No wmk* (20.11.39).

55	**14**	30 h. violet		25	25
56		50 h. green		25	25
57		1 k. vermilion		30	25
58	**15**	2 k. blackish green		45	40
59		3 k. brown		90	80
60		4 k. blue		1·50	1·50

(b) **W 5** (1940–44)

61	**14**	1 k. vermilion (15.9.44)		30	30
62	**16**	5 k. brown-purple (30.11.40)		1·00	1·40
63		10 k. blue-grey (30.11.40)		1·25	1·50
64		20 k. slate-green (30.11.40)		1·50	2·00
55/64		*Set of* 10		7·00	8·00

P 17   **17** Stiavnica Castle

1940. *PERSONAL DELIVERY.* **W 5.** *Imperf.*

P65	P **17**	50 h. blue		75	1·25
		a. Tête-bêche (pair)		1·50	2·50
P66		50 h. carmine		75	1·25
		a. Tête-bêche (pair)		1·50	2·50

1940–41. *NEWSPAPER. Typo.* **W 5.** *Imperf.*

N65	N **7**	5 h. blue		20	20
N66		10 h. brown-lake		20	15
N67		15 h. purple (1941)		20	15
N68		20 h. deep green		40	45
N69		25 h. blue (1941)		30	45
N70		40 h. vermilion (1941)		40	45
N71		50 h. red-brown		65	50
N72		1 k. grey-olive (1941)		65	50
N73		2 k. light green (1941)		1·25	90
N65/73		*Set of* 9		3·75	3·25

1941 (20 May–June). *As T* **17** *(various castles).* **W 5.** *P* 12½.

65		1 k. 20, claret		20	15
66		1 k. 50, carmine (Lietava)		20	15
67		1 k. 60, blue (Spissky Hrad)		25	10
68		2 k. green (Bojnice) (28.6)		20	10
65/68		*Set of* 4		75	40

18 S. M. Daxner and   **19** Wounded Soldier
Bishop Moyses   and Red Cross Orderly

1941 (26 May). 80*th Anniv of Presentation of a Slovak Memorandum to Emperor Francis Joseph.* **W 5.** *P* 12½.

69	**18**	50 h. olive-green		1·40	1·50
70		1 k. slate-blue		6·00	6·00
71		2 k. black		6·00	6·00

(Des Schurmann)

1941 (10 Nov). *Red Cross Fund.* W **5.** P 12½.
72	**19**	50 h. + 50 h. green			40	45
73		1 k. + 1 k. claret			50	50
74		2 k. + 1 k. blue			1·50	1·25

20 Mother and Child   **21** Soldier and Hlinka Youth Member

1941 (10 Dec). *Child Welfare Fund.* W **5.** P 12½.
75	**20**	50 h. + 50 h. green			75	70
76		1 k. + 1 k. brown			75	70
77		2 k. + 1 k. violet			75	70

(Des Schurmann)

1942 (14 Mar). *Hlinka Youth Fund.* W **5.** P 12½.
78	**21**	70 h. + 1 k. brown			30	30
79		1 k. 30 + 1 k. blue			40	40
80		2 k. + 1 k. carmine			1·00	1·00

1942. *Father Hlinka.* As T **4** of 1939, but inscr "SLOVENSKO" *(without "POSTA"), above portrait.* W **5.** P 12½.
81	1 k. 30, violet			40	15

22 Boy Stamp Collector   **23** Dove and St. Stephens

1942 (23 May). *Philatelic Exhibition, Bratislava. T **22** and similar vert designs.* W **5.** P 12½.
82	30 h. green				90	90
83	70 h. carmine				90	90
84	80 h. violet				90	90
85	1 k. 30, brown				90	90
82/85	*Set of 4*				3·25	3·25

Designs:—30 h., 1 k. 30, Posthorn, round various arms, above Bratislava; 80 h. Postmaster-General examining stamps.

1942 (12 Oct). *European Postal Congress.* W **5.** P 14.
86	**23**	70 h. blue-green			80	75
87		1 k. 30, grey-olive			80	75
88		2 k. blue			1·75	2·00

D 24   **24** Inaugural Ceremony

1942. *POSTAGE DUE. No wmk.* P 14.
D89	D **24**	10 h. brown			10	10
D90		20 h. brown			10	15
D91		40 h. brown			10	15
D92		50 h. brown			70	50
D93		60 h. brown			15	15
D94		80 h. brown			20	15

D95	D **24**	1 k. scarlet			20	15
D96		1 k. 10, scarlet			40	45
D97		1 k. 30, scarlet			30	15
D98		1 k. 60, scarlet			40	15
D99		2 k. scarlet			45	15
D100		2 k. 60, scarlet			90	75
D101		3 k. 50, scarlet			6·25	6·25
D102		5 k. scarlet			2·25	2·00
D103		10 k. scarlet			2·75	2·50
D89/103		*Set of 15*			13·50	12·50

1942 (14 Dec). *150th Anniv of Foundation of National Literary Society.* W **5.** P 14.
89	**24**	70 h. black			15	15
90		1 k. red			15	15
91		1 k. 30, blue			15	15
92		2 k. brown			20	15
93		3 k. green			35	35
94		4 k. violet			35	35
89/94		*Set of 6*			1·25	1·10

25 L. Stur   **27** National Costumes   **28**   N **29** Printer's Type

1943 (Jan)–**44.** As T **25** *(portraits).* P 14.

A. W **5.** B. *No wmk* (26.1.44)

			A		B	
95	80h. blackish grn (20.1.44)		†		15	10
96	1 k. brown-lake (20.1.44)		†		20	20
97	1 k. 30, ultramarine		15	10	50	30

Portraits:—1 k. M. Razus; 1 k. 30, Father Hlinka.

1943. *Winter Relief Fund. As T **27** and **28** (national costumes).* W **5.** P 14.
98	50 h. + 50 h. green			30	20
99	70 h. + 1 k. carmine			30	20
100	80 h. + 2 k. blue			30	25

Design:—80 h. Mother and two children.

1943. *NEWSPAPER.* W **5.** *Imperf*
N101	N **29**	10 h. green			15	15
N102		15 h. sepia			15	15
N103		20 h. ultramarine			15	15
N104		50 h. red			20	20
N105		1 k. deep green			40	40
N106		2 k. blue			65	65
N101/106		*Set of 6*			1·50	1·50

1943. *As 1939–42, but no wmk.* P 12½.
101	**7**	10 h. chocolate			15	15
102	–	20 h. blue-grey			40	15
103	**8**	25 h. sepia			40	20
104	–	30 h. chestnut			25	20
105	**9**	70 h. red-brown			45	25
101/105		*Set of 5*			1·50	85

29 Infantry   **30** Railway Tunnel

1943 (28 July). *Fighting Forces. As T **29** (military designs).* W **5.** P 14.
106	70 h. + 2 k. lake				50	70
107	1 k. 30 + 2 k. blue				75	85
108	2 k. + 2 k. olive-green				65	65

Designs: *Horiz*—2 k. Artillery. *Vert*—1 k. 30, Air Force.

1943 (5 Sept). *Opening of the Strazke–Prešov Railway. T* **30** *and similar designs. W* **5**. *P* 14.

109	70 h. purple	..	..	80	1·00
110	80 h. blue	..	..	1·00	1·25
111	1 k. 30, black	..	..	1·00	1·40
112	2 k. red-brown	..	..	1·25	2·00
109/112	Set of 4		..	3·50	5·00

Designs: *Horiz*—70 h. Prešov Church; 2 k. Railway viaduct. *Vert*—80 h. Railway engine.

32 *Trans* "The Slovak Language is Our Life"

33 National Museum

1943 (14 Oct). *Culture Fund. T* **32**/**3** *and similar types. W* **5**. *P* 14.

113	30 h. + 1 k. red-brown	..	..	40	30
114	70 h. + 1 k. green	..	..	50	50
115	80 h. + 2 k. blue	..	..	40	30
116	1 k. 30 + 2 k. brown	..	..	40	30
113/116	Set of 4	..	..	1·50	1·25

Designs: *Horiz*—80 h. Matica Slovenska College. *Vert*—1 k. 30, Agricultural student.

34 Prince Pribina Okolo

35 Footballer

1944 (14 Mar). *5th Anniv of Declaration of Independence. As T* **34** *(princes). P* 14.

117	50 h. green	..	..	10	10
118	70 h. magenta	..	..	10	10
119	80 h. red-brown	..	..	10	10
120	1 k. 30, ultramarine	..	..	15	10
121	2 k. blue	..	..	15	15
122	3 k. brown	..	..	35	25
123	5 k. violet	..	..	65	50
124	10 k. black	..	..	1·75	1·60
117/124	Set of 8	..	..	3·00	2·75

Designs:—1 k. 30, King Svatopluk. Princes—Mojmir (70 h.); Ratislav (80 h.); Kocel (2 k.); Mojmir II (3 k.); Svatopluk II 5 k.); Braslav (10 k.).

1944 (Apr). *As 1939–42 but larger* (18½ × 22½ *mm.*), *No wmk. P* 14.

125	**7** 10 h. carmine	..	..	15	25
126	– 20 h. ultramarine	..	..	15	25
127	**8** 25 h. maroon	..	..	15	25
128	– 30 h. bright purple	..	..	15	25
129	– 50 h. green	..	..	15	25
125/129	Set of 5	..	..	70	1·10

Design:—50 h. Zelené Pleso (as No. 40).

1944 (30 Apr). *As T* **35** *(sports). P* 14.

130	70 h. + 70 h. olive-green	..	..	55	65
131	1 k. + 1 k. violet	..	..	70	75
132	1 k. 30 + 1 k. 30 blue-green	..	..	70	75
133	2 k. + 2 k. red-brown	..	..	75	1·10
130/133	Set of 4	..	..	2·40	3·00

Designs: *Vert*—1 k. Skiing; 1 k. 30, Diving. *Horiz*—2 k. Running.

36 Symbolical of "Protection"

37 Children Playing

38 Mgr. Tiso

1944 (6 Oct). *Protection Series. W* **5**. *P* 14.

134	**36** 70 h. + 4 k. blue	..	..	80	1·10
135	1 k. 30 + 4 k. red-brown	..	..	80	1·10
136	2 k. green	..	..	30	20
137	3 k. 80, purple	..	..	30	40
134/137	Set of 4	..		2·00	2·50

1944 (18 Dec). *Child Welfare. W* **5**. *P* 14.

138	**37** 2 k. + 4 k. blue	..	..	3·00	3·00

Printed in sheets of 8 stamps with centre label depicting arms.

1945. *P* 14. *(a) No wmk.*

139	**38** k. orange	..	..	75	50
140	1 k. 50, brown	..	..	20	15
141	2 k. blue-green	..	..	25	15
142	4 k. carmine	..	..	75	50
143	5 k. blue	..	..	75	50

(b) W **5**

144	**38** 10 k. purple	..	..	50	25
139/144	Set of 6	..	..	3·00	1·90

In May 1945, Slovakia was re-incorporated in Czechoslovakia; Ruthenia was ceded to the Soviet Union on 29 June 1945. Mgr. Tiso was executed on 16 April 1947.

B. SLOVAK REPUBLIC
1 January 1993

The Czech and Slovak Federative Republic (Czechoslovakia) was dissolved on 31 December 1992, the two constituent republics becoming independent.

Stamps of Czechoslovakia remained valid until 30 September 1993.

PRINTERS AND PRINTING PROCESS. All stamps were printed by the Post Office Ptg Wks, Czech Republic, *unless otherwise stated.* Recess*=Printed by a combination of recess-printing and photogravure.

PHOSPHORESCENT PAPER. Many issues are on phosphorescent paper; this reacts *yellow* under an ultra-violet lamp. The non-phosphorescent paper used for other issues reacts *white* under a UV lamp due to brighteners used in the manufacture of the paper.

39 State Arms   **40** Ružomberok   **41** Pres. Michal Kováč

(Des and eng M. Činovský. Recess* (3 k.) or recess (8 k.))

1993 (1–2 Jan). *Phosphorescent paper* (3 k.). *P* 11½.

145	**39** 3 k. multicoloured (2 Jan)	..	..	20	20
146	8 k. multicoloured (26×40 *mm*)	..	..	85	85

No. 146 was issued in sheets of 6 stamps.

(Des and eng J. Herčík (5 k.), J. Bouda (10 k.), M. Činovský (30 k.).
Des D. Kállay; eng M. Činovský (others). Recess*)

1993 (31 Jan–Dec). *T* **40** *and similar designs. Phosphorescent
paper.* P 11½×12 (*horiz*) *or* 12×11½ (*vert*).
147   5 k. deep blue and orange-red 25   15
148 10 k. deep lilac and orange 55   30
150 30 k. black, new blue & brt scarlet (24.9.93) 1·50   75
151 50 k. blue-black, orange & lt blue (31.12.93) 2·75 1·40
147/151 *Set of 4* .. .. .. 4·50 2·40
  Design: *Vert*—10 k. Košice; 50 k. Bratislava. *Horiz*—30 k. Suden
Castle.
  Numbers have been left for additions to this series.

(Des and eng M. Činovský. Recess (2 k.) or recess* (3 k.))

1993 (2 Mar–Nov). *Phosphorescent paper.* P 12×11½.
156 **41** 2 k. blue-black 10 10
157   3 k. chocolate & bright magenta (3 Nov) 15 10

42 St. John and Charles **43** Pedunculate
Bridge, Prague   Oak (*Quercus
                  robur*)

(Des J. Riess. Eng J. Herčík. Recess*)

1993 (11 Mar). *600th Death Anniv of St. John of Nepomuk
*(*patron saint of Bohemia*). *Phosphorescent paper.* P 12×11½.
158 **42** 8 k. multicoloured 50 25

(Des K. Ševellová. Eng M. Ondráček. Recess*)

1993 (14 May). *Trees. T* **43** *and similar vert designs.
Multicoloured. Phosphorescent paper.* P 11½.
159   3 k. Type **43** 15 10
160   4 k. Hornbeam (*Carpinus betulus*) .. 20 10
161 10 k. Scots pine (*Pinus sylvestris*) .. 55 30

44 Ján Levoslav **45** "Woman with Jug"
Bella (composer)   (Marián Čunderlik)

(Des J. Baláž. Eng M. Činovský. Recess*)

1993 (20 May). *Anniversaries. T* **44** *and similar vert designs.
Phosphorescent paper.* P 12×11½.
162   5 k. cream, chestnut and blue .. 25 15
163   8 k. pale cinnamon, sepia & rose-carmine 45 25
164 20 k. pale buff, grey-blue & yellow-orange 1·00 50
  Designs:—5 k. Type **44** (150th birth anniv); 8 k. Alexander
Dubček (statesman) (first death anniv); 20 k. Jan Kollár (poet and
scholar) (birth bicentenary).

(Des and eng K. Pavel. Recess)

1993 (31 May). *Europa. Contemporary Art.* P 11½.
165 **45** 14 k. multicoloured .. .. 1·00 1·00
  Issued in sheets of 4 stamps.

46 Sun   **47** Arms of
                       Dubnica nad
                       Váhom

(Des I. Benca. Eng M. Činovský (166), M. Srb (167). Recess*)

1993 (22 June). *Anniversaries. T* **46** *and similar horiz designs.
Multicoloured. Phosphorescent paper.* P 12×11½.
166 2 k. Type **46** (150th anniv of Slovakian
     written language) 10 10
167 8 k. Sts. Cyril and Methodius (1130th anniv
     of arrival in Moravia) 45 25

(Des and eng M. Činovský. Recess*)

1993 (8 July). *Phosphorescent paper.* P 12×11½.
168 **47** 1 k. silver, black and bright blue .. 10 10

48 "The Big Pets" **49** Canal Lock, Gabčikovo
(Lane Smith)

(Des L. Krátky. Eng R. Ciganik. Recess*)

1993 (2 Sept). 14*th Biennial Exhibition of Book Illustrations for
Children, Bratislava. Phosphorescent paper.* P 11½.
169 **48** 5 k. multicoloured 25 15

(Des J. Baláž. Eng M. Činovský. Recess*)

1993 (12 Nov). *Rhine–Main–Danube Canal. Phosphorescent
paper.* P 11½×12.
170 **49** 10 k. multicoloured 65 35
  No. 170 was issued with *se-tenant* half stamp-size label
showing a map of the river–canal system.

50 Child's Face **51** "Madonna and
in Blood-drop   Child" (Jozef
                 Klemens)

(Des and eng F. Horniak. Recess*)

1993 (15 Nov). *Red Cross. Phosphorescent paper.* P 11½.
171 **50** 3 k. + 1 k. scarlet and grey-blue .. 20 10

(Des and eng M. Činovský. Recess*)

1993 (1 Dec). *Christmas. Phosphorescent paper.* P 11½.
172 **51** 2 k. multicoloured 10 10

52 Milan Štefánik's Tomb, Bradlo

(Des K. Felix. Eng M. Činovský. Recess)

1993 (17 Dec). *Sheet* 70×90 *mm. P* 11½.
MS173 **52** 16 k. multicoloured .. .. 1·00 1·00

53 "The Labourer's Spring" **54** Ski Jumping
(Jozef Kostka)

(Des and eng M. Činovský. Recess)

1993 (31 Dec). *Art. P* 12.
174 **53** 9 k. multicoloured 45 45
Issued in sheets of four stamps.

(Des D. Nágel. Eng F. Horniak. Recess*)

1994 (26 Jan). *Winter Olympic Games, Lillehammer, Norway. Phosphorescent paper. P* 11½.
175 **54** 2 k. black, mauve and blue 10 10

55 Family **56** Antoine de
Saint-Exupéry (writer
and pilot) (50th death)

(Des Z. Tóthová. Eng M. Činovský. Recess*)

1994 (29 Apr). *International Year of the Family. Phosphorescent paper. P* 11½.
176 **55** 3 k. multicoloured 15 10

(Des R. Brun (8 k.), M. Činovský (9 k.). Eng M. Činovský. Recess*)

1994 (25 May). *Anniversaries. T* **56** *and similar horiz design. Phosphorescent paper. P* 11½.
177 8 k. brown-red and new blue 45 25
178 9 k. multicoloured 45 25
Design:—8 k. János András Segner (mathematician and physicist) (290th birth).

57 Jozef Murgaš **58** Cigarettes
(radio-telegraphy
pioneer)

(Des D. Grečner. Eng M. Činovský. Recess)

1994 (27 May). *Europa. Inventions. P* 11½.
179 **57** 28 k. multicoloured .. .. .. 1·40 70

(Des Z. Brázdil. Eng M. Činovský. Recess*)

1994 (31 May). *World No Smoking Day. Phosphorescent paper. P* 11½.
180 **58** 3 k. multicoloured 15 10

59 Football Pitch **60** Ancient Greek Runner
as Tie passing Baton to Modern Athlete

(Des S. Mydlo. Eng B. Šneider. Recess*)

1994 (10 June). *World Cup Football Championship, U.S.A. Phosphorescent paper. P* 11½.
181 **59** 2 k. multicoloured 10 10

(Des I. Schurmann. Eng M. Činovský. Recess*)

1994 (23 June). *Centenary of International Olympic Committee. Phosphorescent paper. P* 12×11½.
182 **60** 3 k. multicoloured 15 10
No. 182 was issued in sheets of 30 stamps and 40 half stamp-size labels showing the emblem of the Slovak Olympic Committee.

61 Golden Eagle **62** Prince Svätopluk
(*Aquila chrysaëtos*)

(Des J. Švec. Eng R. Cigánik. Recess*)

1994 (4 July). *Birds. T* **61** *and similar vert designs. Multicoloured. Phosphorescent paper. P* 11½×12.
183 4 k. Type **61** 20 10
184 5 k. Peregrine falcon (*Falco peregrinus*) .. 25 15
185 7 k. Eagle owl (*Bubo bubo*) 30 15

(Des T. Bártfay. Eng J. Herčík. Recess)

1994 (20 July). *1100th Death Anniv of Prince Svätopluk of Moravia. P* 12.

186 **62** 12 k. lake-brown, buff and black .. 50 50

Issued in sheets of four stamps with gutter label showing a Slavonian sword.

63 Boat with Stamp for Sail	**64** Generals Rudolf Viest and Ján Golian

(Des O. Solga. Eng R. Cigánik. Recess*)

1994 (1 Aug). *120th Anniv of Universal Postal Union. Phosphorescent paper. P* 11½×12.

187 **63** 8 k. multicoloured 35 20

(Des J. Baláž. Eng Činovský. Recess*)

1994 (27 Aug). *50th Anniv of Slovak Uprising. T* **64** *and similar horiz design. Phosphorescent paper. P* 12×11½.

188 6 k. deep violet-blue, bright rose and yellow 25 15
189 8 k. multicoloured 35 20

Design:—8 k. French volunteers and their Memorial.

Each issued in sheets of 30 stamps and 40 half stamp-size labels.

65 Janko Matúška (lyricist) and Allegory of *A Well She Dug* (melody)

(Des V. Hložník. Eng M. Činovský. Recess*)

1994 (1 Sept). *"Over the Tatras Lightning Breaks"* (national anthem). *Sheet* 66×79 *mm. P* 12×11½.

MS190 **65** 34 k. multicoloured .. .. 1·40 1·40

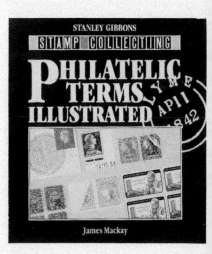

Poland

1860. 100 Kopeks=1 Rouble
1918. 100 Pfennig=1 Mark
1918. 100 Halerzy=1 Korona (South Poland)
1918. 100 Fenigów=1 Marka (North Poland and throughout the country in 1919)
1924. 100 Groszy=1 Zloty

I. RUSSIAN PROVINCE

The ancient Kingdom of Poland was partitioned between Russia, Austria and Prussia in 1772–95. Napoleon I created a Grand Duchy of Warsaw and in 1815 most of this became a new Kingdom of Poland, with the Tsar of Russia as king. Following a revolt in 1830–31, Poland became a Russian province in 1832.

1 Russian Arms

(Eng H. Mejer. Typo Govt Ptg Office, Warsaw)

1860 (1 Jan). *Wove paper. P 11½ to 12½.*
1 **1** 10 k. deep blue and carmine .. £800 £200
 a. Blue and rose .. £475 £170
 b. Pale blue and pale rose .. £475 £160
 c. Frame of oval ptd twice, in rose and in blue .. £1200 £400
 d. Imperf .. — £5000

As 1 January 1860 was a Sunday when post offices were closed, No. 1 was not available until 2 January (local Gregorian calendar). Letters to Russia had to have town postmark in Russian; as Russia still used the Julian calendar at this time the corresponding date was 20 December 1859.

Another Polish revolt in 1863–64 led to the incorporation of Poland in the Russian postal system on 13 February 1865 and the replacement of Polish stamps by Russian stamps. No. 1 was demonetized 13 April 1865 (Gregorian calendar).

II. REPUBLIC

From 1915 to 1918, Poland was in German and Austro-Hungarian occupation. Overprinted German stamps were used in the German Zone (see German Occupation issues at the end of this list) and Austro-Hungarian Military Post stamps in the Austro-Hungarian Zone. On 3 November 1918 a Polish Republic was proclaimed; during 1919–21 Poland acquired large areas from surrounding states. Western Galicia, part of the Austrian Empire, was awarded to Poland by the Powers on 8 May 1919. On 20 November 1919 the Powers agreed that Eastern Galicia (which in 1918–19 had been the West Ukrainian Republic) should be under Polish protection for 25 years; on 14 March 1923 this decision was repealed, and the area was integrated with Poland. The German province of Posen (Poznan) and parts of West Prussia and Lower Silesia were awarded to Poland by the Treaty of Versailles, 28 June 1919, and part of Upper Silesia was awarded to her after plebiscite in 1921. After almost continual warfare between Poland and Russia from 1918 to 1920, the Treaty of Riga, 18 March 1921, gave Poland large parts of White Russia and Volhynia. Central Lithuania was acquired on 8 April 1922.

5 Jan III Sobieski Monument, Warsaw

(6a)   (6b)

(Des E. Trojanowski. Litho)

1918 (17 Nov). *Warsaw issue. Stamps prepared for use by Warsaw Citizens' Post, surch and optd "Poczta Polska" as in T* **2/5.** *Background of central design in buff. Wmk Horiz Wavy Lines. P 11½.*
2 **2** 5 FEN. on 2 g. brown .. 70 60
 a. Surch inverted .. 30·00 27·00
3 **3** 10 FEN. on 6 g. green .. 60 50
 a. Surch inverted .. 3·50 3·25
4 **4** 25 FEN. on 10 g. carmine .. 1·90 1·25
 a. Surch inverted .. 7·50 6·75
5 **5** 50 FEN. on 20 g. blue .. 4·25 3·00
 a. Surch inverted .. £110 85·00

T **6**: Distance between 2nd and 3rd bars:
6a—3¼ mm (1st ptg, 5.12.18); **6**b—4 mm (2nd ptg, 15.1.19)

1918 (5 Dec)–**19.** *Issue for former area of German occupation. Nos. 6 etc. of German Occupation of Poland (German stamps optd "Gen. Gouv. Warschau").*

(a) *Surch as T* **6**a (A) *or* **6**b (B)

			A	B
6	**24**	5 on 2½ pf. grey ..	30	30 25
7	**17**	5 on 3 pf. brown ..	2·25	1·25 20·00 16·00
8	**24**	25 on 7½ pf. orange ..	40	30 65 50

(b) *Optd "Poczta Polska" and bars as in T* **6**a/b

			A	B
9	**17**	pf. brown (15.1.19) ..	†	9·00 6·00
10		5 pf. green ..	40	40 80 45
11		10 pf. carmine ..	20	20 15 15
12	**24**	15 pf. slate-violet ..	20	20 20 15
13	**17**	20 pf. deep blue ..	20	20 20 20
		a. Violet-blue ..	20	20 20 20
		b. Ultram (15.1.19) ..	†	£200 £200
14		30 pf. black & orange/buff ..	20	20 15 15
15		40 pf. black and carmine ..	30	30 30 30
16		60 pf. magenta	30	30 35 35
6/16A		*Set of 10* ..	4·25	3·25 †
6/16B		*Set of 11* ..	†	29·00 22·00

Many of the above exist with inverted or double overprint, with "Pocata" or "Poczto" for "Poczta", or with various letters omitted or inverted.

A. REGIONAL ISSUES

2 Sigismund III Vasa Column, Warsaw

3 Arms of Warsaw

4 Polish Eagle

7

(8)

1918 (5 Dec). *Issue for former zone of Austro-Hungarian occupation. Imperial Welfare Fund stamps of Austro-Hungarian Military Post, optd as in T **7**, at Lublin.*

17 **6**	10 h. green		5·75	5·25
	a. Opt inverted		15·00	17·00
	b. Opt double		85·00	85·00
18 **7**	20 h. claret		5·75	5·25
	a. Opt inverted		15·00	17·00
	b. Opt double		85·00	85·00
19 **6**	45 h. blue		5·75	5·25
	a. Opt inverted		15·00	17·00
	b. Opt double		85·00	85·00

1918 (19–21 Dec). *Second issue for former Austro-Hungarian zone. Emperor Charles stamps of Austro-Hungarian Military Post surch as in T **8**, at Lublin. P 12½.*

(a) With stars

20 **4**	3 h. on 3 h. olive-green		30·00	17·00
	a. Surch inverted		£130	£130
	b. Perf 11½		18·00	12·50
	ba. Surch inverted		£100	£100
	c. Perf 11½×12½		23·00	23·00
21	3 h. on 15 h. rose-pink		3·75	2·00
	a. Surch inverted		12·00	12·00
22	10 h. on 30 h. deep green		3·75	2·00
	a. Surch inverted		12·00	12·00
	b. Surch in violet		35·00	29·00
	ba. Surch inverted		£170	£170
23	25 h. on 40 h. olive		6·00	2·75
	a. Surch inverted		18·00	18·00
	b. Perf 11½		9·00	6·00
	ba. Surch inverted		32·00	32·00
24	45 h. on 60 h. carmine		5·50	2·75
	a. Surch inverted		12·00	12·00
25	45 h. on 80 h. blue		6·00	2·75
	a. Surch inverted		18·00	18·00
26	50 h. on 60 h. carmine		5·50	2·75
	a. Surch inverted		12·00	12·00

On Nos. 22/7 "HAL." is in capital letters.

Most of the above exist with left-hand star omitted. In such cases it is often replaced by a vertical smudge running right across the stamp.

Stamps with cancellations before the date of issue are forged surcharges made on genuine stamps.

(b) With two bars instead of stars

27 **4**	45 h. on 80 h. blue		9·00	6·00
	a. Surch inverted		12·00	12·00

(c) Optd only (21 Dec)

28 **4**	50 h. green		38·00	21·00
	a. Opt inverted		50·00	50·00
29	90 h. violet		5·50	3·00
	a. Opt inverted		12·00	12·00
20/29	Set of 10		£100	55·00

1, 2, 5, 6 and 12 h. values with overprint only are private productions.

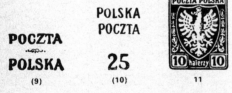

(9) POCZTA POLSKA (9)

(10) POLSKA POCZTA 25 (10)

11 POCZTA POLSKA / 10 halerzy 10

1919 (10 Jan). *Issue for Western Galicia. Austrian stamps of 1916 optd at Cracow.*

*(a) Optd with T **9** (Nos. 45/48) or similar type (others).*

30 **49**	3 h. violet (Imperial Crown)		£170	£130
31	5 h. yellow-green		£170	£130
32	6 h. orange		18·00	12·50
	a. Opt inverted		£1000	
33	10 h. claret		£170	£140
34	12 h. greenish blue		18·00	12·00
35 **60**	15 h. Venetian red (Charles I)		5·25	4·25
36	20 h. deep green		60·00	55·00
37	25 h. blue		£600	£550
38	30 h. dull violet		£120	85·00
39 **51**	40 h. olive (Arms)		12·00	9·50
	a. Opt inverted		60·00	60·00
	b. Opt double		£225	£225

40 **51**	50 h. deep green		4·25	3·50
	a. Opt inverted		£1400	£1400
41	60 h. deep blue		3·25	3·25
	a. Opt inverted		60·00	45·00
42	80 h. red-brown		3·50	3·50
	a. Opt inverted		60·00	60·00
	b. Opt double		75·00	75·00
43	90 h. claret		£500	£400
44	1 k. red/yellow		6·75	4·50
45 **52**	2 k. deep blue (Arms)		3·75	3·75
46	3 k. carmine		45·00	35·00
47	4 k. green		65·00	50·00
48	10 k. deep violet		£3250	£2500
	a. Violet		£3000	£2500

*(b) Surch with T **10***

49 **51**	25 on 80 h. red-brown		2·10	1·90
	a. Surch inverted		35·00	35·00

On Nos. 30/44 the overprint has a diamond shape between "POCZTA" and "POLSKA".

The 3 k. with inverted overprint is a forgery.

1919 (10 Jan). *NEWSPAPER. Newspaper stamps of Austria (Mercury) optd at Cracow similar to T **9** but with diamond shape between "POCZTA" and "POLSKA".*

N50 **N 53**	2 h. brown		10·00	10·00
N51	4 h. green		2·40	2·40
N52	6 h. blue		2·40	2·40
N53	10 h. orange		38·00	38·00
N54	30 h. claret		6·00	6·00
N50/54	Set of 5		55·00	55·00

1919 (10 Jan). *POSTAGE DUE. Postage Due stamps of Austria (Numerals) optd at Cracow with T **9** (Nos. D57/9) or similar type (others).*

D50 **D 55**	5 h. carmine		5·75	5·25
D51	10 h. carmine		£1100	£1200
D52	15 h. carmine		2·40	2·00
	a. Opt inverted		90·00	
D53	20 h. carmine		£300	£300
D54	25 h. carmine		14·00	13·00
D55	30 h. carmine		£550	£475
D56	40 h. carmine		£150	£120
D57 **D 56**	1 k. blue (R.)		£1700	£1700
D58	5 k. blue (R.)		£1700	£1700
D59	10 k. blue (R.)		£6000	£5500
	a. Black opt		£8000	£9500

On Nos. D50/6 the overprint has a diamond shape between "POCZTA" and "POLSKA".

1919 (Jan). *POSTAGE DUE. Nos D287 and D289 of Austria (Francis Joseph I) optd at Cracow similar to T **9** but with diamond shape between "POCZTA" and "POLSKA".*

D60 **50**	15 on 36 h. violet		£180	£120
D61	50 on 42 h. brown		19·00	19·00
	a. Opt double		£170	£170

(Des J. Michalski. Litho at Cracow)

1919 (25 Feb). *Issue for Western Galicia. Stout wove paper. No gum. Imperf.*

50 **11**	2 h. grey		35	45
51	3 h. dull violet		35	45
52	5 h. green		25	45
53	6 h. orange		12·00	15·00
54	10 h. lake		25	30
55	15 h. brown		25	30
56	20 h. olive-green		35	45
57	25 h. carmine		15	15
58	50 h. indigo		25	30
59	70 h. blue		35	45
60	1 k. carmine and grey		60	75
50/60	Set of 11		13·50	17·00

On the 2 and 3 h. the currency is inscribed as "halerze". Stamps printed by typography are forgeries; the 2 and 3 h. can be also identified by the inscription "halerzy".

(12) 5 / Poczta / Polska

(13) 5

(14) 10

1919 (5 Aug). *Poznań provisional issue. Stamps of Germany ("Germania") surch as T* **12.**

61	**17**	5 on 2 pf. grey			22·00	16·00
62	**24**	5 on 7½ pf. orange			2·40	1·00
		a. Surch double			70·00	
63	**17**	5 on 20 pf. blue			1·60	60
64		10 on 25 pf. black and red/*yellow*			6·50	2·75
65		10 on 40 pf. black and carmine			2·40	1·00
61/65		*Set of* 5			32·00	19·00

A 10 on 80 pf. stamp was prepared for use but was never issued.

1919 (15 Sept). *Gniezno provisional issue. Stamps of Germany ("Germania") surch with T* **13** *or* **14.**

66	**24**	5 on 2 pf. yellowish grey (R.)			£200	£110
		a. Surch inverted			£2500	
67		10 on 7½ pf. orange (G.)			£150	85·00

Forgeries of these surcharges exist, including inverts of the "10".

B. ISSUES FOR SOUTHERN POLAND

Austrian Currency

15 **16** **17** Agriculture

18 Ploughing in Peace **19** Polish Uhlan D **20**

(Des E. Trojanowski (**15**) and E. Bartlomiejczyk (**16/19**). Typo)

1919 (27 Jan). *Value in "halerzy" or "korony".*

(a) Imperf

68	**15**	3 h. brown			10	10
69		5 h. bright green			10	10
70		10 h. orange			10	10
71		15 h. scarlet			10	10
72	**16**	20 h. grey-brown			10	10
73		25 h. pale blue			10	10
74		50 h. red-brown			10	10
75	**17**	1 k. green			10	10
76		1 k. 50, brown			3·00	2·10
77		2 k. deep blue			1·50	1·25
78	**18**	2 k. 50, purple			9·50	6·00
79	**19**	5 k. grey-blue			11·00	6·75
68/79		*Set of* 12			23·00	15·00

(b) P 11½

80	**15**	3 h. brown			10	10
81		5 h. bright green			10	10
82		10 h. orange			10	10
83		15 h. scarlet			10	10
84	**16**	20 h. grey-brown			10	10
85		25 h. pale blue			10	10
86		50 h. red-brown			10	10
87	**17**	1 k. green			20	20
88		1 k. 50, brown			90	25
89		2 k. deep blue			1·10	25
90	**18**	2 k. 50, purple			1·10	50
91	**19**	5 k. grey-blue			1·75	90
80/91		*Set of* 12			5·00	2·40

1919 (9 Sept). *POSTAGE DUE. Value in "halerzy". Typo. Wove paper. P* 11½.

D 92	D **20**	2 h. deep blue			10	10
D 93		4 h. deep blue			10	10
D 94		5 h. deep blue			10	10

D 95	D **20**	10 h. deep blue			10	10
D 96		20 h. deep blue			10	10
D 97		30 h. deep blue			10	10
D 98		50 h. deep blue			10	10
D 99		100 h. deep blue			40	50
D100		500 h. deep blue			1·50	1·60
D92/100		*Set of* 9			2·25	2·40

These stamps were originally issued for use as Postage Dues in former Austrian territory, until superseded by Nos. D128/36. The stock on hand was used for ordinary postage for a time, from February, 1920.

Stamps perforated 11 are forgeries.

See also Nos. D128/36 and D144/7.

C. ISSUES FOR NORTHERN POLAND

Polish Currency

1919 (27 Jan). *Value in "fenigów" or "marki". Medium wove paper. Clear impression.*

(a) Imperf

92	**15**	3 f. brown			15	10
93		5 f. green			15	10
94		10 f. purple			15	10
95		15 f. lake			15	10
96	**16**	20 f. blue			15	10
97		25 f. olive			15	10
98		50 f. green			15	10
99	**17**	1 m. violet			1·60	80
100		1 m. 50, green			2·75	1·75
101		2 m. brown			2·75	1·75
102	**18**	2 m. 50, red-brown			14·00	7·00
103	**19**	5 m. purple			16·00	8·00
92/103		*Set of* 12			35·00	18·00

(b) P 11½

104	**15**	3 f. brown			10	10
105		5 f. yellow-green			10	10
106		10 f. purple			10	10
107		15 f. scarlet			10	10
		a. Carmine			10	10
108	**16**	20 f. blue			10	10
109		25 f. olive			10	10
110		50 f. green			10	10
111	**17**	1 m. violet			15	10
112		1 m. 50, green			60	25
113		2 m. brown			1·00	30
114	**18**	2 m. 50, red-brown			1·00	60
115	**19**	5 m. violet			1·25	60
104/115		*Set of* 12			4·25	2·10

From 1 February 1920, this series could be used throughout Poland.

See also Nos. 128/43, 146 and 179 etc.

I POLSKA WYSTAWA MAREK

5 ✛ **5**

(19*a*)

20

21 Prime Minister Paderewski

22 A. Trampczyński **23** Eagle and Ship

1919 (3 May). *First Polish Philatelic Exhibition and Polish White Cross Fund. Such as T 19a, in violet.*

A. *Imperf.* B. *Perf* $11\frac{1}{2}$

			A		B	
116	**15**	5+5 f. yellow-green	15	25	15	15
117		10+5 f. purple	2·00	1·60	30	15
118		15+5 f. lake	40	25	15	15
119	**16**	25+5 f. olive	40	25	20	15
120		50+5 f. green	50	30	75	30
116/120		*Set of 5*	3·00	2·40	1·25	70

(Des E. Bartlomiejczyk (10 f., 50 f., 1 m.), E. Trojanowski (15, 25 f.), F. Polkowski (20 f.) Typo)

1919 (15 June)—**20**. *Opening of First Session of Parliament. Inscr* "SEJM 1919". *P* $11\frac{1}{2}$.

121	**20**	10 f. mauve	15	10
122	**21**	15 f. red	15	10
123	**22**	20 f. brown (21×25 mm)	55	30
124		20 f. brown (17×20 mm) ('20)	1·10	65
125	–	25 f. sage-green	35	15
126	**23**	50 f. greenish blue	40	15
127	–	1 m. violet	55	55
121/127		*Set of 7*	3·00	1·75

Designs: *Horiz* as T **21**—25 f. Gen. Pilsudski. As T **23**—1 m. Griffin and fasces.

1919 (9 Sept). *POSTAGE DUE. Value in* "fenigów". *Typo. Wove paper. P* $11\frac{1}{2}$.

D128	D **20**	2 f. vermilion	25	30
D129		4 f. vermilion	10	10
D130		5 f. vermilion	10	10
D131		10 f. vermilion	10	10
D132		20 f. vermilion	10	10
D133		30 f. vermilion	10	10
D134		50 f. vermilion	10	10
D135		100 f. vermilion	50	30
D136		500 f. vermilion	1·40	70
D128/136		*Set of 9*	2·40	1·75

See also Nos. D144/7.

D. ISSUES FOR THE WHOLE OF POLAND
1 February 1920

O **24**

A	–	B

(Des E. Bartlomiejczyk. Typo)

1920. *OFFICIAL*.

(*a*) *Stars as in A on* 3 *to* 50 *f. Medium wove paper. P* $11\frac{1}{2}$, 10 *or compound* (1 Feb)

O128	O **24**	3 f. scarlet	10	10
O129		5 f. scarlet	10	10
O130		10 f. scarlet	10	10
O131		15 f. scarlet	10	10
O132		25 f. scarlet	10	10
O133		50 f. scarlet	10	10
O134		100 f. scarlet	25	25
O135		150 f. scarlet	30	30
O136		200 f. scarlet	40	40
O137		300 f. scarlet	35	35
O138		600 f. scarlet	50	50
O128/138		*Set of 11*	2·00	2·00

(*b*) *Stars as B. Thin laid paper. P* $11\frac{1}{2}$ (20 Nov)

O139	O **24**	5 f. scarlet	10	10
O140		10 f. scarlet	25	25
O141		15 f. scarlet	20	20
O142		25 f. scarlet	90	90
O143		50 f. scarlet	50	50
O139/143		*Set of 5*	1·75	1·75

The stamps on thin paper are printed from new plates in which the stars are inclined outwards instead of inwards, and the figures are larger.

1920 (Feb). *Thin wove paper. Coarse impression. P* $11\frac{1}{2}$, 10 *or compound.*

128	**15**	5 f. green	10	10
129		10 f. chocolate	10	10
130		15 f. scarlet	10	10
131	**16**	20 f. blue	10	10
132		25 f. olive	10	10
133		50 f. green	10	10
134	**17**	1 m. slate-violet	30	30
128/134		*Set of 7*	55	55

Thin horizontally or vertically laid paper. Coarse impression. P 9 *to* $11\frac{1}{2}$ *and compound*

135	**16**	25 f. dull olive	10	10
136		50 f. dull blue-green	10	10
137	**17**	1 m. slate-violet	20	10
138		2 m. brown	60	10
139	**18**	3 m. red-brown	30	10
140	**19**	5 m. purple	10	10
141		6 m. rose-carmine	10	10
142		10 m. vermilion	25	15
143		20 m. green	50	25
135/143		*Set of 9*	2·00	90

Examples of the 20 m. in *tête-bêche* pairs are postal forgeries.

1920 (May). *POSTAGE DUE. As Nos. D132, etc. but on thin laid paper. P* 9 *to* $11\frac{1}{2}$.

D144	D **20**	20 f. deep blue	45	30
D145		100 f. deep blue	20	20
D146		200 f. deep blue	40	30
D147		500 f. deep blue	25	20
D144/147		*Set of 4*	1·00	80

Though Type D **20** in blue was originally sold for Austrian currency, this reissue on thin paper was taken at face value in "fenigów".

24	25	(26)

(Des E. Bartlomiejczyk. Typo)

1920 (May). *Redrawn value tablet. Thick wove paper. P* 10 *to* $11\frac{1}{2}$ *and compounds.*

146	**24**	40 f. bright violet	10	10

See also Nos. 182 and 184.

(Des E. Trojanowski. Typo)

1920–21. *Thin laid or wove paper. P* 9 *to* $14\frac{1}{2}$ *and compounds.*

147	**25**	1 m. carmine	10	10
148		2 m. green	10	10
149		3 m. pale blue	10	10
150		4 m. rose	10	10
151		5 m. brown-purple	10	10
152		8 m. bistre-brown (1921)	25	20
147/152		*Set of 6*	50	35

The 3 m. comes on laid paper (vertical or horizontal) only; the other values exist both on laid (8 m. horiz only; others vert or horiz) and on wove paper.

1921 (25 Jan). *Surch with T* **26**.

153	**24**	3 m. on 40 f. bright violet	10	10
		a. Surch inverted	12·00	12·00
		b. Surch double	12·00	12·00

6 Mk.

dopłata

30 M5

(D 27)	(27)

1921 (25 Jan). *POSTAGE DUE. Surch as Type* D **27.**

D154	**11**	6 m. on 15 h. brown	..	.. 75	75
		a. Surch double		.. 23·00	
D155		6 m. on 25 h. carmine	..	.. 50	50
		a. Surch inverted	..	.. 23·00	
D156		20 m. on 10 h. lake		.. 95	95
		a. Surch inverted		.. 25·00	
D157		20 m. on 50 h. indigo	..	.. 1·25	1·60
D158		35 m. on 70 h. blue	..	.. 10·00	12·00
D154/158		*Set of* 5	..	.. 12·00	14·00

1921 (5 Mar). *Red Cross Fund. Surch with T* **27**, *in red. P* 9.

154	**19**	5 m. + 30 m. purple ..	..	3·75	8·00
155		6 m. + 30 m. rose-carmine	..	3·75	8·00
156		10 m. + 30 m. vermilion	..	8·00	13·00
157		20 m. + 30 m. green	..	30·00	27·00
154/157		*Set of* 4	..	40·00	50·00

The label issued in 1921 inscribed "PRO JUVENTUTE" is a bogus production. Large labels (25 and 100 m.) inscribed "AERO-TARG: POZNAN 1921", with "T.A.B.R.O.M.I.K." at foot are not a Government issue.

D 28   28   29

30   31 Sower

(Des E. Trojanowski. Typo)

1921 (15 Apr). *POSTAGE DUE. Wove or laid paper. Size* 17×21–22 mm. *P* 9 *to* 14½ *and compound.*

D159	D **28**	1 m. indigo	..	20	10
D160		2 m. indigo	..	20	10
D161		4 m. indigo	..	20	10
D162		6 m. indigo	..	20	10
D163		8 m. indigo	..	20	10
D164		20 m. indigo	..	20	10
D165		50 m. indigo	..	20	10
D166		100 m. indigo	..	40	10
D159/166		*Set of* 8	..	1·25	70

Nos. D159/166 exist on a range of different papers in varying shades.
For stamps size 19×24 mm, see Nos. D199/215.

(Des E. Bartlomiejczyk and W. Huzarski (T **30**). Typo)

1921 (2 May). *New Constitution. P* 11–11½.

158	**28**	2 m. green	..	1·50	1·25
159		3 m. blue	..	1·50	1·25
160		4 m. scarlet	..	70	40
		a. Error. Carmine	..	£120	
161	**29**	6 m. carmine	..	70	40
162		10 m. slate-green	..	1·10	40
163	**30**	25 m. violet	..	2·25	1·25
164		50 m. myrtle-green and buff ..		1·50	90
158/164		*Set of* 7	..	7·00	5·25

(Des B. Wisniewski. Typo)

1921–22. *Peace Treaty with Russia. Laid* (No. 165) *or wove* (all) *paper. P* 9 *to* 14½ *and compounds.*
    (a) *Size* 28×22 mm (May–Aug 1921)

165	**31**	10 m. deep turquoise (*shades*)	..	20	10
166		15 m. orange-brown	..	25	10
167		20 m. red	..	20	10

(b) *Size* 27¼×21½ mm (10 m.) *or* 25½×21 mm (20 m.) (Feb 1922)

168	**31**	10 m. blue-green	..	20	10
169		20 m. brown-red	..	20	10

32   33 Silesian Miner

(Des E. Trojanowski. Typo)

1921–23. (a) *Thick wove paper. P* 9 *to* 14½ *and compounds* (June 1921).

170	**32**	25 m. violet and buff	..	10	10
171		50 m. carmine and buff		10	10
172		100 m. black-brown and orange		10	10
173		200 m. pink and black	..	15	10

(b) *Thin wove paper. P* 10½ *to* 14½ *and compounds* (Feb–Apr 1923)

174	**32**	300 m. yellow-green	..	15	10
175		400 m. chocolate	..	15	10
176		500 m. plum	..	15	10
177		1000 m. orange	..	15	10
178		2000 m. indigo-violet	..	15	10
170/178		*Set of* 9	..	1·00	70

(T **33** des E. Bartlomiejczyk. Typo)

1922 (19 June)–**23.** *Issue for districts of Upper Silesia.*
    (a) *P* 9 *to* 14½ *and compound*

179	**15**	5 f. blue	..	10	10
180		10 f. mauve	..	10	10
181	**16**	20 f. red	..	10	10
182	**24**	40 f. purple-brown	..	10	10
183	**16**	50 f. red-orange	..	10	10
184	**24**	75 f. blue-green (7.22)	..	10	10
185	**33**	1 m. slate (7.22)	..	10	10
186		1.25 m deep green (7.22)	..	10	10
187		2 m. carmine (7.22)	..	10	10
188		3 m. emerald (7.22)	..	10	10
189		4 m. deep ultramarine (7.22)	..	10	10
190		5 m. yellow-brown (7.22)	..	10	10
191		6 m. red-orange (7.22)	..	10	25
192		10 m. pale chocolate (7.22)	..	10	10
193		20 m. deep purple (7.22)	..	10	10
194		50 m. olive (7.22)	..	10	70

    (b) *Thicker paper. P* 10 *to* 13½

195	**33**	80 m. red (3.23)	..	40	1·00
196		100 m. bright violet (3.23)	..	40	1·00
197		200 m. dull orange (3.23)	..	80	1·50
198		300 m. pale blue (15.4.23)	..	2·10	3·25
179/198		*Set of* 20	..	4·50	7·50

Upper Silesia was divided between Germany and Poland after a plebiscite held on 20 March 1921.

1923 (Mar)–**24.** *POSTAGE DUE. Wove paper. Size* 19×24 mm. *P* 12½.

D199	D **28**	50 m. indigo	..	10	10
D200		100 m. indigo	..	10	10
D201		200 m. indigo	..	10	10
D202		500 m. indigo	..	10	10
D203		1000 m. indigo	..	10	10
D204		2000 m. indigo	..	10	10
D205		10000 m. indigo	..	10	10
D206		20000 m. indigo	..	10	10
D207		30000 m. indigo	..	10	10
D208		50000 m. indigo	..	20	10
D209		100000 m. indigo	..	25	10
D210		200000 m. indigo	..	30	10
D211		300000 m. indigo	..	30	20
D212		500000 m. indigo	..	50	15
D213		1000000 m. indigo	..	95	40
D214		2000000 m. indigo	..	1·75	40
D215		3000000 m. indigo	..	1·90	50
D199/215		*Set of* 17	..	6·00	2·00

Nos. D205/215 were issued in the period from January to March 1924.

34 Copernicus   **35** Konarski

1923 (June–Nov). *450th Birth Anniv of Copernicus (astronomer) and 150th Death Anniv of Konarski (educationist). Typo. P 10½–12½ and compounds.*

199	**34**	1000 m. slate	60	25
200	**35**	3000 m. red-brown	35	25
		a. Error "KONAPSKI"	7·00	7·00
201	**34**	5000 m. carmine	60	35

No. 200a occurs in positions 5 and 15.

(36)   (37)

(38)   39

1923–24. *Various stamps surch.*

		(a) With T 36		
202	**32**	10,000 on 25 m. violet and buff	15	10
		(b) As T 37		
203	**31**	25,000 m. on 20 m. red (No. 167)	35	20
204		25,000 m. on 20 m. brown-red (169)	15	10
205		50,000 m. on 10 m. dp turquoise (165)	15	10
205a		50,000 m. on 10 m. blue-green (168)	15	10

On No. 204 the surcharge is smaller.

		(c) As T 38 (1924)		
206	**25**	20,000 m. on 2 m. green	35	15
207		100,000 m. on 5 m. brown-purple	15	10
202/207		*Set of 7*	1·25	65

All the above exist with surcharge inverted and surcharge double.

Nos. 206/7 exist on both laid and wove paper; for No. 205 only the wove paper printing was surcharged.

1923 (Nov). *POSTAGE DUE. Surch in figures.*

D216	D **28**	"10000" on 8 m. indigo	25	10
D217		"20000" on 20 m. indigo	25	20
D218		"50000" on 2 m. indigo	1·50	50

1924 (Jan–Mar). *Typo. P 10 to 13½.*

208	**39**	10,000 m. brown-purple	25	30
209		20,000 m. sage-green	15	10
210		30,000 m. scarlet	80	30
211		50,000 m. apple-green	85	30
212		100,000 m. chestnut	60	25
213		200,000 m. light blue	60	15
214		300,000 m. magenta	60	30
215		500,000 m. brown	60	1·50
216		1,000,000 m. pink	60	3·25
217		2,000,000 m. deep green	95	12·00
208/217		*Set of 10*	5·50	16·00

40   **41** President Wojciechowski   42

(Typo State Graphic Institution)

1924 (1 May). *New Currency. P 10½ to 13½ and compound.*

218	**40**	1 g. yellow-brown	45	40
219		2 g. grey-brown	45	10
220		3 g. orange	55	10
221		5 g. sage-green	75	10
222		10 g. blue-green	75	10
223		15 g. scarlet	75	10
224		20 g. light blue	3·00	10
225		25 g. claret	4·00	15
		a. Error. Slate	£2000	£3250
226		30 g. bright violet	16·00	10
		a. Grey-blue	£160	80·00
227		40 g. slate	4·50	30
228		50 g. magenta	3·50	15
218/228		*Set of 11*	32·00	1·40

No. 225a came from a cliché of the 25 g. in the plate of the 40 g.

1924–26. *POSTAGE DUE. New Currency. Typo. Size 20 × 25½ mm. P 10½ to 13½ and compound.*

D229	D **28**	1 g. brown	15	15
D230		2 g. brown	15	15
D231		4 g. brown	15	15
D232		6 g. brown	25	15
D233		10 g. brown	3·25	15
D234		15 g. brown	3·00	20
D235		20 g. brown	6·50	20
D236		25 g. brown	4·50	20
D237		30 g. brown	85	20
D238		40 g. brown	1·10	20
D239		50 g. brown	1·10	20
D240		1 z. brown	85	30
D241		2 z. brown	85	30
D242		3 z. brown	1·10	1·25
D243		5 z. brown (1926)	1·10	50
D229/243		*Set of 15*	23·00	3·75

See also Nos. D290/5.

(Des F. Aumiller. Litho)

1924 (1 Oct). *P 12 × 11½.*

229	**41**	1 z. scarlet	18·00	1·25

1925 (1 Jan). *National Fund. Typo. P 12½.*

230	**42**	1 g. + 50 g. yellow-brown	17·00	20·00
231		2 g. + 50 g. grey-brown	17·00	20·00
232		3 g. + 50 g. orange	17·00	20·00
233		5 g. + 50 g. sage-green	17·00	20·00
234		10 g. + 50 g. blue-green	17·00	20·00
235		15 g. + 50 g. scarlet	17·00	20·00
236		20 g. + 50 g. light blue	17·00	20·00
237		25 g. + 50 g. claret	17·00	20·00
238		30 g. + 50 g. bright violet	17·00	20·00
239		40 g. + 50 g. slate	17·00	20·00
240		50 g. + 50 g. magenta	17·00	20·00
230/240		*Set of 11*	£170	£180

43 Holy Gate, Vilna   **44** Town Hall, Poznań   **45** King Sigismund Vasa Column, Warsaw

46 Wawel Castle, Cracow

47 Jan III Sobieski Statue, Lwów

48 Galleon

I

II

I. Coarse printing; background lines touch the figures.
II. Redrawn, clearer design; white surround to figures.

III

IV

III. Background lines continue through "GR".
IV. Background lines shortened to give white surround to "GR".

V

VI

V. "40" small, 6 mm across.
VI. "40" larger, 6½ mm, nearer to spire.

1925–27. *Typo.* P 11½ *or* 12½×13 *(13×12½ on 15 and 40 g.).*

241	43	1 g. brown	..	..	25	10
242	47	2 g. brown-olive	..	..	50	25
243	45	3 g. pale blue (I)	..	..	1·50	10
		a. Type II	..	..	1·40	10
244	44	5 g. green (I)	..	..	1·50	10
		a. Type II	..	..	1·40	10
245	45	10 g. violet (I)	..	..	1·50	10
		a. Type II	..	..	1·40	10
246	46	15 g. carmine (I)	..	..	1·50	10
		a. Type II	..	..	1·75	10
247	48	20 g. carmine-red	..	..	3·00	10
248	43	24 g. grey-blue	..	..	8·00	60
249	47	30 g. dull blue (III)	..	..	3·25	10
		a. Type IV	..	..	3·50	10
250	46	40 g. light blue (V) (1927)		..	3·25	10
		a. Type VI	..	..	3·50	10
251	48	45 g. mauve	..	..	10·00	40
241/251		Set of 11	..	..	30·00	1·75

Use of the 1 g. was obligatory on all internal correspondence in payment of a special tax.
The 20 g. printed by lithography is a postal forgery.

49 LVG Schneider Biplane

(Des L. Sowiński. Typo)

1925 (10 Sept). *AIR.* P 12½.

252	49	1 g. pale blue	..	..	65	2·25
253		2 g. orange	..	..	65	2·25
254		3 g. yellow-brown	..	..	65	2·25
255		5 g. brown	..	..	65	50
256		10 g. blue-green	..	..	1·75	60
257		15 g. bright magenta	..	..	2·25	75
258		20 g. olive-green	..	..	12·00	3·50
259		30 g. carmine	..	..	8·00	1·75
260		45 g. deep lilac	..	..	11·00	3·75
252/260		Set of 9	..	..	35·00	16·00

Stamps perforated 11½ are forgeries.

50 Chopin

51 Marshal Pilsudski

52 President Moscicki

(Des Z. Kamiński. Litho)

1927 (1 Mar.). P 11½.
261 **50** 40 g. deep ultramarine .. 13·00 1·25

1927–28. Typo. P 11½ (25 g.) or 12½×13 (both).
262 **51** 20 g. carmine (19.3.27) .. 2·10 10
262a 25 g. yellow-brown (1.2.28) .. 2·10 15
No. 262 has the shading of the central portrait and background formed of dots. In No. 262a, the shading is made up of lines.

1927 (3 May). P 12×11½.
263 **52** 20 g. vermilion .. .. 5·25 35

53

54 Dr. K. Kaczkowski

55 J. Slowacki (poet)

(Des Z. Kamiński. Typo)

1927 (3 May). *Educational Funds. Background of coloured wavy lines.* P 11½.
264 **53** 10 g. +5 g. purple/*green* .. 8·50 10·00
265 20 g. +5 g. indigo/*straw* .. 8·50 10·00

1927 (27 May). *4th International Military Medical Congress, Warsaw. Litho* (10 g.) *or typo* (others). P 11½ or 12½ (40 g.).
266 **54** 10 g. grey-green .. .. 3·00 1·00
267 25 g. carmine .. .. 6·00 2·75
268 40 g. blue .. .. 8·00 2·25

1927 (28 June). *Transference of Slowacki's remains to Cracow. Typo.* P 12½ or 12½×13.
269 **55** 20 g. claret .. .. 5·25 40

56 Marshal Pilsudski

57 Pres. Moscicki

(Des Z. Kamiński. Eng F. Schirnbōck. Recess)

1928 (3 May). *Warsaw Philatelic Exhibition. Sheet* 117×88 mm. *T* **56/7** *in deep sepia.* P 12½.
MS270 50 g. and 1 z. (+1 z. 50)   £300   £225
  See also Nos. 272/3, 328 and **MS**332*b/c*.

63

64 Kosciuszko, Washington and Pulaski

 (Gen. Joseph Bem / H. Sienkiewicz / The ancient Slav God, Swiatowit)

58 Gen. Joseph Bem   **59** H. Sienkiewicz   **60** The ancient Slav God, Swiatowit

(Des T. Gronowski. Typo)

1930 (1 Nov). *Centenary of "November Rising"* (29 Nov. 1830). P 12½×13.
280	**63**	5 g. purple			75	10
281		15 g. blue			3·00	20
282		25 g. red-brown			1·75	10
283		30 g. rosine			10·00	3·25
280/283		*Set of 4*			14·00	3·25

The 25 g. perf 11 is a postal forgery.

1928 (May). *Typo.* P 12½×13.
271 **58** 25 g. bright rose   3·00   20

1928 (May)–**31**. *T* **56** (*wove paper*) *and* **57** (*vertically laid paper*). *Various perfs,* 10½ *to* 13½ *and compounds.*
272	**56**	50 g. bluish slate		3·25	15
272a		50 g. blue-green (5.31)		9·00	15
273	**57**	1 z. slate-black/*cream*		8·75	15
		a. Horiz laid paper (1930)		55·00	2·10

(Des R. Kleczewski. Eng W. Vacek. Recess)

1932 (3 May). *Birth Bicentenary of George Washington. Vert laid paper.* P 11½.
284 **64** 30 g. chocolate/*cream*   2·75   25

(Des E. Gaspé. Typo)

1928 (Oct). *Henryk Sienkiewicz* (author). P 12×12½.
274 **59** 15 g. bright blue   1·90   15

(Des Z. Kaminski. Typo)

1928 (15 Dec). *National Exhibition, Poznan.* P 12½×12.
275 **60** 25 g. red-brown   2·40   15

 (stamps 61, 62 King Jan III Sobieski, D 63)

61   **62** King Jan III Sobieski   **D 63**

(Des Z. Kaminski. Typo)

1928 (15 Dec). P 12×12½.
276	**61**	5 g. violet		20	10
277		10 g. green		60	10
278		25 g. red-brown		40	10

Stamps printed by lithography and the 25 g. with vertical edges imperforate are postal forgeries.

(Des F. Schirnbōck. Typo)

1930 (July). *Birth Tercentenary of King Jan III Sobieski.* P 12×12½.
279 **62** 75 g. purple   5·25   20

1930 (July). *POSTAGE DUE. Typo.* P 12½×13.
D280 **D 63** 5 g. brown   50   15

65   **66**

1932–33. *Typo.* W **66.** P 12×12½.
284a	**65**	5 g. violet (1933)		15	10
285		10 g. green		15	10
285a		15 g. claret (1933)		15	10
286		20 g. grey		50	10
287		25 g. bistre		50	10
288		30 g. scarlet		3·00	10
289		60 g. cobalt		25·00	10
284a/289		*Set of 7*		26·00	40

The 25 and 30 g. on unwatermarked paper are postal forgeries; the 25 g. is line perf 12½, the 30 g. perf 13.

1932. *POSTAGE DUE. Size* 19×24 mm. *Typo.* P 12½.
D290	**D 28**	1 g. brown		20	10
D291		2 g. brown		20	10
D292		10 g. brown		1·00	20
D293		15 g. brown		1·40	10
D294		20 g. brown		3·00	10
D295		25 g. brown		27·00	10
D290/295		*Set of 6*		30·00	45

67 Town Hall, Torun   **68** Franciszek Zwirko (airman) and Stanislaw Wigura (aircraft designer)

1933 (2 Jan). *Seventh Centenary of Torun. Recess.* W **66.** P 11½.
290 **67** 60 g. blue/*cream*   30·00   45

PRINTER. The letters "P.W.P.W." below the designs of some stamps from 1933 onwards stand for "Panstwowa-Wytwornia Papierów Wartosciowych" (the Govt Ptg Wks).

MINIMUM PRICE

The minimum price quoted is 10p which represents a handling charge rather than a basis for valuing common stamps. For further notes about prices see introductory pages.

(Des R. Kleczewski. Eng W. Vacek. Recess)

1933 (15 Apr). *Victory in Flight round Europe Air Race*, 1932.
W **66**. *P* 11½ *or* 12½.
292 **68** 30 g. grey-green .. .. .. 15·00 1·50

1933 (21 May). *Torun Philatelic Exhibition. Recess.* W **66**.
P 11½.
293 **67** 60 g. scarlet/*cream* .. .. .. 17·00 15·00
No. 293 was sold at 1 z., at the Exhibition.

69 Altar piece, St. Mary's Church,
Cracow

O 70

(Des R. Kleczewski. Eng W. Vacek. Recess)
1933 (10 July). *Fourth Death Centenary of Veit Stoss* (*sculptor*).
Vert laid paper. P 11½.
294 **69** 80 g. red-brown/*cream* .. .. 13·00 1·40

1933 (1 Aug). *OFFICIAL. Type O* **70** (*and similar type*). *Typo.*
W **66**. *P* 12×12½.

(a) *Inscr* "ZWYCZAJNA" (*Ordinary*)
O295 (30 g.) mauve 75 15

(b) *Inscr* "POLECONA" (*Registered*)
O296 (80 g.) scarlet .. .. .. 1·75 25
See also Nos. O306/7.

70 "The Liberation of Vienna",
by J. Matejko

71 Cross of
Independence

(Des R. Kleczewski. Eng W. Vacek. Recess)
1933 (12 Sept). *250th Anniv of Relief of Vienna. Vert laid
paper. P* 12×11½ *or* 11½.
295 **70** 1 z. 20, blue/*cream* .. .. 32·00 12·00

1933 (11 Nov). *15th Anniv of Proclamation of Republic.
Typo.* W **66**. *P* 12½×13.
296 **71** 30 g. scarlet .. .. 7·75 30

**Wyst. Filat.
1934
Katowice**
(72)

73 Pilsudski and Legion
of Fusiliers' Badge

**20
groszy**
(D 74)

1934 (5 May). *Katowice Philatelic Exhibition. Optd with T* **72**.
W **66**. *P* 12×12½.
297 **65** 20 g. grey (R.) .. .. .. 38·00 26·00
298 30 g. scarlet .. .. .. 38·00 26·00
Overprints reading "1934 r." in the centre are proofs.

(Des R. Kleczewski. Eng W. Vacek. Recess)
1934. *20th Anniv of Formation of Polish Legion. P* 11½.
299 **73** 25 g. blue (1 Oct) 95 20
300 30 g. sepia (6 Aug) .. .. 2·40 30

1934–38. *POSTAGE DUE. Postage Due stamps of 1924–26
surch as Type D* **74**.
D301 D **28** 10 g. on 2 z. brown (1938) .. 20 15
D302 15 g. on 2 z. brown (30.11.36) .. 20 15
D303 20 g. on 1 z. brown (30.11.36) .. 20 15
D304 20 g. on 5 z. brown (6.8.34) .. 1·90 40
D305 25 g. on 40 g. brown (7.37) .. 50 40
D306 30 g. on 40 g. brown (7.37) .. 70 40
D307 50 g. on 40 g. brown (7.37) .. 70 40
D308 50 g. on 3 z. brown (1935) .. 1·90 70
D301/308 Set of 8 .. .. .. 5·50 2·50

**Challenge
1934**
(74)

DOPŁATA

10 GR.

55 gr.
(75)

1 zł.
(76)

(D 77)

1934 (28 Aug). *International Air Tournament. Optd in red with
T* **74** *or larger overprint* (18½×8½ *mm.*).
301 **49** 20 g. olive-green .. .. .. 14·00 8·50
302 **68** 30 g. grey-green .. .. .. 8·00 2·00

1934 (1 Oct)–**35**. *Surch as T* **75** (303/4) *or* **76**.
303 **69** 25 g. on 80 g. red-brown/*cream* .. 5·25 45
a. "gr." lower than "25" .. 50·00 2·25
304 **65** 50 g. on 60 g. cobalt .. .. 5·00 25
305 **70** 1 z. on 1 z. 20, blue/*cream* (R.) .. 17·00 4·00
a. "l" 4½ mm. (1935) .. .. 17·00 4·00
No. 303. Surcharge in each of the upper corners over
original value.
No. 305. Surcharge in the centre at the foot with bars in
upper corners obliterating original value. Figure "1" of surcharge
measures 5½ mm.

1934–36. *POSTAGE DUE. No. 273a surch as Type D* **77**
(*differing in size and detail for each value*). *Horiz laid paper.*
D309 **57** 10 g. on 1 z. (R.) (1.6.36) 80 10
a. Vert laid paper .. .. 30·00 20·00
D310 20 g. on 1 z. (Br.) (15.2.36) .. 1·75 45
D311 25 g. on 1 z. (B.) (1.10.34) .. 80 20
a. Vert laid paper .. .. 22·00 18·00

1935 (1 Apr). *OFFICIAL. Redrawn types resembling Nos.*
O295/6.
O306 (30 g.) violet-blue ("ZWYCZAJNA") .. 10 10
O307 (80 g.) brown red ("POLECONA") .. 20 10

77 Marshal Pilsudski

**Kopiec
Marszałka
Piłsudskiego**
(78)

(Des M. R. Folak. Litho (308, 309/10) or typo (others))

1935. *Mourning for Marshal Pilsudski. P* 11½×13 *(No.* 308)
or 11 *(others)*.

306 **77**	5 g. black (7.35)	70	10
307	15 g. black (7.35)	70	25
308	25 g. black (*litho*) (16.5.35)	1·10	10
308a	25 g. black (*typo*) (7.35)	1·10	10
309	45 g. black (28.5.35)	3·00	1·40
310	1 z. black (28.5.35)	5·00	3·00

Nos. 285a and 299 optd with T **78**

311 **65**	15 g. claret (B.) (31.5.35)	70	65
312 **73**	25 g. blue (R.) (31.5.35)	2·50	1·60
306/312	*Set of* 8	13·50	6·50

See also No. **MS**358a.

79 Pieskowa Skala
(Dog's Rock)

80 President Moscicki

(Des R. Kleczewski (313/5, 324), L. Sowinski (316, 321/3, 325/6), W. Borowski (317/20). Eng W. L. Vacek (313, 316, 322, 324/5, 327), M. R. Polak (314, 316, 317/9, 321, 323, 326), J. Piwczyk (320))

1935–37. *As T* **79** *(various views, ship and buildings) and T* **80**.

(a) *Typo. P* 13×12½

313	5 g. violet-blue (16.8.35)	40	10
314	10 g. yellow-green (1.12.35)	40	10
315	15 g. greenish blue (5.8.35)	3·25	10
316	20 g. violet-black (1.12.35)	90	10

(b) *Recess. P* 13×12½ (5 *to* 20 *g.,* 25 (II), 45, 50 (II) *g.) or* 13 *(others)*.
Plate I 28.3×21.3 *mm,* Plate II 28.5×22 *mm*

317	5 g. violet (1.4.37)	15	10
318	10 g. yellow-green (1.4.37)	75	10
319	15 g. brown-lake (1.4.37)	30	10
320	20 g. brown-orange (1.4.37)	45	10
321	25 g. deep blue-green (I) (1.12.35)	3·00	10
	a. Plate II (1937)	80	10
322	30 g. scarlet (1.12.35)	1·75	15
323	45 g. magenta (I) (16.1.36)	2·50	15
	a. Plate II (1937)	1·75	15
324	50 g. black (I) (16.1.36)	2·50	15
	a. Plate II (1937)	2·25	15
325	55 g. blue (I) (16.1.36)	6·50	40
	a. Plate II (1937)	9·00	40
326	1 z. sepia (16.1.36)	4·00	90
327	3 z. sepia (15.9.35)	2·50	2·25
313/327	*Set of* 15 (*cheapest*)	23·00	4·50

Designs: *As T* **79**—No. 314, Lake Morskie Oko; 315, *Pilsudski* (liner); 316, Pieniny-Czorsztyn; 317, Monastery of Jasna Góra, Czestochowa; 318, Sea passenger terminal, Gdynia; 319, University, Lwow; 320, Adminstrative Buildings, Katowice; 25 g. Belvedere Palace, Warsaw; 30 g. Castle at Mir; 45 g. Castle at Podhorce; 50 g. Cloth Hall, Cracow; 55 g. Raczynski Library, Poznan; 1 z. Vilna Cathedral.

1936 (3 June). 10*th Anniv of Moscicki Presidency. As T* **57**
but inscr "1926. 3. VI. 1936" *below design. P* 12½.

328 **57**	1 z. bright blue	6·00	5·50

GORDON-BENNETT 30.VIII.
1936

(81)

1936 (15 Aug). *Gordon-Bennett International Balloon Race*
Optd with T **81**.

329	30 g. scarlet (B.) (No. 322)	10·50	5·00
330	55 g. blue (R.) (No. 325)	10·50	5·00

82 Marshal Smigly-Rydz   **83** President Moscicki

(Des S. Chrostowski. Eng M. R. Folak. Recess)

1937. *P* 12½.

331 **82**	25 g. slate-blue (1 July)	35	10
332	55 g. blue (Aug)	50	10

See also No. **MS**358a.

1937 (1 Sept). *Visit of King of Rumania. Three sheets each*
102×125 mm. each containing a block of four of earlier
types in new colours. P 12½.

MS332a **82**	25 g. sepia	18·00	23·00
MS332b **56**	50 g. slate-blue	18·00	23·00
MS332c **57**	1 z. black	18·00	23·00

(Eng J. Piwczyk. Recess)

1938 (1 Feb). *President's 70th Birthday. P* 12½.

333 **83**	15 g. greenish slate	20	10
334	30 g. purple	40	10

84 Kosciuszko, Paine
and Washington

84a Postal Coach   **84b** Stratosphere
Balloon

(Des W. Boratynski. Eng W. Vacek. Recess)

1938 (17 Mar). 150*th Anniv of U.S. Constitution. P* 12×12½.

335 **84**	1 z. deep blue	1·60	1·40

(Des W. Boratynski. Eng W. Vacek. Recess)

1938 (3 May). *Fifth Philatelic Exhibition, Warsaw. Sheet*
130×103 *mm. P* 12×12½ *or imperf.*

MS335a **84a**	45 g. (×2) green and	£110	95·00
	55 g. (×2) blue		

(Des L. Sowiński. Eng W. Vacek. Recess)

1938 (15 Sept). *Proposed Polish Stratosphere Flight. Sheet*
75×125 *mm. P* 12½×12.

MS335b **84b**	75 g. (+1 z. 25) violet	80·00	70·00

85 Boleslaw   **85a** (No. 338)   **86** Marshal Pilsudski
the Brave

(Des W. Boratyński (5 g. to 1 z.), M. Watorek (2 z.) and
Z. Rozwadowski (3 z.). Eng H. Dutczyński (5 g., 45 g., 50 g.,
1 z.), J. Piwczyk (10 g., 30 g., 55 g., 75 g.) and M. R. Folak
(others). Recess)

1938 (11 Nov). *20th Anniv of Independence.* (a) *Designs as*
T 85 and T 85a (5 g. to 2 z.) and T 86. P 12½×13 *or* 13×12½
(3 z.).

336	5 g. red-orange			10	10
337	10 g. green			10	10
338	15 g. red-brown			15	15
339	20 g. greenish blue			35	10
340	25 g. purple			10	10
341	30 g. rose-red			55	10
342	45 g. black			85	15
343	50 g. magenta			1·90	10
344	55 g. bright blue			45	10
345	75 g. blue-green			2·75	1·40
346	1 z. orange			2·75	1·40
347	2 z. carmine			9·00	7·00
348	3 z. slate-blue			9·00	13·00
336/348	*Set of 13*			25·00	22·00

(b) *Sheet* 102×125 *mm. containing four portraits as T 83 but*
with value and inscr transposed, all in purple. Recess. P 12½.

MS348a	25 g. Marshal Piłsudski	
	25 g. Fres. Narutowicz	
	25 g. Fres. Moscicki	13·00 20·00
	25 g. Marshal Smigly-Rydz	

Designs:—10 g. Casimir the Great; 15 g. King Wladislaw
Jagiello and Queen Jadwiga; 20 g. Casimir Jagiellon; 25 g.
Sigismund August; 30 g.Stefan Batory; 45 g. Chodkiewicz and
Zolkiewski; 50 g. Jan III Sobieski; 55 g. Symbol of Constitution of
3 May, 1791; 75 g. Kosciuszko, Poniatowski and Dabrowski; 1 z.
November Uprising, 1830–31; 2 z. Romuald Traugutt.
For stamp as No. 338, but without crossed swords in fore-
ground, see No. 357.

87 "Teschen comes   D 88   88 "Warmth"
    to Poland"

(Des W. Boratyński. Eng W. Vacek. Recess)

1938 (11 Nov). *Acquisition of Teschen.* P 12½×13.

349	87	25 g. purple		1·40	35

1938 (25 Nov)–**39**. *POSTAGE DUE. Typo.* P 12½×12.

D350	D 88	5 g. blue-green	15	10
D351		10 g. blue-green	15	10
D352		15 g. blue-green (1939)	15	10
D353		20 g. blue-green (1939)	40	15
D354		25 g. blue-green (1939)	15	15
D355		30 g. blue-green (1939)	20	10
D356		50 g. blue-green (1939)	55	70
D357		1 z. blue-green (1939)	2·10	1·40
D350/357		*Set of 8*	3·50	2·50

(Des W. Boratyński. Eng J. Piwczyk. Recess)

1938–39. *Winter Relief Fund.* P 13×12½.

350	88	5 g.+5 g. red-orange (21.12.38)	40	70
351		25 g.+10 g. purple (10.1.39)	85	1·60
352		55 g.+15 g. bright blue (15.3.39)	1·60	2·50

89 Tatra Mountaineer   89a (No. 357)

(Des W. Boratyński. Eng M. Dutczynski. Recess)

1939 (6 Feb). *International Ski Championships, Zakopane.*
P 12½×13.

353	89	15 g. red-brown			1·00	70
354		25 g. purple			1·50	80
355		30 g. carmine			2·00	90
356		55 g. bright blue			7·00	4·50
353/356		*Set of 4*			10·50	6·25

1939 (2 Mar). *As No. 338, but crossed swords in foreground*
replaced by ornamental dais.

357	89a	15 g. red-brown	25	20

90 Marshal Pilsudski and Polish Legionaries

(Des W. Boratynski. Eng J. Piwczyk. Recess)

1939 (1 Aug). *25th Anniv of Battles of First Polish Legions.*
(a) P 12½×13

358	90	25 g. purple		80	40

(b) *Sheet* 103×125 *mm. comprising former types printed in*
violet-grey. Recess. P 12½

MS358a	25 g. T 90; 25 g. T 77; 25 g. T 82	23·00	28·00

III. GERMAN OCCUPATION
1939–45

German armies invaded Poland on 1 September 1939 and
on 17 September Russian troops invaded from the east. On 28
September Poland was divided between Russia and Germany.
Germany annexed the territory she had lost in 1919–21 and also
parts of the provinces of Lodz, Warsaw, Cracow and Bialystok;
on 12 October the rest of the area seized by Germany became
a protectorate called the General-Government. Russian stamps
were used in the area to the east of River Bug, annexed by the
Soviet Union.

16 Groschen 16

Deutsche Post
OSTEN
(91)

2 2
GR.
General-
Gouvernement
(92)

1939 (1–4 Dec). *T 94 of Germany (Hindenburg) surch as T 91.*
Wmk Swastikas. P 14×14½.

359	6 g. on 3 pf. bistre-brown			20	40
360	8 g. on 4 pf. slate-blue			20	30
361	12 g. on 6 pf. deep green			20	25
362	16 g. on 8 pf. orange-red (4 Dec)			75	1·00
363	20 g. on 10 pf. chocolate (4 Dec)			25	25
364	24 g. on 12 pf. carmine			25	20
365	30 g. on 15 pf. claret (4 Dec)			65	85
366	40 g. on 20 pf. light blue (4 Dec)			50	40
367	50 g. on 25 pf. ultramarine			60	50
368	60 g. on 30 pf. bronze-green			60	25
369	80 g. on 40 pf. magenta (4 Dec)			70	70
370	1 z. on 50 pf. black and green			1·90	1·25
371	2 z. on 100 pf. black and yellow			3·75	3·00
359/371	*Set of 13*			9·50	8·50

1940 (Feb–Mar). *Stamps of Poland, 1937–39, optd as T 92,*
at State Ptg Wks, Vienna.

372	2 g. on 5 g. red-orange (336)		20	30
373	4 g. on 5 g. red-orange (336)		20	30
374	6 g. on 10 g. green (337)		20	30

375	8 g. on 10 g. green (337)		20	30
376	10 g. on 10 g. green (337)		20	30
377	12 g. on 15 g. red-brown (l) (357)		20	30
	a. Type II		2·50	3·00
378	16 g. on 15 g. red-brown (357)		20	30
379	24 g. on 25 g. slate-blue (331)		20	30
380	24 g. on 25 g. purple (340)		80	80
381	30 g. on 30 g. rose-red (341)		40	40
382	30 g. on 5 g. + 5 g. red-orange (350)		40	50
383	40 g. on 30 g. purple (334)		50	75
384	40 g. on 25 g. + 10 g. purple (351)		40	40
385	50 g. on 50 g. magenta (l) (343)		25	40
	a. Type II		2·50	3·25
386	50 g. on 55 g. blue (332)		40	40
386a	50 g. on 20 g. blue-green (D353)		1·00	1·90
386b	50 g. on 25 g. blue-green (D354)		16·00	14·00
386c	50 g. on 30 g. blue-green (D355)		40·00	32·00
386d	50 g. on 50 g. blue-green (D356)		1·50	1·90
386e	50 g. on 1 z. blue-green (D357)		1·50	1·90
387	60 g. on 55 g. bright blue (344)		10·00	8·50
388	80 g. on 75 g. blue-green (345)		10·00	8·50
388a	1 z. on 55 g. + 15 g. blue (352)		9·00	6·00
389	1 z. on 1 z. orange (346)		10·00	8·50
390	2 z. on 2 z. carmine (347)		7·50	6·00
391	3 z. on 3 z. slate-blue (348)		7·50	6·00
372/391	Set of 26		£110	90·00

Two types of 12 g. and 50 g. Type I is as in T **92**. In Type II the figures of value are very close to the "G" and "I" of "General".

PRINTER. All stamps from Nos. O392 to 477 were printed at the State Printing Works, Vienna.

O **93**

93 Copernicus Memorial, Cracow   **(94)**

(Des Kreb. Design photo; figures of value typo)

1940 (5 Apr–5 Aug). OFFICIAL. As Type O **93**.

(a) 31 × 23 mm. P 12½ (5 Apr)

O392	6 g. pale brown		1·50	1·50
O393	8 g. grey		1·50	1·50
O394	10 g. pale green		1·50	1·50
O395	12 g. deep green		1·75	1·75
O396	20 g. deep brown		1·75	3·00
O397	24 g. brown-red		25·00	1·00
O398	30 g. crimson-lake		2·25	3·50
O399	40 g. deep violet		2·50	6·00
O400	48 g. pale olive		10·00	7·00
O401	50 g. blue		2·50	2·50
O402	60 g. deep olive		1·75	2·00
O403	80 g. purple		1·75	2·00

(b) 35 × 26 mm. P 13½ × 14 (5 Apr)

O404	1 z. purple and grey		5·00	5·00
O405	3 z. red-brown and grey		5·00	5·00
O406	5 z. orange and grey		6·00	6·00
O392/406	Set of 15		65·00	45·00

(c) Size 21 × 16 mm.

O407	6 g. brown (5 Aug)		1·00	1·25
O408	8 g. grey (5 Aug)		1·50	1·75
O409	10 g. blue-green (5 Aug)		2·00	2·00
O410	12 g. deep green (5 Aug)		2·00	2·00
O411	20 g. deep brown (22 July)		1·00	1·25
O412	24 g. brown-red (5 Aug)		80	85
O413	30 g. crimson-lake (22 July)		1·75	2·00
O414	40 g. deep violet (22 July)		2·00	2·00
O415	50 g. blue (22 July)		2·00	2·00
O407/415	Set of 9		12·50	13·50

(Des Prof. Fuchinger. Photo)

1940 (5 Aug)–41. Views as T **93**. P 14.

392	6 g. brown		25	60
393	8 g. chestnut		25	60

394	8 g. blue-black (8.9.41)		25	40
395	10 g. emerald		15	15
396	12 g. deep green		3·00	25
397	12 g. violet (8.9.41)		30	15
398	20 g. deep brown		10	10
399	24 g. lake		10	10
400	30 g. reddish violet		10	15
401	30 g. purple (8.9.41)		20	30
402	40 g. blue-black		20	15
403	48 g. red-brown (8.9.41)		70	1·00
404	50 g. blue		20	15
405	60 g. deep olive		20	20
406	80 g. deep violet		25	25
407	1 z. reddish purple (9.9.40)		2·00	1·10
408	1 z. blue-green (8.9.41)		45	40
392/408	Set of 17		7·75	5·50

Designs:—6 g. Florian Gate, Cracow; 8 g. Castle Keep, Cracow; 10 g. Cracow Gate, Lublin; 20 g. Church of the Dominicans, Cracow; 24 g. Wawel Castle, Cracow; 30 g. Old Church in Lublin; 40 g. Arcade, Cloth Hall, Cracow; 48 g. Town Hall, Sandomir; 50 g. Town Hall, Cracow; 60 g. Courtyard of Wawel Castle, Cracow; 80 g. St. Mary's Church, Cracow; 1 z. Bruhl Palace, Warsaw.

95   **96**

(Nos. 413/9. Des O. Engelhardt-Kyffhäuser. Eng F. Lorber. Recess)

1940 (26 Oct). First Anniv of German Occupation. T **95** and similar types. Thick straw-coloured paper. P 14½.

413	12 g. + 38 g. deep green		1·75	1·90
414	24 g. + 26 g. red		1·75	1·90
415	30 g. + 20 g. deep violet		3·00	2·75

Designs:—24 g. Woman with scarf; 30 g. Fur-capped peasant (as T **96**).

1940 (1 Dec). Winter Relief Fund. P 12½.

416	**96**	12 g. + 8 g. deep green	1·00	75
417		24 g. + 16 g. red	1·40	1·50
418		30 g. + 30 g. purple-brown	1·75	1·75
419		50 g. + 50 g. blue	2·40	2·50
416/419	Set of 4		6·00	6·00

D **97**   **97** Cracow

1940 (1 Dec). DELIVERY. Photo. P 14.

D420	D **97**	10 g. red-orange	25	90
D421		20 g. red-orange	35	1·00
D422		30 g. red-orange	35	1·00
D423		50 g. red-orange	1·25	1·60
D420/423	Set of 4		2·00	4·00

Ordinary postage stamps only paid for delivery to the nearest sub-office and the above were applied in addition to pay for delivery to the addressee.

(Des Gessner and W. Kreb. Eng F. Lorber. Recess)

1941 (20 Apr). *P* 14½.
420 **97** 10 z. grey and red .. .. 2·25 1·50
Issued in sheets of 8.

98 The Barbican, Cracow   **99** Adolf Hitler

(Des Fahringer and Gessner. Eng F. Lorber. Recess)

1941. *T* **98** *and similar horiz design. P* 13½×14.
421 2 z. blue (22 May) 35 55
422 4 z. green (10 July) 50 70
Design:—4 z. Tyniec Monastery.
See also Nos. 465/8.

(Des W. Dachauer. Eng F. Lorber)

1941 (26 Oct)–**44**. (*a*) *Photo. P* 14.
423 **99** 2 g. grey 10 20
424 6 g. yellow-brown 10 20
425 8 g. deep grey-blue 10 20
426 10 g. yellow-green 10 10
427 12 g. deep violet 10 10
428 16 g. red-orange 35 40
429 20 g. deep brown 10 15
430 24 g. lake 10 10
431 30 g. purple 30 15
432 32 g. deep blue-green 15 35
433 40 g. blue 10 15
434 48 g. chocolate 40 40
435 50 g. deep blue (7.43) 10 15
436 60 g. olive (7.43) 10 15
437 80 g. deep purple (7.43) 10 15
       (*b*) *Recess. P* 12½ (7.4.42–44)
438 **99** 50 g. deep blue 30 40
439 60 g. olive 30 40
440 80 g. reddish purple 30 40
441 1 z. deep green 30 40
    a. Perf 14 (1944) 45 70
442 1 z. 20, purple-brown 35 45
    a. Perf 14 (1944) 55 80
443 1 z. 60, violet-indigo 45 60
    a. Perf 14 (1944) .. .. 60 1·25
423/443 *Set of 21* .. .. 4·00 5·00

1942 (20 Apr). *Hitler's 53rd Birthday. As T* **99**, *but premium inserted in design. Recess. Thick straw-coloured paper. P* 11.
444 30 g.+1 z. reddish purple 30 35
445 50 g.+1 z. blue 30 35
446 1 z. 20+1 z. brown 30 35

100 Modern Lublin   **101** Copernicus

1942 (15 Aug). *600th Anniv of Lublin. T* **100** *and similar design. Photo. P* 12½.
447 – 12 g. + 8 g. purple 10 15
448 **100** 24 g. + 6 g. red-brown 10 15
449 – 50 g. + 50 g. dull blue 15 25
450 **100** 1 z. + 1 z. green 50 60
447/450 *Set of 4* .. .. 75 1·00
Designs:—12 g., 50 g. Lublin, after an ancient engraving.

(Des W. Dachauer. Eng F Lorber. Recess)

1942 (20 Nov). *Third Anniv of German Occupation. T* **101** *and similar portraits. P* 13½×14.
451 12 g.+18 g. vio (Veit Stoss (Vit Stvosz)) 15 15
452 24 g.+26 g. lake (Hans Dürer) .. 15 15
453 30 g.+30 g. purple (J. Schuch) .. 15 15
454 50 g.+50 g. blue (J. Elsner) .. 15 20
455 1 z.+1 z. green 60 35
451/455 *Set of 5* .. .. .. 1·00 90

O **102**   **102** Adolf Hitler

(Des W. Kreb. Design photo; value typo)

1943 (16 Feb). *OFFICIAL. P* 14.
O456 O **102** 6 g. yellow-brown .. 10 20
O457 8 g. grey-blue 10 20
O458 10 g. light green 10 20
O459 12 g. violet 25 20
O460 16 g. brown-orange .. 10 30
O461 20 g. brown-olive .. 15 20
O462 24 g. brown-lake .. 25 20
O463 30 g. reddish purple .. 15 20
O464 40 g. blue 15 20
O465 60 g. olive 15 20
O466 80 g. dull purple .. 20 20
O467 100 g. slate 25 60
O456/467 *Set of 12* .. .. 1·60 2·50

(Des W. Dachauer. Eng F. Lorber. Recess)

1943 (20 Apr). *Hitler's 54th Birthday. P* 14.
456 **102** 12 g.+1 z. violet .. 15 20
457 24 g.+1 z. carmine .. 15 20
458 84 g.+1 z. green 30 35

102*a*   **103** Cracow Gate, Lublin

1943 (24 May). *400th Death Anniv of Nicolas Copernicus* (*astronomer*). *T* **101** (*colour changed*) *optd with T* **102***a*.
459 **101** 1 z. + 1 z. reddish purple 60 65
Issued in sheets of 10.
Examples of the 1 z. reddish purple without overprint exist; their status is unclear.

PUZZLED ?

Then you need
PHILATELIC TERMS ILLUSTRATED
to tell you all you need to know about printing methods, papers, errors, varieties, watermarks, perforations, etc. 192 pages, some in full colour, soft cover. Third Edition.

(Des W. Kreb. Frame photo. Centre embossed)

1943 (13 Aug–Sept). *Third Anniv of Nazi Party in German-occupied Poland. T* **103** *and similar designs. P* 14.

460	12 g. + 38 g. green			10	15
461	24 g. + 76 g. red			10	15
462	30 g. + 70 g. purple			10	15
463	50 g. + 1 z. blue			10	15
464	1 z. + 2 z. grey			15	25
460/464	*Set of* 5			40	75

Designs:—24 g. Cloth Hall, Cracow; 30 g. Administrative Building, Radom; 50 g. Bruhl Palace, Warsaw; 1 z. Town Hall, Lwow.

103a Lwow   104 Adolf Hitler

(Des Fahringer (2 z., 4 z.), F. Prufimeyer (6 z.), Gessner (10 z.). Eng F. Lorber. Recess)

1943–44. *T* **103** *and similar horiz designs. P* 13½×14 *or* 14×13½ (10 z.).

465	2 z. deep green (10.4.44)			10	10
466	4 z. slate-violet (10.4.44)			20	25
467	6 z. agate (11.2.44)			35	40
468	10 z. grey and chestnut (26.10.43)			40	50
465/468	*Set of* 4			95	1·10

Designs:—2 z. The Barbican, Cracow; 4 z. Tyniec Monastery; 10 z. Cracow.

(Des W. Kreb. Photo)

1944 (20 Apr). *Hitler's* 55*th Birthday. P* 14.

469	**104**	12 g. + 1 z. green			10	15
470		24 g. + 1 z. red-brown			10	15
471		84 g. + 1 z. violet			15	20

105 Konrad Celtis   105a Cracow Castle

(Des W. Dachauer. Eng F. Lorber. Recess)

1944 (15 July). *Culture Funds. T* **105** *and similar portraits. P* 14

472	12 g. + 18 g. green			10	10
473	24 g. + 26 g. red			10	10
474	30 g. + 30 g. purple			10	10
475	50 g. + 50 g. blue			20	25
476	1 z. + 1 z. brown			20	25
472/476	*Set of* 5			50	65

Designs:—24 g. Andreas Schluter; 30 g. Hans Boner; 50 g. Augustus the Strong; 1 z. Gottlieb Fusch.

(Des P. Stubinger. Eng R. Zenziger. Recess)

1944 (26 Oct). 5*th Anniv of German Occupation. P* 13½.

477	**105a**	10 z. + 10 z. greenish black & car	18·00	20·00
		a. Grey-black and red	6·00	10·00

Issued in sheets of 8.

IV. ISSUES OF POLISH EXILED GOVERNMENT IN LONDON
1941–44

For correspondence on Polish sea-going vessels and, on certain days, from Polish military camps in Great Britain.

106 Ruins of Ministry   107 Vickers-Armstrong
of Finance, Warsaw   Wellington and Hawker
                            Hurricanes used by Poles in
                            Great Britain

(Eng E. Dawson (5, 25, 75 g.), P. S. Hall (10, 80 g.), A. B. Hill (25 g.), E. Warner (1 z.), R. Godbehear (1 z. 50). Recess Bradbury, Wilkinson)

1941 (15 Dec). *T* **106/7** *and similar designs. P* 12½×13 (*vert*) *or* 11½×12 (*horiz*).

478	5 g. claret				15	60
479	10 g. myrtle green				20	70
480	25 g. slate-black				40	1·25
481	55 g. deep blue				70	1·75
482	75 g. brown-olive				2·50	4·00
483	80 g. carmine				2·50	4·00
484	1 z. slate-blue				6·00	5·00
485	1 z. 50, red-brown				6·00	5·00
478/485	*Set of* 8				17·00	22·00

Designs: *As T* **106**—5 g. Ruins of U.S.A. Embassy, Warsaw; 25 g. Destruction of Mickiewicz Monument, Cracow; 1 z. 50, Polish submarine *Orzel. As T* **107**—55 g. Ruins of Warsaw; 75 g. Polish machine-gunners; 80 g. Polish tank in Great Britain.

108 Vickers-Armstrong   109 Merchant Navy
Wellington and U-boat

(Des A. Horowicz. Eng P. S. Hall (5, 25, 55 g.), E. Dawson (10, 75, 80 g.), R. Godbehear (12 g.), A. B. Hill (1 z. 50). Recess Bradbury, Wilkinson)

1943 (1 Nov). *T* **108/9** *and similar designs. P* 12½×13 (*vert*) *or* 11½×12 (*horiz*).

486	5 g. claret				1·00	85
487	10 g. bright green				60	90
488	25 g. violet				60	90
489	55 g. ultramarine				65	1·25
490	75 g. red-brown				1·40	2·00
491	80 g. carmine				1·75	2·25
492	1 z. blackish olive				3·00	3·00
493	1 z. 50, black				2·00	4·00
486/493	*Set of* 8				10·00	13·50

Designs: *As T* **108**—25 g. Anti-tank gun in France; 55 g. Poles at Narvik; 1 z. Saboteurs damaging railway line. *As T* **109**—75 g. The Tobruk road; 80 g. Gen. Sikorski visiting Polish troops in Middle East; 1 z. 50, Underground newspaper office.

ALBUM LISTS   Please write for our latest lists of albums and accessories. These will be sent free on request.

MONTE CASSINO
18. V. 1944

Gr 55
≡≡≡

(110)

111 Folish Partisans

1944 (27 June). *Capture of Monte Cassino. Nos. 482/5 surch as T* **110**, *or smaller (No. 497).*

494	45 g. on 75 g. olive-green (B.)	..	10·00	13·00
495	55 g. on 80 g. carmine (B.)	..	10·00	13·00
	a. No stop after "18"	..	10·00	
496	80 g. on 1 z. slate-blue (B.)	..	10·00	13·00
497	1 z. 20 on 1 z. 50, red-brown (B.)	..	10·00	13·00
494/497	Set of 4	..	35·00	48·00

(Des A. Horowicz. Eng W. Vacek. Recess De La Rue)

1945 (3 Feb). *Relief Fund for Survivors of Warsaw Rising.*
P 11½.

498	**111**	1 z.+2 z. green	.. 5·25	7·00

V. REPUBLIC

In July 1944 a Provisional Government with Soviet sympathies was formed at Lublin, in the part of Poland reconquered by the Red Army. On 28 June 1945 a "Government of National Unity" was formed; by 1948 Poland had gradually been transformed into a Communist state.

112
Romuald Traugutt

113 White Eagle

114 Grunwald
Memorial, Cracow

(Des J. Ogórkiewicz. Litho J. Pietrzykowski, Lublin)

1944 (7 Sept). *National Heroes. T* **112** *and similar portraits. No gum. P* 11½.

499	25 g. rose-red (shades) ..	..	42·00	55·00
	a. Imperf (pair)	..	70·00	
500	50 g. green (T. Kościuszko)	..	48·00	65·00
	a. Imperf (pair)	..	70·00	
501	1 z. blue (H. Dabrowski)	..	50·00	55·00
	a. Imperf (pair)	..	70·00	

(Des J. Grubecki. Photo State Ptg Wks, Moscow)

1944 (13 Sept). *P* 12½.

502	**113**	25 g. brown-red	.. 50	25
503	**114**	50 g. slate-green	.. 50	15

No. 502 was printed in photogravure, but unoverprinted copies also exist from a typographed printing in dull red, which arrived too late for issue in this condition. See Nos. 516a, 536a and 602.

— 1 zł —

31.XII.1943

K. R. N.

31.XII.1944

(115)

— 2 zł —

P. K. W. N.

31.XII.1944

(116)

— 3 zł —

31.XII.1944

R. T. R. P.
(117)

22.I.1863.
(118)

"K.R.N." = Krajowa Rada Narodowa (National Federal Council).
"P.K.W.N." = Polski Komitet Wolnosci Narodowej (Polish National Liberation Committee).
"R.T.R.P." = Rzad Tymczasowy Rzeczpospolitej Polskiej (Provisional Government of the Polish Republic).

(Surch typo J. Pietrzykowski, Lublin)

1944–45. *No.* 502 *surch with T* **115** *to* **117**.

504	**113**	1 z. on 25 g. brown-red (31.12.44)	1·75	2·00
505		2 z. on 25 g. brown-red (15.1.45) ..	1·75	2·00
506		3 z. on 25 g. brown-red (15.1.45) ..	1·75	2·00

The 1 z. with spacing of 5 mm between the second and third and the third and fourth lines of the surcharge are postal forgeries.

1945 (22 Jan). *82nd Anniv of 1863 Revolt against Russia. T* **112** *surch with T* **118**.

507	**112**	5 z. on 25 g. cinnamon	.. 35·00	42·00

— 3 zł —

Bydgoszcz

23. I. 1945
(119)

120 Flag-bearer
and War Victim

121 Lodz
Factories

1945 (12 Feb). *Liberation Issue. No.* 502 *surch as T* **119** (*various town names with dates of liberation, as shown below*), *in blue.*

508	3 z. on 25 g. "Bydgoszcz 23.1.1945"		4·25	5·00
509	3 z. on 25 g. "Czestochowa 17.1.1945"		4·25	5·00
510	3 z. on 25 g. "Gniezno 22.1.1945"	..	4·25	5·00
511	3 z. on 25 g. "Kalisz 24.1.1945"		4·25	5·00
512	3 z. on 25 g. "Kielce 15.1.1945"		4·25	5·00
513	3 z. on 25 g. "Kraków 19.1.1945"		4·25	5·00
514	3 z. on 25 g. "Lódz 19.1.1945"	..	4·25	5·00
515	3 z. on 25 g. "Radom 16.1.1945"		4·25	5·00
516	3 z. on 25 g. "Warszawa 17.1.1945"		10·50	14·00
	a. Dull red (typo)		90·00	£100
517	3 z. on 25 g. "Zakopane 29.1.1945"		6·50	6·50
508/517	Set of 10	..	45·00	55·00

(T **120**/1 des J. Ogórkiewicz. Typo Postal Ptg Inst, Lódz)

1945 (9 Mar). *Liberation of Warsaw. White or grey paper. P* 11.

518	**120**	5 z. scarlet ..	.. 2·00	2·00

1945 (15 Mar). *Liberation of Lodz. P* 11.

519	**121**	1 z. ultramarine	.. 65	20

5 zł. ≡≡

24. III. 1794
(122)

123 Grunwald
Memorial, Cracow

1945 (9 Apr). 151*st Anniv of Kościuszko's Oath of Allegiance.*
No. 500 surch with T **122.**
520   5 z. on 50 g. green (R.)   . .   . .   9·00   10·00

USED PRICES. From 1945 most commemorative issues were
available cancelled-to-order from the Philatelic Bureau. and
used prices are for stamps in this condition. Postally used
stamps may be worth more.

(Des J. Wilczyk. Photo at Cracow)

1945 (10 Apr).   *Cracow Monuments. T* **123** *and similar designs.*
P 11.
521   50 g. chocolate   15   10
       a. Perf 11½   15   10
       b. Designer's name omitted (*p* 11)   . .   90   25
522   1 z. lake-brown   20   10
       a. Perf 11½   20   20
523   2 z. blue   75   15
524   3 z. plum   85   25
525   5 z. blue-green . .   . .   . .   5·00   7·00
521/525   *Set of* 5   . .   . .   . .   6·25   7·00
   Designs: *Vert*—1 z. Kosciuszko Memorial; 3 z. Copernicus
Memorial. *Horiz*—2 z. Cloth Hall; 5 z. Wawel Castle.

125 H.M.S. *Dragon* (cruiser)   D **126** Posthorn and
                                              Thunderbolts

(Typo at Lódz)

1945 (24 Apr). *25th Anniv of Polish Maritime League. T* **125**
and similar type inscr "Liga Morska". *P* 11.
526   50 g. + 2 z. reddish orange   . .   . .   8·50   6·50
527   1 z. + 3 z. royal blue   . .   . .   4·50   6·50
528   2 z. + 4 z. scarlet   . .   . .   3·50   5·50
529   3 z. + 5 z. deep green   . .   . .   3·50   5·50
526/529   *Set of* 4   . .   . .   . .   18·00   22·00
   Designs: *Vert*—1 z. *Dar Pomorza* (cadet ship); 2 z. Naval
ensigns. *Horiz*—3 z. Crane and Old Grain Tower, Gdansk.

1945 (20 May). *POSTAGE DUE. Litho. Size* 26×19½ *mm.*
P 11.
D530   D **126**   1 z. orange-brown   10   10
D531   2 z. orange-brown   10   10
D532   3 z. orange-brown   15   15
D533   5 z. orange-brown   20   15
D530/533   *Set of* 4   45   40
   For stamps in larger size, see Nos. D571/7 and D646/52.

126 Town Hall, Poznań   **127** Kościuszko
                                    Memorial, Lódź

(Des J. Wilczyk.   Photo Postal Ptg Inst, Lódz)

1945 (16 June).   *Postal Employees' Congress. P* 11
530   **126**   1 z. + 5 z. green   . .   . .   18·00   23·00

(Des Dobrowald.   Litho at Lódź)

1945 (1 July).   *P* 11.
531   **127**   3 z. purple   70   25

O **128**   **128** Grunwald, 1410   **129** Eagle
                                           and Manifesto

(Des J. Ogorkiewicz. Photo at Cracow)

1945 (1 July)—**46**. *OFFICIAL. With control numbers at bottom
right.*
   (*a*) *Control numbers* M-01705 (5 z.) *or* M-01706 (10 z.). *P* 11
O532   O **128**   (5 z.) deep violet-blue   . .   20   10
O533   (10 z.) red   30   15

(*b*) *Redrawn. Control number* M-01709 (May 1946). A. *P* 11.
                                                B. *Imperf.*
                                                A   B
O534   O **128**   (5 z.) dp violet-bl   15   10   15   10
O535   (10 z.) red   25   15   25   15
   The blue stamps are inscribed "ZWYKLA" (Ordinary) and the
red stamps "POLECONA" (Registered).
   Although the control number is the easiest method of
identifying the two issues, it is often blurred with the final figure
illegible. The redrawn stamps have fewer lines of shading on the
eagle and the diagonal lines in each corner are narrower. The 10 z.
stamps can be further distinguished by the horizontal
measurement of the design: No. O533 is 17 mm, No. O535 is
16½ mm.
   See also Nos. O748 and O804/6.

(Des M. Watorski.   Photo at Cracow)

1945 (16 July). *535th Anniv of Battle of Grunwald. P* 11.
532   **128**   5 z. blue   . .   . .   . .   8·00   9·00

(Des J. Wilczyk.   Photo at Cracow)

1945 (22 July).   *First Anniv of Liberation. P* 11.
533   **129**   3 z. carmine . .   . .   . .   10·00   13·00

130 Westerplatte

(Des J. Wilczyk.   Photo at Cracow)

1945 (1 Sept). *6th Anniv of Defence of Westerplatte. P* 11.
534   **130**   1 z. + 9 z. slate   . .   . .   20·00   24·00
   The premium was for a fund for sanatoria and rest homes.

1 ZŁ   1·50
(131)   ZŁ
                                  (132)

1945. *Surch with T* **131/2,** *in brown.*
535	**114**	1 z. on 50 g. slate-green (10 Sept)		45	15
		a. Surch inverted		20·00	
536	**113**	1.50 z. on 25 g. brown-red (1 Sept)		£375	£190
		a. Dull red (typo)		45	15

133 Crane Tower   **135** St. John's Cathedral

(Des J. Wilczyk. Photo at Cracow)

1945 (15 Sept). *Liberation of Gdańsk. T* **133** *and similar types inscr* "GDANSK. 30 III 1945". *P* 11.
537		1 z. blackish olive		10	10
538		2 z. blue (Stock Exchange)		20	10
539		3 z. purple (High Gate (*horiz*))		60	15
		a. Imperf (pair)		50	10

(Des J. Wilczyk. Photo at Cracow)

1945–46. "*Warsaw, 1939–45". T* **135** *and similar views of Warsaw before and after destruction. Imperf.*
540		1.50 z. carmine (Royal Castle) (15.10.45)		20	10
541		3 z. blue (25.11.45)		25	10
542		3.50 z. green (City Hall) (5.12.45)		1·10	30
543		6 z. slate (G.P.O.) (1.1.46)		25	15
544		8 z. brown (War Ministry) (1.1.46)		3·00	30
545		10 z. purple (Church of the Holy Cross) (10.1.46)		65	20
540/545		Set of 6		5·00	1·00

136 United Workers

(Des J. Wilczyk. Photo at Cracow)

1945 (18 Nov). *Trades' Union Congress. P* 11.
546	**136**	1.50 z. + 8.50 z. slate		7·25	8·00

137 Soldiers of 1830 and Jan III Sobieski Statue

(Des J. Wilczyk. Photo at Cracow)

1945 (29 Nov). *115th Anniv of 1830 Revolt against Russia. P* 11.
547	**137**	10 z. slate		8·50	10·50

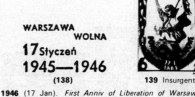

WARSZAWA WOLNA

17 Styczeń
1945—1946
(138)   **139** Insurgent

1946 (17 Jan). *First Anniv of Liberation of Warsaw. Nos. 540/5 optd with T* **138.**
548		1.50 z. carmine		1·75	2·50
549		3 z. blue		1·75	2·50
550		3.50 z. green		1·75	2·50
551		6 z. slate		1·75	2·50
552		8 z. brown		1·75	2·50
553		10 z. purple		1·75	2·50
548/553		Set of 6		9·50	13·50

(Des M. Konarski, after A. Grottger. Photo at Cracow)

1946 (22 Jan). *83rd Anniv of 1863 Revolt. P* 11.
554	**139**	6 z. blue		6·75	8·00

140 Lisunov Li-2   **141** Fighting in Spain
over ruins of Warsaw

(Des J. Wilczyk. Photo at Cracow)

1946. *AIR. P* 11.
555	**140**	5 z. slate-grey (25 June)		35	10
		a. Slate-black		1·25	15
		b. Control Number omitted		4·00	30
556		10 z. purple (20 May)		45	15
557		15 z. blue (1 Nov)		2·50	20
558		20 z. claret (5 Mar)		1·10	15
559		25 z. green (10 Sept)		2·00	35
560		30 z. scarlet (15 Mar)		3·00	45
555/560		Set of 6		8·50	1·25

Nos. 557 and 559 are without control "M-07741" at foot.

(Des M. Watorski. Photo at Cracow)

1946 (10 Mar). *Polish Legion in the Spanish Civil War. P* 11.
561	**141**	3 z. + 5 z. scarlet		4·00	3·75

142 Bydgoszcz   **143** "Death" over Majdanek
Concentration Camp

(Des M. Watorski. Photo at Cracow)

1946 (19 Apr). *600th Anniv of Bydgoszcz. P* 11.
562	**142**	3 z. + 2 z. grey-black		6·50	6·00

(Des J. Wilczyk. Photo at Cracow)

1946 (29 Apr). *Majdanek Concentration Camp.* P 11.
563 **143** 3 z.+5 z. slate-green   3·00   3·00

144 Shield and   **145** Infantry   **146** Polish Coastline
Soldiers

(Des M. Watorski. Photo at Cracow)

1946 (2 May). *Silesian Uprisings* (1919–21 and 1939–45).
P 11.
564 **144** 3 z.+7 z. brown   90   65

(Des S. Jasiński. Photo at Cracow)

1946 (9 May). *First Anniv of Peace.* P 11.
565 **145** 3 z. chocolate   40   25

(Des P. Marczewski. Photo)

1946 (21 July). *Maritime Festival.* P 11.
566 **146** 3 z.+7 z. blue   1·75   2·25

147 Pres Bierut, Premier O. Morawski   **148** Bedzin Castle
and Marshal Zymierski

(Des T. Gronowski. Photo)

1946 (22 July). *Second Anniv of Polish Committee of National
Liberation Manifesto.* P 11.
567 **147** 3 z. violet   3·25   3·75

(Des S. K. Dawski (568/9), S. Zechowski (570). Photo)

1946. T **148** *and similar designs. Imperf* (5 z., 10 z.) *or*
P 11 (6 z.).
568   5 z. olive-black (*shades*) (13.8)   15   10
568a   5 z. chocolate (*shades*) (14.12)   20   10
569   6 z. black (1.9)   35   10
570   10 z. blue (16.12)   70   15
568/570   *Set of 4*   1·25   35
Designs: *Vert*—6 z. Tombstone of Henry IV. *Horiz*—10 z. Castle
at Lanckorona.

1946 (Aug). *POSTAGE DUE. Photo. Size* 29×21½ *mm.
Imperf.*
D571 D **126**   2 z. orange-brown   10   10
D572   3 z. orange-brown   10   10
D573   5 z. orange-brown   10   10
D574   6 z. orange-brown   10   10
D575   10 z. orange-brown   15   15
D576   15 z. orange-brown   20   15
D577   25 z. orange-brown   30   15
D571/577   *Set of 7*   90   70
See also Nos. D646/52 for perf stamps.

149 Crane, Monument and   **150** Schoolchildren
Crane Tower   at Desk

(Des S. Żechowski. Photo)

1946 (14 Sept). *The Fallen in Gdansk.* P 11.
571 **149** 3 z.+12 z. slate   2·00   2·00

(Des E. Bartlomiejczyk. Photo Courvoisier)

1946 (10 Oct). *Polish Work for Education and Fund for
International Bureau of Education.* T **150** *and similar designs.
Granite paper.* P 11½.
571a   3 z.+22 z. vermilion   25·00   42·00
571b   6 z.+24 z. blue   25·00   42·00
571c   11 z.+19 z. green   25·00   42·00
MS571d 128×80 mm. Nos. 571a/c. Colours
slightly changed (sold at 25+75 z.)   £400   £750
Designs:—6 z. Court of Jagiellonian University, Cracow;
11 z. Gregor Piramowicz (1735–1801), founder of the Education
Commission.
Nos. 571a/c were issued in small sheets of 12.

152 Stojalowski, Bojko, Stapinski and Witos

(Des S. Zechowski. Photo)

1946 (1 Dec). *Fiftieth Anniv of Peasant Movement and Relief
Fund.* P 11.
572 **152** 5 z.+10 z. blue-green   1·25   1·40
573   5 z.+10 z. blue   1·25   1·40
574   5 z.+10 z. brown-olive   1·25   1·40

(153)

SEJM
USTAWODAWCZY
19 I 1947

1947 (4 Feb). *Opening of Polish Parliament. No.* 567 *surch
with* T **153**.
575 **147** 3 z.+7 z. violet (R.)   7·25   7·75

5 + 15 zł

XXII
MISTRZOSTWA
NARCIARSKIE
POLSKI
1947

(154)   **(155)**

1947 (21 Feb). *22nd National Ski Championships, Zakopane. No.*
502 *surch with* T **154**.
576 **113** 5 + 15 z. on 25 g. brown-red (B.)   3·25   4·00

1947 (25 Feb). *No.* 569 *surch with T* **155**.
577 5 z. on 6 z. black (R.) 60 25
   a. Orange surch 85 35

156 Home of Emil   **157** Frédéric Chopin
   Zegadlowicz   (musician)

158 Boguslawski, Modrzejewska   **159** Wounded Soldier,
   and Jaracz (actors)   Nurse and Child

(Des F. Suknarowski. Photo)

1947 (1 Mar). *Emil Zegadlowicz Commemoration. P* 11.
578 **156** 5 z.+15 z. grey-green .. .. 1·10 1·40

(Des S. Żechowski. Photo)

1947 (Mar)—**48**. *Polish Culture. As T* **157/8** (*Polish Celebrities*).
                   A. *P* 11.   B. *Imperf*
579 1 z. blue 20 15 25 15
580 1 z. blue-slate 20 15 50 25
581 2 z. brown 25 15 60 25
582 2 z. orange 15 15 40 10
583 3 z. turquoise-green .. 80 20 90 20
584 3 z. grey-olive .. .. 1·75 30 2·00 25
585 5 z. greenish black .. 55 15 55 15
586 5 z. sepia 20 15 60 15
587 6 z. greenish grey .. 90 20 1·50 25
588 6 z. carmine 35 15 80 15
589 10 z. grey .. .. 1·25 15 2·00 20
590 10 z. pale blue .. .. 1·40 25 1·40 25
591 15 z. slate-violet .. .. 1·50 40 2·75 30
592 15 z. red-brown .. .. 1·25 30 1·00 35
593 20 z. slate-black .. 2·25 60 3·00 50
594 20 z. dull purple .. 1·00 50 1·50 60
579/594 *Set of* 16 .. .. 12·50 3·50 18·00 3·75
MS594*a* 210×128 mm. in shades similar to
second issue of colours listed above. P 11½
(sold at 62+438 z.) £225 £250
  Portraits: *Horiz*—1 z. Matejko, Malczewski and Chelmonski
(painters); 6 z. Swietochowski, Zeromski and Prus (writers);
15 z. Wyspianski, Slowacki and Kasprowicz (poets). *Vert*—2 z.
Brother Albert of Cracow (founder of Albertine Social Service
Order); 10 z. Marie Curie (scientist); 20 z. A. Mickiewicz (poet).
  Dates of issue:—1st set of colours, Mar–May, 1947; 2nd set
of colours, May–Oct, 1947; Sheet, 10.6.48.

(Des M. Konarski. Photo)

1947 (1 June). *Red Cross Fund. Cross in red. P* 11.
595 **159** 5 z.+5 z. grey and red .. 2·40 3·50

THE WORLD CENTRE FOR
FINE STAMPS IS 399 STRAND

161 Steelworker   (**162**)

(Des S. Zechowski and M. Watorski (15 z.). Eng G. Barlangue,
  Cottet, Dufresne and Mazelin. Recess Govt Ptg Wks, Paris)

1947 (20 Aug). *As T* **161** (*occupations*). *P* 13.
596 5 z. brown-lake .. .. .. 1·00 30
597 10 z. emerald-green (Harvester) .. 30 15
598 15 z. blue (Fisherman) 60 25
599 20 z. black (Miner) .. .. 1·00 30
596/599 *Set of* 4 .. .. .. 2·50 80

1947 (10 Sept). *AIR. Nos.* 502/3 *surch with T* **162** *or similar*
surch. (*a*) *Design photo, surch typo.*
600 **114** 40 z. on 50 g. slate-green (R.) .. 2·00 50
601 **113** 50 z. on 25 g. brown-red .. 3·25 2·00
        (*b*) *Design and surch typo*
602 **113** 50 z. on 25 g. dull red .. 3·00 1·75

163 Brother Albert   **164** Sagittarius
   of Cracow

(Des S. Żechowski. Photo)

1947 (21 Dec). *Winter Relief Fund. P* 11.
603 **163** 2 z.+18 z. violet .. .. 1·10 2·40

(Des S. Żechowski. Photo)

1948 (9 Feb–25 Apr). *AIR. P* 11.
604 **164** 15 z. violet (25 Apr) .. 1·90 25
605 25 z. blue (25 Apr) .. 1·25 15
606 30 z. chocolate (25 Apr) .. 1·25 40
607 50 z. green .. .. 2·40 45
608 75 z. black (15 Mar) .. 2·40 60
609 100 z. vermilion .. .. 2·40 60
604/609 *Set of* 6 .. .. 10·50 2·25

165 Chainbreaker   **166** Generals H. Dembinski
                    and J. Bem

(T **165** des M. Watorski; others des S. Zechowski. Photo)

1948 (15 Mar–15 July). *Revolution Centenaries. T* **165** *and*
portraits as T **166**. *P* 11.
610 15 z. sepia 35 15
611 30 z. sepia (15 July) .. .. 1·25 35
612 35 z. olive-green (15 July) .. 2·75 60
613 60 z. scarlet (15 July) .. 1·50 70
610/613 *Set of* 4 .. .. 5·25 1·60
  Portraits: 35 z. S. Worcell, P. Sciegienny and E. Dembowski;
60 z. Friedrich Engels and Karl Marx.

167 Insurgents   **168** Wheel and Streamers

(Des J. Tom. Photo)

1948 (19 Apr). *Fifth Anniv of Warsaw Ghetto Defence.* P 11.
614 **167** 15 z. black .. .. 1·10 1·40

(Des T. Gronowski. Design photo, blue portion litho)
1948 (1 May). *Warsaw-Prague Cycle Race.* P 11.
615 **168** 15 z. carmine and blue .. .. 3·00 1·10

169 Cycle Race   **170** *Oliwa* under
Construction

(Des N. Jarczewska and K. Witkowski. Photo)
1948 (22 June). *Seventh Circuit of Poland Cycle Race.* P 11.
616 **169** 3 z. grey-black .. .. .. 2·00 1·75
617   6 z. brown .. .. .. 2·00 1·75
618   15 z. green .. .. 2·75 2·50

(Des T. Gronowski. Photo)
1948 (22 June). *Merchant Marine. As T* **170**. P 11.
619   6 z. bright violet .. .. .. 1·90 1·25
620   15 z. carmine-lake .. .. .. 2·25 2·00
621   35 z. slate .. .. 3·50 3·25
    Designs: *Horiz*—15 z. Freighter; 35 z. *General M. Zaruski* (cadet ketch).

173 Firework Display   **174** "Youth"

(Des E. Bartlomiejczyk. Photo)
1948 (15 July). *Wroclaw Exhibition.* P 11.
622 **173** 6 z. greenish blue 40 30
623   15 z. scarlet 65 20
624   18 z. claret .. .. .. 1·10 40
625   35 z. brown .. .. 1·10 40
622/625 *Set of 4* .. .. 2·75 1·10

(Des T. Tuszewski. Photo)
1948 (8 Aug). *International Youth Conference, Warsaw.* P 11.
626 **174** 15 z. blue 50 25

175 Roadway, St Anne's   **176** Torun Ramparts
Church and Palace   and Mail Coach

(Des Z. Skibiński. Photo)
1948 (1 Sept). *Charity. Warsaw Reconstruction Fund.* P 11.
627 **175** 15 z.+5 z. green 25 25

(Des A. Suchanek. Photo)
1948 (4 Sept). *Philatelic Congress, Torun.* P 11.
628 **176** 15 z. sepia 65 25

177 Locomotive,   **178** President Bierut
Clock and Winged Wheel

(Des E. Bartlomiejczyk. Photo)
1948 (6 Oct). *European Railway Conference.* P 11½.
629 **177** 18 z. blue .. .. 5·50 7·75

(Des M. Watorski. Photo)
1948–49. P 11½ (6 z.) or 11 (*others*).
629a **178** 2 z. dull orange (15.2.49) .. 10 10
629b   3 z. deep blue-green (15.5.49) .. 10 10
    ba. Perf 11½ .. 10 10
630   5 z. brown (1.12.48) .. 10 10
    a. Perf 11½ .. 10 10
631   6 z. blue-black (1.12.48) .. 60 10
631a   10 z. violet (15.5.49) .. 15 10
    ab. Perf 11½ .. 15 10
632   15 z. carmine-red (14.10.48) .. 50 10
    a. Perf 11½ .. 50 10
633   18 z. deep dull green (1.12.48) .. 70 20
    a. Perf 11½ .. 70 20
634   30 z. blue (1.12.48) .. 1·25 20
    a. Perf 11½ .. 1·25 20
635   35 z. brown-purple (1.12.48) .. 2·00 40
629a/635 *Set of 9* .. .. .. 5·00 1·00

179 Workers and Flag   **180** Baby

(Des E. John (5 z.), T. Gronowski (others). Photo)
1948 (8 Dec). *Workers Class Unity Congress. T* **179** *and similar horiz designs.* P 11.
636   5 z. carmine-red 80 50
    a. Perf 11½ 80 50
637   15 z. blackish purple 80 50
    a. Perf 11½ 80 50
638   25 z. brown 80 50
    a. Perf 11½ 80 50
    Designs:—15 z. Flags and portraits of Engels, Marx, Lenin and Stalin; 25 z. Workers marching and portrait of L. Warynski.

1948 (15 Dec). *As Nos. 636/8, but colours changed and inscr "XII 1948" instead of "8 XII 1948". P 11 (25 z.) or 11½ (others).*

639	5 z. plum				2·25	1·75
640	15 z. blue				2·25	1·75
641	25 z. green				3·00	2·00

(Des T. Trepkowski. Photo)

1948 (16 Dec). *Anti-tuberculosis Fund. T 180 and similar baby portraits. P 11½ (3 z.) or 11 (others).*

642	3 z. + 2 z. bronze green			3·00	2·50
643	5 z. + 5 z. reddish brown			3·00	2·50
	a. Perf 11½			3·00	2·50
644	6 z. + 4 z. plum			1·50	2·50
645	15 z. + 10 z. deep rose-red			1·25	1·75
642/645	*Set of 4*			8·00	8·50

Nos. 642/5 were each issued with *se-tenant* stamp-sized labels in 10 different designs.

180a President Franklin D. Roosevelt

181 Workers

(Des T. Granowski. Photo Courvoisier)

1948 (30 Dec). *AIR. Honouring Presidents Roosevelt, Pulaski and Kosciuszko. T 180a and similar horiz designs. P 11½.*

645a	80 z. blackish violet			22·00	28·00
645b	100 z. purple (Pulaski)			24·00	22·00
645c	120 z. blue (Kościuszko)			24·00	22·00

MS645d 160 × 95 mm. Nos. 645a/c 300 + 200 z.

colours changed £275 £400

Nos. 645a/c were issued in small sheets of 16 plus four attached labels.

The sale of this issue was restricted and it is doubtful if many were used, except philatelically.

1949 (15 Feb). **—50**. *POSTAGE DUE. As P 11½ (1, 2 z.) or 11 (others).*

D646	D **126**	1 z. yellow-brown ('50)		10	10
D647		2 z. yellow-brown ('50)		10	10
D648		3 z. yellow-brown ('50)		10	10
D649		15 z. yellow brown (2.50)		15	15
D650		25 z. yellow-brown ('50)		30	15
D651		100 z. orange-brown		75	25
D652		150 z. orange-brown		1·40	25
D646/652		*Set of 7*		2·50	90

(Des E. John. Photo)

1949 (31 May). *Trades Union Congress, Warsaw. T 181 and similar types inscr "II./VIII. KONGRES . ZWIAZKOW ZAWODOWYCH . MAJ. 1949". P 11½.*

646	3 z. carmine			90	90
647	5 z. blue			90	90
648	15 z. green			1·25	1·25

Designs:—5 z. Factory, tractor and worker; 15 z. Three workers.

PUZZLED ?

Then you need
PHILATELIC TERMS ILLUSTRATED
to tell you all you need to know about printing methods, papers, errors, varieties, watermarks, perforations, etc. 192 pages, some in full colour, soft cover. Third Edition.

---

182 Banks of R. Vistula

183 Pres. Bierut

(Des W. Borowski (10 z., 15 z.), R. Kleczewski (35 z.). Eng B. Brandt (10 z.), M. R. Polak (15 z.), S. Lukaszewski (35 z.). Litho)

1949 (22 July). *Fifth Anniv of National Liberation Committee. T 182/3 and similar vert design. P 13.*

649	10 z. black			2·00	1·50
650	15 z. deep mauve			2·00	1·50
651	35 z. grey-blue (Radio station, Raszyn)		2·00	1·50
	a. Perf 11			2·00	1·50

184 Mail Coach and Map

185 Worker and Tractor

(Des R. Kleczewski. Eng B. Brandt (6 z.), S. Lukaszewski (30 z.) and M. R. Polak (80 z.). Recess)

1949 (10 Oct). *75th Anniv of U.P.U. Various forms of transport as T 184 inscr "75 LAT SWIATOWEGO ZWIAZKU POCZTOWEGO". P 13 × 12½.*

652	6 z. slate-purple			1·00	1·25
653	30 z. deep blue (Liner)			1·75	1·60
654	80 z. myrtle green (Aeroplane)			3·50	3·50

(Des L. Dabrowski and D. Piotrowski. Eng S. Lukaszewski. Recess)

1949. *Congress of Peasant Movement. P 13 × 12½.*

655	**185**	5 z. claret (20.12)		85	20
656		10 z. red (20.12)		20	10
657		15 z. green (26.11)		20	10
658		35 z. brown (20.12)		1·00	70
655/658		*Set of 4*		2·00	95

186 Frédéric Chopin

187 Mickiewicz and Pushkin

188 Postman

(Des M. Watorski. Eng M. R. Polak (10 z.), S. Lukaszewski (15 z.) and B. Brandt (35 z.). Recess)

1949 (5 Dec). *T 186 and similar portraits. P 12½ × 13.*

659	10 z. purple (Adam Mickiewicz)			2·00	1·50
660	15 z. brown-red			2·75	1·50
661	35 z. blue (Julius Slowacki)			2·00	1·50

(Des M. Milberger. Eng B. Brandt. Recess)

1949 (15 Dec). *Polish-Russian Friendship Month. P 12½ × 13.*

662	**187**	15 z. slate-violet		2·40	2·40

(Des R. Kleczewski. Eng B. Brandt. Recess)

1950 (21 Jan). *Third Congress of Postal Workers.* P 12½×13.
663 **188** 15 z. bright purple .. .. .. 2·00 1·40

189 Mechanic, Hangar and Aeroplane   **D 190**   **190** President Bieruť

(Des W. Borowski. Eng B. Brandt. Recess)

1950 (6 Feb). *AIR.* P 12½×13.
664 **189** 500 z. brown-lake .. .. 5·00 6·75

(Des R. Kleczewski. Eng S. Lukaszewski. Recess)

1950. *POSTAGE DUE.* P 12×12½.

D665 D **190**	5 z. brown-red (20.10) ..	15	10
D666	10 z. brown-red (25.2) ..	15	10
D667	15 z. brown-red (5.7) ..	15	10
D668	20 z. brown-red (20.10) ..	15	10
D669	25 z. brown-red (5.7) ..	25	15
D670	50 z. brown-red (24.5) ..	40	15
D671	100 z. brown-red (20.10) ..	70	45
D665/671	*Set of 7* ..	1·60	1·00

See also Nos. D701/12, D804/14 and D2699/2702.

(Des W. Borowski. Eng M. R. Polak. Recess)

1950 (25 Feb). P 12×12½.
665 **190** 15 z. red 50 15

191 J. Marchlewski   **192** Workers   **193** Worker and Flag

(Des from photo by W. Kwinta. Photo)

1950 (23 Mar). *25th Death Anniv of Julian Marchlewski* (*patriot*). P 11½.
666 **191** 15 z. blue-black 65 40
    a. Perf 11 .. .. 65 40

(Des M. Bylina. Photo)

1950 (15 Apr). *Reconstruction of Warsaw.* P 12.
667 **192** 5 z. deep brown 10 10
    a. Perf 11 .. .. 10 10
    b. Perf 13×11 .. .. .. 10 10
    c. Perf 11½×12 .. .. .. 10 10
    d. Perf 13×11½ 10 10
See also No. 695.

(Des E. John (10 z.), M. Bylina (15 z.). Photo)

1950 (26 Apr). *60th Anniv of May Day Manifesto.* T **193** *and vert type inscr* "I MAJ 1890 1950". P 11½×12 (*horiz*), 12×11½ (*vert*).
668 10 z. magenta .. .. .. 1·60 30
669 15 z. olive-green .. .. .. 1·60 15
    Design:—15 z. Three workers and flag.

THE WORLD CENTRE FOR FINE STAMPS IS 399 STRAND

194 Statue   **195** Dove and Globe   **195a** President Bieruť

(Des J. Wilczyk. Photo)

1950 (27 Apr). *23rd International Fair, Posnań.* P 11½.
670 **194** 15 z. red-brown 25 15

(Des T. Trepkowski. Photo)

1950 (15 May). *International Peace Conference.* P 11.
671 **195** 10 z. deep green 70 20
672   15 z. deep sepia 30 15
    a. Perf 11½ 30 15

(Des W. Borowski. Eng S. Lukaszewski. Recess)

1950 (25 June–20 Oct). P 12×12½.

673 **195a**	5 z. green (25.7) ..	10	10
674	10 z. scarlet (10.8) ..	10	10
675	15 z. blue (20.10) ..	85	10
676	20 z. violet ..	35	10
677	25 z. red-brown (25.7) ..	35	10
678	30 z. claret (10.8) ..	50	10
679	40 z. brown ..	70	10
680	50 z. brown-olive ..	1·40	20
673/680	*Set of 8* ..	4·00	60

See also Nos. 687/94.

196 Industrial and Agricultural Worker   **197** Hibner, Kniewski, Rutkowski   **198** Worker and Dove

(Des W. Zakrzewski. Eng M. R. Polak. Recess)

1950 (20 July). *Six Year Reconstruction Plan.* P 12½×13.
681 **196** 15 z. ultramarine 20 10
    a. Grey-blue 20 10
For similar stamps see Nos. 696/e and **MS**721a.

(Des Cz. Kaczmarczyk. Photo at Cracow)

1950 (18 Aug). *25th Death Anniv of Hibner, Kniewski, Rutkowski* (*revolutionaries*). P 11½.
682 **197** 15 z. deep blue-grey .. .. 2·00 60

(Des T. Gronowski. Eng M. R. Polak. Recess)

1950 (31 Aug). *First Polish Peace Congress.* P 12½×13.
683 **198** 15 z. grey-green 30 10

Currency Revaluation
100 Old Zlotys = 1 New Zloty

By a decree of 28 October 1950 1 old zloty became worth 1 new groszy and all post offices were empowered to handstamp existing stocks of stamps with the word "Groszy" or "gr". About 50 types of these handstamps are known. These are outside the scope of this catalogue.

The stamps which were authorised for handstamping are Nos. 579/94 perf and imperf, 596/615, 619/645, 646/658, 673/80, D530/3, D571/7, D646/52 and D665/71. Handstamps on other stamps were not authorised.

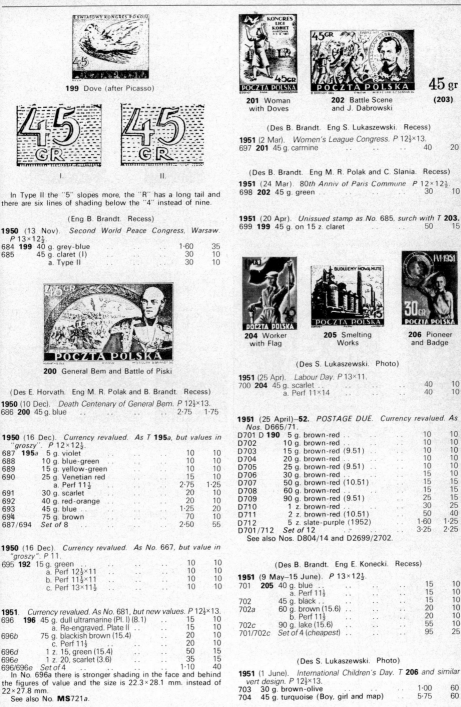

199 Dove (after Picasso)

I.

II.

In Type II the "5" slopes more, the "R" has a long tail and there are six lines of shading below the "4" instead of nine.

(Eng B. Brandt. Recess)

1950 (13 Nov). *Second World Peace Congress, Warsaw.* P 13×12½.

684	**199**	40 g. grey-blue		1·60	35
685		45 g. claret (I)		30	10
		a. Type II		30	10

200 General Bem and Battle of Piski

(Des E. Horvath. Eng M. R. Polak and B. Brandt. Recess)

1950 (10 Dec). *Death Centenary of General Bem.* P 12½×13.

686	**200**	45 g. blue		2·75	1·75

1950 (16 Dec). *Currency revalued. As T 195a, but values in "groszy".* P 12×12½.

687	**195**a	5 g. violet		10	10
688		10 g. blue-green		10	10
689		15 g. yellow-green		10	10
690		25 g. Venetian red		15	10
		a. Perf 11½		2·75	1·25
691		30 g. scarlet		20	10
692		40 g. red-orange		20	10
693		45 g. blue		1·25	20
694		75 g. brown		70	10
687/694		*Set of 8*		2·50	55

1950 (16 Dec). *Currency revalued. As No. 667, but value in "groszy".* P 11.

695	**192**	15 g. green		10	10
		a. Perf 12½×11		10	10
		b. Perf 11½×11		10	10
		c. Perf 13×11½		10	10

1951. *Currency revalued. As No. 681, but new values.* P 12½×13.

696	**196**	45 g. dull ultramarine (Pl. I) (8.1)		15	10
		a. Re-engraved. Plate II		15	10
696b		75 g. blackish brown (15.4)		20	10
		c. Perf 11½		20	10
696d		1 z. 15, green (15.4)		50	15
696e		1 z. 20, scarlet (3.6)		35	15
696/696e		*Set of 4*		1·10	40

In No. 696a there is stronger shading in the face and behind the figures of value and the size is 22.3×28.1 mm. instead of 22×27.8 mm.
See also No. **MS**721a.

201 Woman with Doves

202 Battle Scene and J. Dabrowski

45 gr (203)

(Des B. Brandt. Eng S. Lukaszewski. Recess)

1951 (2 Mar). *Women's League Congress.* P 12½×13.

697	**201**	45 g. carmine		40	20

(Des B. Brandt. Eng M. R. Polak and C. Slania. Recess)

1951 (24 Mar). *80th Anniv of Paris Commune* P 12×12½.

698	**202**	45 g. green		30	10

1951 (20 Apr). *Unissued stamp as No. 685, surch with T 203.*

699	**199**	45 g. on 15 z. claret		50	15

204 Worker with Flag

205 Smelting Works

206 Pioneer and Badge

(Des S. Lukaszewski. Photo)

1951 (25 Apr). *Labour Day.* P 13×11.

700	**204**	45 g. scarlet		40	10
		a. Perf 11×14		40	10

1951 (25 April)–**52.** *POSTAGE DUE. Currency revalued. As Nos. D665/71.*

D701	D **190**	5 g. brown-red		10	10
D702		10 g. brown-red		10	10
D703		15 g. brown-red (9.51)		10	10
D704		20 g. brown-red		10	10
D705		25 g. brown-red (9.51)		10	10
D706		30 g. brown-red		15	10
D707		50 g. brown-red (10.51)		15	15
D708		60 g. brown-red		15	15
D709		90 g. brown-red (9.51)		25	15
D710		1 z. brown-red		30	25
D711		2 z. brown-red (10.51)		50	40
D712		5 z. slate-purple (1952)		1·60	1·25
D701/712		*Set of 12*		3·25	2·25

See also Nos. D804/14 and D2699/2702.

(Des B. Brandt. Eng E. Konecki. Recess)

1951 (9 May–15 June). P 13×12½.

701	**205**	40 g. blue		15	10
		a. Perf 11½		15	10
702		45 g. black		15	10
702a		60 g. brown (15.6)		20	10
		b. Perf 11½		20	10
702c		90 g. lake (15.6)		55	10
701/702c		*Set of 4 (cheapest)*		95	25

(Des S. Lukaszewski. Photo)

1951 (1 June). *International Children's Day.* T **206** and similar vert design. P 12½×13.

703		30 g. brown-olive		1·00	60
704		45 g. turquoise (Boy, girl and map)		5·75	60

207 St. Staszic

208 Wroblewski and Olszewski

(Des M. R. Polak (25 g.), S. Lukaszewski (40 g.), C. Slania (45 g.), B. Brandt (60 g., 1 z. 20), R. Kleczewski (1 z. 15). Photo)

1951 (25 June). *First Polish Scientific Congress.* T **207** and *similar vert designs and* T **208**. P 14×10½ (45 g.) *or* 12½×13 (others).

705	25 g. carmine	..	2·75	2·75
706	40 g. blue (Marie Curie)	..	60	20
707	45 g. violet	..	7·75	65
708	60 g. green (M. Nencki)	..	60	20
709	1 z. 15, purple (Copernicus)	..	90	50
710	1 z. 20, grey (Dove and book)	..	1·75	20
705/710	*Set of 6*	..	13·00	4·00

BLOCKED VALUES. Starting with the above issue most commemorative issues up to 1963 contained one "blocked value" which was not available at most post offices but could only be obtained in strictly limited quantities at the Philatelic Bureau. Their relative scarcity is reflected in the prices quoted. It is understood that this practice was intended to restrict the export of stamps by private individuals.

209 F. Dzerzhinsky

210 Pres Bierut, Industry and Agriculture

(Des B. Brandt. Eng S. Lukaszewski. Recess)

1951 (5 July). *25th Death Anniv of Dzerzhinsky (Russian politician).* P 12×12½.

711	**209**	45 g. brown	..	..	25	15

(Des S. Lukaszewski. Eng M. R. Polak and C. Slania. Recess)

1951 (22 July). *Seventh Anniv of People's Republic.* P 12½×13.

712	**210**	45 g. carmine	..	..	60	15
713		60 g. grey-green	..	..	15·00	5·75
714		90 g. deep blue	..	..	3·50	70

(212)

211 Young People and Globe

213 Sports Badge

(Des B. Brandt. Photo)

1951 (5 Aug). *Third World Youth Festival, Berlin.* P 11 *or* 12½×10½.

715	**211**	40 g. blue	..	..	85	25

1951 (1 Sept). *Unissued stamp as Nos.* 673/80 *surch with* T **212.**

716	**196**a	45 g. on 35 z. orange	..	25	15
		a. Figure "4" shorter than "5"	..	3·50	90

(Des E. Konecki. Photo)

1951 (8 Sept). *Spartacist Games.* P 14×11 *or* 12½×13.

717	**213**	45 g. green	..	..	1·10	40

214 Stalin

215 Chopin and Moniuszko

(Des and eng S. Lukaszewski. Recess)

1951 (30 Oct). *Polish–Soviet Friendship.* P 12½×13.

718	**214**	45 g. brown-carmine	..	15	10
719		90 g. blackish brown	..	35	20

(Des and eng E. Konecki. Recess)

1951 (15 Nov). *Polish Music Festival.* P 13×12½.

720	**215**	45 g. black	..	30	10
721		90 g. red	..	90	50

1951 (15 Nov). *Warsaw Stamp Day. Sheet* 90×120 mm *comprising Nos.* 696a/e *printed in red-brown.* P 12½×13.

MS721a	**196**	Sold at 5 z.	..	..	20·00	12·00

216 Mining Machinery

217 Building Modern Flats

218 Installing Electric Cable

(Des and eng C. Slania. Recess)

1951 (4 Dec)–**52.** *Six Year Plan (Mining).* P 13×12½.

722	**216**	90 g. purple-brown	..	25	10
723		1 z. 20, grey-blue	..	30	10
724		1 z. 20+15 g. red-orange (18.10.52)	..	25	15

(Des R. Kleczewski. Eng B. Brandt. Recess)

1951 (10 Dec)–**52.** *Six Year Plan (Reconstruction).* P 12½×13.

725	**217**	30 g. green	..	10	10
		a. Perf 12×11½	..	10	10
726		30 g. + 15 g. brown-red (1.6.52)	..	20	10
727		1 z. 15, maroon	..	25	10
		a. Perf 12×11½	..	25	10

(Des R. Kleczewski. Eng M. R. Polak. Recess)

1951 (15 Dec)–**52.** *Six Year Plan (Electrification).* P 12½×13.

728	**218**	30 g. black	..	10	10
729		45 g. scarlet	..	15	10
730		45 g.+15 g. brown (1.6.52)	..	50	15

219 M. Nowotko   **220** Women and Banner   **221** Gen Swierczewski

224 Cyclists and City Arms   **225** Workers and **226** J. I. Kraszewski Banner

(Des C. Slania, eng E. Konecki (45 g.); des and eng B. Brandt (90 g.); des M. R. Polak, eng S. Lukaszewski (I z. 15). Recess)

1952 (18 Jan). *Tenth Anniv of Polish Workers' Coalition. T 219 and similar vert portrait designs. P 12½×13.*

731	45 g.+15 g. lake	..	15	10
732	90 g. chocolate (P. Finder)	..	30	15
733	1 z. 15 orange-red (M. Fornalska)	..	30	15

(Des and eng S. Lukaszewski. Recess)

1952 (8 Mar). *International Women's Day. P 12½×12.*

734	**220** 45 g.+15 g. purple-brown	..	35	10
735	1 z. 20, scarlet	..	45	20

(Des and eng C. Slania. Recess)

1952 (28 Mar). *Fifth Death Anniv of General Swierczewski. P 12½×13.*

736	**221** 45 g.+15 g. purple-brown	..	35	10
737	90 g. indigo..	..	45	25

IMPERF STAMPS. From 1952 until 1961 some sets exist imperf from limited printings and issued at special prices by the Philatelic Bureau. We do not list these but they are mentioned in footnotes.

222 Ilyushin Il-12 over Farm   **223** President Bierut

(Des C. Slania (55 g., 1 z. 40), B. Brandt (others). Eng B. Brandt (55 g.), E. Konecki (90 g.), C. Slania (1 z. 40) and M. R. Polak (5 z.). Recess)

1952 (10 Apr). *AIR. T 222 and similar horiz designs showing aeroplanes and views. P 12×12½.*

738	55 g. grey-blue (Tug and freighters)	..	40	25
739	90 g. deep green	..	35	30
740	1 z. 40, maroon (Warsaw)	..	50	30
741	5 z. black (Steelworks)	..	1·50	40
738/741	Set of 4	..	2·50	1·10

These exist imperforate.

(Des Rolicz. Eng B. Brandt. Recess)

1952 (18 Apr). *Pres Bierut's 60th Birthday. P 13×12½.*

742	**223** 45 g.+15 g. scarlet ..	..	30	25
743	90 g. grey-green	..	55	60
744	1 z. 20+15 g. bright blue ..	..	70	25

(Des P. Swiatkowski and K. Maleszewski. Photo)

1952 (25 Apr). *Fifth Warsaw–Berlin–Prague Peace Cycle Race. P 13×12½.*

745	**224** 40 g. blue	.. ..	1·50	80

(Des S. Lukaszewski. Eng B. Brandt. Recess)

1952 (1 May). *Labour Day. P 12½×13.*

746	**225** 45 g.+15 g. scarlet ..	..	15	10
747	75 g. green ..	..	40	25

1952. *OFFICIAL. As No. O534 but no control number and litho. Inscr "ZWYKLA". P 11.*

O748	O **128** (60 g.) pale blue	25	10

See also Nos. O804/6.

(Des and eng M. R. Polak. Recess)

1952 (5 May). *140th Birth Anniv of Jozef Ignacy Kraszewski (writer). P 12½×13.*

748	**226** 25 g. maroon	.. ..	40	25

227 Maria Konopnicka   **228** H. Kollataj   **229** Leonardo da Vinci

(Des and eng E. Konecki. Recess)

1952 (10 May). *110th Birth Anniv of Maria Konopnicka (poet). P 12½×13.*

749	**227** 30 g.+15 g. deep green	..	45	15
750	1 z. 15, brown-red	..	65	45

(Des and eng S. Lukaszewski. Recess)

1952 (20 May). *140th Death Anniv of Hugo Kollataj (educationist and politician). P 12½×13.*

751	**228** 45 g.+15 g. brown ..	..	15	10
752	1 z. olive-green	..	25	15

(Des M. R. Polak. Eng B. Brandt. Recess)

1952 (1 June). *500th Birth Anniv of Leonardo da Vinci (artist). P 12½×13.*

753	**229** 30 g. + 15 g. deep blue	..	75	35

230 President Bierut and Children   **231** N. V. Gogol

(Des C. Slania. Photo)

1952 (1 June). *International Children's Day*. P 14.
754 **230** 45 g.+15 g. blue .. .. 2·25 60

(Des B. Brandt. Eng C. Slania. Recess)

1952 (5 June). *Death Centenary of Nikolai Gogol (Russian writer)*. P 12½×13.
755 **231** 25 g. deep green 60 25

232 Cement Works   **233** Swimmers   **234** Yachts

(Des C. Slania. Eng B. Brandt. Recess)

1952 (17 June). *Construction of Cement Works, Wierzbica*. P 12½×13.
756 **232** 3 z. black .. .. .. 1·25 35
757 10 z. scarlet .. .. .. 1·60 30

(Des P. Swiatkowski. Photo)

1952 (21 June). *Sports Day.* T **233** *and similar vert designs.* P 12½×13.
758 30 g. + 15 g. blue .. .. 4·50 1·00
759 45 g. + 15 g. violet (Footballers) .. 1·60 15
760 1 z. 15, green (Runners) .. 1·40 1·40
761 1 z. 20, rose-red (High jumper) .. 85 55
758/761 *Set of 4* .. .. .. 7·50 2·75

(Des B. Brandt (30 g.), C. Slania (45 g.), R. Kleczewski (90 g.). Eng M. R. Polak (30 g.), S. Lukaszewski (45 g.), E. Konecki (90 g.). Recess)

1952 (28 June). *Shipbuilders' Day.* T **234** *and similar designs.* P 13×12½ (30 g.) or 12½×13 (others).
762 30 g. + 15 g. dull blue-green .. 3·00 85
763 45 g. + 15 g. deep violet-blue .. 75 20
764 90 g. maroon 75 75
Designs: *Vert*—45 g. Cadet ship *Dar Pomorza*; 90 g. Shipbuilding worker.

235 Young Workers   **236** "New Constitution"   **237** L. Warynski

(Des R. Kleczewski (30 g.), B. Brandt (45 g.) and M. R. Polak (90 g.). Eng B. Brandt (45 g.), S. Lukaszewski (others). Recess)

1952 (17 July). *Youth Festival, Warsaw.* T **235** *and similar designs with flag inscr "20 22 VII WARSZAWA 1952".* P 12×12½ (45 g.) or 12½×12 (others).
765 30 g.+15 g. deep green .. 35 25
766 45 g.+15 g. scarlet .. 60 15
767 90 g. brown 35 30
Designs: *Horiz*—45 g. Girl and boy students; 90 g. Boy bugler.

POLISH PEOPLE'S REPUBLIC

The above title was officially adopted on 22 July 1952.

(Des T. Gronowski. Photo)

1952 (22 July). *Adoption of New Constitution.* P 11×11½ (45 g.) or 11½×13 (3 z.).
768 **236** 45 g.+15 g. green and purple-brown 1·00 15
769 3 z. violet and deep brown .. 40 35

(Des R. Kleczewski. Eng C. Slania. Recess)

1952 (31 July). *70th Anniv of the Party "Proletariat".* P 13×12½.
770 **237** 30 g.+15 g. brown-red .. 45 15
771 45 g.+15 g. purple-brown .. 45 15

238 Jaworzno Power Station   **239** Frydman

(Des C. Slania. Eng E. Konecki. Recess)

1952 (7 Aug). *Electricity Power Station, Jaworzno.* P 13×12½.
772 **238** 45 g. + 15 g. red 65 10
773 1 z. black 60 40
774 1 z. 50, deep green 60 15
 a. Perf 11½×12 .. .. 60 15

(Des Z. Polasińska. Photo)

1952 (18 Aug). *Pieniny Mountain Resorts.* T **239** *and similar vert designs.* P 12½×13.
775 45 g.+15 g. dull purple .. 45 10
776 60 g. green (Grywald) .. 30 40
777 1 z. rose-red (Niedzica) .. 90 10
 a. Error "NIEDZIGA" .. 2·75 80

240 Pilot and Glider   **241** Avicenna

(Des E. Konecki, eng B. Brandt (30 g.). Des C. Slania, eng M. R. Polak (45 g.). Des and eng S. Lukaszewski (90 g.). Recess)

1952 (23 Aug). *Aviation Day.* T **240** *and similar horiz designs.* P 13×12½.
778 30 g. + 15 g. deep green .. .. 1·40 20
779 45 g. + 15 g. scarlet .. .. 2·25 70
780 90 g. deep blue 40 30
Designs:—45 g. Pilot and Yakovlev Yak-18U; 90 g. Parachutists descending.

(Des and eng C. Slania. Recess)

1952 (1 Sept). *Birth Millenary of Avicenna (Arab physician).* P 12½×13.
781 **241** 75 g. brown-red 30 15

HAVE YOU READ THE NOTES AT THE BEGINNING OF THIS CATALOGUE?

These often provide answers to the enquiries we receive.

242 Victor Hugo   **243** Ship-building

(Des E. Konecki. Eng C. Slania. Recess)

1952 (1 Sept). *150th Birth Anniv of Victor Hugo (French author).*
P 12½×13.

782	**242**	90 g. chocolate	30	15

(Des B. Świderska. Eng E. Konecki. Recess)

1952 (10 Sept). *Gdansk Shipyards.* P 12½×13.

783	**243**	5 g. deep green	15	10
		a. Perf 11½	15	10
784		15 g. brown-red	15	10

244 H. Sienkiewicz   **245** Assault on Winter
(author)   Palace, Petrograd

(Des R. Kleczewski. Eng C. Slania. Recess)

1952 (25 Oct). P 12½×13.

785	**244**	45 g. + 15 g. chocolate	25	10

(Des and eng B. Brandt. Recess)

1952 (7 Nov). *35th Anniv of Russian Revolution.* P 12×12½.

786	**245**	45 g. + 15 g. brown-red	1·00	20
787		60 g. blackish brown	40	30

These exist imperforate.

246 Lenin   **247** Miner   **248** H. Wieniawski
(violinist)

(Des and eng M. R. Polak. Recess)

1952 (7 Nov). *Polish–Soviet Friendship Month.* P 12½×13.

788	**246**	30 g. + 15 g. dull purple	30	15
789		45 g. + 15 g. brown	55	25
		a. "LENIN" omitted	—	20·00

(Des E. Konecki. Eng S. Lukaszewski. Recess)

1952 (4 Dec). *Miners' Day.* P 12½×13.

790	**247**	45 g. + 15 g. brown-black	15	10
791		1 z. 20 + 15 g. brown	55	30

(Des K. Sopoćko. Photo)

1952 (5 Dec). *Second Wieniawski International Violin
Competition.* P 12½×13.

792	**248**	30 g. + 15 g. deep green	1·00	40
793		45 g. + 15 g. violet	2·75	50

249 Car Factory,   **250** Dove of Peace
Zeran

(Des and eng C. Slania. Recess)

1952 (12 Dec). *Zeran Car Workers' Fund.* P 13×12½.

794	**249**	45 g. + 15 g. deep grey-green	15	10
795		1 z. 15, brown	55	25

(Des R. Kleczewski. Photo)

1952 (12 Dec). *Peace Congress, Vienna.* P 12½×13.

796	**250**	30 g. green	70	25
797		60 g. bright blue	1·25	35

251 Soldier and Flag   **252** Lorry Factory

(Des E. Szancer. Photo)

1953 (2 Feb). *Tenth Anniv of Battle of Stalingrad.* P 11.

798	**251**	60 g. carmine-red and grey-olive	5·00	1·50
799		80 g. carmine-red and slate	60	30

(Des C. Slania. Eng M. R. Polak. Recess)

1953 (20 Feb). *Lublin Lorry Builders' Fund.* P 13×12½.

800	**252**	30 g. + 15 g. deep blue	20	10
801		60 g. + 20 g. dull purple	20	10

253 Karl   **254** Globe   **255** Cyclists and
Marx   and Flag   Arms of Warsaw

1953 (14 Mar). *70th Death Anniv of Marx.* P 12½×13.

802	**253**	60 g. grey-blue	17·00	10·00
803		80 g. sepia	1·25	30

1953 (April). *POSTAGE DUE. As Nos. D701/12 but photo
and without imprint at foot.* P 12×12½, *also* 11 (5 g.),
12½×11 (10 g.) *and* 10×13 (1 z.).

D804	D **190**	5 g. red-brown	10	10
D805		10 g. red-brown	10	10
D806		15 g. red-brown	10	10
D807		20 g. red-brown	10	10
D808		25 g. red-brown	10	10
D809		30 g. red-brown	15	10
D810		50 g. red-brown	20	15
D811		60 g. red-brown	30	20
D812		90 g. red-brown	40	35
D813		1 z. red-brown	50	35
D814		2 z. red-brown	1·10	80
D804/814		*Set of 11*	2·75	2·25

1953–54. *OFFICIAL. As Nos. O534/5 but no control number and litho. Inscr "ZWYKLA" (60 g.) or "POLECONA" (1.55 z.). P 11 to 14 and compound.*

O804	O 128	(60 g.) blue	20	10
O805		(60 g.) indigo ('54)	65	30
O806		(1.55 z.) red	40	15

(Des Cz. Kaczmarczyk. Photo)

1953 (28 Apr). *Labour Day. P 12½×13.*

804	254	60 g. dull vermilion	5·00	3·25
805		80 g. carmine-red	40	10

(Des Cz. Kaczmarczyk. Photo)

1953 (30 Apr). *Sixth International Peace Cycle Race. T 255 and similar vert designs. P 12½×13.*

806	—	80 g. deep green	70	25
807	255	80 g. sepia	70	25
808	—	80 g. brown-red	13·00	7·00

Designs:—No. 806, Cyclists and Arms of Berlin; No. 808, Cyclists and Arms of Prague.

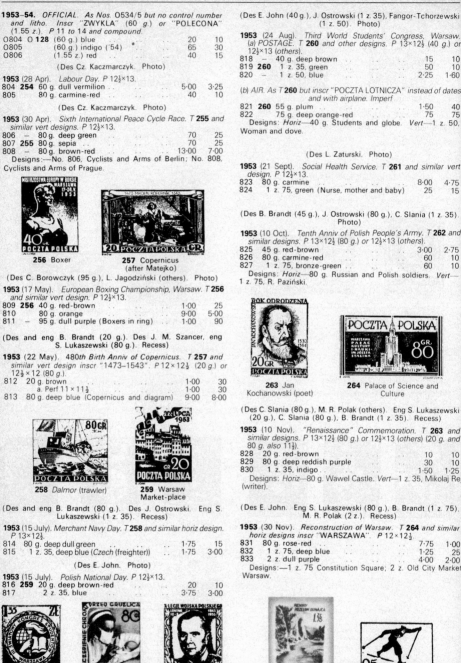

256 Boxer

257 Copernicus (after Matejko)

(Des C. Borowczyk (95 g.), L. Jagodziński (others). Photo)

1953 (17 May). *European Boxing Championship, Warsaw. T 256 and similar vert design. P 12½×13.*

809	256	40 g. red-brown	1·00	25
810		80 g. orange	9·00	5·00
811	—	95 g. dull purple (Boxers in ring)	1·00	90

(Des and eng B. Brandt (20 g.). Des J. M. Szancer, eng S. Lukaszewski (80 g.). Recess)

1953 (22 May). *480th Birth Anniv of Copernicus. T 257 and similar vert design inscr "1473–1543". P 12×12½ (20 g.) or 12½×12 (80 g.).*

812		20 g. brown	1·00	30
		a. Perf 11 × 11½	1·00	30
813		80 g. deep blue (Copernicus and diagram)	9·00	8·00

258 *Dalmor* (trawler)

259 Warsaw Market-place

(Des and eng B. Brandt (80 g.). Des J. Ostrowski. Eng S. Lukaszewski (1 z. 35). Recess)

1953 (15 July). *Merchant Navy Day. T 258 and similar horiz design. P 13×12½.*

814		80 g. deep dull green	1·75	15
815		1 z. 35, deep blue (*Czech* (freighter))	1·75	3·00

(Des E. John. Photo)

1953 (15 July). *Polish National Day. P 12½×13.*

816	259	20 g. deep brown-red	20	10
817		2 z. 35, blue	3·75	3·00

260 Students' Badge

261 Nurse feeding Baby

262 M. Kalinowski

(Des E. John (40 g.), J. Ostrowski (1 z. 35), Fangor-Tchorzewski (1 z. 50). Photo)

1953 (24 Aug). *Third World Students' Congress, Warsaw. (a) POSTAGE. T 260 and other designs. P 13×12½ (40 g.) or 12½×13 (others).*

818	—	40 g. deep brown	15	10
819	260	1 z. 35, green	50	10
820	—	1 z. 50, blue	2·25	1·60

(b) *AIR. As T 260 but inscr "POCZTA LOTNICZA" instead of dates and with airplane. Imperf.*

821	260	55 g. plum	1·50	40
822		75 g. deep orange-red	75	75

Designs: *Horiz*—40 g. Students and globe. *Vert*—1 z. 50, Woman and dove.

(Des L. Zaturski. Photo)

1953 (21 Sept). *Social Health Service. T 261 and similar vert design. P 12½×13.*

823		80 g. carmine	8·00	4·75
824		1 z. 75, green (Nurse, mother and baby)	25	15

(Des B. Brandt (45 g.), J. Ostrowski (80 g.), C. Slania (1 z. 35). Photo)

1953 (10 Oct). *Tenth Anniv of Polish People's Army. T 262 and similar designs. P 13×12½ (80 g.) or 12½×13 (others).*

825		45 g. red-brown	3·00	2·75
826		80 g. carmine-red	60	10
827		1 z. 75, bronze-green	60	10

Designs: *Horiz*—80 g. Russian and Polish soldiers. *Vert*—1 z. 75, R. Paziński.

263 Jan Kochanowski (poet)

264 Palace of Science and Culture

(Des C. Slania (80 g.), M. R. Polak (others). Eng S. Lukaszewski (20 g.), C. Slania (80 g.), B. Brandt (1 z. 35). Recess)

1953 (10 Nov). *"Renaissance" Commemoration. T 263 and similar designs. P 13×12½ (80 g.) or 12½×13 (others) (20 g. and 80 g. also 11½).*

828		20 g. red-brown	10	10
829		80 g. deep reddish purple	30	10
830		1 z. 35, indigo	1·50	1·25

Designs: *Horiz*—80 g. Wawel Castle. *Vert*—1 z. 35, Mikolaj Rej (writer).

(Des E. John. Eng S. Lukaszewski (80 g.), B. Brandt (1 z. 75). M. R. Polak (2 z.). Recess)

1953 (30 Nov). *Reconstruction of Warsaw. T 264 and similar horiz designs inscr "WARSZAWA". P 12×12½.*

831		80 g. rose-red	7·75	1·00
832		1 z. 75, deep blue	1·25	25
833		2 z. dull purple	4·00	2·00

Designs:—1 z. 75 Constitution Square; 2 z. Old City Market Warsaw.

265 Dunajec Canyon, Pieniny Mts.

266 Skiing

(Des B. Brandt (20 g.), M. R. Polak (80 g.), S. Lukaszewski (others). Photo)

1953 (16 Dec). *Tourist Series. Views as T* **265**. *P* 12½×13 (*vert*) *or* 13×12½ (*horiz*).

834	20 g. brown-lake and blue		15	10
	a. Perf 13		15	10
835	80 g. deep lilac and blue-green		2·50	1·50
836	1 z. 75, slate-green and bistre-brown		70	15
837	2 z. black and vermilion		1·00	10
834/837	*Set of 4*		4·00	1·60

Designs: *Horiz*—20 g. Krynica Spa; 2 z. Ciechocinek Spa. *Vert*—80 g. Morskie Oko Lake, Tatra Mts.

(Des J. Rajewicz (80 g.), H. Przeżdziecka (95 g.), T. Gronowski (2 z. 85). Litho)

1953 (31 Dec). *Winter Sports. T* **266** *and similar vert designs. P* 13×12½ (95 g.) *or* 12½×13 (others).

838	80 g. pale blue (Ice-skating)		1·25	25
839	95 g. blue-green		1·50	25
840	2 z. 85, brown-red (Ice-hockey)		4·00	1·90

267 Infants Playing	**268** Electric Locomotive

(Des H. Tomaszewski (1 z. 50), J. Ostrowski (others). Photo)

1953 (31 Dec). *Children's Education. T* **267** *and similar horiz designs. P* 13×12½.

841	10 g. violet		50	10
842	80 g. lake-brown		75	25
843	1 z. 50, slate-green		5·00	2·75

Designs:—80 g. Girls and school; 1 z. 50. Two schoolgirls writing.

(Des Cz. Kaczmarczyk. Eng S. Lukaszewski (60 g.), B. Brandt (80 g.). Recess)

1954 (26 Jan). *Electrification of Railways. T* **268** *and similar horiz design. P* 13×12½.

844	60 g. Prussian blue		9·00	4·00
845	80 g. red-brown		1·00	25

Design:—60 g. Electric commuter train.

269 Mill Girl	**270** Flags and Mayflowers	**271** "Warsaw-Berlin-Prague"

(Des S. Lukaszewski (20 g.), H. Przeżdziecka (others). Photo)

1954 (24 Mar). *International Women's Day. T* **269** *and similar vert designs. P* 12½×13.

846	20 g. slate-green		2·00	1·75
847	40 g. deep blue (Postwoman)		50	10
848	80 g. chocolate (Woman driving tractor)		50	10

(Des R. Kleczewski. Photo)

1954 (28 Apr). *Labour Day. P* 12½×13.

849	**270** 40 g. chocolate		55	30
850	60 g. blue		55	15
851	80 g. bright carmine-red		60	15

(Des H. Przeżdziecka. Photo)

1954 (29 Apr). *Seventh International Peace Cycle Race. T* **271** *and similar vert design. P* 12½×12 (*No.* 853 *also* 12×11).

852	80 g. brown (Type **271**)		70	20
853	80 g. deep blue (Dove and cycle wheel)		70	20

272 Symbols of Labour	**272a** Postal Coach and 'Plane

(Des B. Brandt. Eng J. Miller. Recess)

1954 (30 Apr). *Third Trades Union Congress, Warsaw. P* 12×11½.

854	**272** 25 g. indigo		60	25
855	80 g. lake		25	10

(Des R. Kleczewski. Eng B. Brandt. Recess)

1954 (23 May). *AIR. Third Polish Philatelic Society Congress. Sheet* 57×76 mm. *P* 12½×13.

MS855a **272a** 5 z.+(2 z. 50) greyish green .. 26·00 18·00
Exists imperforate.

273 Glider and Flags	**274** Paczkow

(Des Cz. Kaczmarczyk. Photo)

1954 (31 May). *International Gliding Competition. T* **273** *and similar horiz designs. P* 13 (857, 859a) *or* 13×12½ (others).

856	45 g. deep green		60	15
857	**273** 60 g. deep lilac		1·75	70
858	60 g. brown		1·25	15
859	1 z. 35, dull blue		2·25	30
	a. Light blue		1·90	25
856/859a	*Set of 4* (cheapest)		5·00	1·10

Designs:—45 g., 1 z. 35, Glider in flight (859 blue clouds, 859a white clouds).

(Des B. Brandt (1 z. 50), C. Slania (others). Eng J. Miller (60 g.), C. Slania (80 g., 1 z. 50), S. Lukaszewski (1 z. 15), B. Brandt (1 z. 55), M. R. Polak (1 z. 95). Recess)

1954 (13 July). *AIR. T* **274** *and similar vert designs. P* 12½×13.

860	60 g. myrtle green		25	10
861	80 g. scarlet		30	15
	a. Perf 12×11½		30	15
862	1 z. 15, black		1·40	1·50
863	1 z. 50, claret		70	15
864	1 z. 55, deep blue		70	10
	a. Perf 12×11½		70	10
865	1 z. 95, deep brown		85	15
860/865	*Set of 6*		3·75	1·75

Designs: Ilyushin Il-12 airplane over—80 g. Market-place, Kazimierz Dolny; 1 z. 15, Wawel Castle, Cracow; 1 z. 50, Town Hall, Wroclaw; 1 z. 55, Lazienki Palace, Warsaw; 1 z. 95, Cracow Tower, Lublin.

275 Fencing	**276** Spartacist Games Badge

(Des H. Przezdziecka (1 z.), L. Jagozinski (others). Photo)
1954 (13 July). *Second Spartacist Games (1st issue)*. T **275** and
similar designs. P 13 (60 g.) or 13×12½ (others).
866	25 g. dull purple		1·25	35
867	60 g. greenish blue		1·25	20
868	1 z. ultramarine		2·40	40

Designs: *Vert*—60 g. Gymnastics. *Horiz*—1 z. Running.

(Des K. Mann. Photo)
1954 (17 July). *Second Spartacist Games (Second issue)*.
P 12×12½.
869	**276**	60 g. red-brown	1·00	20
870		1 z. 55, deep slate-blue	1·00	30

O **277**

277 Battlefield

(Des B. Brandt. Eng W. Falkowski. Recess)
1954 (18 Aug). *OFFICIAL*. P 11×11½ (No. O872 *also*
12×12½).
O871	O **277**	60 g.) deep blue	20	10
O872		(1.55 z.) red	40	15

No. O872 is inscribed "POLECONA".

(Des J. Ostrowski. Photo)
1954 (24 Aug). *Tenth Anniv of Liberation and Battle of
Studzianki*. T **277** and similar horiz design. P 12½×13.
871	60 g. green		1·50	40
872	1 z. ultramarine		5·00	2·75

Design: —1 z. Soldier, airman and tank.

278 Steel Works

279 Signal

(Des Cz. Kaczmarczyk. Eng (b) S. Lukaszewski (10 g., 60 g.),
J. Miller (20 g., 25 g.), M. R. Polak (40 g., 1 z. 15), B. Brandt
(45 g., 2 z. 10), C. Slania (1 z. 40, 1 z. 55). (a) Centres litho.
(b) Centres recess. Frames photo)
1954 (Aug)—**55**. *Tenth Anniv of Second Republic*. T **278** and
similar horiz designs. P 12½×12.
873	10 g. sepia & red-brown (b)	(23.12.54)	90	10
874	20 g. dp myrtle-grn & rose (b)		45	10
875	25 g. grey-black and yellow-brown (a)		3·00	70
876	25 g. grey-black & yellow-brown (b)	('55)	1·50	10
877	40 g. pur-brn & orge-yell (b)	(23.12.54)	70	10
878	45 g. dl purple & dl mauve (b)	(23.12.54)	70	10
879	60 g. purple-brown and green (a)		1·10	20
880	60 g. purple-brown and green (b)	('55)	75	10
881	1 z. 15, blk & brt bl-grn (b)	(23.12.54)	3·75	20
882	1 z. 40, dp brn & orge (b)	(23.12.54)	14·00	2·50
883	1 z. 55, dp bl & dl grnsh bl (b)	(23.12.54)	3·25	55
884	2 z. 10, dp bl & cobalt (b)	(23.12.54)	5·00	1·50
873/884	*Set of 12*		32·00	5·50

Designs: —10 g. Coal mine; 20 g. Soldier and flag. 40 g.
Worker on holiday; 45 g. House-builders; 60 g. Tractor and
binder; 1 z. 15, Lublin Castle; 1 z. 40, Customers in bookshop;
1 z. 55, *Soldek* (freighter) alongside wharf; 2 z. 10, Battle of
Lenino.

(Des T. Gronowski (40 g.), E. John, after A. Porebski (60 g.).
Photo)
1954 (9 Sept). *Railway Workers' Day*. T **279** and similar vert
design. P 13 (40 g.) or 12½×13 (60 g.).
885	40 g. deep blue		3·25	50
886	60 g. black (Night train)		2·50	40

280 Picking Apples

281 Elblag

(Des H. Przeździecka. Photo)
1954 (15 Sept). *Polish–Russian Friendship*. P 12½×13.
887	**280**	40 g. slate-violet	1·25	60
888		60 g. black	50	15

(Des S. Zukowski (45 g.), K. Gorska (1 z. 40), E. John (1 z.
55), Cz. Kaczmarczyk (others). Eng B. Brandt (20 g.), M. R.
Polak (45 g.), J. Miller (60 g.), S. Lukaszewski (1 z. 40),
C. Slania (1 z. 55). Recess)
1954 (16 Oct). *500th Anniv of Return of Pomerania to
Poland*. T **281** and similar horiz designs showing mediaeval
views. P 12×12½.
889	20 g. carmine/*blue*		1·50	60
	a. Perf 11×12		1·50	60
890	45 g. brown/*lemon* (Gdańsk)		15	10
891	60 g. deep blue-green/*pale green* (Torun)		20	10
892	1 z. 40, deep ultramarine/*pink* (Malbork)		50	15
893	1 z. 55, chocolate/*cream* (Olsztyn)		75	10
889/893	*Set of 5*		2·75	85

282 Chopin and
Grand Piano

283 Battle Scene

(Des Cz. Kaczmarczyk. Photo)
1954 (8 Nov). *Fifth International Chopin Piano Competition,
Warsaw (1st issue)*. P 12½×13.
894	**282**	45 g. deep brown	40	10
895		60 g. deep myrtle-green	85	10
	a. Perf 11		1·75	1·75
896		1 z. blue	2·50	1·40

See also Nos. 906/7.

(Des after W. Kossak (40 g.), after J. Matejko (60 g.). Eng
S. Lukaszewski (40 g.), C. Slania (60 g.). Des and eng
B. Brandt (1 z. 40). Recess)
1954 (30 Nov). *160th Anniv of Kosciuszko's Insurrection*. T **283**
and similar horiz designs. P 12½×13.
897	40 g. blackish olive		40	15
898	60 g. deep brown-purple		60	15
899	1 z. 40, slate-black		1·50	70

Designs: —60 g. Kosciuszko on horse-back with insurgents;
1 z. 40, Street battle.

284 European Bison

285 "The Liberator"

(Des C. Borowczyk. Eng B. Brandt (45 g.), S. Lukaszewski (60 g.), M. R. Polak (1 z. 90), C. Slania (3 z.). Background photo; remainder recess)

1954 (22 Dec). *Protected Animals. Vert designs as T* **284**.

900	45 g. black-brown and deep yellow-green		45	15
901	60 g. brown and bright green	..	45	15
902	1 z. 90, black-brown and cobalt		90	15
903	3 z. brown and deep turquoise-green	..	1·40	60
900/903	Set of 4	..	3·00	90

Designs:—60 g. Elk; 1 z. 90, Chamois; 3 z. Eurasian beaver.
These exist imperforate.

(Des J. Ostrowski (40 g.), T. Trepkowski (60 g.). Photo)

1955 (17 Jan). *Tenth Anniv of Liberation of Warsaw. T* **285** *and similar horiz design. P* 12½×13.

904	40 g. chocolate	..	1·40	30
905	60 g. grey-blue ("Spirit of Poland")	..	1·40	50

286 Bust of Chopin (after L. Isler)

287 Mickiewicz Monument

288 Flags and Tower

(Des K. Podlasiecki. Eng C. Slania. Recess)

1955 (22 Feb). *Fifth International Chopin Piano Competition, Warsaw (2nd issue). P* 12½×13.

906	**286**	40 g. purple-brown	30	10
907		60 g. deep blue ..	90	20

(Des R. Kleczewski (15 g., 45 g., 1 z. 55), E. John (others). Eng M. R. Polak (5 g.), S. Lukaszewski (10 g., 45 g.), J. Miller (15 g., 20 g.), C. Slania (40 g.), B. Brandt (60 g., 1 z. 55). Recess)

1955 (Mar–May). *Warsaw Monuments. T* **287** *and similar vert designs. P* 12½×13.

908	5 g. myrtle green/*olive-yellow* ..		10	10
	a. Perf 12×11½	..	20	15
909	10 g. maroon/*yellow*	..	10	10
	a. Perf 12×11½	..	20	10
910	15 g. brownish black/*pale green* ..		10	10
	a. Perf 12×11½	..	20	10
911	20 g. deep blue/*pink* (31.5)	..	10	10
	a. Perf 12×11½	..	20	10
912	40 g. deep violet/*reddish lilac* (31.5)		30	10
	a. Perf 12×11½	..	40	10
913	45 g. purple brown/*pale orange* ..		65	20
914	60 g. blue/*olive-grey* (31.5)	..	10	10
915	1 z. 55, deep bluish green/*olive-grey*		1·00	25
908/915	Set of 8	..	2·00	70

Designs:—*Vert*—5 g. "Siren"; 10 g. Dzerzhinsky Statue; 15 g. King Sigismund III Statue; 20 g. "Brotherhood in Arms"; 40 g. Copernicus Monument; 45 g. Marie Curie Statue; 1 z. 55, Kilinski Statue.

(Des E. Kleczewski (40 g.), W. Borowczyk (60 g.). Photo)

1955 (21 Apr). *Tenth Anniv of Russo–Polish Treaty of Friendship. T* **288** *and similar vert design. P* 11½×11.

916	**288**	40 g. rose-red	..	20	10
		a. Perf 12½×12	..	20	10
917		40 g. chestnut	..	50	35
		a. Perf 12½×12	..	50	35
918	—	60 g. turquoise-blue	..	20	10
		a. Perf 12½×12 ..	..	20	10
919	—	60 g. deep olive-brown	..	20	10
		a. Perf 12½×12	..	20	10
916/919	Set of 4	..	1·00	50

Design:—60 g. Statue of "Friendship".

289

290 Town Hall, Poznań

291 Festival Emblem

(Des Cz. Kaczmarczyk (40 g.), S. Jasiński (60 g.). Photo)

1955 (25 Apr). *Eighth International Peace Cycle Race. T* **289** *and similar vert design. P* 12½×13 (40 g.) *or* 13 (60 g.).

920	40 g. purple-brown	..	..	45	20
921	60 g. cobalt	..	..	25	10

Design:—60 g. "VIII" and doves of peace.

(Des Cz. Kazmarczyk. Photo)

1955 (10 June). *24th International Fair, Poznań. P* 12½×13.

922	**290**	40 g. deep bright blue	..	25	10
923		60 g. red	..	..	15	10

See also Nos. **MS**926*a/b*.

(Des W. Chomicz. Litho)

1955 (16 June). *Cracow Festival. T* **291** *and similar design. P* 12.

924	**291**	20 g. ochre, sepia, red-brn & bluish grn	50	20
925	—	40 g. bluish grn, blk, chestnut & lilac	25	15
926	**291**	60 g. yellow-brown, black, rose & bl	1·00	25

Design: *Horiz*—40 g. Centre as T **291**.

1955 (7 July). *Sixth Polish Philatelic Exhibition, Poznań. Two sheets* 50×70 *mm. as T* **290**. *Imperf*.

MS926*a*	2 z.+(1 z.) black and blue-green	..	3·00	1·75
MS926*b*	3 z.+(1 z. 50), black and carmine	..	15·00	8·75

292 "Peace"

293 Motor Cyclists

294 Stalin Palace of Culture and Science, Warsaw

(Des J. Woznicki (Nos. 928, 931), S. Malecki (others). Litho)

1955 (13 July). *Fifth International Youth Festival, Warsaw. T* **292** *and similar vert designs. P* 12 (*Nos.* 928 *and* 930 *also* 11).

927	—	25 g. purple-brown, rose and yellow	20	10
928	—	40 g. grey and pale blue	..	20	10
929	—	45 g. lake, magenta and yellow		35	10
930	**292**	60 g. ultramarine and pale blue	..	30	10
931	—	60 g. black and yellow-orange		30	10
932	**292**	1 z. deep slate-purple and pale blue	70	50
927/932	Set of 6	..	1·90	85

Designs:—25 g., 45 g. Pansies and dove; 40 g., 60 g. (No. 931), Dove and tower.
These exist imperforate.
See also Nos. **MS**944*a/b*.

(Des J. Woźnicki. Photo)

1955 (20 July). *13th International Tatra Mountains Motor Cycle Race. P* 12½×13.

933	**293**	40 g. deep brown	..	..	30	10
934		60 g. green	..	..	20	10

(Des K. Podlasiecki. Photo)

1955 (21 July).   *Polish National Day.* P 12½×13.

935	**294**	60 g. bright blue	15	10
		a. Pair. Nos. 935/6	30	20
936		60 g. bluish grey	15	10
937		75 g. turquoise-green	50	20
		a. Pair. Nos. 937/8	1·00	40
938		75 g. brown	50	20
935/938		*Set of 4*	1·10	50

Nos. 935/6 and 937/8 were printed together in sheets containing alternate vertical rows of each colour *se-tenant.*

295 Athletes

296 Szczecin

297 Peasants and Flag

(Des J. Karolkiewicz. Photo)

1955 (27 July).   *Second International Games.* T **295** *and similar designs.* P 13×12½ (60 g.) or 12½×13 (*others*).

939	20 g. sepia	15	10
940	40 g. brown-purple	20	10
941	60 g. dull greenish blue	35	10
942	1 z. red-orange	50	10
943	1 z. 35, dull purple	70	10
944	1 z. 55, blue-green	1·40	50
939/944	*Set of 6*	3·00	80

Designs: *Vert*—40 g. Throwing the hammer; 1 z. Net-ball; 1 z. 35, Sculling; 1 z. 55, Swimming. *Horiz*—60 g. Stadium. These exist imperforate.

1955 (3 Aug).   *International Philatelic Exhibition, Warsaw. Two sheets* 61×84 *mm. Imperf.*

MS944*a*	1 z. (+1 z.) As No. 929	3·00	2·00
MS944*b*	2 z. (+1 z.) As No. 932	15·00	10·00

(Des S. Jasiński. Eng B. Brandt (25 g.), J. Miller (40 g.). M. R. Polak (others). Recess)

1955 (22 Sept).   *Tenth Anniv of Return of Western Territories.* T **296** *and similar vert designs.* P 12½×13.

945	25 g. deep blue-green	15	10
	a. Perf 12×11½	15	10
946	40 g. red-brown (Wroclaw)	25	10
947	60 g. deep violet-blue (Zielona Gora)	45	10
948	95 g. brown-black (Opole)	1·25	50
945/948	*Set of 4*	1·90	60

(Des M. Bylina. Photo)

1955 (30 Sept).   *50th Anniv of 1905 Revolution.* P 12½×13.

949	**297**	40 g. sepia	25	15
950		60 g. carmine-red	15	10

298 Mickiewicz

299 Statue

(Des H. Przeździecka (20 g.), W. Chmielewski (others). Photo)

1955 (10 Oct).   *Death Centenary of Adam Mickiewicz (poet).* T **298** *and vert designs as* T **299**. P 12×12½ (20 g.) or 12½×13 (*others*).

951	20 g. sepia	20	10
952	40 g. sepia and brown-orange	20	10
953	60 g. sepia & dull green (Sculptured head)	30	10
954	95 g. black and brown-red (Statue)	1·25	50
951/954	*Set of 4*	1·75	60

300 Teacher and Pupil

301 Rook and Hands

302 Ice Skates

(Des R. Kleczewski (40 g.), H. Przeździecka (60 g.). Photo)

1955 (21 Oct).   *50thn Anniv of Polish Teachers' Union.* T **300** *and similar vert design.* P 12½×13.

955	40 g. brown	1·25	30
956	60 g. bright blue (Open book and lamp)	2·25	65

(Des Cz. Kaczmarczyk. Photo)

1956 (9 Feb).   *First World Chess Championship of the Deaf and Dumb.* T **301** *and similar vert design.* P 12½×13.

957	40 g. brown-red	4·00	1·00
958	60 g. dull greenish blue	2·50	10

Design:—60 g. Knight and hands.

(Des Cz. Kaczmarczyk. Litho)

1956 (7 Mar).   *11th World Students' Winter Sports Championship.* T **302** *and similar vert designs.* P 12½×13.

959	20 g. black and blue	4·00	1·60
960	40 g. ultramarine and bright blue-green	1·00	10
	a. Perf 11	1·00	10
961	60 g. claret and mauve	1·00	10
	a. Perf 11	1·00	10

Designs:—40 g. Ice-hockey sticks and puck; 60 g. Skis and ski sticks.

303 Officer and *Kilinski* (freighter)

304 Racing Cyclist

(Des S. Lukaszewski. Eng J. Miller (10 g.), M. R. Polak (45 g.), S. Lukaszewski (60 g.), B. Brandt (others). Recess)

1956 (16 Mar).   *Merchant Navy.* T **303** *and similar horiz designs.* P 12×12½ or 11×11½.

962	5 g. deep bluish green	15	10
963	10 g. crimson	20	10
964	20 g. deep blue	30	10
965	45 g. red-brown	85	40
966	60 g. deep violet-blue	50	10
962/966	*Set of 5*	1·75	70

Designs:—10 g. Tug and barges; 20 g. *Pokoj* (freighter) in dock; 45 g. Building *Marceii Nowatka* (freighter); 60 g. *Fryderyk Chopin* (freighter) and *Radunia* (trawler).

(Des H. Przeździecka. Photo)

1956 (25 Apr).   *Ninth International Peace Cycle Race.* P 13×12½.

967	**304**	40 g. deep blue	1·10	30
968		60 g. deep green	20	10

305 Lodge, Tatra Mountains

(306)

(Des Cz. Kaczmarczyk, J. Kończak and S. Jasinski. Photo)

1956 (25 May). *Tourist Propaganda. T **305** and similar vert designs.* P 12½×13.

969	30 g. bottle green			15	10
	a. Perf 13			15	10
970	40 g. chestnut			15	10
971	60 g. blue			1·40	70
972	1 z. 15, deep dull purple			50	10
969/972	*Set of 4*			2·00	90

Designs:—40 g. Compass, rucksack and map; 60 g. Canoe and map; 1 z. 15, Skis and mountains.

1956 (6 July). *No. 829 surch as T **306**.*

973	10 g. on 80 g. deep reddish purple			40	20
974	40 g. on 80 g. deep reddish purple			25	10
975	60 g. on 80 g. deep reddish purple			25	10
976	1 z. 35 on 80 g. deep reddish purple			1·25	90
973/976	*Set of 4*			1·90	1·10

307 Ghetto Heroes Monument **308** "Economic Co-operation"

(Des E. John. Eng C. Slania (30 g.), M. R. Polak (40 g.), E. Konecki (1 z. 55). Recess)

1956 (10 July). *Warsaw Monuments. T **307** and similar vert designs.* P 12½×13 (Nos. 977 and 979 also 12×11½).

977	30 g. black			15	10
978	40 g. red-brown/*green*			50	15
979	1 z. 55, brown-purple/*pink*			40	15

Designs:—40 g. Statue of King Jan III Sobieski; 1 z. 55, Statue of Prince Joseph Poniatowski.

(Des S. Gospodarek (40 g.), S. Malecki (60 g.). Litho)

1956 (14 Sept). *Russo–Polish Friendship Month. T **308** and similar horiz design.* P 12½×12.

980	40 g. deep brown and rose-pink			40	20
	a. Perf 11			40	20
981	60 g. red and bistre			25	15

Design:—40 g. Polish and Russian dancers.

309 Ludwika Wawrzynska (teacher) **310** "Lady with a Weasel" (Leonardo da Vinci)

(Des H. Przeździecka. Photo)

1956 (17 Sept). *Ludwika Wawrzynska Commemoration.* P 13.

982	**309**	40 g. chocolate		75	25
983		60 g. deep blue		25	10

(Des Cz. Kaczmarczk. Eng E. Konecki (40 g.), S. Lukaszewski (60 g.), B. Brandt (1 z. 55). Recess)

1956. *International Campaign for Museums. T **310** and similar vert designs.* P 11½×11.

984	40 g. myrtle-green (19.11)			2·25	1·40
985	60 g. deep violet (19.11)			1·00	15
986	1 z. 55, blackish chocolate (23.10)			2·00	20

Designs:—40 g. Niobe (bust); 60 g. Madonna (Vit Stvosz).

310a Music Quotation and Profiles of Chopin and Liszt **311** Honey Bee and Hive

(Des S. Gospodarek. Photo)

1956 (25 Oct). *Stamp Day. Sheet 55×75 mm. Imperf.*
MS986a **310**a 4 z.(+2 z.) deep bluish green 26·00 14·00

(Des J. Kończak (40 g.), S. Gospodarek (60 g.). Litho)

1956 (30 Oct). *50th Death Anniv of Jan Dzierzon (apiarist). T **311** and similar vert design.* P 12½×13.

987	40 g. brown/*orange-yellow*			85	30
988	60 g. brown/*orge-yell* (Dr. J. Dzierzon)			20	10

312 Fencing **313** 15th-century Postman

(Des Cz. Kaczmarczyk. Eng E. Konecki (10 g.), S. Lukaszewski (20 g.), M. R. Polak (25 g.), B. Brandt (40 g.), C. Slania (60 g.), J. Miller (1 z. 55). Centres recess (except No. 995, photo); frames litho)

1956 (2 Nov–12 Dec). *Olympic Games. T **312** and similar designs inscr "MELBOURNE 1956".* P 11½.

989	10 g. brown and slate			15	10
990	20 g. blackish lilac and bistre-brown			20	10
991	25 g. black and pale blue			60	15
992	40 g. chocolate and blue-green			30	10
993	60 g. brown-black and carmine			50	10
994	1 z. 55, sepia and bright violet			2·50	1·00
995	1 z. 55, reddish brown & orange (12.12)			1·00	25
989/995	*Set of 7*			4·75	1·50

Designs:—20 g. Boxing; 25 g. Rowing; 40 g. Steeplechase; 60 g. Javelin throwing; No. 994, Gymnastics; No. 995, Long jumping (Elizabeth Duńska-Krzesińska's gold medal).

(Des S. Bernacinsky. Litho)

1956 (30 Nov). *Re-opening of Postal Museum, Wroclaw.* P 12½×13.
996 **313** 60 g. grey-black/*pale blue* 85 75

MINIMUM PRICE

The minimum price quoted is 10p which represents a handling charge rather than a basis for valuing common stamps. For further notes about prices see introductory pages.

314 Snow Crystals and Skier of 1907 **315** Apple Tree and Globe

(Des J. Konczak. Photo)

1957 (18 Jan). *Fifty years of Skiing in Poland. T* **314** *and similar designs.* P 13.

997	40 g. blue			30	10
998	60 g. deep bluish green			30	10
999	1 z. purple			70	20

Designs: *Vert*—60 g. Snow crystals and skier jumping. *Horiz*—1 z. Snow crystals and skier standing.

(Des S. Malecki. Photo)

1957 (26 Feb). *United Nations Organization. T* **315** *and similar designs.* P 12½×12 (5 g.) or 12×12½ (others).

1000	5 g. crimson and deep turquoise-blue	25	15
1001	15 g. blue and pale grey	40	15
1002	40 g. blue-green and pale grey	70	50

MS1002*a* 55×70 mm. 1 z. 50, blue and bright blue-green. Imperf   ..   ..   20·00   13·00

Designs: *Vert*—15 g. U.N.O. emblem; 40 g., 1 z. 50, U.N.O. Headquarters, New York.

Nos. 1000/2 exist imperforate.

316 Skier   **317** Winged Letter

(Des S. Gospodarek. Photo)

1957 (22 Mar). *12th Death Anniv of Bronislaw Czech and Hanna Marusarzowna (skiers).* P 12½×13.

1003	**316** 60 g. deep brown	..	..	..	90	25
1004	60 g. blue	..	..	..	50	15

(Des S. Jasiński. Photo)

1957. *AIR. 7th Polish National Philatelic Exhibition, Warsaw.* P 11½.

1005 **317** 4 z.+2 z. blue (28.3)   ..   ..   2·75   2·75
MS1005*a* 55×75 mm. 4 z.+2 z. violet-blue (T **317**). Imperf (18.5)   ..   ..   8·75   5·25

No. 1005 is printed in sheets of 12 stamps with four labels.

318 Foil, Sword and Sabre on Map   **319** Dr. S. Petrycy (philosopher)   **320** Cycle Wheel and Flower

(Des J. Kończak (40 g.), S. Jasiński (others). Photo)

1957 (20 Apr). *World Youth Fencing Championships, Warsaw. T* **318** *and similar horiz designs.* P 13×12½.

1006	40 g. purple	..	..	55	15
1007	60 g. deep rose-red	..	..	25	15
	a. Pair. Nos. 1007/8	..	..	50	30
1008	60 g. bright blue	..	..	25	15

Designs:—Nos. 1007/8 are arranged in *se-tenant* pairs in the sheet, and together show two fencers duelling.

(Des J. Desselberger. Eng J. Miller (10 g.), B. Brandt (20 g., 3 z.), M. R. Polak (40 g.), E. Konecki (60 g., 1 z. 35), S. Lukaszewski (2 z. 50). Recess and typo)

1957 (27 Apr–30 Sept). *Polish Doctors. T* **319** *and similar designs.* P 12×11½.

1009	10 g. sepia and ultramarine	..	..	10	10
1010	20 g. lake and emerald	..	..	10	10
1011	40 g. black and rose-red	..	..	10	10
1012	60 g. dull purple and pale blue	..	..	40	20
1013	1 z. blue-grey & yellow-orange (30.9)		20	10
1014	1 z. 35, black-brown and blue-green	..	15	10
1015	2 z. 50, slate-violet and cerise	..	35	10
1016	3 z. deep olive-brown and violet	..	45	10
1009/1016	*Set of 8*	..	..	1·50	50

Portraits:—20 g. Dr. W. Oczko; 40 g. Dr. J. Sniadecki; 60 g. Dr. T. Chalubinski; 1 z. Dr. W. Bieganski; 1 z. 35, Dr. J. Dietl; 2 z. Dr. B. Dybowski; 3 z. Dr. H. Jordan.

(Des S. Szymański. Photo)

1957 (4 May). *Tenth International Peace Cycle Race. T* **320** *and similar design.* P 12½×13.

1017	60 g. blue	30	15
1018	1 z. 50, rose-magenta (Cyclist)	..	40	15

321 Fair Emblem   **322** Carline Thistle

(Des A. Borys. Litho)

1957 (8 June). *26th International Fair, Poznań.* P 13 (60 g.) or 12½×13 (2 z. 50).

1019	**321** 60 g. light ultramarine	..	..	20	10
1020	2 z. 50, blue-green	..	..	20	10

(Des Cz. Borowczyk. Photo)

1957 (12 Aug). *Wild Flowers. T* **322** *and similar floral designs.* P 12×12½.

1021	60 g. yellow, blue-green and pale grey	45	10
1022	60 g. deep blue-green and pale blue	..	45	10
1023	60 g. olive-green and grey	..	45	10
1024	60 g. yellow, brown-red & pl bluish grn	80	25
1025	60 g. maroon and blue-green	..	45	10
1021/1025	*Set of 5*	..	..	2·40	45

Designs:—No. 1021, *T* **322**; 1022, Sea holly; 1023, Edelweiss; 1024, Lady's Slipper orchid; 1025, Turk's Cap lily.

323 Fireman   **324** Town Hall, Leipzig   **325** "The Letter" (after Fragonard)

(Des S. Szymański (40 g.), S. Gospodarek (60 g.), S. Malecki (2 z. 50). Photo)

1957 (11 Sept). *International Fire Brigades Conference, Warsaw. T* **323** *and similar vert designs.* P 12×12½.

1026	40 g. black and red	..	..	15	10
1027	60 g. deep bluish green and orange-red	15	10
1028	2 z. 50, violet and vermilion	..	45	15

Designs:—60 g. Flames enveloping child; 2 z. 50, Ear of corn in flames.

(Des H. Macierewicz. Photo)

1957 (25 Sept). *Fourth International Trade Unions Congress, Leipzig.* P 12½×13.
1029 **324** 60 g. violet 20 10

(Des H. Przeżdziecka. Photo)

1957 (9 Oct). *Stamp Day.* P 12×12½.
1030 **325** 2 z. 50, deep myrtle green 50 15

326 Red Banner

327 Karol Libelt (founder)

328 H. Wieniawski (violinist)

(Des Cz. Kaczmarczyk. Photo)

1957 (7 Nov). *40th Anniv of Russian Revolution. T* **326** *and similar vert design.* P 12½×13.
1031 60 g. red and deep blue 10 10
1032 2 z. 50, chestnut and black 20 10
Design:—2 z. 50, Lenin Monument, Poronin.

(Des J. Skoracki. Photo)

1957 (15 Nov). *Centenary of Poznań Scientific Society.* P 12½×13.
1033 **327** 60 g. crimson 15 10

(Des S. Jasiński. Photo)

1957 (2 Dec). *Third Wieniawski International Violin Competition.* P 12½×13.
1034 **328** 2 z. 50, blue 25 15

POCZTA LOTNICZA

329 Ilyushin Il-14P over Steel Works

330 Multiple Posthorns

There are four different types of W **330**, which also come inverted.

(Des J. Miller. Eng S. Lukaszewski (90 g.), E. Konecki (1 z. 50), J. Miller (3 z. 40, 3 z. 90), M. R. Polak (4 z.), B. Brandt (15 z.). Recess, background photo)

1957 (6 Dec)–**58**. *AIR. Pictorial designs as T* **329**. W **330** (5, 10, 20, 30, 50 z.) *or no wmk (others)*. P 12½.
1035 90 g. black and pink 15 10
1036 1 z. 50, brown and salmon 15 10
1037 3 z. 40, sepia and buff 45 10
1038 3 z. 90, deep brown and olive-yellow 90 55
1039 4 z. Prussian blue and pale green .. 45 10
1039*a* 5 z. brown-purple and grey (15.12.58) 55 15
1039*b* 10 z. sepia and pale turquoise (15.12.58) 90 30
1040 15 z. deep bluish violet & turquoise-blue 1·60 35
1040*a* 20 z. slate-violet & pl yellow (15.12.58) 1·75 80
1040*b* 30 z. olive-green and buff (15.12.58) . . 2·75 1·10
1040*c* 50 z. deep blue and pale drab (15.12.58) 7·00 1·90
1035/1040c *Set of 11* 15·00 5·00
Designs: Ilyushin Il-14P over—1 z. 50, Castle Square, Warsaw; 3 z. 40, Market, Cracow; 3 z. 90, Szczecin; 4 z. Karkonosze Mountains; 5 z. Old Market, Gdańsk; 10 z. Liw Castle; 15 z.

Lublin; 20 z. Cable railway, Kasprowy Wierch; 30 z. Porabka Dam; 50 z. *Batory* (liner).
For stamp as No. 1039*b*, but printed in slate-purple only, see No. 1095.

330*a* J. A. Komensky (Comenius)

331 A. Strug

(Des S. Jasiński. Photo)

1957 (11 Dec). *300th Anniv of Publication of Komensky's "Opera Didactica Omnia".* P 12.
1041 **330***a* 2 z. 50, bright carmine .. 25 10

(Des S. Szymanski. Photo)

1957 (16 Dec). *20th Death Anniv of Andrzej Strug (writer).* P 12½×13.
1042 **331** 2 z. 50, brown 25 10

332 Joseph Conrad and Full-rigged Sailing Ship *Torrens*

333 Postman of 1558

(Des S. Lukaszewski. Recess)

1957 (30 Dec). *Birth Centenary of Joseph Conrad (Korzeniowski), author.* P 12×12½.
1043 **332** 60 g. chocolate/turquoise .. 30 10
1044 2 z. 50, deep blue/pink .. 1·10 10

(Des S. Malecki. Litho)

1958 (24 Feb). *400th Anniv of Polish Postal Service (1st issue).* P 12½×13.
1045 **333** 2 z. 50, blackish violet and blue .. 25 10
See also Nos. 1063/7.

334 Town Hall, Biecz

335 Perch

I

II

Two types of 20 g.:
I. Central part of building more lightly shaded; no stops in engraver's name.
II. Building evenly shaded; stops in engraver's name.

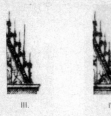

III. IV.

Two types of 40 g.:
III. Second needle from bottom on right-hand side of roof very long; triangular area at top of door unshaded.
IV. Second needle same size as other needles; triangular area shaded.

(Des S. Gospodarek. Eng B. Szymańska (20 g., 40 g., 2 z. 10), E. Tirdiszek (others). Recess)

1958 (29 Mar). *Ancient Polish Town Halls. Designs as T* **334.** P 12×11½ (2 z. 50), 12½×13 (20, 40 g., 2 z. 10) or 13×12½ (60 g.).

1046	20 g. blue-green (I)	10	10
	a. Type II	10	10
	ab. Perf 12×11½	10	10
1047	40 g. brown (Wroclaw) (III)	10	10
	a. Type IV	10	10
	ab. Perf 12×11½	10	10
1048	60 g. deep blue (Tarnow) (*horiz*)	10	10
1049	2 z. 10, lake (Gdansk)	15	10
1050	2 z. 50, violet (Zamosc)	55	25
1046/1050	*Set of 5*	75	35

(Des S. Malecki. Photo)

1958 (22 Apr). *Fishes. Designs as T* **335.** P 12×12½ (*vert*) or 12½×12 (*horiz*).

1051	40 g. yellow, black & dp turquoise-blue	15	10
1052	60 g. ultramarine, indigo and light green	25	10
1053	2 z. 10, yellow, indigo and blue	40	10
1054	2 z. 50, green, black and reddish violet	1·25	30
1055	6 z. 40, bistre-brown, vermilion, black and deep turquoise-green	1·10	40
1051/1055	*Set of 5*	2·75	80

Designs: *Vert*—60 g. Salmon; 2 z. 10, Pike; 2 z. 50, Trout. *Horiz*—6 z. 40, Grayling.

336 Warsaw University   **337** Fair Emblem   **338**

(Des S. Jasiński. Photo)

1958 (14 May). *140th Anniv of Warsaw University.* P 12½×13.
1056 **336** 2 z. 50, deep violet-blue   25   10

(Des Z. Kaja. Litho)

1958 (9 June). *27th International Fair, Poznań.* P 12½×13.
1057 **337** 2 z. 50, red and black   30   10

(Des J. Desselberger. Litho)

1958 (14 June). *Seventh International Gliding Championships. T* **338** *and similar vert design.* P 12½×13.
1058   60 g. black and slate-blue   10   10
1059   2 z. 50, black and grey   30   10
Design:—2 z. 50, as T **338** but design in reverse.

339 Armed Postman   **340** Polar Bear on Iceberg

(Des Cz. Kaczmarczyk. Eng E. Konecki. Recess)

1958 (1 Sept). *19th Anniv of Defence of Gdansk Post Office.* P 11×11½.
1060 **339** 60 g. deep blue   25   10

(Des S. Jasiński. Photo)

1958 (30 Sept). *International Geophysical Year. T* **340** *and similar vert design.* P 12½×12.
1061   60 g. black   15   10
1062   2 z. 50, blue   70   15
Design:—2 z. 50, Sputnik and track of rocket.

341 Tomb of Prosper Prowano (First Polish Postmaster)   **342** Envelope, Quill and Postmark   **343** Partisans' Cross

(Des S. Malecki. Litho)

1958 (8 Oct). *400th Anniv of Polish Postal Service* (2nd issue). *T* **341** *and similar vert designs.* P 12½×13.

1063	40 g. maroon and cobalt	40	10
1064	60 g. black and lilac	10	10
1065	95 g. violet and yellow-bistre	10	10
1066	2 z. 10, ultramarine and grey	60	25
1067	3 z. 40, red-brown & turquoise-blue	35	20
1063/1067	*Set of 5*	1·40	60

Designs:—60 g. Mail coach and Church of Our Lady, Cracow; 95 g. Mail coach (rear view); 2 z. 10, 16th-century postman; 3 z. 40, Kogge. Nos. 1064/67 show various forms of modern transport in clear silhouette in the background.

(Des S. Gospodarek. Litho)

1958 (9 Oct). *Stamp Day.* P 12½×13.
1068 **342** 60 g. blue-green, red and black   55   40

(Des Cz. Kacmarczyk. Photo)

1958 (10 Oct). *15th Anniv of Polish People's Army. Polish decorations as T* **343.** P 11.
1069   40 g. buff, black and green   15   10
1070   60 g. brown, yellow, black and blue   15   10
1071   2 z. 50, yellow, black, red and green   55   15
Decorations:—60 g. Virtuti Military Cross; 2 z. 50, Grunwald Cross.

344 "Mail Coach in the Kielce District" 345 Galleon
(after painting by A. Kedzierski)

(Des H. Przeździecka. Eng S. Lukaszewski. Recess)

1958 (26 Oct). *Polish Postal Service 400th Anniv Exhibition.*
W 330. P 12½×13.
1072 **344** 2 z. 50, olive-black/buff 85 55
No. 1072 was printed in sheets of six (*Price £7·75 un*). These
sheets normally measure 139 mm in height but examples also
exist 20 mm taller with an extra line of perforations in the top
margin. These were attached to the fronts of special brochures
(*Price £50 un*).
See also No. **MS**1078*a*.

(Des S. Jasiński. Photo)

1958 (29 Oct). *350th Anniv of Polish Emigration to America.*
T 345 and similar vert design inscr "1608" etc. P 11.
1073 60 g. blackish green .. 15 10
1074 2 z. 50, carmine-red (Polish emigrants) 30 15

346 U.N.E.S.C.O. 347 S. Wyspiański 348 "Human
Headquarters, Paris (dramatist and painter) Rights"

(Des Cz. Kaczmarczyk. Photo)

1958 (3 Nov). *Inauguration of U.N.E.S.C.O. Headquarters*
Buildings, Paris. P 13×12½.
1075 **346** 2 z. 50, black and green 55 15

(Des J. Kończak. Eng B. Brandt (60 g.). E. Tirdiszek (2 z. 50).
Recess)

1958 (25 Nov). *Famous Poles. T 347 and similar vert design.*
P 12½×13.
1076 60 g. violet 10 10
1077 2 z. 50, deep green 45 15
Portrait:—2 z. 50, S. Moniuszko (composer).

(Des S. Gospodarek. Litho)

1958 (10 Dec). *Tenth Anniv of Declaration of Human Rights.*
P 12½×13.
1078 **348** 2 z. 50, red-brown and light brown .. 55 15

348*a* Coach and Horses 349 Party
(after A. Kedzierski) Flag

(Des H. Przeździecka. Eng S. Lukaszewski. Recess on silk)

1958 (12 Dec). *400th Anniv of Polish Postal Service. Sheet*
86×76 mm. Imperf.
MS1078*a* 348*a* 50 z. slate-blue .. 13·00 13·00

(Des A. Balcerzak. Photo)

1958 (16 Dec). *40th Anniv of Polish Communist Party. P 12½×13.*
1079 **349** 60 g. red and reddish purple .. 10 10

350 Yacht 351 The "Guiding Hand"

(Des J. Macierewicz. Photo)

1959 (3 Jan). *Sports. T 350 and similar vert designs. P 12½×13.*
1080 40 g. ultramarine and pale blue .. 35 10
1081 60 g. deep purple and salmon .. 35 10
1082 95 g. purple and green .. 70 20
1083 2 z. deep blue and pale green .. 35 20
1080/1083 *Set of 4* .. .. 1·50 50
Designs:—60 g. Archer; 95 g. Footballers; 2 z. Horseman.

(Des J. Kończak (40 g.), S. Biernaciński (60 g.), S. Malecki
(1 z. 55). Photo)

1959 (10 Mar).*Third Polish United Workers' Party Congress. T 351*
and similar designs. W 330. P 13×12½ (60 g.) or 12½×13
(others).
1084 40 g. black, yellow-brown and red .. 10 10
1085 60 g. black, red, yellow and bluish green 10 10
1086 1 z. 55, vermilion, grey, purple & black 40 10
Designs: *Horiz*—60 g. Hammer and ears of corn. *Vert*—
1 z. 55, Nowa Huta foundry.

352 Death Cap
(*Amanita phalloides*)

(Des C. Borowczyk. Photo)

1959 (8 May). *Mushrooms. Triangular designs as T 352.*
W 330. P 11½.
1087 20 g. yellow, brown and green .. 1·60 25
1088 30 g. red, olive, brown & orange-yellow 30 10
1089 40 g. red, green, yellow & dull mauve 65 10
1090 60 g. yellow, brown, green & deep green 65 10
1091 1 z. yellow, brown, green and blue .. 1·00 10
1092 2 z. 50, sepia, green and blue .. 1·50 30
1093 3 z. 40, red, yellow, green and black . 1·75 35
1094 5 z. 60, chocolate, green & olive-yellow 4·50 1·75
1087/1094 *Set of 8* .. .. 11·00 2·50
Mushrooms:—30 g. Butter mushroom (*Boletus luteus*); 40 g.
Cep (*Boletus edulis*); 60 g. Saffron milk cap (*Lactarius deliciosus*);
1 z. Chanterelle (*Cantharellus cibarius*); 2 z. 50, Field mushroom
(*Psalliota campestris*); 3 z. 40, Fly agaric (*Amanita muscaria*);
5 z. 60, Brown beech bolete (*Boletus scaber*).

1959 (23 May). *AIR. 65 Years of Philately in Poland and*
Sixth Polish Philatelic Association Congress, Warsaw.
Design as No. 1039b but in one colour only. Litho and
photo. W 330. P 12½.
1095 10 z. slate-purple .. .. .. 2·75 2·75
No. 1095 is printed in sheets of six stamps *se-tenant* with
variously inscribed labels in slate-purple and pale green each
bearing a premium "+5 zl.".

MINIMUM PRICE

The minimum price quoted is 10p which represents a handling charge rather than a basis for
valuing common stamps. For further notes
about prices see introductory pages.

353 "Storks" (after Chełmoński)

354 Miner

(Des J. Desselberger. Eng E. Konecki (40 g.), B. Szymańska (60 g.), S. Łukaszewski (1 z.), M. R. Polak (1 z. 50), J. Miller (6 z. 40). Recess)

1959 (29 June–22 Sept). *Polish Paintings. Various designs as T 353. W 330. P 13×12 (1 z.) or 12 (others).*

1096	40 g. bronze-green		15	10
1097	60 g. deep maroon		30	10
1098	1 z. black (22.9)		30	10
1099	1 z. 50, sepia		70	25
1100	6 z. 40, deep blue		2·75	1·00
1096/1100	*Set of* 5		3·75	1·25

Paintings: *Vert*—60 g. "Motherhood" (after Wyspiański); 1 z. "Madame de Romanet" (after Rodakowski); 1 z. 50, "Death" (after Malczewski). *Horiz*—6 z. 40, "The Sandmen" (after Gierymski).

(Des S. Malecki. Litho)

1959 (1 July). *Third International Miners' Congress, Katowice. W 330. P 12½×13.*

1101	**354**	2 z. 50, multicoloured	40	15

355 Sheaf of Wheat ("Agriculture")

356 Dr L. Zamenhof

357 "Flowering Pink" (Map of Austria)

(Des S. Malecki. Litho)

1959 (21 July). *15th Anniv of People's Republic. T 355 and similar vert designs inscr "XV LAT PRL". W 330. P 12×12½.*

1102	40 g. blue-green and black		10	10
1103	60 g. red and black		10	10
1104	1 z. 50, pale blue and black		20	10

Designs:—60 g. Crane ("Building"); 1 z. 50, Corinthian column, and book ("Culture and Science").

(Des B. Brandt (60 g.), R. Dudzicki (1 z. 50). Litho)

1959 (24 July). *International Esperanto Congress, Warsaw, and Birth Centenary of Dr. Ludwig Zamenhof (inventor of Esperanto). T 356 and similar vert design. W 330. P 12½×13.*

1105	60 g. black and green/*light olive*	10	10
1106	1 z. 50, blue-green, red and violet/*grey*	60	20

Design:—1 z. 50, Esperanto Star, and Globe.

(Des E. Konecki. Litho)

1959 (27 July). *Seventh World Youth Festival, Vienna. W 330. P 12½×12.*

1107	**357**	60 g. multicoloured	10	10
1108		2 z. 50, multicoloured	35	15

358

359 Parliament House, Warsaw

(Des J. Kończak. Litho)

1959 (24 Aug). *30th Anniv of Polish Airlines "LOT". W 330. P 13×12½.*

1109	**358**	60 g. light blue, bluish violet & black	15	15

(Des S. Jasiński. Litho)

1959 (27 Aug). *48th Inter-Parliamentary Union Conference, Warsaw. W 330. P 12×12½.*

1110	**359**	60 g. green, red and black	10	10
1111		2 z. 50, dull purple, red and black	40	15

BALPEX I - GDAŃSK 1959
(360)

1959 (30 Aug). *Baltic States' International Philatelic Exhibition, Gdańsk. No. 890 optd with T 360.*

1112	45 g. brown/*lemon* (B.)		60	50

361 Dove and Globe

362 Nurse with Bag

(Des A. Balcerzak and S. Nargiello. Photo)

1959 (1 Sept). *Tenth Anniv of World Peace Movement. W 330. P 13×12½.*

1113	**361**	60 g. grey and blue	35	10

(Des Cz. Kaczmarczyk. Litho)

1959 (21 Sept). *40th Anniv of Polish Red Cross. T 362 and similar designs. W 330. P 11 (2 z. 50) or 12½×13 (others).*

1114	40 g. red, black and green		15	10
1115	60 g. red, brown and yellow-brown		15	10
1116	2 z. 50, red, black & light Venetian red	60	30

Designs: *Vert*—60 g. Nurse with bottle and bandages. *Square* (23 mm. × 23 mm.)—2 z. 50, J. H. Dunant.

363 Emblem of Polish-Chinese Friendship Society

364

(Des S. Malecki. Litho)

1959 (28 Sept). *Polish-Chinese Friendship. W 330. P 11.*

1117	**363**	60 g. red, yellow, blue and violet	35	15
1118		2 z. 50, red, yellow, blue & bl-grn	25	10

(Des S. Bernacinski. Litho)

1959 (9 Oct). *Stamp Day. W 330. P 12½×13.*

1119	**364**	60 g. red, olive-green & lt turquoise	15	10
1120		2 z. 50, violet-blue, blue-grn & red	30	10

365 "Sputnik 3"

(Des Cz. Kaczmarczyk. Photo)

1959 (7 Nov). *Cosmic Flights.* **T 365** *and similar horiz designs.* W **330**. P 12½.

1121	40 g. black and turquoise-blue	15	10
1122	60 g. black and brown-lake	30	10
1123	2 z. 50, deep blue and blue-green	1·25	50

Designs:—60 g. Rocket "Mieczta" encircling Sun; 2 z. 50, Moon rocket "Lunik 2".

Nos. 1121/3 exist imperforate.

366 Schoolgirl

367 Darwin

(40 g. des W. Górka; eng B. Szymańska. Recess, background photo. 60 g. des H. Hilscher; eng E. Tirdiszek. Recess and typo, background photo)

1959 (14 Nov). *"1000 Schools for Polish Millennium"* **T 366** *and similar vert design inscr* "TYSIAC SZKOL NA TYSIACLECIE". W **330**. P 11½.

1124	40 g. sepia and deep green	10	10
1125	60 g. red, black and blue	10	10

Designs:—60 g. Children going to school.

(Des S. Chludziński. Eng E. Tirdiszek (20 g.), E. Konecki (40 g.), J. Miller (60 g.), B. Brandt (1 z. 50), B. Kowalska (1 z. 55), S. Lukaszewski (2 z. 50). Recess)

1959 (10 Dec). *Famous Scientists. Vert portraits as* **T 367**. W **330**. P 11×11½.

1126	20 g. deep blue	10	10
1127	40 g. deep olive (Mendeleev)	10	10
1128	60 g. brown-purple (Einstein)	15	10
1129	1 z. 50, chocolate (Pasteur)	20	10
1130	1 z. 55, deep myrtle-green (Newton)	50	10
1131	2 z. 50, violet (Copernicus)	80	50
1126/1131	Set of 6	1·60	70

368 Costumes of Rzeszów **369**

(Des Cz. Kaczmarczyk. Eng S. Lukaszewski (20 g.), B. Konecki (60 g.), J. Miller (1 z.), B. Brandt (2 z. 50), M. R. Polak (5 z. 60). Recess; background photo)

1959 (18 Dec). *Provincial Costumes* (1st series). **T 368/9** *and similar vert designs.* W **330**. P 12.

1132	20 g. greenish black and grey-green	10	10
	a. Pair. Nos. 1132/3	20	
1133	20 g. greenish black and grey-green	10	10
1134	60 g. agate and salmon-pink	15	10
	a. Pair. Nos. 1134/5	30	
1135	60 g. agate and salmon-pink	15	10
1136	1 z. brown-red and pale blue	20	10
	a. Pair. Nos. 1136/7	40	
1137	1 z. brown-red and pale blue	20	10
1138	2 z. 50, blue-green and lavender-grey	40	10
	a. Pair. Nos. 1138/9	80	
1139	2 z. 50, blue-green and lavender-grey	40	10
1140	5 z. 60, Prussian blue & greenish yellow	1·60	40
	a. Pair. Nos. 1140/1	3·25	

1141	5 z. 60, Prussian blue & greenish yellow	1·60	40
1132/1141	Set of 10	4·50	1·40

Designs:— Male and female costumes of: Nos. 1134/5, Kurpie; Nos. 1136/7, Silesia; Nos. 1138/9, Mountain regions; Nos. 1140/1, Szamotuly.

Stamps of the same value were issued together in *se-tenant* pairs within their sheets.

These also exist imperforate.

See also Nos. 1150/9.

370 Piano

371 Polish 10 k. Stamp of 1860 and Postmark

(Des S. Malecki. Litho (60 g., 1 z. 50). Eng B. Kowalska. Recess (2 z. 50))

1960 (22 Feb). *150th Birth Anniv of Chopin, and Chopin Music Competition, Warsaw.* **T 370** *and similar vert designs inscr* "1810–1960". W **330**. P 12 (60 g., 1 z. 50) or 12½×12 (2 z. 50).

1142	60 g. black and bright violet	45	15
1143	1 z. 50, black, red and light blue	70	15
1144	2 z. 50, blackish brown	2·00	1·25

Designs: (22×35½ *mm.*).—1 z. 50, Portion of Chopin's music. (25×39½ *mm.*)—2 z. 50, Portrait of Chopin.

(Des A. Balcerzak. Litho)

1960 (21 Mar). *Stamp Centenary.* **T 371** *and similar vert designs.* W **330**. P 11½×11.

1145	40 g. rose, blue, black & lt turquoise-bl	15	10
1146	60 g. blue, black and violet	25	10
1147	1 z. 35, blue, red and grey	65	35
1148	1 z. 55, carmine, black and bluish green	80	25
1149	2 z. 50, dp myrtle-grn, blk & lt yell-ol	1·40	60
1145/1149	Set of 5	3·00	1·25

Designs:—1 z. 35, Emblem inscr "1860 1960". Reproductions of Polish stamps: 60 g. No. 356; 1 z. 55, No.533; 2 z. 50, No. 1030; with appropriate postmarks.

A set of five miniature sheets, each containing a value of Nos. 1145/9 in block of four, was presented to subscribers to the first volume of *Polskie Znaki Pocztowe* (*Price £325 mint per set*).

(Des Cz. Karczmarczyk. Eng M. R. Polak (1150), S. Lukaszewski (1152, 1156), B. Brandt (1154), E. Konecki (1155), B. Szymanska (1157), E. Tirdiszek (1158), J. Miller (others). Recess; background photo)

1960 (28 May). *Provincial Costumes* (2nd series). Vert designs as **T 368/9**. W **330**. P 12.

1150	40 g. carmine and light blue	10	10
	a. Pair. Nos. 1150/1	20	
1151	40 g. carmine and light blue	10	10
1152	2 z. ultramarine and greenish yellow	25	10
	a. Pair. Nos. 1152/3	50	
1153	2 z. ultramarine and greenish yellow	25	10
1154	3 z. 10, grey-green and sage green	40	15
	a. Pair. Nos. 1154/5	80	
1155	3 z. 10, grey-green and sage green	40	15
1156	3 z. 40, brown and pale blue	50	20
	a. Pair. Nos. 1156/7	1·00	
1157	3 z. 40, brown and pale blue	50	20
1158	6 z. 50, violet and green	1·60	40
	a. Pair. Nos. 1158/9	3·25	
1159	6 z. 50, violet and green	1·60	40
1150/1159	Set of 10	5·25	1·75

Designs:—Male and female costumes of: Nos. 1150/1,

Cracow; Nos. 1152/3, Lowicz; Nos. 1154/5, Kujawy; Nos. 1156/7, Lublin; Nos. 1158/9, Lubusz.

Stamps of the same value were issued together in *se-tenant* pairs within their sheets.

These also exist imperforate.

372 Throwing the Discus   **373** King Wladislaw Jagiello's Tomb, Wawel Castle

(Des S. Malecki. Litho; centres embossed)

1960 (15 June). *Olympic Games, Rome. T* **372** *and similar horiz designs. P* 12×13.

1160	60 g. greenish blue and black	15	15
	a. Block of 4. Nos. 1160/3	60	
1161	60 g. magenta and black	15	15
1162	60 g. bright violet and black	15	15
1163	60 g. bright blue-green and black	15	15
1164	2 z. 50, ultramarine and black	70	25
	a. Block of 4. Nos. 1164/7	2·75	
1165	2 z. 50, orange-brown and black	70	25
1166	2 z. 50, orange-vermilion and black	70	25
1167	2 z. 50, emerald and black	70	25
1160/1167	*Set of 8*	3·00	1·40

Designs (Polish successes in previous Olympic Games):—No. 1161, Running; 1162, Cycling; 1163, Show jumping; 1164, Trumpeters; 1165, Boxing; 1166, Olympic Flame; 1167, Long jumping.

Stamps of the same value were issued together in *se-tenant* blocks of four stamps within the sheet, each block illustrating a complete circuit of the stadium track.

These also exist imperforate.

(Des Cz. Kaczmarczyk. Eng E. Konecki (60 g.), S. Lukaszewski (90 g.), J. Miller (2 z. 50). Recess)

1960 (15 July). *550th Anniv of Battle of Grunwald. T* **373** *and other designs inscr* "GRUNWALD 1410–1960". *W* **330**. *P* 11×11½.

1168	60 g. chocolate	25	15
1169	90 g. deep bronze-green	55	30
1170	2 z. 50, black	2·25	1·25

Designs: *Vert*—90 g. Proposed Grunwald monument. *Horiz* (78×35½ *mm.*) —"Battle of Grunwald" (after Matejko).

374 1860 Stamp and Postmark   **375** I. Lukaszewski (inventor of petrol lamp)

(Des A. Balcerzak. Litho)

1960 (4 Sept). *International Philatelic Exhibition, Warsaw. W* **330**. *P* 11×11½.

1171 **374** 10 z.+10 z. red, black and blue   7·75   7·75
Printed in sheets of four and sold only at the Exhibition.

(Des J. Desselberger. Eng E. Konecki. Recess; background photo)

1960 (14 Sept). *Lukasiewicz Commemoration and Fifth Pharmaceutical Science Congress, Poznań. W* **330**. *P* 11×11½.

1172 **375** 60 g. black and olive-yellow   15   10

376 "The Annunciation"   **377** Paderewski

(Des R. Kleczewski. Eng E. Konecki (20 g., 2 z. 50), E. Tirdiszek (30 g.), B. Brandt (40 g.), B. Szymanska (60 g.), J. Miller (5 z. 60), S. Lukaszewski (10 z.). Recess)

1960 (20 Sept). *Altar Wood Carvings of St. Mary's Church, Cracow, by Veit Stoss. T* **376** *and similar horiz designs. W* **330**. *P* 12½×12 *or imperf* (10 z.).

1173	20 g. slate-blue	20	10
1174	30 g. red-brown	15	10
1175	40 g. violet	20	10
1176	60 g. deep grey-green	20	10
1177	2 z. 50, deep claret	90	30
1178	5 z. 60, sepia	5·50	3·75
1173/1178	*Set of 6*	6·50	3·75

MS1178a 86×107 mm. 10 z. grey-black   7·00   4·75
Designs:—30 g. "The Nativity"; 40 g. "Homage of the Three Kings"; 60 g. "The Resurrection"; 2 z. 50, "The Ascension"; 5 z. 60, "The Descent of the Holy Ghost". *Vert* (72×95 *mm.*) —10 z. The Assumption of the Virgin.

(Des J. Desselberger. Eng E. Konecki. Recess)

1960 (26 Sept). *Birth Centenary of Paderewski. W* **330**. *P* 13×12½.

1179 **377** 2 z. 50, black   35   15

DZIEŃ ZNACZKA 1960

(378)   **379** Gniezno

1960 (9 Oct). *Stamp Day. Optd with T* **378**.
1180 **371** 40 g. rose, blue, black & lt turq-bl   1·40   55

(Des W. Chomicz. Eng S. Lukaszewski (5 g., 1 z. 15, 3 z. 10), A. Szklarczyk (10 g., 50 g., 5 z. 60), B. Kowalska (20 g., 60 g. (1187)), E. Tirdiszek (40 g., 95 g., 1 z. 50, 2 z. 10), E. Konecki (60 g. (1186), 90 g., 1 z. 35, 1 z. 55, 2 z. 50), B. Brandt (80 g.), J. Miller (1 z., 2 z.). Recess)

1960 (15 Nov)–**61**. *Old Polish Towns. Horiz designs as T* **379**. *P* 13×12½ (95 g.) *or* 11½×12 (*others*).

1181	5 g. red-brown	10	10
	a. Perf 13×12½	10	10
1182	10 g. blue-green	10	10
	a. Perf 13×12½	10	10
1183	20 g. sepia	10	10
	a. Perf 13×12½	10	10
1184	40 g. vermilion	10	10
	a. Perf 13×12½	10	10
1185	50 g. violet	10	10
1186	60 g. brown-lilac	10	10
	a. Perf 13×12½	10	10
1187	60 g. dull ultramarine (12.5.61)	10	10
1188	80 g. deep violet-blue	15	15
	a. Perf 13×12½	15	15
1189	90 g. brown (12.5.61)	10	10
1190	95 g. blackish olive	30	10
1191	1 z. orange-red and pale lilac	10	10
1192	1 z. 15, bottle grn & pale orge (28.12.60)	30	10
1193	1 z. 35, magenta & pale green (28.12.60)	15	10

1194	1 z. 50, bistre-brown & pale bl (28.12.60)		30	10
1195	1 z. 55, brown-lilac & pale yell (28.12.60)		30	10
1196	2 z. deep blue and pale lilac (28.12.60)		20	10
1197	2 z. 10, agate and pale yellow (28.12.60)		20	10
1198	2 z. 50, violet and pale green (28.12.60)		25	10
1199	3 z. 10, brt scarlet & pale grey (28.12.60)		30	20
1200	5 z. 60, slate & lt grey-green (28.12.60)		60	25
1181/1200	Set of 20		3·25	90

Towns:—10 g. Cracow; 20 g. Warsaw; 40 g. Poznań; 50 g. Plock; 60 g. (1186) Kalisz; 60 g. (1187) Tczew; 80 g. Frombork; 90 g. Toruń; 95 g. Puck; 1 z. Slupsk; 1 z. 15, Gdańsk; 1 z. 35, Wroclaw; 1 z. 50, Szczecin; 1 z. 55, Opole; 2 z. Kolobrzeg; 2 z. 10, Legnica; 2 z. 50, Katowice; 3 z. 10, Lódź; 5 z. 60, Walbrzych.

380 Great Bustard
(*Otis tarda*)

381 Front page of newspaper *Proletaryat* (1883)

(Des J. Desselberger. Photo)

1960 (26 Nov). *Birds. Designs as T 380. Multicoloured. P 11½.*

1201	10 g. Type **380**		20	10
1202	20 g. Raven (*Corvus corax*)		20	10
1203	30 g. Common cormorant (*Phalacrocorax carbo*)		20	10
1204	40 g. Black stork (*Ciconia nigra*)		35	10
1205	50 g. Eagle owl (*Bubo bubo*)		65	15
1206	60 g. White-tailed sea eagle (*Haliaeëtus albicilla*)		65	15
1207	75 g. Golden eagle (*Aquila chrysaëtos*)		70	15
1208	90 g. Short-toed eagle (*Circaëtus gallicus*)		75	20
1209	2 z. 50, Rock thrush (*Monticola saxatilis*)		4·00	1·40
1210	4 z. Common kingfisher (*Alcedo atthis*)		3·25	1·00
1211	5 z. 60, Wallcreeper (*Tichodroma muraria*)		5·50	1·10
1212	6 z. 50, Common roller (*Coracias garrulus*)		8·00	2·00
1201/1212	Set of 12		22·00	6·00

(Des Cz. Kaczmarczyk. Litho. "300" embossed)

1961 (3 Jan). *300th Anniv of Polish Newspaper Press. T 381 and similar vert designs. W 330. P 12.*

1213	40 g. green, blue and black		50	25
1214	60 g. yellow, brown-red and black		50	25
1215	2 z. 50, blue, violet and black		2·75	2·50

Designs:—As T 381 but showing front page of newspapers. 40 g. *Merkuriusz* (first issue, 1661); 2 z. 50, *Rzeczpospolita* (1944).

382 Ice-hockey

383 Congress Emblem

(Des J. Grabiański. Litho)

1961 (1 Feb). *First Winter Military Spartakiad. T 382 and similar vert designs. W 330. P 12.*

1216	40 g. black, olive-yellow and lilac		40	10
1217	60 g. black, carmine, violet-blue & cobalt		1·00	30

1218	1 z. olive, black, red, dp blue & lt blue	5·50	1·90
1219	1 z. 50, black, yellow & lt turquoise-bl	90	30
1216/1219	Set of 4	7·00	2·40

Designs:—60 g. Ski jumping; 1 z. Rifle-shooting; 1 z. 50, Slalom.

(Des S. Jasiński. Litho)

1961 (11 Feb). *Fourth Polish Engineers' Conference. W 330. P 12½ × 13.*

1220	**383**	60 g. black and red	15	10

384 Yuri Gagarin

385 Fair Emblem

(Des A. Heidrich. Photo)

1961 (27 Apr). *World's First Manned Space Flight. T 384 and similar horiz design inscr "12.IV.1961". W 330. P 12.*

1221	40 g. black, red and brown-red		75	20
1222	60 g. red, black and blue		75	25

Design:—60 g. Globe and star.

(Des Z. Kaja. Litho)

1961 (25 May). *30th International Fair, Poznań. W 330. P 12½.*

1223	**385**	40 g. black, orange-red and blue	10	10
1224		1 z. 50, black, blue and orange-red	20	10

See also No. **MS**1245*a*.

386 King Mieszko I

(Des A. Heidrich. Eng A. Szklarczyk (1225), S. Lukaszewski (1226), J. Miller (1227), E. Tirdiszek (1228), E. Konecki (1229), B. Kowalska (1230). Recess: background photo)

1961 (15 June). *Famous Poles (1st series). T 386 and similar horiz portrait designs. W 330. P 11 × 12.*

1225	60 g. black and blue		10	10
1226	60 g. black and claret		10	10
1227	60 g. black and grey-green		10	10
1228	60 g. black and violet		70	20
1229	60 g. black and light brown		10	10
1230	60 g. black and olive-brown		10	10
1225/1230	Set of 6		90	50

Portraits:—No. 1225, T **386**; No. 1226, King Casimir the Great; No. 1227, King Casimir Jagiellon; No. 1228, Copernicus; No. 1229, A. F. Modrzewski; No. 1230, Kosciuszko.
See also Nos. 1301/6 and 1398/1401.

387 *Leskov* (trawler support ship)

(Des J. Desselberger. Litho)

1961 (24 June). *Shipbuilding Industry. T 387 and similar horiz designs. Multicoloured. P 11.*

1231	60 g. Type **387**		25	10
1232	1 z. 55, *Severodvinsk* (depot ship)		40	15
1233	2 z. 50, *Rambutan* (coaster)		70	30
1234	3 z. 40, *Krynica* (freighter)		1·00	40

1235   4 z. *B54* (freighter) .. .. .. 1·75   70
1236   5 z. 60, *Bavsk* (tanker) .. .. .. 4·50 1·75
1231/1236 *Set of* 6 .. .. 7·75 3·00
   Sizes: *As* T **387**—2 z. 50. 81×21 *mm*—1 z.55, 3 z. 40, 4 z.
108×21 *mm*—5 z.60.

388 Posthorn and
Telephone Dial

389 Opole Seal

390 Beribboned
Paddle

(Des S. Malecki. Litho)

1961 (26 June). *Communications Ministers' Conference,
Warsaw.* T **388** *and similar designs. No wmk or* W **330**
(*No.* **MS**1239*a*). P 11.
1237   40 g. orange-red, dp green & slate-blue   10   10
1238   60 g. brt violet, yellow & lt slate-purple 15   10
1239   2 z. 50, ultramarine, lt blue & bistre-brn 50   20
MS1239*a* 108×66 mm. Nos. 1237/9 (sold at
5 z.) .. .. 3·75 2·50
   Designs: Posthorn and —60 g. Radar screen; 2 z. 50.
Conference emblem.

(Des Cz. Kaczmarczyk. Eng A. Szklarczyk (1240), E Konecki (1241,
1243*b*), S. Lukaszewski (1242), B. Kowalska (1243), E. Tirdiszek
(1243*a*, 1244), J. Miller (1245). Recess and photo)

1961 (21 July)-**62**. *Polish Western Provinces.* T **389** *and similar
designs.* W **330**. P 11.
1240   40 g. deep chocolate and grey-brown .. 10   10
      a. Block. Nos. 1240/1 plus label   30
1241   40 g. deep chocolate and grey-brown .. 10   10
1242   60 g. deep reddish violet and pink   10   10
      a. Block. Nos. 1242/3 plus label   30
1243   60 g. deep reddish violet and pink   10   10
1243*a* 95 g. myrtle green & turq-bl (23.2.62) .. 15   10
      ab. Block. Nos. 1243*a*/*b* plus label   50
1243*b* 95 g. myrtle green & turq-bl (23.2.62) .. 15   10
1244   2 z. 50, bronze green and yellow-olive 30   15
      a. Block. Nos. 1244/5 plus label   70
1245   2 z. 50, bronze green and yellow-olive 30   15
1240/1245 *Set of* 8 .. .. 1·60   60
   Designs: *Vert*—No. 1240, Type **389**; 1242, Henry IV's tomb;
1243*a*, Seal of Conrad II; 1244, Prince Barnim's seal. *Horiz*—
No. 1241, Opole cement-works; 1243, Wroclaw apartment-
house; 1243*b*, Factory interior, Zielona Góra; 1245, Szczecin
harbour.
   Stamps of the same value were issued together *se-tenant* with ⅔
stamp-size inscribed label.
   See also Nos. 1308/13.

1961 (29 July). *"Intermess II" Stamp Exhibition. Sheet*
121×51 *mm. containing pair of No.* 1224 *but imperf.*
MS1245*a* 1 z. 50 (×2) (sold at 4 z. 50+2 z. 50) 5·25 2·75

(Des R. Dudzicki. Litho)

1961 (18 Aug). *Sixth European Canoeing Championships.* T **390**
and similar designs. W **330**. P 12½.
1246   40 g. red, yellow, green, blue & turq 15   10
1247   60 g. red, yellow, violet and blue   15   10
1248   2 z. 50, red, yell, vio, grey-grn & slate 1·25   40
   Designs: *Horiz*—40 g. Two canoes within letter "E"; 60 g.
Two four-seater canoes at finishing post.
   These also exist imperforate.

391 Titov and Orbit
within Star

392 Monument

(Des S. Bernaciński. Photo)

1961 (24 Aug). *Second Russian Manned Space Flight.* T **391**
*and similar horiz design inscr "700,000 KM W KOSMOSIE"
etc.* P 12×13.
1249   40 g. black, red and pale pink . 40   10
1250   60 g. blue and black . 40   10
   Design: —60 g. Dove and spaceman's orbit around globe.

(Des J. Desselberger. Litho)

1961 (15 Sept). *40th Anniv of Third Silesian Uprising.* T **392**
*and similar vert design inscr "40 ROCZNICA TRZECIEGO"
etc.* W **330**. P 12.
1251   60 g. grey and emerald   10   10
1252   1 z. 55, grey and light blue   20   10
   Design: —1 z. 55, Cross of Silesian uprisers.

393 P.K.O. Emblem
and Ant

394 "Mail Cart"
(after J. Chelmonski)

(Des S. Malecki. Litho)

1961 (30 Sept). *Savings Month.* T **393** *and similar horiz
designs.* W **330**. P 12.
1253   40 g. orange-red, yellow and black 15   10
1254   60 g. brown, yellow and black   15   10
1255   60 g. blue, violet and pink   15   10
1256   60 g. green, orange-red and black 15   10
1257   2 z. 50, magenta, grey and black 2·40 1·25
1253/57 *Set of* 5 . 2·75 1·50
   Designs:—No. 1253, Savings Bank motif; 1254, T **393**;
1255, Bee; 1256, Squirrel; 1257, Savings Bank book.

(Des Cz. Kaczmarczyk. Eng J. Miller. Recess)

1961 (9 Oct). *Stamp Day and 40th Anniv of Postal Museum.*
W **330**. P 12×12½.
1258 **394** 60 g. chocolate . 25   10
1259   60 g. deep green . 25   10

395 Congress Emblem

396 Emblem of
Kopasyni mining
family, 1284

(Des S. Jasiński. Eng B. Kowalska. Recess)

1961 (20 Nov). *Fifth World Federation of Trade Unions'
Congress, Moscow.* W **330**. P 12×12½.
1260 **395** 60 g. black . 10   10

(Des S. Miklaszewski. Litho)

1961 (4 Dec). *Millenary of Polish Mining Industry.* As T **396,** *inscr* "TYSIACLECIE GORNICTWA POLSKIEGO". W **330.** P 11×11½

1261	40 g. brown-purple, orange & lt orange	15	10
1262	60 g. grey-blue, ultramarine & lt blue	15	10
1263	2 z. 50, green, black and light green	60	25

Designs: —60 g. 14th-century seal of Bytom; 2 z. 50, Emblem of International Mine Constructors' Congress, Warsaw, 1958.

397 Child and Syringe

398 Cogwheel and Wheat

(Des S. Gospodarek. Litho)

1961 (11 Dec). *15th Anniv of UNICEF.* T **397** *and similar designs inscr* "1961 XV ROCZNICA POWSTANIA UNICEF". W **330.** P 12×12½ (60 g.) or 12½×12 (others)

1264	40 g. black and light blue	10	10
1265	60 g. black and yellow-orange	10	10
1266	2 z. 50, black and turquoise-green	60	25

Designs: *Horiz* —60 g. Children of three races. *Vert* —2 z. 50, Mother and child, and feeding bottle.

(Des Cz. Kaczmarczyk. Litho)

1961 (12 Dec). *15th Economic Co-operative Council Meeting, Warsaw.* T **398** *and similar horiz design.* W **330.** P 12.

| 1267 | 40 g. crimson, yellow and black | 15 | 10 |
| 1268 | 60 g. red, light blue and ultramarine | 15 | 10 |

Design: —60 g. Oil pipeline map, E. Europe.

399 Caterpillar-hunter (*Calosoma sycophanta*)

400 Worker with Flag and Dove

(Des J. Desselberger (1269/74), A. Balcerzak (1275/8), A. Heidrich (1279/80). Photo)

1961 (30 Dec). *Insects.* T **399** *and similar multicoloured designs.* P 13×12 (20 g. to 80 g.) or 11½ (1 z. 15 to 5 z. 60).

1269	20 g. Type **399**	20	10
1270	30 g. Violet ground beetle (*Carabus violaceus*)	20	10
1271	40 g. Alpine longhorn beetle (*Rosalia alpina*)	20	10
1272	50 g. *Cerambyx cerdo* (longhorn beetle)	20	10
1273	60 g. *Carabus auronitens* (ground beetle)	20	10
1274	80 g. Stag beetle (*Lucanus cervus*)	35	10
1275	1 z. 15, Clouded apollo (*Parnassius mnemosyne*)	70	15
1276	1 z. 35, Death's-head hawk moth (*Acherontia atropos*)	45	15
1277	1 z. 50, Scarce swallowtail (*Papilio podalirius*)	90	15
1278	1 z. 55, Apollo (*Parnassius apollo*)	90	15

1279	2 z. 50, Red wood ant (*Formica rufa*)	1·50	40
1280	5 z. 60, White-tailed bumble bee (*Bombus*)	8·00	4·25
1269/1280	*Set of 12*	12·50	5·25

Sizes: As T **399**—20 g. to 80 g. 36½×36½ mm—1 z. 15 to 5 z. 60.

(Des J. Desselberger. Litho)

1962 (5 Jan). *20th Anniv of Polish Workers' Coalition.* T **400** *and similar vert designs.* P 12½×12.

1281	60 g. sepia, black and vermilion	15	10
1282	60 g. bistre, black and vermilion	15	10
1283	60 g. violet, black and vermilion	15	10
1284	60 g. slate-green, black and vermilion	15	10
1285	60 g. grey-blue, black and vermilion	15	10
1281/1285	*Set of 5*	50	25

Designs: —1282, Steersman; 1283, Worker with hammer; 1284, Soldier with weapon; 1285, Worker with trowel and rifle.

401 Two Skiers Racing

(Des S. Toepfer. Litho. Central figures embossed in colour)

1962 (14 Feb). *F.I.S. International Ski Championships, Zakopane.* T **401** *and similar designs.* P 12×12½ (1 z. 50), 12½×12 (40, 60 g.) or imperf (10 z.).

1286	**401** 40 g. slate-blue, grey and red	10	10
1287	— 40 g. grey-blue, bistre-brown & red	1·00	20
1288	— 60 g. slate-blue, grey and red	20	10
1289	— 60 g. indigo, bistre-brown and red	1·25	70
1290	— 1 z. 50, slate-blue, grey and red	35	10
1291	— 1 z. 50, violet, grey and red	1·75	1·25
1286/1291	*Set of 6*	4·25	2·25

MS1291*a* 67×80 mm. 10 z. (+5 z.) slate-blue, grey and red | 4·75 | 3·75

Designs: *Horiz* —60 g. Skier racing. *Vert* —1 z. 50, Ski-jumper; 10 z. F.I.S. emblem.

Nos. 1286, 1288 and 1290 also exist in sheets of four, perf 11×11½ or 11½×11 (*Price per set of 3 sheets* £110 *un*).

402 Majdanek Monument   **403** Racing Cyclist

(Des S. Jasiński. Eng J. Miller (40 g.), E. Konecki (60 g.), B. Kowalska (1 z. 50). Recess)

1962 (2 Apr). *Concentration Camp Monuments.* T **402** *and similar designs.* W **330.** P 11½.

1292	40 g. deep blue	10	10
1293	60 g. black	30	10
1294	1 z. 50, violet	40	15

Designs: *Vert* (20×31 *mm.*) —40 g. Broken carnations and portion of prison clothing (Oswiecim or Auschwitz Camp); 1 z. 50, Treblinka Monument.

(Des S. Malecki. Litho)

1962 (27 Apr). *15th International Peace Cycle Race.* T **403** *and similar horiz designs.* W **330.** P 12.

1295	60 g. black and blue	20	10
1296	2 z. 50, black and yellow	40	10
1297	3 z. 40, black and light reddish violet	70	25

Designs: —(74½×22 *mm.*) 2 z. 50, Cyclists and "XV"; (As T **403**) 3 z. 40, Arms of Berlin, Prague and Warsaw, and cycle wheel.

405 Lenin walking **406** General K. Swierczewski-Walter (monument) **407** *Crocus scepusiensis* (Borb)

(Des S. Malecki. Eng E. Tirdiszek (40 g.), A. Szklarczyk (60 g.), B. Kowalska (2 z. 50). Recess)

1962 (25 May). *50th Anniv of Lenin's Sojourn in Poland. T* **405** *and similar vert designs inscr "1912–1962". W* **330.** *P* $11 \times 11\frac{1}{2}$.

1298	40 g. deep bluish green and pale green	35	10
1299	60 g. lake and pale pink	15	10
1300	2 z. 50, sepia and pale yellow	35	10

Designs:—60 g. Lenin; 2 z. 50, Lenin wearing cap, and St. Mary's Church, Cracow.

(Des A. Heidrich; eng S. Lukaszewski (1301), J. Miller (1302). Recess; background photo. Des A. Heidrich. Litho (others))

1962 (20 June). *Famous Poles* (*2nd series*). *Portrait designs as T* **386.** *W* **330.** *P* 11×12 (*Nos* 1301/2) *or* $12 \times 12\frac{1}{2}$ (*others*).

1301	60 g. black and light grey-green	10	10
1302	60 g. black and orange-brown	10	10
1303	60 g. black and blue	50	10
1304	60 g. black and brown-bistre	10	10
1305	60 g. black and reddish purple	10	10
1306	60 g. black and deep bluish green	10	10
1301/1306	Set of 6	90	45

Portraits:—1301, A. Mickiewicz (poet); 1302, J. Slowacki (poet); 1303, F. Chopin (composer); 1304, R. Traugutt (patriot); 1305, J. Dabrowski (revolutionary); 1306, Maria Konopnicka (poet).

(Des S. Jasiński. Eng J. Miller. Recess)

1962 (14 July). *15th Anniv of Death of General K. Swierczewski-Walter* (*patriot*). *P* $11 \times 11\frac{1}{2}$.

1307	**406** 60 g. black	10	10

(Des Cz. Kaczmarczyk. Eng E. Tirdszek (1308), A. Szklarczyk (1309), Z. Kowalski (1310), E. Konecki (1311, 1312), J. Miller (1313). Recess and photo)

1962 (21 July). *Polish Northern Provinces. Designs as T* **389.** *P* 11.

1308	60 g. deep violet-blue and bluish grey	10	10
	a. Block. Nos. 1308/9 plus label	30	
1309	60 g. deep violet-blue and bluish grey	10	10
1310	1 z. 55, sepia and pale yellow	20	10
	a. Block. Nos. 1310/11 plus label	50	
1311	1 z. 55, sepia and pale yellow	20	10
1312	2 z. 50, greenish slate and greenish grey	50	15
	a. Block. Nos. 1312/13 plus label	1·25	
1313	2 z. 50, greenish slate and greenish grey	50	15
1308/1313	Set of 6	1·75	60

Designs: *Vert*—No. 1308, Princess Elizabeth's seal; 1310, Gdańsk Governor's seal; 1312, Frombork Cathedral. *Horiz*—No. 1309, Insulator factory, Szczecinek; 1311, Gdańsk shipyard; 1313, Laboratory of Agricultural College, Kortowo.

Stamps of the same value were issued together *se-tenant* with $\frac{2}{3}$ stamp-size inscribed label.

(Des A. Balcerzak. Photo)

1962 (8 Aug). *Polish Protected Plants. T* **407** *and similar vert designs. Plants in natural colours. P* 12.

1314	60 g. yellow	20	10
1315	60 g. cinnamon	80	30
1316	60 g. pink	20	10
1317	90 g. yellow-green	25	10
1318	90 g. yellow-olive	25	10
1319	90 g. green	25	10
1320	1 z. 50, grey-blue	35	15
1321	1 z. 50, light green	45	15
1322	1 z. 50, bluish green	35	15
1323	2 z. 50, grey-green	90	50
1324	2 z. 50, turquoise	90	50
1325	2 z. 50, violet-blue	1·25	60
1314/1325	Set of 12	5·50	2·50

Plants:—No. 1314, T **407**; 1315, *Platanthera bifolia* (Rich); 1316, *Aconitum callibotryon* (Rchb); 1317, *Gentiana clusii* (Perr. et Song); 1318, *Dictamnus albus* (L); 1319, *Nymphaea alba* (L.); 1320, *Daphne mezereum* (L.); 1321, *Pulsatilla vulgaris* (Mill.); 1322, *Anemone Silvestris* (L.); 1323, *Trollius europaeus* (L.); 1324, *Galanthus nivalis* (L.); 1325, *Adonis vernalis* (L.).

408 "The Poison Well", after J. Malczewski **409** Pole Vault

(Des J. Desselberger. Eng E. Tirdiszek. Recess)

1962 (25 Aug). *F.I.P. Day* (*1st Sept —Federation Internationale de Philatélie*). *W* **330.** *P* $11\frac{1}{2}$.

1326	**408** 60 g. black/cream	30	10

No. 1326 was printed in sheets of 40 stamps *se-tenant* with labels inscribed "FILA-TELISTYKA ZBLIZA LUDZI WSZYSTKICH KRAJOW" ("Philately unites people of all countries"). It also exists in sheets of 4 stamps and 4 labels.

(Des R. Dudzicki. Litho)

1962 (12 Sept). *Seventh European Athletic Championships, Belgrade. T* **409** *and similar horiz designs. Multicoloured. P* 11.

1327	40 g. Type **409**	10	10
1328	60 g. 400-metres relay	10	10
1329	90 g. Throwing the javelin	10	10
1330	1 z. Hurdling	10	10
1331	1 z. 50, High-jumping	15	10
1332	1 z. 55, Throwing the discus	15	10
1333	2 z. 50, 100-metres	45	15
1334	3 z. 40, Throwing the hammer	1·10	25
1327/1334	Set of 8	1·75	70

The above exist imperforate.

410 Mosquito **411** Cosmonauts "in Flight" **412** "A Moment of Determination" (after painting by A. Kamienski)

(Des S. Malecki. Litho)

1962 (1 Oct). *Malaria Eradication. T* **410** *and similar vert designs. W* **330.** *P* 13×12 *or imperf* (3 z.).

1335	60 g. olive-brown and deep bluish green	10	10
1336	1 z. 50, pink, grey, violet and red	15	10
1337	2 z. 50, orange, yellow-green, ultramarine and greenish grey	55	20
MS1337a	60 × 81 mm. 3 z. multicoloured	1·10	50

Designs:—1 z. 50, Malaria parasites in blood; 2 z. 50, Cinchona plant; 3 z. Anopheles mosquito.

(Des J. Desselberger. Litho)

1962 (6 Oct). *First "Team" Manned Space Flight.* **T 411** *and similar vert design.* W **330.** P 12½×12 *or* 11½×11 (10 z.).
1338   60 g. yellow-green, black & bluish violet   15   10
1339   2 z. 50, red, black and turquoise-blue   35   15
MS1339a 70×94 mm. 10 z. red, black and
   turquoise-blue   2·40   2·40
   Design: —2 z. 50, 10 z. Two stars (representing space-ships)
in orbit.

(Des H. Przezdziecka. Eng B. Kowalska. Recess)

1962 (9 Oct). *Stamp Day.* W **330.** P 13×12.
1340 **412** 60 g. black   10   10
1341   2 z. 50, red-brown   45   20

413 Mazovian   **414** Cruiser *Aurora*
Princes' Mansion,
Warsaw

(Des Cz. Kaczmarczyk. Litho)

1962 (13 Oct). *25th Anniv of Polish Democratic Party.* W **330.**
P 13×12.
1342 **413** 60 g. black/*red*   15   10

(Des S. Malecki. Eng Z. Kowalski. Recess and photo)

1962 (3 Nov). *45th Anniv of Russian Revolution.* W **330.**
P 11.
1343 **414** 60 g. grey-blue and orange-red   30   10

415 J. Korczak   **416** Old Town, Warsaw
(bust after
Dunikowski)

(Des J. Srokowski. Litho)

1962 (12 Nov). *20th Death Anniv of Janusz Korczak (child educator).* **T 415** *and similar vert designs.* P 13×12.
1344   40 g. sepia, light bistre and red-brown   15   10
1345   60 g. multicoloured   15   10
1346   90 g. multicoloured   30   15
1347   1 z. multicoloured   30   10
1348   2 z. 50, multicoloured   70   40
1349   5 z. 60, multicoloured   2·10   90
1344/1349   *Set of 6*   3·25   1·50
   Designs: —60 g. to 5 z. 60, Illustrations from Korczak's
children's books.

(Des A. Heidrich. Litho)

1962 (26 Nov). *Fifth Trade Unions Congress, Warsaw.* W **330.**
P 11.
1350 **416** 3 z. 40, grey-blue, red, blk & cream   45   15
   Also printed in sheets of four.

417 Master   **418** R. Traugutt (insurgent leader)
Buncombe

(Des J. M. Szancer. Litho)

1962 (31 Dec). *Maria Konopnicka's Fairy Tale "The Dwarfs and Orphan Mary".* **T 417** *and similar vert designs. Multicoloured.* P 12½×12.
1351   40 g. Type **417**   45   10
1352   60 g. Lardie the Fox and Master Buncombe   2·25   1·25
1353   1 z. 50, Bluey and the frog   60   15
1354   1 z. 55, Peter's kitchen   60   20
1355   2 z. 50, Saraband's concert   75   35
1356   3 z. 40, Orphan Mary and Subearthy   2·40   1·50
1351/1356   *Set of 6*   6·25   3·25

(Des A. Heidrich. Litho)

1963 (31 Jan). *Centenary of January (1863) Rising.* W **330.**
P 11½×11.
1357 **418** 60 g. black, pale pink & turquoise-bl   10   10

419 Tractor and Wheat

(Des A. Heidrich. Litho)

1963 (25 Feb). *Freedom from Hunger.* **T 419** *and similar horiz designs. Multicoloured.* W **330.** P 12×12½.
1358   40 g. Type **419**   10   10
1359   60 g. Millet and hoeing   60   25
1360   2 z. 50, Rice and mechanical harvester   55   15

420 Cocker Spaniel   **421** Egyptian Galley
                    (15th Century, B.C.)

(Des J. Grabiański. Litho)

1963 (25 Mar). *Dogs. Designs as T 420.* P 12½.
1361   20 g. orange, red, black and lilac   15   10
1362   30 g. black and carmine   15   10
1363   40 g. yellow-ochre, black and lilac   20   10
1364   50 g. yellow-ochre, black and blue   35   10
1365   60 g. black and light blue   35   10
1366   1 z. black and yellow-green   90   30
1367   2 z. 50, brown, yellow and black   1·40   40

1368	3 z. 40, black and vermilion		3·00	1·40
1369	6 z. 50, black and greenish yellow		6·00	3·75
1361/1369	Set of 9		11·00	5·75

Dogs: *Horiz*—30 g. Sheep-dog; 40 g. Boxer, 2 z. 50, Gun-dog "Ogar"; 6 z. 50. Great Dane. *Vert*—50 g. Airedale terrier; 60 g. French bulldog; 1 z. French poodle; 3 z. 40, Podhale sheep-dog.

(Des S. Malecki. Eng Z. Kowalski (5 g., 1 z. 15), A. Szklarczyk (10 g., 60 g.), J. Miller (20 g.), B. Kowalska (30 g., 40 g.), E. Tirdiszek (1 z.). Recess and photo)

1963 (5 Apr). *Sailing Ships* (1st series). *Horiz designs as* T **421**. P 11½×12.

1370	5 g. red-brown/*light bistre*		10	10
1371	10 g. deep bluish green/*light green*		15	10
1372	20 g. ultramarine/*light violet*		15	10
1373	30 g. black/*yellow-olive*		20	10
1374	40 g. blue/*light blue*		20	10
1375	60 g. purple/*light grey-brown*		35	10
1376	1 z. black/*light blue*		40	10
1377	1 z. 15, green/*light pink*		65	10
1370/1377	Set of 8		2·00	60

Ships:—10 g. Phoenician merchantman (15th cent. B.C.); 20 g. Greek trireme (5th cent. B.C.); 30 g. Roman merchantman (3rd cent. A.D.); 40 g. *Mora* (Norman ship, 1066); 60 g. Hanse kogge (14th cent.); 1 z. Hulk (16th cent.); 1 z. 15, Carrack (15th cent.).
See also Nos. 1451/66.

422 Insurgent

423 Centenary Emblem

(Des S. Jasiński. Eng J. Miller. Recess and photo)

1963 (19 Apr). 20*th Anniv of Warsaw Ghetto Uprising*. W **330**. P 11½×11.

1378	**422**	2 z. 50, deep purple-brown & pl bl	25	10

(Des F. Winiarski. Litho)

1963 (8 May). *Red Cross Centenary*. P 12½×12.

1379	**423**	2 z. 50, red, blue & greenish yellow	60	20
	a. Tête-bêche (pair)		2·25	1·50

No. 1379 is arranged in sheets with alternate horizontal rows inverted.

424 Lizard

425 Epée, Foil, Sabre and Knight's Helmet

(Des J. Desselberger. Photo)

1963 (10 June). *Protected Reptiles and Amphibians*. T **424** *and similar designs. Reptiles in natural colours; inscriptions and values black; background colours given.* P 11½.

1380	30 g. grey-green		10	10
1381	40 g. olive		10	10
1382	50 g. light brown		15	10
1383	60 g. drab		15	10
1384	90 g. myrtle		15	10
1385	1 z. 15, grey		20	10
1386	1 z. 35, grey-blue		20	10
1387	1 z. 50, turquoise-green		45	20
1388	1 z. 55, pale grey-blue		40	10
1389	2 z. 50, lavender		40	25
1390	3 z. myrtle-green		1·00	30
1391	3 z. 40, slate-purple		2·50	1·75
1380/1391	Set of 12		5·25	2·75

Reptiles:—40 g. Copperhead (snake); 50 g. Marsh tortoise; 60 g. Grass snake; 90 g. Blindworm; 1 z. 15, Tree toad; 1 z. 35, Mountain newt; 1 z. 50, Crested newt; 1 z. 55, Green toad; 2 z. 50, "Bombina" toad; 3 z. Salamander; 3 z. 40, "Natterjack" (toad).

(Des K. Tarkowska. Litho)

1963 (29 June). *World Fencing Championships, Gdańsk*. T **425** *and similar designs*. P 11×11½ (**MS**1397*a*), 13×12 (6 z. 50) or 12×13 (others).

1392	20 g. orange-yellow and red-brown		10	10
1393	40 g. light blue and blue		15	10
1394	60 g. light red and carmine-red		15	10
1395	1 z. 15, light green and green		20	10
1396	1 z. 55, reddish violet and violet		50	15
1397	6 z. 50, yell, brn-pur & lt bistre-brn		1·60	75
1392/1397	Set of 6		2·40	1·00
MS1397*a*	110×93 mm. Nos. 1393/6		40·00	40·00

Designs: *Horiz*—Fencers with background of: 40 g. Knights jousting; 60 g. Dragoons in sword-fight; 1 z. 15, 18th-century duellists; 1 z. 55, Old Gdansk. *Vert*—6 z. 50, Inscription, and Arms of Gdańsk.

(Des A. Heidrich. Litho)

1963 (20 July). *Famous Poles* (3rd series). *Portrait designs as* T **386**. W **330**. P 12×12½.

1398	60 g. black and brown-red		10	10
1399	60 g. black and sepia		10	10
1400	60 g. black and light greenish blue		35	10
1401	60 g. black and green		10	10
1398/1401	Set of 4		55	20

Portraits:—No. 1398, L. Waryński (patriot); 1399, L. Krzywicki (economist); 1400, M. Sklodowska-Curie (scientist); 1401, K. Świerczewski (patriot).

426 Bykovsky and "Vostok 5"

(Des T. Michaluk. Litho)

1963 (26 Aug). *Second "Team" Manned Space Flights*. T **426** *and similar horiz designs*. P 11.

1402	40 g. black, green and blue		15	10
1403	60 g. black, blue and bluish green		15	10
1404	6 z. 50, green, blue, black and red		1·10	45

Designs:—60 g. Tereshkova and "Vostok 6"; 6 z. 50, "Vostoks 5 and 6" in orbit.

427 Basketball

428 Missile

(Des T. Michaluk. Litho)

1963 (16 Sept). 13*th European (Men's) Basketball Championships, Wroclaw*. T **427** *and similar designs*. P 11½ or imperf (10 z.).

1405	40 g. green, brown black and yellow		10	10
1406	50 g. green, black and pink		10	10
1407	60 g. black, light green and red		10	10
1408	90 g. violet, red-brown, black & lt emer		10	10

1409	2 z. 50, black, orange, red-brn & cobalt	30	10
1410	5 z. 60, black, cream, lt green & blue	1·50	35
1405/1410	Set of 6	1·90	50
MS1410a	76×86 mm. 10 z. (+5 z.) multicoloured	2·25	1·10

Designs:—50 g. to 2 z. 50, As T **427** but with ball, players and hands in various positions; 5 z. 60, Hands placing ball in net; 10 z. Town Hall, People's Hall and Arms of Wroclaw.

(Des R. Dudzicki. Litho)

1963 (1 Oct). *20th Anniv of Polish People's Army. T* **428** *and similar horiz designs. Multicoloured. P* 12×12½.

1411	20 g. Type **428**	10	10
1412	40 g. *Blyskawica* (destroyer)	15	10
1413	60 g. PZL-106 Kruk (airplane)	15	10
1414	1 z. 15, Radar scanner	15	10
1415	1 z. 35, Tank	20	10
1416	1 z. 55, Missile carrier	30	10
1417	2 z. 50, Amphibious troop carrier	40	10
1418	3 z. Ancient warrior, modern soldier and two swords	50	30
1411/1418	Set of 8	1·75	50

429 "A Love Letter" (after Czachorski)

(430)

(Des Cz. Kaczmarczyk. Eng E. Konecki. Recess)

1963 (9 Oct). *Stamp Day. P* 11½.

1419	**429** 60 g. red-brown	45	30

1963 (23 Oct). *Visit of Soviet Cosmonauts to Poland. Nos. 1402/4 optd diagonally as T* **430**, *or horiz in small capitals at foot (6 z. 50).*

1420	40 g. black, green and blue (R.)	25	10
1421	60 g. black, blue and bluish green	40	10
1422	6 z. 50, green, blue, black and red	1·60	1·00

431 Tsiolkovsky's Rocket and Formula

432 Mazurian Horses

(Des J. Desselberger. Litho)

1963 (25 Nov). *"The Conquest of Space". T* **431** *and similar vert designs. P* 13×12.

1423	30 g. deep turquoise-green and black	10	10
1424	40 g. yellow-olive and black	10	10
1425	50 g. violet-blue and black	10	10
1426	60 g. orange-brown and black	10	10
1427	1 z. blue-green and black	10	10
1428	1 z. 50, brown-red and black	15	10
1429	1 z. 55, blue and black	15	10
1430	2 z. 50, purple and black	30	10
1431	5 z. 60, yellow-green and black	90	25
1432	6 z. 50, turquoise-blue and black	1·50	40
1423/1432	Set of 10	3·00	95
MS1432a	78×106 mm. Nos. 1431/2 (two of each)	42·00	42·00

Designs:—40 g. "Sputnik 1"; 50 g. "Explorer 1"; 60 g. Banner carried by "Lunik 2"; 1 z. "Lunik 3"; 1 z. 50, "Vostok 1"; 1 z. 55, "Friendship 7"; 2 z. 50, "Vostoks 3 and 4"; 5 z. 60, "Mariner 2"; 6 z. 50, "Mars 1".

(Des L. Maciag. Photo)

1963 (31 Dec). *Polish Horse-breeding. Designs as T* **432**. *Multicoloured. P* 11½×11 (20, 30, 40 g.), 12½×12 (50, 90 g., 4 z.) *or* 13×12 (*others*).

1433	20 g. Arab stallion "Comet"	10	10
1434	30 g. Wild horses	10	10
1435	40 g. Sokolski horse	15	10
1436	50 g. Arab mares and foals	15	10
1437	60 g. Type **432**	15	10
1438	90 g. Steeplechasers	25	10
1439	1 z. 55, Arab stallion "Witez II"	50	15
1440	2 z. 50, Head of Arab horse (facing right)	95	15
1441	4 z. Mixed breeds	2·25	55
1442	6 z. 50, Head of Arab horse (facing left)	3·25	2·00
1433/1442	Set of 10	7·00	3·00

Sizes:—*Triangular* (55×27½ mm.), 20 g., 30 g., 40 g. *Horiz* (75×26 mm.), 50 g., 90 g., 4 z. *Vert as T* **432**, 60 g., 1 z. 55, 2 z. 50, 6 z. 50.

433 Ice Hockey

434 "Flourishing Tree"

(Des F. Winiarski. Litho)

1964 (25 Jan). *Winter Olympic Games, Innsbruck. Horiz designs as T* **433**. *Multicoloured. P* 12×13 *or* 11×11½ (*No.* **MS**1450a).

1443	20 g. Type **433**	10	10
1444	30 g. Slalom	10	10
1445	40 g. Downhill skiing	10	10
1446	60 g. Speed skating	10	10
1447	1 z. Ski-jumping	20	10
1448	2 z. 50, Tobogganing	50	10
1449	5 z. 60, Cross-country skiing	90	25
1450	6 z. 50, Pairs, figure-skating	1·90	70
1443/1450	Set of 8	3·50	1·00
MS1450a	110×94 mm. Nos. 1448 and 1450 (two of each)	32·00	32·00

(Des S. Malecki 5 g. to 1 z. 15 eng as Nos. 1370/7; others eng E. Konecki (1 z. 35, 3 z. 40), E. Tirdiszek (1 z. 50), A. Szklarczyk (1 z. 55), Z. Kowalski (2 z., 2 z. 50), J. Miller (2 z. 10), B. Kowalska (3 z.). Recess)

1964 (19 Mar)–**65**. *Sailing Ships (2nd series). Designs as T* **421** *but without coloured backgrounds. P* 12½×13 (*vert*) *or* 13×12½ (*horiz*).

1451	5 g. reddish brown (25.1.65)	10	10
1452	10 g. deep dull green (25.1.65)	10	10
1453	20 g. slate-blue (25.1.65)	15	10
	a. Perf 11½×12	15	10
1454	30 g. bronze green (25.1.65)	20	10
1455	40 g. grey-blue (25.1.65)	20	10
1456	60 g. deep claret (25.1.65)	20	10
	a. Perf 11½×12	20	10
1457	1 z. chestnut (25.1.65)	40	10
	a. Perf 11½×12	40	10
1458	1 z. 15, red-brown (25.1.65)	40	10
1459	1 z. 35, blue	40	10
1460	1 z. 50, maroon	40	10
1461	1 z. 55, black	40	10
	a. Perf 12×11½	40	10
1462	2 z. deep reddish violet	40	10
1463	2 z. 10, blue-green	40	10
	a. Perf 11½×12	40	10
1464	2 z. 50, magenta	45	10
1465	3 z. deep olive	70	10
	a. Perf 11½×12	70	10
1466	3 z. 40, brown	1·00	10
1451/1466	Set of 16	5·50	1·10

Ships: *Horiz*—5 g. to 1 z. 15, As Nos. 1370/7; 1 z. 50, *Ark Royal* (English galleon, 1587); 2 z. 10, Ship of the line (18th cent.); 2 z. 50, Sail frigate (19th cent.); 3 z. *Flying Cloud* (clipper, 19th cent.). *Vert*—1 z. 35, *Santa Maria* (Columbus's ship); 1 z. 55, *Wodnik* (17th-century Polish warship); 2 z. Dutch fleute (17th cent.); 3 z. 40, *Dar Pomorza* (cadet ship).

(Des A. Heidrich. Litho)

1964 (15 Apr). *20th Anniv of People's Republic (1st issue).*
T **434** *and similar horiz design.* P 12×12½.
1467　60 g. red, ochre, blue, blk & grn (T **434**)　10　10
1468　60 g. black, orange-yellow and red　.. 　10　10
　Design:—No. 1468, Emblem composed of symbols of
agriculture and industry.
　See also Nos. 1497/1506.

435 European Cat　**436** Casimir the Great
　　　　　　　　　　　　　(founder)

(Des J. Grabianski. Litho)

1964 (30 Apr). *Domestic Cats. T* **435** *and similar designs.*
P 12½.
1469　30 g. black and greenish yellow　.. 　20　10
1470　40 g. light grey-green, pink, blk & orge　20　10
1471　50 g. black, turquoise-green and yellow　20　10
1472　60 g. multicoloured　.. 　.. 　.. 　40　10
1473　90 g. multicoloured　.. 　.. 　.. 　30　10
1474　1 z. 35, yell-ochre, yell-orge, blk & emer　30　10
1475　1 z. 55, sepia, lt blue, black & ultram　60　10
1476　2 z. 50, greenish yellow, black & violet　90　50
1477　3 z. 40, grey-violet, orge, blk & rose-car　2·00　1·00
1478　6 z. 50, black, yell-grn, cerise & vio　4·00　1·75
1469/1478　*Set of 10*　.. 　.. 　.. 　8·00　3·50
　Cats: *Vert* (European)—40 g., 2 z. 50, 6 z. 50. (Siamese)—
50 g. (Persian)—3 z. 40. *Horiz* (European)—60 g., 1 z. 55.
(Persian)—90 g. 1 z. 35.

(Des S. Malecki. Eng E. Tirdiszek (1479), J. Miller (1480),
E. Konecki (1481), Z. Kowalski (1482), B. Kowalska (1483).
Recess)

1964 (5 May). *600th Anniv of Jagiellonian University, Cracow.*
T **436** *and similar designs. P* 11½ (2 z. 50) or 11×11½
(others).
1479　40 g. purple (T **436**)　.. 　.. 　.. 　10　10
1480　40 g. deep green　.. 　.. 　.. 　10　10
1481　60 g. violet ·　.. 　.. 　.. 　10　10
1482　60 g. deep violet-blue　.. 　.. 　10　10
1483　2 z. 50, sepia　.. 　.. 　.. 　60　15
1479/1483　*Set of 5* .. 　.. 　.. 　80　35
　Portraits:—No. 1480, Hugo Kollataj (educationist and
politician); No. 1481, Jan Dlugosz (geographer and historian); No.
1482, Copernicus (astronomer); No. 1483, (36×37 *mm.*), King
Wladyslaw Jagiello and Queen Jadwiga.

437 Lapwing (*Vanellus vanellus*)

(Des J. Desselberger. Photo)

1964 (5 June). *Birds. Designs as T* **437**. *Multicoloured.*
P 11½.
1484　30 g. Type **437** .. 　.. 　.. 　15　10
1485　40 g. Bluethroat (*Luscinia svecica*)　.. 　15　10
1486　50 g. Black-tailed godwit (*Limosa limosa*)　15　10
1487　60 g. Osprey (*Pandion haliaëtus*)　.. 　25　10
1488　90 g. Grey heron (*Ardea cinerea*)　.. 　35　10
1489　1 z. 35, Little gull (*Larus minutus*)　60　10
1490　1 z. 55, Common shoveler (*Spatula
　　　 clypeata*) .. 　.. 　.. 　60　15
1491　5 z. 60, Black-throated diver (*Gavia
　　　 arctica*) .. 　.. 　.. 　1·25　50
1492　6 z. 50, Great crested grebe (*Podiceps
　　　 cristatus*) .. 　.. 　.. 　1·75　70
1484/1492　*Set of 9*　.. 　.. 　4·75　1·60
　Nos. 1487/9 are vert (35×48 mm), the rest as T **437**.

438 Red Flag on Brick Wall

(Des A. Heidrich (1493), R. Dudzicki (others). Litho)

1964 (15 June). *Fourth Polish United Workers' Party Congress,
Warsaw. T* **438** *and similar horiz designs. Multicoloured.*
P 11.
1493　60 g. Type **438**　.. 　.. 　.. 　10　10
1494　60 g. Beribboned hammer　.. 　.. 　10　10
1495　60 g. Hands reaching for Red Flag　.. 　10　10
1496　60 g. Hammer and corn emblems　.. 　10　10
1493/1496　*Set of 4*　.. 　.. 　.. 　35　20

439 Factory　　　　　　　　　**440** Gdańsk Shipyard
and Cogwheel

(Des T. Michaluk. Photo (1497/1500). Des S. Malecki
(others). Eng E. Tirdiszek (1501), J. Miller (1502), B.
Kowalska (1503), Z. Kowalski (1504). E. Konecki (1505/6).
Recess and photo)

1964 (21 July). *20th Anniv of People's Republic (2nd issue).
Various designs. P* 11.

(*a*) *As T* **439**
1497　60 g. black and blue (T **439**) .. 　.. 　10　10
1498　60 g. black and green　.. 　.. 　10　10
1499　60 g. red and orange　.. 　.. 　10　10
1500　60 g. ultramarine and grey　.. 　10　10
　Designs: *Vert*—No. 1498, Tractor and ear of wheat; No.
1499, Mask and symbols of the arts; No. 1500, Atomic symbol
and book.

(*b*) *As T* **440**
1501　60 g. ultramarine and turquoise-green .. 　10　10
1502　60 g. reddish violet and magenta　.. 　10　10
1503　60 g. sepia and slate-violet　.. 　10　10
1504　60 g. bronze-green and green .. 　.. 　10　10
1505　60 g. reddish purple and salmon-red　.. 　10　10
1506　60 g. sepia and olive-yellow　.. 　10　10
1497/1506　*Set of 10*　.. 　.. 　90　40
　Designs: *Horiz*—No. 1501, T **440**; 1502, Lenin Foundry,
Nowa Huta; 1503, Cement works, Chelm; 1504, Turoszow
power station; 1505, Petro-chemical plant, Plock; 1505,
Tarnobrzeg sulphur mine.

441 Battle Scene   **442** Relay-racing

(Des R. Dudzicki. Litho)

1964 (1 Aug). *20th Anniv of Warsaw Insurrection.* P 12½×12.
1507 **441** 60 g. multicoloured 15 10

(Des J. Korolkiewicz and J. Jaworowski (**MS**1515*b*). Litho)

1964. *Olympic Games, Tokyo. (a) T* **442** *and similar designs.*
Multicoloured. P 11×11½ (5 z. 60, 6 z. 50) *or* 11½ (*others*)
(25 Aug)

1508	20 g. Triple-jumping ..	10	10
1509	40 g. Rowing ..	10	10
1510	60 g. Weightlifting	10	10
1511	90 g. Type **442**	10	10
1512	1 z. Boxing ..	15	10
1513	2 z. 50, Football	35	10
1514	5 z. 60, Highjumping (women)	1·00	40
1515	6 z. 50, High-diving ..	1·50	75
1508/1515	*Set of 8* ..	3·00	1·25

MS1515*a* 83×111 mm. Nos. 1514/5 (two of
each) (31 Aug) .. .. 42·00 26·00
Sizes: *Diamond*—20 g. to 60 g.; *Square*—90 g. to 2 z. 50;
Vert (23½×36 mm.) 5 z. 60, 6 z. 50.

(*b*) *Sheet* 79×106 *mm. containing four diamond-shaped*
stamps. Multicoloured. Imperf (31 Aug)
MS1515*b* 2 z. 50, Rifle-shooting
2 z. 50, Canoeing
5 z. Fencing
5 z. Basketball }3·75 1·40

443 Congress   **444** Hand holding   **445** S. Zeromski
Emblem   Hammer

(Des T. Michaluk. Litho)

1964 (7 Sept). *15th International Astronautical Congress,*
Warsaw. P 13×12.
1516 **443** 2 z. 50, black and bright violet .. 40 15

(Des F. Winiarski. Litho)

1964 (21 Sept). *Third Congress of Fighters for Freedom and*
Democracy Association, Warsaw. P 11×11½.
1517 **444** 60 g. red, black and blue-green .. 10 10

ALBUM LISTS

Write for our latest lists of albums
and accessories.
These will be sent free on request.

(Des M. Zeromska. Photo)

1964 (21 Sept). *Birth Centenary of Stefan Żeromski (writer).*
P 12½×13.
1518 **445** 60 g. olive-brown 10 10

446 Globe and   **447** 18th-Century Stage Coach
Red Flag   (after J. Brodowski)

(Des J. Desselberger. Photo)

1964 (28 Sept). *Centenary of "First International".* P 12½.
1519 **446** 60 g. black and orange-red .. 10 10

(Des A. Heidrich. Eng B. Kowalska. Recess)

1964 (9 Oct). *Stamp Day.* P 11½.
1520 **447** 60 g. green 20 10
1521 60 g. bistre-brown 20 10

448 Eleanor   **449** Battle of Studzianki
Roosevelt   (after S. Zoltowski)

(Des A. Heidrich. Eng E. Konecki. Recess)

1964 (10 Oct). *80th Birth Anniv of Eleanor Roosevelt.*
P 12½×13.
1522 **448** 2 z. 50, sepia 25 10

(Des S. Malecki. Eng J. Miller (1523), E. Konecki (1524),
E. Tirdiszek (1525, 1527), Z. Kowalski (1526). Recess)

1964 (16 Nov). *"Poland's Struggle" (World War II) (1st issue).*
T **449** *and similar designs.* P 11×11½ (*horiz*) *or* 11½×11
(*vert*)

1523	40 g. black ..	10	10
1524	40 g. slate-violet ..	10	10
1525	60 g. deep blue	15	10
1526	60 g. deep bluish green	15	10
1527	60 g. bronze-green (T **449**)	15	10
1523/1527	*Set of 5* ..	60	20

Designs: *Vert*—No. 1523, Virtuti Militari Cross; 1524,
Westerplatte Memorial, Gdańsk; 1525, Bydgoszcz Memorial.
Horiz—1526. Soldiers crossing the Oder (after S. Zoltowski).
Printed in sheets of 50 stamps and 20 inscribed labels or 56
stamps and 14 labels.
See also Nos. 1610/12.

449*a* W. Komarov   **450** Cyclamen

(Des A. Heidrich. Litho)

1964 (20 Nov). *Russian Three-manned Space Flight. Sheet 114×63 mm. depicting crew. P* 11½.
MS1527a 60 g. black and red (T **449***a*)
    60 g. black & green (Feoktistov) } 1·00   60
    60 g. black and blue (Yegorov)

(Des A. Balcerzak. Photo)

1964 (30 Nov). *Garden Flowers. T* **450** *and similar designs. Multicoloured. P* 11½ (20 *g. to* 90 *g.*) *or* 13×12 (*others*).
1528	20 g. Type **450**	10	10
1529	30 g. Freesia	10	10
1530	40 g. Rose	10	10
1531	50 g. Peony	10	10
1532	60 g. Lily	10	10
1533	90 g. Poppy	15	10
1534	1 z. 35, Tulip	15	10
1535	1 z. 50, Narcissus	65	25
1536	1 z. 55, Begonia	25	10
1537	2 z. 50, Carnation	60	15
1538	3 z. 40, Iris	90	30
1539	5 z. 60, Japanese camelia	1·50	70
1528/1539	*Set of* 12	4·25	1·75

Sizes: *As T* **450**—20 g. to 90 g.; *Vert* (26½×37 *mm.*)— others.

451 Spacecraft of the Future

452 "Siren" of Warsaw

(Des T. Michaluk. Litho)

1964 (30 Dec). *Space Research. T* **451** *and similar designs. Multicoloured. P* 13×12.
1540	20 g. Type **451**	10	10
1541	30 g. Launching rocket	10	10
1542	40 g. Dog "Laika" and rocket	10	10
1543	60 g. "Lunik 3" and Moon	10	10
1544	1 z. 55, Satellite	20	10
1545	2 z. 50, "Elektron 2"	50	10
1546	5 z. 60, "Mars I"	1·25	50
1547	6 z. 50+2 z. Gagarin seated in capsule	1·75	85
1540/1547	*Set of* 8	3·50	1·50

(Des T. Michaluk. Eng E. Konecki. Recess)

1965 (15 Jan). *20th Anniv of Liberation of Warsaw. P* 11×11½.
1548 **452** 60 g. grey-green 10   10

453 Edaphosaurus

(Des A. Heidrich. Litho)

1965 (5 Mar). *Prehistoric Animals* (1st series). *T* **453** *and similar designs. Multicoloured. P* 12½.
1549	20 g. Type **453**	15	10
1550	30 g. Cryptocleidus	15	10
1551	40 g. Brontosaurus	15	10
1552	60 g. Mesosaurus	15	10
1553	90 g. Stegosaurus	15	10
1554	1 z. 15, Brachiosaurus	20	10

1555	1 z. 35, Styracosaurus	25	10
1556	3 z. 40, Corythosaurus	70	20
1557	5 z. 60, Rhamphorhynchus	1·75	50
1558	6 z. 50, Tyrannosaurus	2·50	60
1549/1558	*Set of* 10	5·50	1·40

The 30 g., 60 g., 1 z. 15, 3 z. 40 and 5 z. 60 are vert designs, the rest horiz.
See also Nos. 1639/47.

454 Petro-chemical Works, Plock, and Polish and Soviet Flags

(Des S. Malecki. Litho)

1965 (21 Apr). *20th Anniv of Polish-Soviet Friendship Treaty. T* **454** *and similar design. P* 13×12 (*No.* 1559) *or* 13×12½ (*No.* 1560).
1559	60 g. carmine, black, yellow & grey-grn	10	10
1560	60 g. black, carmine, red & yellow-olive	10	10

Design: *Vert* (27×38½ *mm.*)—No. 1559, Seal.

455 Polish Eagle and Civic Arms

456 Dove of Peace

(Des T. Michaluk. Eng E. Konecki. Recess)

1965 (8 May). *20th Anniv of Return of Western and Northern Territories to Poland. P* 11½.
1561 **455** 60 g. carmine-red 10   10

(Des S. Jasiński. Litho)

1965 (8 May). *20th Anniv of Victory. P* 12×12½.
1562 **456** 60 g. red and black 10   10

457 I.T.U. Emblem

458 Clover-leaf Emblem and *The Friend of the People* (journal)

(Des S. Malecki. Litho)

1965 (17 May). *Centenary of International Telecommunications Union. P* 13×12.
1563 **457** 2 z. 50, black, reddish violet & new bl   45   15

(Des A. Kalczyńska. Litho)

1965 (5 June). *70th Anniv of Peasant Movement. T* **458** *and similar design. P* 11×11½ (40 *g.*) *or* 11½×11 (60 *g.*).
1564	40 g. green, black, drab & lt bluish violet	10	10
1565	60 g. yell-orge, ultram, blk & bluish grn	10	10

Design: *Horiz*—60 g. Ears of corn and industrial plant.

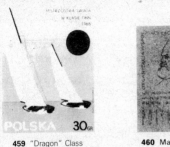

459 "Dragon" Class
Yachts

460 Marx and Lenin

(Des J. Jaworowski and R. Dudzicki (15 z.). Litho)

1965 (14 June). *World Finn Class Sailing Championships, Gdynia. T 459 and similar designs. Multicoloured. P 12½ or 11 (15 z.).*

1566	30 g. Type **459**	..	..	10	10
1567	40 g. "5.5 m." class	..	..	10	10
1568	50 g. "Finn" class	..	..	15	10
1569	60 g. "V" class	..	..	15	10
1570	1 z. 35, "Cadet" class	..	..	20	10
1571	4 z. "Star" class	..	..	90	30
1572	5 z. 60, "Flying Dutchman" class	..	1·50	60
1573	6 z. 50, "Amethyst" Class	..	2·25	75
1566/1573	*Set of 8*	..	..	4·75	1·75
MS1573a	79×59 mm. 15 z. "Finn" class		2·00	1·25

The 50 g., 1 z. 35, 4 z. and 6 z. 50 are horiz.

(Des J. Desselberger. Eng E. Konecki. Recess and photo)

1965 (14 June). *Postal Ministers' Congress, Peking. P 11½×11.*

1574	**460**	60 g. black/red	..	15	10

461 17th-Century
Arms of Warsaw

462 "Nike" Memorial and
Old Warsaw Seal

(Des Cz. Kaczmarczyk. Eng E. Konecki (5 g.), B. Kowalska (10 g., 2 z. 50), E. Tirdiszek (20 g., 60 g.), J. Miller (40 g., 1 z. 55), Z. Kowalski (1 z. 50). Recess. Des S. Malecki. Eng E. Konecki (3 z. 40). Recess and photo)

1965 (21 July). *700th Anniv of Warsaw. T 461 and similar designs and T 462. P 11½×12 (5, 10 g.) or 12×11½ (others).*

1575	5 g. carmine	..	..	10	10
	a. Perf 12×12½			10	10
1576	10 g. myrtle green	..	..	10	10
	a. Perf 12×12½			10	10
1577	20 g. deep blue	..	..	10	10
	a. Perf 12½×12			10	10
1578	40 g. red-brown	..	..	10	10
	a. Perf 12½×12			10	10

1579	60 g. orange-red	..	..	..	10	10
	a. Perf 12½×12				10	10
1580	1 z. 50, black ..	..	..	..	15	10
	a. Perf 12½×12				15	10
1581	1 z. 55, greenish blue	..		20	10
	a. Perf 12½×12				20	10
1582	2 z. 50, reddish purple	..		35	10
	a. Perf 12½×12				35	10
1575/1582	*Set of 8*	..	..	..	90	30
MS1583	51×62 mm. 3 z. 40, black and bistre	90	55

Designs: *Vert*—10 g. 13th-century antiquities. *Horiz*—20 g. Tombstone of last Masovian dukes; 40 g. Old Town Hall; 60 g. Barbican; 1 z. 50, Arsenal; 1 z. 55, National Theatre; 2 z. 50, Staszic Palace; 3 z. 40, T **462.**

463 I.Q.S.Y.
Emblem

464 *Odontoglossum
grande*

(Des T. Michaluk. Litho)

1965 (9 Aug). *International Quiet Sun Year. T 463 and similar designs. Multicoloured; background colours given. P 11½.*

1584	60 g. ultramarine	..	..	10	10
1585	60 g. bluish violet	..	..	10	10
1586	2 z. 50, red	..	..	35	10
1587	2 z. 50, brown-red	..	..	35	10
1588	3 z. 40, orange	..	..	45	20
1589	3 z. 40, greyish olive	..	..	45	20
1584/1589	*Set of 6* ..	..	..	1·60	55

Designs:—2 z. 50, Solar scanner; 3 z. 40, Solar System.

(Des G. Dokalski. Photo)

1965 (6 Sept). *Orchids. T 464 and similar vert designs. Multicoloured. P 13×12.*

1590	20 g. Type **464**	..	..	15	10
1591	30 g. *Cypripedium hibridum*	..	15	10
1592	40 g. *Lycaste skinneri*	..	15	10
1593	50 g. *Cattleya warszewicza*	..	15	10
1594	60 g. *Vanda sanderiana*	..	15	10
1595	1 z. 35, *Cypripedium hibridum*	..	40	10
1596	4 z. *Sobralia*	..	..	70	35
1597	5 z. 60, *Disa grandiflora*	..	1·75	50
1598	6 z. 50, *Cattleya labiata*	..	2·75	1·00
1590/1598	*Set of 9* ..	..	..	5·75	2·00

The 30 g. and 1 z. 35 are different designs.

465 Weightlifting

466 "The Post Coach"
(after P. Michalowski)

(Des S. Malecki. Photo)

1965 (8 Oct). *Olympic Games, Tokyo. Polish Medal Winners.*
T **465** *and similar vert designs. Multicoloured with backgrounds*
of bronze (7 z. 10), silver (50 g., 90 g.) or gold (others), according
to medals. P 13×12.

1599	30 g. Type **465**		..	10	10
1600	40 g. Boxing	..	..	10	10
1601	50 g. Relay-racing	..	..	10	10
1602	60 g. Fencing	..	..	10	10
1603	90 g. Hurdling (women's 80-m.)			10	10
1604	3 z. 40, Relay-racing (women's)			50	10
1605	6 z. 50, "Hop, step and jump"			90	60
1606	7 z. 10, Volleyball (women's)			1·10	50
1599/1606	*Set of 8* ..		..	2·50	1·40

Nos. 1599/1606 were each issued in sheets of 8, two panes
of 4 being divided by 2 *se-tenant* labels showing the reverse
and obverse of the medals.

(Des A. Balcerzak. Eng B. Kowalska (60 g.), E. Tirdiszek
(2 z. 50). Recess)

1965 (9 Oct). *Stamp Day. T* **466** *and similar horiz design.*
P 11×11½.

1607	60 g. brown	..	..	15	10
1608	2 z. 50, bronze-green	..	..	25	10

Design:—2 z. 50, "Coach about to leave" (after P. Michalowski). Nos. 1607/8 were each in sheets of 50 with attached
se-tenant labels inscr "DZIEN ZNACZKA 1965 R.".

467 U.N. Emblem

468 Memorial, Holy
Cross Mountains

(Des A. Kalczyńska. Litho)

1965 (24 Oct). *20th Anniv of U.N.O. P* 13×12.
1609	**467**	2 z. 50, bright blue	..	..	30	10

(Des S. Malecki. Eng E. Tirdiszek (1610), B. Kowalska (1611),
J. Miller (1612). Recess)

1965 (29 Nov). *"Poland's Struggle" (World War II) (2nd*
issue). T **468** *and similar designs. P* 11×11½ *(No.* 1612) *or*
11½×11 *(others).*

1610	**468**	60 g. deep brown ..	..	..	15	10
1611	—	60 g. bronze-green	..	..	15	10
1612	—	60 g. blackish brown	..	..	15	10

Designs: *Vert*—No. 1611, Memorial, Plaszow. *Horiz*—1612,
Memorial, Chelm-on-Ner.

Nos. 1610/11 were each printed in sheets of 56 stamps and
14 inscribed labels, and No. 1612 in sheets of 50 stamps and
20 labels.

469 Wolf

(Des J. Desselberger. Photo)

1965 (30 Nov). *Forest Animals. T* **469** *and similar designs.*
Multicoloured. P 11½.

1613	20 g. Type **469**	..	..	10	10
1614	30 g. Lynx	..	..	10	10
1615	40 g. Red fox	..	..	10	10
1616	50 g. Eurasian badger	..	..	10	10
1617	60 g. Brown bear	..	..	10	10
1618	1 z. 50, Wild boar	..	..	70	10
1619	2 z. 50, Red deer	..	..	70	15
1620	5 z. 60, European bison	..		1·60	45
1621	7 z. 10, Elk	..	..	2·50	1·00
1613/1621	*Set of 9* ..		..	5·25	1·90

470 Gig

(Des J. Miller. Litho)

1965 (30 Dec). *Horse-drawn Carriages in Lancut Museum.*
T **470** *and similar horiz designs. Multicoloured. P* 11.

1622	20 g. Type **470**	..	..	10	10
1623	40 g. Coupe	..	..	10	10
1624	50 g. Ladies' "basket" (trap)		..	10	10
1625	60 g. "Vis-à-vis"	..	..	10	10
1626	90 g. Cab	..	..	15	10
1627	1 z. 15, Berlinka	..	..	20	10
1628	2 z. 50, Hunting brake	..	..	50	10
1629	6 z. 50, Barouche	..	..	1·40	45
1630	7 z. 10, English brake	..	..	2·00	1·00
1622/1630	*Set of 9* ..		..	4·25	1·75

Nos. 1627/9 are 77×22 mm. and No. 1630 is 104×22 mm.

471 Congress Emblem and Industrial Products

(Des A. Heidrich. Litho)

1966 (11 Feb). *Fifth Polish Technicians Congress. Katowice.*
P 11.
1631	**471**	60 g. multicoloured	..	..	15	10

No. 1631 has *se-tenant* commemorative label.

(Des A. Heidrich. Litho)

1966 (10 Feb–21 May). *Twentieth Anniv of Industrial*
Nationalisation. Designs similar to T **471***. Multicoloured.*
P 11.

1632	60 g. Pithead gear (10.2)	..	..	15	10
1633	60 g. Freighter ..	..	..	15	10
1634	60 g. Petro-chemical works, Plock	..	15	10
1635	60 g. Combine-harvester	..	..	15	10
1636	60 g. Electric train	..	..	20	10
1637	60 g. Exhibition Hall, 35th Poznan Fair		15	10
1638	60 g. Crane	..	..	15	10
1632/1638	*Set of 7* ..		..	90	40

Nos. 1632 and 1638 are vertical. Each stamp has *se-tenant*
commemorative label.

(Des A. Heidrich. Litho)

1966 (5 Mar). *Prehistoric Animals (2nd series). Designs as*
T **453**. *Multicoloured. P* 12½.

1639	20 g. Dinichthys	..	..	15	10
1640	30 g. Eusthenopteron	..	..	15	10
1641	40 g. Ichthyostega	..	..	15	10

1642	50 g. Mastodonsaurus..			15	10
1643	60 g. Cynognathus	..	..	25	10
1644	2 z. 50, Archaeopteryx	..	..	40	10
1645	3 z. 40, Brontotherium		..	60	10
1646	6 z. 50, Machairodus		..	95	50
1647	7 z. 10, Mammuthus..		..	2·00	95
1639/1647	*Set of 9* ..		..	4·25	1·75

The 2 z. 50 is vertical and the rest are horizontal designs.

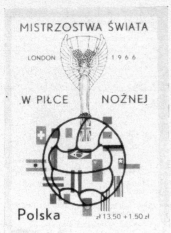

472 H. Sienkiewicz (novelist)

473 Footballers (Montevideo, 1930)

(Des T. Michaluk. Eng E. Tirdiszek. Recess)

1966 (30 Mar). *50th Death Anniv of Henryk Sienkiewicz.*
P 11½ × 11.

1648	**472**	60 g. blackish brown/*light buff*	15	10

(Des J. Jaworowski. Litho)

1966 (6 May). *World Cup Football Championship.* (a) *T* **473** *and similar vert designs showing football scenes representing World Cup finals.* Multicoloured. *P* 13 × 12.

1649	20 g. Type **473**		..	10	10
1650	40 g. Rome, 1934		..	10	10
1651	60 g. Paris, 1938		..	10	10
1652	90 g. Rio de Janeiro, 1950		..	10	10
1653	1 z. 50, Berne, 1954		..	65	15
1654	3 z. 40, Stockholm, 1958		..	65	15
1655	6 z. 50, Santiago, 1962		..	1·25	65
1656	7 z. 10, "London", 1966 (elimination match Glasgow 1965)		..	1·75	1·25
1649/1656	*Set of 8* ..		..	4·25	2·25

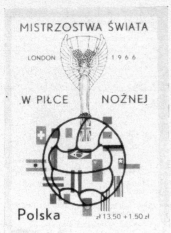

474 Jules Rimet Cup, Flags and Football

(*b*) *Sheet* 61 × 81 *mm.* Litho. Multicoloured. *Imperf*

MS1657	**474**	13 z. 50 + 1 z. 50	..	2·75	1·40

POLSKA 60

DZIEŃ ZWYCIĘSTWA
9.V.1945

475 Soldier with Flag and Dove of Peace

476 Women's Relay-racing

477 Long-distance Running

(Des T. Michaluk. Eng E. Konecki. Typo, litho and recess)

1966 (9 May). *21st Anniv of Victory Day. P* 11 × 11½.

1658	**475**	60 g. red and black/*silver*	..	..	10	10

(Des S. Malecki. Litho)

1966 (18 June). *Eighth European Athletic Championships, Budapest. T* **476** *and similar designs.* Multicoloured. *P* 11½ × 11 (*vert*) or 11 × 11½ (*horiz*).

1659	20 g. Runner starting race		..	10	10
1660	40 g. Type **476**		..	10	10
1661	60 g. Throwing the javelin		..	10	10
1662	90 g. Women's hurdles		..	10	10
1663	1 z. 35, Throwing the discus..		..	15	10
1664	3 z. 40, Finish of race		..	55	10
1665	6 z. 50, Throwing the hammer		..	95	35
1666	7 z. 10, High-jumping		..	1·25	60
1659/1666	*Set of 8* ..		..	3·00	1·10
MS1667	**477**	110 × 66 mm. 5 z. Imperf		1·50	80

The 20 g., 60 g., 1 z. 35 and 6 z. 50 are vert.

478 White Eagle

479 Flowers and Produce

(Des F. Winiarski. Photo and embossed)

1966 (21 July). *Polish Millenary* (1*st issue*). *Each printed in red and black on gold. P* 12½ × 12.

1668	60 g. Type **478**		..	10	10
	a. Pair. Nos. 1668/9	..	..	20	15
1669	60 g. Polish flag		..	10	10
1670	2 z. 50, Type **478**	..	..	30	15
	a. Pair. Nos. 1670/1	..	..	60	30

179

1671   2 z. 50, Polish flag   30   15
1668/71   *Set of 4*   70   40
  Nos. 1668/9 and 1670/1 were issued respectively in *se-tenant* pairs within sheets of 10 stamps.
  See also Nos. 1717/18.

(Des H. Matuszewska. Photo)

1966 (15 Aug). *Harvest Festival. T* **479** *and similar designs. Multicoloured. P* 11.
1672   40 g. Type **479**   25   10
1673   60 g. Woman and loaf   25   10
    a. Silver (value and bottom inscr) omitted
1674   3 z. 40, Festival bouquet   65   30
  The 60 g. is vert as Type **479** and the 3 z. 40 is 49×48 mm.

480 Chrysanthemum

481 Tourist Map

(Des S. Malecki. Photo)

1966 (1 Sept). *Flowers. T* **480** *and similar designs. Multi-coloured. P* 11.
1675   10 g. Type **480**   10   10
1676   20 g. Poinsettia   10   10
1677   30 g. Centaury   10   10
1678   40 g. Rose   10   10
1679   60 g. Zinnia   10   10
1680   90 g. Nasturtium   15   10
1681   5 z. 60, Dahlia   90   35
1682   6 z. 50, Sunflower   ..   ..   1·25   45
1683   7 z. 10, Magnolia   ..   ..   2·00   50
1675/1683   *Set of 9*   ..   ..   4·00   1·50

(Des T. Michaluk. Eng J. Miller (10 g., 60 g.—No. 1688, 1 z. 35), B. Kowalska (20 g., 1 z. 15), Z. Kowalski (40 g., 2 z.), E. Tirdiszek (60 g.—No. 1687), B. Brandt (1 z. 55). Recess)

1966 (15 Sept). *Tourism. T* **481** *and similar horiz designs. A. Perf* 13×12. *B. Perf* 11×12.

			A		B	
1684	10 g. rose	.. ..	10	10	10	10
1685	20 g. drab	.. ..	10	10	10	10
1686	40 g. slate-blue	.. ..	10	10	10	10
1687	60 g. brown	.. ..	10	10	10	10
1688	60 g. black	.. ..	10	10	10	10
1689	1 z. 15, deep green	..	10	10	10	10
1690	1 z. 35, vermilion	..	20	10	20	10
1691	1 z. 55, dp reddish violet		20	10	20	10
1692	2 z. slate-green	..	40	10	40	10
1684/1692	*Set of 9*	..	1·00	40	1·00	40

  Designs:—20 g. Hela Lighthouse; 40 g. Yacht; 60 g. (No. 1687), Poniatowski Bridge, Warsaw; 60 g. (No. 1688), Mining Academy, Kielce; 1 z. 15, Dunajec Gorge; 1 z. 35, Old oaks, Rogalin; 1 z. 55, Silesian Planetarium; 2 z. *Batory* (liner).

482 Roman Capital

483 Stable-man with Percherons

(Des R. Dudzicki. Eng E. Tirdiszek. Recess and photo)

1966 (7 Oct). *Polish Culture Congress. P* 11.
1693 **482** 60 g. cerise and deep chocolate   10   10

(Des J. Miklaszewski (after paintings by P. Michalowski). Eng E. Konecki (60 g.), E. Tirdiszek (2 z. 50). Recess)

1966 (8 Oct). *Stamp Day. T* **483** *and similar horiz design. P* 11×12.
1694   60 g. sepia   15   10
1695   2 z. 50, myrtle-green   25   10
  Design:—2 z. 50, Stable-men with horses and dogs.

484 Soldier in Action

485 Woodland Birds

(Des A. Heidrich. Litho)

1966 (20 Oct). *30th Anniv of Jaroslav Dabrowski Brigade in Spain. P* 11×11.
1696 **484** 60 g. black, olive-green and red   ..   15   10

(Des T. Michaluk (10 g), J. Desselberger (others). Photo)

1966 (17 Nov). *Woodland Birds. T* **485** *and similar square designs. Multicoloured. P* 11.
1697   10 g. Type **485**   25   10
1698   20 g. Green woodpecker (*Picus viridis*)   ..   25   10
1699   30 g. Jay (*Garrulus glandarius*)   ..   30   10
1700   40 g. Golden oriole (*Oriolus oriolus*)   ..   30   10
1701   60 g. Hoopoe (*Upupa epops*)   ..   30   10
1702   2 z. 50,   Redstart   (*Phoenicurus phoenicurus*)   65   40
1703   4 z. Siskin (*Carduelis spinus*)   ..   2·25   50
1704   6 z. 50, Chaffinch (*Fringilla coelebs*)   ..   2·25   80
1705   7 z. 10, Great tit (*Parus major*)   ..   2·50   85
1697/1705   *Set of 9*   ..   ..   8·00   2·75
  Type **485** shows the species depicted on Nos. 1698/1705.

486 Ram (ritual statuette)

487 "Vostok 1"

(Des K. Tarkowska. Eng E. Konecki (1706), Z. Kowalski (1707), B. Kowalska (1708). Recess)

1966 (10 Dec). *Polish Archaeological Research. T* **486** *and similar designs. P* 11×11 (*No.* 1708) *or* 11×11 (*others*).
1706   60 g. slate-blue   15   10
1707   60 g. myrtle-green   15   10
1708   60 g. brown   15   10
  Designs: *Vert*—No. 1706, T **486**; 1707, Plan of Biskupin settlement. *Horiz*—1708, Brass implements and ornaments.

1966 (20 Dec). *Space Research. T **487** and similar vert designs showing spacecraft. Multicoloured. P 11½×11.*

1709	20 g. Type **487**	..	10	10
1710	40 g. "Gemini"	..	10	10
1711	60 g. "Ariel 2"	..	10	10
1712	1 z. 35, "Proton 1"	..	15	10
1713	1 z. 50, "FR 1"	..	25	10
1714	3 z. 40, "Alouette"	..	40	10
1715	6 z. 50, "San Marco 1"	..	1·25	25
1716	7 z. 10, "Luna 9"	..	1·50	40
1709/1716	Set of 8	..	3·25	90

488 Polish Eagle and Hammer

(Des S. Malecki. Litho)

1966 (20 Dec). *Polish Millenary (2nd issue). T **488** and similar horiz design. P 11.*

1717	40 g. purple-brown, lilac and light red	..	10	10
1718	60 g. purple-brown, sage-green & lt red		10	10

Design:—60 g. Polish eagle and agricultural and industrial symbols.

489 Dressage

(Des B. Kamiński. Photo)

1967 (25 Feb). *150th Anniv of Racehorse Breeding in Poland. T **489** and similar horiz designs. Multicoloured. P 12½.*

1719	10 g. Type **489**	..	20	10
1720	20 g. Cross-country racing	..	20	10
1721	40 g. Horse-jumping	..	20	10
1722	60 g. Jumping fence in open country	..	30	10
1723	90 g. Horse-trotting	..	35	10
1724	5 z. 90, Playing polo	..	1·00	20
1725	6 z. 60, Stallion "Ofir"	..	1·40	60
1726	7 z. 25, Stallion "Skowronek"	..	2·25	85
1719/1726	Set of 8	..	5·25	1·90

490 Striped Butterfly

491 Auschwitz Memorial

(Des J. Desselberger. Litho)

1967 (1 Apr). *Exotic Fishes. T **490** and similar horiz designs. Multicoloured. P 11×11½.*

1727	5 g. Type **490**	..	10	10
1728	10 g. Imperial Angelfish	..	10	10
1729	40 g. Banded Butterfly	..	10	10
1730	60 g. Spotted Triggerfish	..	10	10
1731	90 g. Undulate Triggerfish	..	15	10
1732	1 z. 50, Picasso Fish	..	25	10
1733	4 z. 50, Black Eyed Butterfly	..	80	30
1734	6 z. 60, Blue Angelfish	..	1·10	60
1735	7 z. Saddleback Butterfly	..	1·40	80
1727/1735	Set of 9	..	3·75	2·00

(Des K. Rogaczewska. Eng E. Tirdiszek (1736, 1738), B. Kowalska (1737). Recess)

1967 (10 Apr). *Polish Martyrdom and Resistance, 1939–45 (1st series). T **491** and similar designs. P 11½×11 (No. 1736) or 11×11½ (others).*

1736	**491**	40 g. olive-brown	10	10
1737	—	40 g. black	10	10
1738	—	40 g. deep reddish purple	10	10

Designs: *Vert*—No. 1737, Auschwitz-Monowitz Memorial; 1738, Memorial guide's emblem.
See also Nos. 1770/2, 1798/9, 1865/9.

492 Cyclists

(Des T. Michaluk. Litho)

1967 (2 May). *20th International Peace Cycle Race. P 11.*

1739	**492**	60 g. multicoloured	..	15	10

493 Running

494 Socialist Symbols

(Des F. Winiarski. Litho)

1967 (24 May). *Olympic Games (1968). T **493** and similar horiz designs. Multicoloured. P 11.*

1740	20 g. Type **493**	..	10	10
1741	40 g. Horse-jumping	..	10	10
1742	60 g. Relay-running	..	10	10
1743	90 g. Weightlifting	..	10	10
1744	1 z. 35, Hurdling	..	10	10
1745	3 z. 40, Gymnastics	..	45	15
1746	6 z. 60, High-jumping	..	60	25
1747	7 z. Boxing	..	1·10	65
1740/1747	Set of 8	..	2·25	1·00
MS1748	65×86 mm. 10 z.+5 z. mult Imperf	..	1·90	1·10

Design: *Diamond (30×30 mm.)*—10 z. Kusocinski winning 10,000 metres race at Olympic Games, Los Angeles, 1932.

The face value is expressed outside the "stamp" which has facsimile perforations. Nos. 1740/7 are each in sheets of eight (2×4) with intervening *se-tenant* labels showing the Olympic torch and rings.

(Des A. Heidrich. Litho)

1967 (2 June). *Polish Trade Unions Congress, Warsaw. P 11.*

1749	**494**	60 g. multicoloured	..	10	10

Issued with *se-tenant* label showing Congress emblem, both in sheets in 20 and sheets of four.

495 *Arnica montana*

496 Katowice Memorial

(Des A. Heidrich. Litho)

1967 (14 June). *Protected Plants. T* **495** *and similar vert designs. Multicoloured. P* 11½×11.

1750	40 g. Type **495**		10	10
1751	60 g. *Aquilegia vulgaris*		10	10
1752	3 z. 40, *Gentiana punctata*		40	10
1753	4 z. 50, *Lycopodium clavatum*		45	10
1754	5 z. *Iris sibirica*		65	15
1755	10 z. *Azalea pontica*		1·25	20
1750/1755	*Set of 6*		2·50	65

(Des R. Dudzicki. Litho)

1967 (21 July). *Inauguration of Katowice Memorial. P* 11½.

1756	**496**	60 g. multicoloured	10	10

497 Marie Curie

498 "Fifth Congress of the Deaf" (sign language)

(Des S. Malecki. Eng J. Miller (1757), E. Tirdiszek (1758), B. Kowalska (1759). Recess)

1967 (1 Aug). *Birth Centenary of Marie Curie. T* **497** *and similar vert designs. P* 11½×11.

1757	**497**	60 g. lake	15	10
1758	–	60 g. sepia	15	10
1759	–	60 g. violet	15	10

Designs:—No. 1758, Marie Curie's Nobel Prize diploma; No. 1759, Statue of Marie Curie, Warsaw.

(Des Cz. Kaczmarczyk. Litho)

1967 (1 Aug). *Fifth World Federation of the Deaf Congress, Warsaw. P* 11×12.

1760	**498**	60 g. black and new blue	15	10

499 Bouquet

500 "Wilanów Palace" (from painting by W. Kasprzycki)

(Des T. Michaluk. Photo)

1967 (5 Sept). *"Flowers of the Meadow". T* **499** *and similar square designs. Multicoloured. P* 11½.

1761	20 g. Type **499**		10	10
1762	40 g. Red poppy		10	10
1763	60 g. Field bindweed		10	10
1764	90 g. Wild pansy		15	10
1765	1 z. 15, Tansy		15	10
1766	2 z. 50, Corn cockle		25	10
1767	3 z. 40, Field scabious		50	25
1768	4 z. 50, Scarlet pimpernel		1·60	40
1769	7 z. 90, Chicory		1·75	65
1761/1769	*Set of 9*		4·25	1·50

(Des K. Rogaczewska. Eng B. Kowalska (1770), J. Miller (1771), E. Tirdiszek (1772). Recess)

1967 (9 Oct). *Polish Martyrdom and Resistance, 1939–45 (2nd series). Designs as T* **491**. *P* 11½×11 (*No.* 1770) or 11×11½ (*others*).

1770	40 g. ultramarine		10	10
1771	40 g. bronze-green		10	10
1772	40 g. black		10	10

Designs: *Horiz*—No. 1770, Stutthof Memorial. *Vert*—1771, Walcz Memorial; 1772, Lodz-Radogoszcz Memorial.

(Des S. Malecki. Eng J. Miller. Recess and photo)

1967 (9 Oct). *Stamp Day. P* 11½.

1773	**500**	60 g. olive-brown and pale blue	15	10

501 Cruiser *Aurora*

(Des K. Tarkowska. Litho)

1967 (9 Oct). *50th Anniv of October Revolution. T* **501** *and similar horiz designs. All in black, grey and brown-red. P* 11.

1774	60 g. Type **501**		30	10
1775	60 g. Lenin		30	10
1776	60 g. "Luna 10"		30	10

502 Peacock (*Vanessa io*)

503 Kościuszko

(Des J. Desselberger. Litho)

1967 (14 Oct). *Butterflies. T* **502** *and similar square designs. Multicoloured. P* 11½.

1777	10 g. Type **502**		15	10
1778	20 g. Swallowtail (*Papilio machaon*)		15	10
1779	40 g. Small tortoiseshell (*Vanessa urticae*)		15	10
1780	60 g. Camberwell beauty (*Vanessa antiopa*)		20	10
1781	2 z. Purple emperor (*Apatura iris*)		35	10
1782	2 z. 50 Red admiral (*Pyrameis atalanta*)		45	10
1783	3 z. 40, Pale clouded yellow (*Colias hyale*)		45	15
1784	4 z. 50, Marbled white (*Melanargia galathea*)		2·00	80
1785	7 z. 90, Large blue (*Maculinea arion*)		2·25	80
1777/1785	*Set of 9*		5·50	2·10

(Des R. Dudzicki. Eng E. Konecki. Recess and photo)

1967 (14 Oct). 150th Death Anniv of Tadeusz Kosciuszko (national hero). P 12×11.

1786	**503**	60 g. chocolate & lt yellow-brown	10	10
1787		2 z. 50, myrtle-green and carmine	20	10

504 "The Lobster" (Jean de Heem)

(Des J. S. Miklaszewski. Photo)

1967 (15 Nov). Famous Paintings. T **504** and similar designs. P 11×11½ (4 z. 50, 6 z. 60) or 11½×11 (others).

1788	20 g. multicoloured	20	10
1789	40 g. multicoloured	10	10
1790	60 g. multicoloured	10	10
1791	2 z. multicoloured	25	15
1792	2 z. 50, multicoloured	30	15
1793	3 z. 40, multicoloured	55	15
1794	4 z. 50, multicoloured	1·00	50
1795	6 z. 60, multicoloured	1·25	60
1788/1795	Set of 8	3·25	1·50

Paintings from the National Museums, Warsaw and Cracow:
Vert—20 g. "Lady with a Weasel" (Leonardo da Vinci); 40 g. "The Polish Lady" (Watteau); 60 g. "Dog Fighting Heron" (A. Hondius); 2 z. "Fowler Tuning Guitar" (J.-B. Greuze); 2 z. 50, "The Tax Collectors" (M. van Reymerswaele); 3 z. 40, "Daria Fiodorowna" (F. S. Rokotov). Horiz—6 z. 60, "Parable of the Good Samaritan" (landscape, Rembrandt).
Printed in sheets of 5 stamps with one stamp-size se-tenant label.

505 W. S. Reymont

507 Ice Hockey

506 J. M. Ossolinski (medallion), Book and Flag

(Des R. Dudzicki. Litho)

1967 (12 Dec). Birth Centenary of W. S. Reymont (novelist). P 11×11½.

1796	**505**	60 g. sepia, red and ochre	10	10

(Des R. Dudzicki. Litho)

1967 (12 Dec). 150th Anniv of Ossolineum Foundation. P 11

1797	**506**	60 g. yell-brn, red, grnsh bl & lt bl	10	10

(Des K. Rogaczewska. Eng B. Kowalska (1798), E. Tirdiszek (1799). Recess)

1967 (28 Dec). Polish Martyrdom and Resistance, 1939–45 (3rd series). Designs as T **491**. P 11×1·1½ (No. 1798) or 11½×11 (1799).

1798	40 g. claret	10	10
1799	40 g. brown	10	10

Designs: Vert—No. 1798, Zagan Memorial. Horiz—1799, Lambinowice Memorial.

(Des F. Winiarski. Litho)

1968 (10 Jan). Winter Olympic Games, Grenoble. T **507** and similar horiz designs. Multicoloured. P 11×11½.

1800	40 g. Type **507**	10	10
1801	60 g. Ski-jumping	10	10
1802	90 g. Slalom	15	10
1803	1 z. 35, Speed-skating	15	10
1804	1 z. 55, Ski-walking	15	10
1805	2 z. Tobogganing	25	10
1806	7 z. Rifle-shooting on skis	60	40
1807	7 z. 90, Ski-jumping (different)	1·10	50
1800/1807	Set of 8	2·40	1·10

508 "Puss in Boots"

509 Passiflora quadrangularis

(Des H. Matuszewska. Litho)

1968 (15 Mar). Fairy Tales. T **508** and similar vert designs. Multicoloured. P 12½.

1808	20 g. Type **508**	10	10
1809	40 g. "The Raven and the Fox"	10	10
1810	60 g. "Mr. Twardowski"	15	10
1811	2 z. "The Fisherman and the Fish"	25	10
1812	2 z. 50, "Little Red Riding Hood"	35	10
1813	3 z. 40, "Cinderella"	50	10
1814	5 z. 50, "The Waif"	1·25	50
1815	7 z. "Snow White"	1·50	65
1808/1815	Set of 8	3·75	1·40

(Des T. Michaluk. Litho)

1968 (15 May). Flowers. T **509** and similar square designs. Multicoloured. P 11½.

1816	10 g. Clianthus dampieri	10	10
1817	20 g. Type **509**	10	10
1818	30 g. Strelitzia reginae	10	10
1819	40 g. Coryphanta vivipara	10	10
1820	60 g. Odontonia	10	10
1821	90 g. Protea cynaroides	15	10
1822	4 z. + 2 z. Abutilon	75	40
1823	8 z. + 4 z. Rosa polyantha	1·90	85
1816/1823	Set of 8	3·00	1·50

510 "Peace" (poster by H. Tomaszewski)

511 Zephyr Glider

(Des A. Heidrich. Litho)

1968 (29 May). *2nd International Poster Biennale, Warsaw.* T **510** *and similar vert design. Multicoloured.* P 11½×11.
1824   60 g. Type **510**   10   10
1825   2 z. 50, Gounod's "Faust" (poster by Jan Lenica)   20   10

(Des J. Jaworowski. Litho)

1968 (29 May). *11th World Gliding Championships, Leszno.* T **511** *and similar horiz designs showing gliders. Multicoloured.* P 12½.
1826   60 g. Type **511** ..   10   10
1827   90 g. Stork   ..   10   10
1828   1 z. 50, Swallow   20   10
1829   3 z. 40 Fly   50   20
1830   4 z. Seal   1·00   30
1831   5 z. 50, Pirate   1·25   35
1826/1831   Set of 6 ..   2·75   95

512 Child with "Stamp"   **513** Part of Monument

(Des T. Michaluk. Litho)

1968 (2 July). *"75 Years of Polish Philately". Multicoloured.* T **512** *and similar vert design.* P 11½×11.
1832   60 g. Type **512** ..   10   10
    a. Pair. Nos. 1832/3 ..   20   15
1833   60 g. Balloon over Poznan   10   10
Nos. 1832/3 were printed together *se-tenant* in sheets of 12.

(Des W. Chrucki. Eng B. Brandt. Recess and photo)

1968 (20 July). *Silesian Insurrection Monument, Sosnowiec.* P 11×11½.
1834 **513** 60 g. black and bright purple   10   10

PUZZLED ?

Then you need
PHILATELIC TERMS ILLUSTRATED
to tell you all you need to know about printing
methods, papers, errors, varieties, watermarks,
perforations, etc. 192 pages, some in full
colour, soft cover. Third Edition.

POLSKA ~ 40 gr

514 Relay-racing   **515** "Knight on a Bay Horse" (P. Michalowski)

(Des T. Michaluk. Litho)

1968 (2 Sept). *Olympic Games, Mexico.* T **514** *and similar horiz designs. Multicoloured.* P 11×11½ or 11½ (10 z.).
1835   30 g. Type **514**   10   10
1836   40 g. Boxing ..   10   10
1837   60 g. Basketball   10   10
1838   90 g. Long-jumping   10   10
1839   2 z. 50, Throwing the javelin ..   20   10
1840   3 z. 40, Gymnastics   35   10
1841   4 z. Cycling   45   30
1842   7 z. 90, Fencing   80   40
1843   10 z.+5 z. Torch Runner and Aztec bas-relief (56×45 *mm.*)   2·00   1·25
1835/1843   Set of 9 ..   3·75   2·00

(Des A. Heidrich. Photo)

1968 (10 Oct). *Polish Paintings.* T **515** *and similar multicoloured designs.* P 11½×11 *(vert)* or 11×11½ *(horiz).*
1844   40 g. Type **515**   10   10
1845   60 g. "Fisherman" (L. Wyczolkowski) .. 10   10
1846   1 z. 15, "Jewish Woman with Lemons" (A. Gierymski) ..   10   10
1847   1 z. 35, "Eliza Parenska" (S. Wyspianski) ..   15   10
1848   1 z. 50, "Manifesto" (W. Weiss)   40   20
1849   4 z. 50, "Stanczyk" (Jan Matejko) ..   40   25
1850   5 z. "Children's Band" (T. Makowski)   65   40
1851   7 z. "Feast II" (Z. Waliszewski) ..   70   45
1844/1851   Set of 8 ..   2·40   1·25
The 4 z. 50, 5 z. and 7 z. are horiz designs.
Printed in sheets of four stamps and 2 labels.

516 "September, 1939" (Bylina)

(Des S. Malecki. Eng E. Konecki (1852, 1854, 1860, 1861), E. Tirdiszek (1853, 1856, 1859), B. Brandt (1855), B. Kowalska (1857), J. Miller (1858). Recess, typo and photo)

1968 (12 Oct). *25th Anniv of Polish People's Army.* T **516** *and similar horiz designs, showing paintings.* P 11½.
1852   40 g. reddish violet and olive/*pale yellow*   10   10
1853   40 g. dp ultram & reddish violet/*pale lilac*   10   10
1854   40 g. olive-green & deep blue/*pale grey*   10   10
1855   40 g. black and orange-brown/*pl orange*   10   10
1856   40 g. purple & bronze-green/*pale green*   10   10
1857   60 g. blackish brown & ultram/*pl blue*   15   10
1858   60 g. maroon & olive-green/*pl yell-grn*   15   10

1859 60 g. blackish olive & carmine-red/*pl pk* 15 10
1860 60 g. emerald-green & chocolate/*pl rose* 30 10
1861 60 g. indigo & turquoise/*pl grnsh blue* 20 10
1852/1861 Set of 10 1·25 40

Paintings and painters:—No. 1852, T **516**; 1853, "Partisans" (Maciag); 1854 "Lenino" (Bylina); 1855, "Monte Cassino" (Boratynski); 1856, "Tanks before Warsaw" (Garwatowski); 1857, "Neisse River" (Bylina); 1858, "On the Oder" (Mackiewicz); 1859, "In Berlin" (Bylina); 1860, "*Blyskawica*" (destroyer) (Mokwa); 1861, "Pursuit" (Mikoyan Gurevich MiG-17 aircraft) (Kulisiewicz).

517 "Party Members" (F. Kowarski)

(Des F. Winiarski. Litho)

1968 (11 Nov). *Fifth Polish United Workers' Party Congress, Warsaw.* T **517** *and similar multicoloured designs showing paintings.* P 11×11½ (No. 1862) or 11½×11 (others).
1862 60 g. Type **517** 10 10
1863 60 g. "Strike" (S. Lentz) 10 10
1864 60 g. "Manifesto" (W. Weiss) 10 10
Nos. 1863/4 are vert designs.

(Des K. Rogaczewska. Eng E. Tirdiszek (1865, 1867), J. Miller (1866), B. Kowalska (1868), B. Brandt (1869). Recess)

1968 (15 Nov). *Polish Martyrdom and Resistance, 1939–45 (4th series).* Designs as T **491**. P 11½×11 (horiz) or 11×11½ (vert).
1865 40 g. slate-grey 10 10
1866 40 g. blackish brown 10 10
1867 40 g. sepia 10 10
1868 40 g. deep ultramarine 10 10
1869 40 g. lake-brown 25 20
1865/1869 Set of 5 .. ..

Designs: Horiz—No. 1865, Tomb of Unknown Soldier, Warsaw; 1866, Partisans' Monument, Kartuzy. Vert—1867, Insurgents' Monument, Poznan; 1868, People's Guard Insurgents' Monument, Polichno; 1869, Rotunda, Zamosc.

518 "Start of Hunt" (W. Kossak)

(Des S. Malecki. Litho)

1968 (20 Nov). *Paintings. Hunting Scenes.* T **518** *and similar horiz designs. Multicoloured.* P 11.
1870 20 g. Type **518** 10 10
1871 40 g. "Hunting with Falcon" (J. Kossak) 10 10
1872 60 g. "Wolves' Raid" (A. Wierusz-Kowalski) 10 10
1873 1 z. 50, "Home-coming with a Bear" (J. Falat) 40 10
1874 2 z. 50, "The Fox-hunt" (T. Sutherland) 30 10
1875 3 z. 40, "The Boar-hunt" (F. Snyders) 40 15
1876 4 z. 50, "Hunters' Rest" (W. G. Pierow) 1·50 50
1877 8 z. 50, "Hunting a Lion in Morocco" (Delacroix) 1·40 70
1870/1877 Set of 8 .. 3·75 1·40

519 Maltese Terrier **520** House Sign

(Des J. Grabiański. Litho)

1969 (2 Feb). *Pedigree Dogs. Multicoloured designs as* T **519**. P 11½×11 (vert) or 11×11½ (horiz).
1878 20 g. Type **519** 20 10
1879 40 g. Wire-haired fox-terrier 30 15
1880 60 g. Afghan hound 30 20
1881 1 z. 50, Rough-haired terrier 30 20
1882 2 z. 50, English setter 60 20
1883 3 z. 40, Pekinese 75 25
1884 4 z. 50, Alsatian 1·60 50
1885 8 z. 50, Pointer 3·00 1·00
1878/1885 Set of 8 .. 6·25 2·40
The 40 g., 4 z. 50 and 8 z. 50 are vert.

(Des K. Rogaczewska. Litho)

1969 (23 Feb). *Ninth Polish Democratic Party Congress.* P 11½×11.
1886 **520** 60 g. carmine-red, black and grey .. 10 10

521 "Dove" and Wheat-ears **522** Running

(Des K. Sliwka. Litho)

1969 (29 Mar). *Fifth Congress of United Peasants' Party.* P 11½.
1887 **521** 60 g. multicoloured 10 10

(Des J. Jaworowski. Litho)

1969 (25 Apr). *75th Anniversary of International Olympic Committee and 50th Anniv of Polish Olympic Committee.* T **522** *and similar vert designs. Multicoloured.* P 11½×11.
1888 10 g. Type **522** 10 10
1889 20 g. Gymnastics 10 10
1890 40 g. Weightlifting 10 10
1891 60 g. Throwing the javelin 10 10
1892 2 z. 50+50 g. Throwing the discus .. 20 10
1893 3 z. 40+1 z. Running 30 15
1894 4 z.+1 z. 50, Wrestling 75 25
1895 7 z.+2 z. Fencing 1·40 35
1888/1895 Set of 8 .. 2·50 90

523 Pictorial Map of Świętokrzyski National Park

(Des A. Heidrich. Litho)

1969 (20 May). *Tourism (1st series). T* **523** *and similar multicoloured designs.* P 11.

1896	40 g. Type **523**		10	10
1897	60 g. Niedzica Castle (*vert*)		10	10
1898	1 z. 35, Kolobrzeg Lighthouse and yacht		30	10
1899	1 z. 50, Szczecin Castle and Harbour		30	10
1900	2 z. 50, Torun and River Vistula		25	10
1901	3 z. 40, Klodzko, Silesia (*vert*)		35	10
1902	4 z. Sulejów		55	25
1903	4 z. 50, Kazimierz Dolny market-place (*vert*)		60	25
1896/1903	Set of 8		2·25	90

Nos. 1896/1903 were each issued with *se-tenant* half stamp-size labels showing either flora or arms.

See also Nos. 1981/5.

524 Route Map and *Opty*

525 Copernicus (after woodcut by T. Stimer) and Inscription

526 "Memory" Flame and Badge

(Des A. Heidrich. Litho)

1969 (21 June). *Leonid Teliga's World Voyage in Yacht "Opty".* P 11×11½.
1904	**524**	60 g. multicoloured	30	10

(Des H. Chylinski. Eng Z. Kowalski (40 g.), E. Konecki (60 g.), B. Kowalska (2 z. 50). Recess and litho)

1969 (26 June). *500th Birth Anniversary of Copernicus (1973) (1st issue). T* **525** *and similar horiz designs.* P 11½.
1905	40 g. blackish brown, red and yellow		15	10
1906	60 g. dp slate-blue, red & light grey-grn		20	10
1907	2 z. 50, olive, red & light brown-purple		50	15

Designs:—60 g. Copernicus (after J. Falck) and 15th-century globe; 2 z. 50, Copernicus (after painting by J. Matejko) and diagram of heliocentric system.

See also Nos. 1995/7, 2069/72, 2167/**MS**2171, 2213/4, 2217/2221.

(Des T. Michaluk. Eng E. Tirdiszek. Recess, litho and typo)

1969 (19 July). *Fifth National Alert of Polish Boy Scout Association. T* **526** *and similar vert designs.* P 11×11½.
1908	60 g. black, red and light blue		10	10
1909	60 g. red, black and green		10	10
1910	60 g. black, green and rose		10	10

Designs:—No. 1908, Type **526**; No. 1909, "Defence" eagle and badge; No. 1910, "Labour" map and badge.

MINIMUM PRICE

The minimum price quoted is 10p which represents a handling charge rather than a basis for valuing common stamps. For further notes about prices see introductory pages.

527 Frontier Guard and Arms

528 Coal-miner

(Des T. Michaluk. Litho and embossed (Nos. 1911/15). Des F. Winiarski. Litho (others))

1969 (21 July). *25th Anniv of Polish People's Republic. Multicoloured.* P 11. (*a*) *Vert designs as T* **527**
1911	60 g. Type **527**		10	10
	a. Horiz strip of 5. Nos. 1911/15		50	
1912	60 g. Plock petro-chemical plant		10	10
1913	60 g. Combine-harvester		10	10
1914	60 g. Grand Theatre, Warsaw		10	10
1915	60 g. Curie statue and University, Lublin		10	10

(*b*) *Horiz designs as T* **528**
1916	60 g. Type **528**		10	10
	a. Horiz strip of 4. Nos. 1916/19		40	
1917	60 g. Sulphur worker		10	10
1918	60 g. Steel worker		10	10
1919	60 g. Shipbuilder		10	10
1911/1919	Set of 9		80	30

Nos. 1911/15 and 1916/19 respectively were issued in horizontal *se-tenant* strips within their sheets.

529 Astronauts and Module on Moon

531 "Nike" Statue

530 "Motherhood" (S. Wyspiański)

(Des A. Balcerzak. Litho)

1969 (21 Aug). *First Man on the Moon.* P 12×12½.
1920	**529**	2 z. 50, multicoloured	65	35

Issued in sheets of eight stamps and two different stamp-size *se-tenant* labels.

(Des R. Dudzicki. Photo)

1969 (4 Sept). *Polish Paintings. Multicoloured designs as T* **530**. *P* 11½×11 (*vert*) or 11×11½ (*horiz*).

1921	20 g.	Type **530**			10	10
1922	40 g.	"Hamlet" (J. Malczewski)			10	10
1923	60 g.	"Indian Summer" (J. Chelmonski)			10	10
1924	2 z.	"Two Girls" (O. Boznańska) (*vert*)			25	10
1925	2 z. 50,	"The Sun of May" (J. Mehoffer) (*vert*)			15	10
1926	3 z. 40,	"Woman combing her Hair" (W. Slewiński)			30	20
1927	5 z. 50,	"Still Life" (J. Pankiewicz)			65	30
1928	7 z.	"Abduction of the King's Daughter" (W. Wojtkiewicz)			1·25	35
1921/1928		*Set of 8*			2·50	1·10

Issued in sheets of four stamps and two *se-tenant* labels inscribed with the artist's name.

(Des K. Śliwka. Litho)

1969 (19 Sept). *Fourth Congress of Fighters for Freedom and Democracy Association. P* 11½ × 11.

1929	**531**	60 g. red, black and bistre		10	10

532 Majdanek Memorial

(Des K. Rogaczewska. Litho)

1969 (20 Sept). *Inauguration of Majdanek Memorial. P* 11.

1930	**532**	40 g. black and bright mauve		15	10

533 Krzczonow (Lublin) Costumes   **534** "Pedestrians— Keep Left"   **535** "Welding" and I.L.O. Emblem

(Des S. Malecki. Litho)

1969 (30 Sept). *Provincial Costumes. T* **533** *and similar vert designs. Multicoloured. P* 11½×11.

1931	40 g.	Type **533**			10	10
1932	60 g.	Lowicz (Lodz)			10	10
1933	1 z. 15,	Rozbark (Katowice)			15	10
1934	1 z. 35,	Lower Silesia (Wroclaw)			15	10
1935	1 z. 50,	Opoczno (Lodz)			30	10
1936	4 z. 50,	Sacz (Cracow)			60	15
1937	5 z.	Highlanders (Cracow)			50	30
1938	7 z.	Kurpie (Warsaw)			70	35
1931/1938		*Set of 8*			2·25	1·00

(Des K. Śliwka. Litho)

1969 (4 Oct). *Road Safety. T* **534** *and similar vert designs. Multicoloured. P* 11.

1939	40 g.	Type **534**			10	10
1940	60 g.	"Drive Carefully" (horses on road)			10	10
1941	2 z. 50,	"Do Not Dazzle" (cars on road at night)			30	15

(Des J. Desselberger. Litho)

1969 (20 Oct). *50th Anniversary of International Labour Organization. P* 11×11½.

1942	**535**	2 z. 50, chalky blue and gold	25	10

536 "The Bell-founder"   **537** "Angel" (19th-century)

(Des J. Rapnicki and F. Winiarski. Litho)

1969 (12 Nov). *Miniatures from Behem's Code of* 1505. *T* **536** *and similar vert designs. Multicoloured. P* 12½.

1943	40 g.	Type **536**		10	10
1944	60 g.	"The Painter"		10	10
1945	1 z. 35,	"The Woodcarver"		15	10
1946	1 z. 55,	"The Shoemaker"		20	10
1947	2 z. 50,	"The Cooper"		25	10
1948	3 z. 40,	"The Baker"		30	10
1949	4 z. 50,	"The Tailor"		60	30
1950	7 z.	"The Bowyer"		1·00	40
1943/1950		*Set of 8*		2·40	1·00

(Des S. Malecki. Litho)

1969 (19 Dec). *Polish Folk Sculpture. T* **537** *and similar vert designs. Multicoloured. P* 11½×11 (5 z. 50, 7 z.) *or* 12½ (*others*).

1951	20 g.	Type **537**		10	10
1952	40 g.	"Sorrowful Christ" (19th-century)		10	10
1953	60 g.	"Sorrowful Christ" (19th-century) (*diff*)		10	10
1954	2 z.	"Weeping Woman" (19th-century)		20	10
1955	2 z. 50,	"Adam and Eve" (F. Czajkowski)		20	10
1956	3 z. 40,	"Girl with Birds" (L. Kudla)		35	10
1957	5 z. 50+1 z. 50,	"Choir" (A. Zegadlo)		80	30
1958	7 z.+1 z. 50,	"Organ-grinder" (Z. Skretowicz)		90	50
1951/1958		*Set of 8*		2·40	1·10

Nos. 1957/8 are larger, 25×35 mm.

538 Leopold Staff   **539** Nike Monument

(Des R. Dudzicki. Eng B. Kowalska (40 g.), J. Miller (60 g., 2 z. 50, 3 z. 40), E. Konecki (others). Recess, typo and photo)

1969 (30 Dec). *Modern Polish Writers. T* **538** *and similar horiz portraits. P* 11×11½.

1959	40 g.	black, olive-green & pale sage-grn		10	10
1960	60 g.	black, carmine-red and pale pink		10	10
1961	1 z. 35,	black, royal blue & pale blue		10	10
1962	1 z. 50,	black, dp bluish vio & pale lilac		10	10

1963	1 z. 55, black, dp emer & pale turq-grn		15	10
1964	2 z. 50, black, ultramarine & pale blue		20	10
1965	3 z. 40, black, red-brown & pale brn		30	20
1959/1965	Set of 7		90	45

Designs:—60 g. Wladyslaw Broniewski; 1 z. 35, Leon Kruczkowski; 1 z. 50, Julian Tuwim; 1 z. 55, Konstanty Ildefons Galczyński; 2 z. 50, Maria Dabrowska; 3 z. 40, Zofia Nalkowska.

(Des F. Baracz. Photo)

1970 (17 Jan). *25th Anniversary of Liberation of Warsaw.*
P 11½.

1966	**539**	60 g. multicoloured		25	10

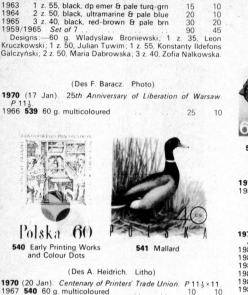

540 Early Printing Works and Colour Dots

541 Mallard

(Des A. Heidrich. Litho)

1970 (20 Jan). *Centenary of Printers' Trade Union. P 11½ × 11.*

1967	**540**	60 g. multicoloured		10	10

(Des J. Desselberger. Litho)

1970 (28 Feb). *Game Birds. T* **541** *and similar square designs. Multicoloured. P 11½.*

1968	40 g. Type **541**			20	10
1969	60 g. Ring-necked pheasant			40	10
1970	1 z. 15, Woodcock			30	10
1971	1 z. 35, Ruff			40	10
1972	1 z. 50, Wood pigeon			40	15
1973	3 z. 40, Black grouse			45	15
1974	7 z. Grey partridge			2·50	1·00
1975	8 z. 50, Capercaillie			2·75	1·00
1968/1975	Set of 8			6·75	2·25

542 Lenin at Desk

(Des K. Tarkowska. Eng J. Miller (40 g.), E. Konecki (60 g.), B. Brandt (2 z. 50). Recess and typo)

1970 (22 Apr). *Birth Centenary of Lenin. T* **542** *and similar horiz designs. P 11.*

1976	40 g. deep olive-grey and brown-red		10	10
1977	60 g. sepia and magenta		10	10
1978	2 z. 50, black and vermilion		20	10
MS1979	134×81 mm. No. 1977×4 (10 Oct)		1·10	40

Designs:—60 g. Lenin addressing meeting; 2 z. 50, Lenin in Party Conference.

No. **MS**1979 was issued for Cracow Philatelic Exhibition.

543 Polish and Russian Soldiers in Berlin

544 Polish "Flower"

(Des A. Heidrich. Litho)

1970 (9 May). *25th Anniversary of Liberation. P 11×11½.*

1980	**543**	60 g. multicoloured		15	10

(Des A. Heidrich. Litho)

1970 (9 May). *Tourism (2nd series). Multicoloured designs as T* **523**. *P 11.*

1981	60 g. Town Hall, Wroclaw (*vert*)		15	10
1982	60 g. View of Opole		15	10
1983	60 g. Legnica Castle		15	10
1984	60 g. Bolkow Castle		15	10
1985	60 g. Town Hall, Brzeg		15	10
1981/1985	Set of 5		65	25

Issued with *se-tenant* labels as described for the first series.

(Des K. Rogaczewska. Eng E. Konecki. Recess, litho and typo)

1970 (9 May). *25th Anniv of Return of Western Territories. P 11½.*

1986	**544**	60 g. red, silver & deep bluish green	15	10

545 Movement Flag

546 U.P.U. Emblem and New Headquarters

(Des K. Syta. Litho)

1970 (15 May). *75th Anniversary of Peasant Movement. P 11½.*

1987	**545**	60 g. multicoloured		10	10

(Des H. Chyliński. Litho)

1970 (20 May). *New U.P.U. Headquarters Building, Berne. P 11½.*

1988	**546**	2 z. 50, bright blue & lt grnish blue	20	10

Polska 60

547 Footballers

POLSKA 60 GR

548 Hand with "Lamp of Learning"

(Des H. Matuszewska. Litho)

1970 (30 May). *Gornik Zabrze v. Manchester City, Final of European Cup-winners Cup Championship.* P 11½×11.
1989 **547** 60 g. multicoloured 20 10
  Issued with *se-tenant* stamp-size label with inscription giving results of previous matches.

(Des H. Chyliński. Litho)

1970 (3 June). *150th Anniversary of Plock Scientific Society.* P 11½.
1990 **548** 60 g. yellow-olive, red and black .. 10 10

549 "Olympic Runners" (from Greek amphora)

550 Copernicus (after miniature by Bacciarelli), and Bologna

(Des F. Winiarski (Nos. 1991 & 1993), W. Skoczylas (No. 1992), Z. Kaminski (**MS**1994). Photo)

1970 (16 June). *Tenth Session of International Olympic Academy.* T **549** *and similar horiz designs.* P 11×12.
1991 60 g. vermilion, orange-yellow & black 10 10
1992 60 g. dp violet-blue, bright blue & black 10 10
1993 60 g. multicoloured 10 10
MS1994 71×101 mm. 10 z.+5 z. multicoloured
  Imperf .. .. 1·75 90
  Designs:—No. 1992, "The Archer"; No. 1993, Modern runners; No. **MS**1994, "Horse of Fame" emblem of Polish Olympic Committee.

(Des H. Matuszewska. Eng E. Tirdiszek (40 g.), B. Kowalska (60 g.), B. Brandt (2 z. 50). Recess, photo and typo)

1970 (26 June). *500th Birth Anniv of Copernicus* (1973) (*2nd issue*). *Vert designs as* T **550**. P 11½.
1995 40 g. bronze-grn, red-orge & redsh lilac 15 10
1996 60 g. reddish lilac, bronze-grn & orge-yell 15 10
1997 2 z. 50, brown, ultram & light emerald 50 10
  Designs:—60 g. Copernicus (after miniature by Lesseur), and Padua; 2 z. 50, Copernicus (by Zinck after lost Goluchowska portrait), and Ferrara.

HAVE YOU READ THE NOTES AT THE BEGINNING OF THIS CATALOGUE?

These often provide answers to the enquiries we receive.

551 "Aleksander Orlowski" (self-portrait)

552 U.N. Emblem within "Eye"

(Des T. Michaluk. Litho and photo)

1970 (27 Aug). *Polish Miniatures.* T **551** *and similar vert portraits. Multicoloured.* P 11½×11.
1998 20 g. Type **551** 10 10
1999 40 g. "Jan Matejko" (self-portrait) 10 10
2000 60 g. "Stefan Batory" (unknown artist) 10 10
2001 2 z. "Maria Leszczynska" (unknown artist) 10 10
2002 2 z. 50. "Maria Walewska" (Marie-Victoire Jacquetot) .. 20 10
2003 3 z. 40, "Tadeusz Kosciuszko" (J. Rustem) 25 10
2004 5 z. 50, "Samuel Linde" (G. Landolfi) 70 40
2005 7 z. 50, "Michal Oginski" (Nanette Windisch) .. 1·40 55
1998/2005 *Set of* 8 .. .. 2·50 1·25
  Issued in sheets of four stamps and two inscribed stamp-sized *se-tenant* labels.

(Des F. Baracz. Photo)

1970 (8 Sept). *25th Anniv of United Nations.* P 11½.
2006 **552** 2 z. 50, multicoloured 25 10

553 Piano Keyboard and Chopin's Signature

554 Population Pictograph

(Des S. Malecki. Eng E. Tirdiszek. Recess and photo)

1970 (8 Sept). *8th International Chopin Piano Competition.* P 11.
2007 **553** 2 z. 50, black and violet 25 10

(Des K. Rogaczewska. Litho)

1970 (15 Sept). *National Census.* T **554** *and similar vert design. Multicoloured.* P 11½×11.
2008 40 g. Type **554** 10 10
2009 60 g. Family in "house" 15 10

555 Destroyer *Piorun*

(Des K. Rogaczewska. Eng B. Kowalska (40 g.), E. Tirdiszek (60 g.), B. Brandt (2 z. 50). Recess and photo)

1970 (25 Sept). *Polish Warships of World War II. T* **555** *and similar horiz designs. P* 11½×11.

2010	40 g. blackish brown				25	10
2011	60 g. black				40	15
2012	2 z. 50, deep brown			1·00	30

Designs:—60 g. *Orzel* (submarine); 2 z. 50, H.M.S. *Garland* (destroyer loaned to Polish Navy).

556 "Expressions"	**557** "Luna 16"
(Maria Jarema)	landing on Moon

(Des S. Malecki. Photo)

1970 (9 Oct). *Stamp Day. Contemporary Polish Paintings. T* **556** *and similar multicoloured designs. P* 11½×12 (*vert*) *or* 12×11½ (*horiz*).

2013	20 g. "The Violin-cellist" (J. Nowosielski) (*vert*)		10	10
2014	40 g. "View of Lodz" (B. Liberski) (*vert*)		10	10
2015	60 g. "Studio Concert" (W. Taranczew-ski) (*vert*)		10	10
2016	1 z. 50, "Still Life" (Z. Pronaszko) (*vert*)		10	10
2017	2 z. "Hanging-up Washing" (A. Wrób-lewski) (*vert*)		15	10
2018	3 z. 40, Type **556**		25	10
2019	4 z. "Canal in the Forest" (P. Potworowski)		55	20
2020	8 z. 50, "The Sun" (W. Strzeminski)		1·10	50
2013/2020	*Set of 8*		2·25	90

(Des Z. Stasik. Litho)

1970 (20 Nov). *Moon Landing of "Luna 16". P* 11½×11.

2021	**557** 2 z. 50, multicoloured	35	15

Issued in sheets of eight stamps and two different stamp-size *se-tenant* labels, showing Space scenes.

558 "Stag" (detail from "Daniel" tapestry)	**560** Chęciny Castle

559 Cadet Ship *Dar Pomorza*

(Des H. Matuszewska. Photo)

1970 (23 Dec). *Tapestries in Wawel Castle. T* **558** *and similar vert designs. Multicoloured. P* 11½.

2022	60 g. Type **558**		10	10
2023	1 z. 15, "White Stork" (detail)		30	10
2024	1 z. 35, "Panther fighting Dragon"		15	10
2025	2 z. "Man's Head" (detail, "Deluge" tapestry)		20	10
2026	2 z. 50, "Child with Bird" (detail, "Adam Tilling the Soil" tapestry)		25	10
2027	4 z. "God, Adam and Eve" (detail, "Happiness in Paradise" tapestry)		50	25
2028	4 z. 50, Royal Monogram tapestry		80	35
2022/2028	*Set of 7*		2·00	90

MS2029 Two sheets each 62×89 mm. Imperf.
(a) 5 z. 50, Polish coat-of-arms ⎱ *Pair* 2·00 1·50
(b) 7 z.+3 z. Monogram and satyrs ⎰
The designs on the miniature sheets are larger, 45×55 mm.

(Des S. Malecki. Photo)

1971 (20 Feb). *Polish Ships. T* **559** *and similar horiz designs. Multicoloured. P* 11.

2030	40 g. Type **559**		15	10
2031	60 g. Liner *Stefan Batory*		15	10
2032	1 z. 15, Ice-breaker *Perkun*		25	10
2033	1 z. 35, Lifeboat *R-1*		35	10
2034	1 z. 50, Bulk carrier *Ziemia Szczecinska*		40	10
2035	2 z. 50, Tanker *Beskidy*		50	10
2036	5 z. Fast freighter *Hel*		1·00	20
2037	8 z. 50, Ferry *Gryf*		2·10	50
2030/2037	*Set of 8*		4·50	90

(Des T. Michaluk. Litho)

1971 (5 Mar). *Polish Castles. T* **560** *and similar horiz designs. Multicoloured. P* 11×12.

2038	20 g. Type **560**		10	10
2039	40 g. Wiśnicz		10	10
2040	60 g. Będzin		10	10
2041	2 z. Ogrodzieniec		15	10
2042	2 z. 50, Niedzica		15	10
2043	3 z. 40, Kwidzyn		30	10
2044	4 z. Pieskowa Skala		35	15
2045	8 z. 50, Lidzbark Warminski		80	60
2038/2045	*Set of 8*		1·75	1·00

561 Battle of Pouilly,	**562** Plantation
J. Dabrowski and W. Wróblewski	

(Des H. Matuszewska. Litho)

1971 (10 Mar). *Centenary of Paris Commune. P* 12½.

2046	**561** 60 g. purple-brn, bright bl & rosine	15	10

(Des Z. Stasik. Photo)

1971 (30 Mar). *Forestry Management. T* **562** *and similar vert designs. Multicoloured. P* 12½ (60 g.) *or* 11½×11 (*others*).

2047	40 g. Type **562**		10	10
2048	60 g. Forest		10	10
2049	1 z. 50, Tree-felling		30	10

The 60 g. is larger, 27×47 mm.

563 "Bishop Marianos" **565** "Soldiers"

564 Revolutionaries

(Des H. Chylinski. Photo)

1971 (20 Apr). *Fresco Discoveries made by Polish Expedition at Faras, Nubia. T 563 and similar vert designs. Multicoloured.* P 11½×11.
2050	40 g. Type **563**	10	10
2051	60 g. "St. Anne"	10	10
2052	1 z. 15, "Archangel Michael"	10	10
2053	1 z. 35, "The Hermit, Anamon"	10	10
2054	1 z. 50, "Head of Archangel Michael"	15	10
2055	4 z. 50, "Evangelists' Cross"	35	10
2056	5 z. "Christ protecting a nobleman"	55	25
2057	7 z. "Archangel Michael" (half-length)	65	40
2050/2057	*Set of 8*	1·90	1·00

(Des J. W. Brzoza. Photo)

1971 (3 May). *50th Anniversary of Silesian Insurrection.* P 11.
2058	**564** 60 g. red-brown and gold	15	10
MS2059 108×106 mm. No. 2058×3 (17 June)		1·60	50

No. 2058 was issued in sheets of 15 stamps with half stamp-size *se-tenant* labels dated "1971".

No. **MS**2059 also contains three such labels, and was issued in connection with a Philatelic Exhibition at Katowice.

(Des H. Matuszewska from children's drawings. Photo)

1971 (29 May). *25th Anniversary of U.N.I.C.E.F. Children's Drawings. T* **565** *and similar multicoloured designs.* P 11½×11 *(vert)* or 11×11½ *(horiz).*
2060	20 g. "Peacock" *(vert)*	10	10
2061	40 g. Type **565**	10	10
2062	60 g. "Lady Spring" *(vert)*	10	10
2063	2 z. "Cat and Ball"	15	10
2064	2 z. 50, "Flowers in Jug" *(vert)*	20	10
2065	3 z. 40, "Friendship"	30	10
2066	5 z. 50, "Clown" *(vert)*	70	35
2067	7 z. "Strange Planet"	90	40
2060/2067	*Set of 8*	2·25	1·00

(Des H. Chyliński. Photo)

1971 (1 June). *40th International Fair, Poznań.* P 11½×11.
2068	**566** 60 g. multicoloured	10	10

(Des A. Heidrich. Litho)

1971 (1 June). *500th Birth Anniv of Copernicus* (1973) (3rd series). *T* **567** *and similar multicoloured designs.* P 11.
2069	40 g. Type **567**	10	10
2070	60 g. Collegium Maius, Jagiellonian University, Cracow (*horiz*)	10	10
2071	2 z. 50, Olsztyn Castle (*horiz*)	20	10
2072	4 z. Frombork Cathedral	60	25
2069/2072	*Set of 4*	85	35

Each value issued with different half stamp-size *se-tenant* label showing Copernicus (40 g.) or aspects of his work.

(Des J. Jaworowski. Recess and photo)

1971 (12 July). *Folk Art Paper "Cut-outs". T* **568** *and similar vert designs showing different patterns.* P 12×11½.
2073	20 g. black, emerald and pale blue	10	10
2074	40 g. indigo, deep olive and pale cream	10	10
2075	60 g. dp brn, greenish blue & pale grey	10	10
2076	1 z. 15, maroon, yellow-brn & pale buff	10	10
2077	1 z. 35, deep bluish green, vermilion and pale yellow-green	20	10
2073/2077	*Set of 5*	40	20

569 "Head of Worker" (X. Dunikowski) **570** Congress Emblem and Computer Tapes

(Des J. W. Brzoza. Photo)

1971 (21 July). *Modern Polish Sculpture. T* **569** *and similar vert designs. Multicoloured.* P 11½×11.
2078	40 g. Type **569**	10	10
2079	40 g. "Foundryman" (X. Dunikowski)	10	10
2080	60 g. "Miners" (M. Więcek)	15	10
2081	60 g. "Harvester" (S. Horno-Poplawski)	15	10
2078/2081	*Set of 4*	40	20
MS2082 158×85 mm. Nos. 2078/81. P 12½×12 (27 Oct)		2·50	75

No. **MS**2082 was issued in connection with a Philatelic Exhibition at Szczecin.

(Des H. Chyliński. Litho)

1971 (2 Sept). *Sixth Polish Technical Congress, Warsaw.* P 11×11½.
2083	**570** 60 g. violet and red	15	10

566 Fair Emblem **567** Copernicus's House, Toruń **568** Folk Art Pattern **571** "Angel" (J. Mehoffer) **572** "Mrs. Fedorowicz" (W. Pruszkowski)

(Des K. Tarkowska. Photo)

1971 (15 Sept). *Stained-glass Windows. T* **571** *and similar vert designs. Multicoloured.* P 11½×11.

2084	20 g. Type **571**		10	10
2085	40 g. "Lilies" (S. Wyspianski)		10	10
2086	60 g. "Iris" (S. Wyspianski)		10	10
2087	1 z. 35, "Apollo" (S. Wyspianski)		15	10
2088	1 z. 55, "Two Wise Men" (14th-century)		15	10
2089	3 z. 40, "The Flight into Egypt" (14th-century)		30	20
2090	5 z. 50, "Jacob" (14th-century)		60	25
2091	8 z. 50+4 z. "Madonna" (15th-century)		90	50
2084/2091	*Set of 8*		2·10	1·10

The 40 g., 60 g., 1 z. 35 and 8 z. 50 are larger, 26×39 mm.

(Des K. Śliwka. Litho)

1971 (25 Sept). *Contemporary Art from National Museum, Cracow. T* **572** *and similar multicoloured designs.* P 11×11½.

2092	40 g. Type **572**		10	10
2093	50 g. "Woman with Book" (T. Czyżewski)		10	10
2094	60 g. "Girl with Chrysanthemums" (O. Boznanska)		10	10
2095	2 z. 50, "Girl in Red Dress" (J. Pankiewicz) (*horiz*)		15	10
2096	3 z. 40, "Reclining Nude" (L. Chwistek) (*horiz*)		30	15
2097	4 z. 50, "Strange Garden" (J. Mehoffer)		45	15
2098	5 z. "Wife in White Hat" (Z. Pronaszko)		55	15
2099	7 z.+1 z. "Seated Nude" (W. Weiss)		75	50
2092/2099	*Set of 8*		2·25	1·10

Issued in sheets of four stamps and two stamp-size *se-tenant* labels bearing inscription.

573 PZL P-11C Fighters

574 Royal Castle, Warsaw (pre-1939)

(Des J. Brodowski. Photo)

1971 (14 Oct). *Polish Aircraft of World War II. T* **573** *and similar horiz designs. Multicoloured.* P 11×11½.

2100	90 g. Type **573**		15	10
2101	1 z. 50, PZL 23A Karas fighters		25	10
2102	3 z. 40, PZL P-37 Łoś bomber		40	10

(Des K. Śliwka. Photo)

1971 (14 Oct). *Reconstruction of Royal Castle, Warsaw.* P 11×11½.

2103	**574** 60 g. black, red and gold		15	10

575 Astronauts in Moon Rover

576 "Lunokhod 1"

(Des A. Balcerzak. Photo)

1971 (17 Nov). *Moon Flight of "Apollo* 15". P 11×11½.

2104	**575** 2 z. 50, multicoloured		45	15
MS2105	122×157 mm. No. 2104×6 plus 2 stamp-size *se-tenant* labels, showing Space scenes		4·00	2·25

(Des Z. Stasik. Photo)

1971 (17 Nov). *Moon Flight of "Lunik* 17" *and "Lunokhod* 1" P 11½×11.

2106	**576** 2 z. 50, multicoloured		45	15
MS2107	158×118 mm. No. 2106×6 plus 2 stamp-size *se-tenant* labels, showing Space scenes		4·00	2·25

577 Worker at Wheel   **578** Ship-building

(Des S. Malecki (Nos. 2108/9) or J. W. Brzoza (others). Photo)

1971 (6 Dec)–**72**. *Sixth Polish United Workers' Party Congress.*

(*a*) *Party Posters. T* **577** *and similar vert design.* P 11½×11

2108	**577** 60 g. red, violet-blue and pale grey		10	10
	a. Strip. Nos. 2108/9 plus label		20	15
2109	– 60 g. red & pale grey (Worker's head)		10	10

(*b*) *Industrial Development. T* **578** *and similar horiz designs. Each gold, black and red.* P 11×11½

2110	60 g. Type **578**		10	10
	a. Block of 6. Nos. 2110/15		55	
2111	60 g. Building construction		10	10
2112	60 g. Combine harvester		10	10
2113	60 g. Motor-car production		10	10
2114	60 g. Pit-head		10	10
2115	60 g. Petro-chemical plant		10	10
2108/2115	*Set of 8*		70	65
MS2116	102×115 mm. Nos. 2110/15 (4.72)		80	45

Nos. 2108/9 were issued *se-tenant* within the sheet with an intervening stamp-size label inscr "PZPR".

Nos. 2110/15 were issued together *se-tenant* in blocks of six within the sheet, forming an outline map of Poland.

579 *Prunus cerasus*

(Des A. Balcerzak. Litho)

1971 (28 Dec). *Flowers of Trees and Shrubs. T* **579** *and similar horiz designs. Multicoloured.* P 12½.

2117	10 g. Type **579**		10	10
2118	20 g. *Malus niedzwetzkyana*		10	10
2119	40 g. *Pyrus L.*		10	10
2120	60 g. *Prunus persica*		10	10
2121	1 z. 15, *Magnolia kobus*		15	10
2122	1 z. 35, *Crataegus oxyacantha*		15	10
2123	2 z. 50, *Malus M.*		20	10
2124	3 z. 40, *Aesculus carnea*		30	10
2125	5 z. *Robinia pseudacacia*		1·00	25
2126	8 z. 50, *Prunus avium*		1·90	60
2117/2126	*Set of 10*		3·75	1·25

HAVE YOU READ THE NOTES AT THE BEGINNING OF THIS CATALOGUE?

These often provide answers to the enquiries we receive.

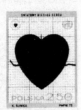

580 "Worker" (sculpture, J. Januszkiewicz)

582 "Heart" and Cardiogram Trace

581 Tobogganing

(Des J. Brzoza. Recess and photo)

1972 (5 Jan). *30th Anniversary of Polish Workers' Coalition* P 11½.
2127 **580** 60 g. black and red 15 10

(Des H. Matuszewska. Photo)

1972 (12 Jan). *Winter Olympic Games, Sapporo, Japan.* T **581** *and similar multicoloured designs.* P 11.
2128 40 g. Type **581** 10 10
2129 60 g. Slalom (*vert*) 10 10
2130 1 z. 65, Biathlon (*vert*) .. 30 10
2131 2 z. 50, Ski jumping 45 20
2128/2131 *Set of 4* 85 40
MS2132 85×68 mm. 10 z. + 5 z. Downhill skiing. Imperf .. .. .. 2·10 1·25

(Des K. Śliwka. Photo)

1972 (28 Mar). *World Heart Month.* P 11½×11.
2133 **582** 2 z. 50, multicoloured 20 10

583 Running

584 Cyclists

(Des W. Swierzy. Photo)

1972 (25 Apr). *Olympic Games, Munich.* T **583** *and similar vert designs. Multicoloured.* P 11½×11.
2134 20 g. Type **583** 10 10
2135 30 g. Archery 10 10
2136 40 g. Boxing 10 10
2137 60 g. Fencing 10 10
2138 2 z. 50, Wrestling 15 10
2139 3 z. 40, Weightlifting .. 20 10
2140 5 z. Cycling 75 30
2141 8 z. 50, Shooting .. .. 1·25 45
2134/2141 *Set of 8* .. .. 2·10 95
MS2142 70×80 mm. 10 z. +5 z. As 30 g. .. 1·75 1·40

(Des T. Michaluk. Photo)

1972 (2 May). *25th International Peace Cycle Race.* P 11.
2143 **584** 60 g. multicoloured 20 10

585 Polish War Memorial, Berlin

586 "Rodlo" Emblem

(Des S. Malecki. Eng E. Tirdiszek. Recess)

1972 (9 May). *"Victory Day, 1945".* P 11½×11.
2144 **585** 60 g. blackish green 15 10

(Des J. Klopocka. Photo)

1972 (28 May). *50th Anniv of Polish Posts in Germany.* P 11½×11.
2145 **586** 60 g. scarlet, myrtle-grn & pale bistre 15 10

587 Polish Knight of 972 A.D.

589 L. Waryński (founder)

588 Cheetah

(Des J. Wysocki. Photo)

1972 (12 June). *Millenary of Battle of Cedynia.* P 11½×11.
2146 **587** 60 g. multicoloured 15 10

(Des J. Grabianski. Litho)

1972 (21 Aug). *Zoo Animals.* T **588** *and similar multicoloured designs on pale buff paper.* P 12½.
2147 20 g. Type **588** 15 10
2148 40 g. Giraffe (*vert*) 20 10
2149 60 g. Toco Toucan 30 10
2150 1 z. 35 Chimpanzee 20 10
2151 1 z. 65, Common gibbon .. 30 10
2152 3 z. 40, Crocodile 40 10
2153 4 z. Red kangaroo 70 15
2154 4 z. 50, Tiger (*vert*) .. .. 2·75 1·00
2155 7 z. Mountain zebra .. .. 3·00 1·25
2147/2155 *Set of 9* .. .. .. 7·25 2·75

(Des K. W. Brzoza. Photo)

1972 (1 Sept). *90th Anniv of Proletarian Party.* P 11.
2156 **589** 60 g. multicoloured 15 10
No. 2156 was issued together with *se-tenant* stamp-sized labels bearing a facsimile of the front page of *Proletaryat.*

590 F. Dzerzhinsky   **591** Global Emblem

(Des Z. Stasik. Photo)

1972 (11 Sept). *95th Birth Anniv of Feliks Dzerzhinsky (Russian politician).* P 11 × 11½.
2157 **590** 60 g. black and red 15 10

(Des M. Wieczorek. Photo)

1972 (15 Sept). *25th International Co-operative Federation Congress.* P 11½ × 11.
2158 **591** 60 g. multicoloured 15 10

592 Scene from *In Barracks* (ballet)   **593** "Copernicus the Astronomer"

(Des J. Desselberger. Eng B. Kowalska (10 g., 2 z. 50), B. Brandt (20 g., 1 z. 35, 1 z. 55), E. Tirdiszek (40 g., 60 g.) and E. Konecki (1 z. 15). Recess and photo)

1972 (15 Sept). *Death Centenary of Stanislaus Moniuszko (composer). Scenes from Works.* T **592** and similar vert designs. P 11½.
2159   10 g. violet and gold 10 10
2160   20 g. black and gold 10 10
2161   40 g. myrtle-green and gold .. 10 10
2162   60 g. indigo and gold 15 10
2163   1 z. 15, deep blue and gold .. 15 10
2164   1 z. 35, deep blue and gold .. 15 10
2165   1 z. 55, olive-grey and gold .. 15 15
2166   2 z. 50, blackish brown and gold 50 25
2159/2166   Set of 8 .. .. .. 1·10 50
Designs:—20 g. *The Countess* (opera); 40 g. *The Haunted Manor* (opera); 60 g. *Halka* (opera); 1 z. 15, *New Don Quixote* (ballet); 1 z. 35, *Verbum Nobile* (opera); 1 z. 55, *Ideal* (operetta); 2 z. 50, *Pariah* (opera).

(Des W. Andrzejewski. Eng B. Kowalska (10 z.). Litho or recess and typo (10 z.))

1972 (28 Sept). *500th Birth Anniv of Nicolas Copernicus (1973) (4th issue),* and *"Polska 73" Stamp Exhibition, Poznan.* T **583** and similar designs. P 11 × 11½ or 11½ (10 z.).
2167   40 g. black and bright blue .. 10 10
2168   60 g. black and yellow-orange .. 15 10
2169   2 z. 50, black and bright red .. 50 10
2170   3 z. 40, black and yellow-green .. 60 30
2167/2170   Set of 4 .. .. .. 1·25 50
MS2171 62 × 102 mm. 10 z. + 5 z. multicoloured 2·50 1·50
Designs:—*Horiz*—60 g. Copernicus and Medal of 1530; 2 z. 50, Copernicus and Polish eagle; 3 z. 40, Copernicus and page of book. *Vert* (29 × 48mm.)—10 z. + 5 z. Copernicus charting the planets.

PIOTR MICHAŁOWSKI

1 50 Zł

(595)

594 "Amazon" (P. Michalowski)   **596** "The Little Soldier" (E. Piwowarski)

(Des T. Michaluk. Photo)

1972 (28 Sept). *Stamp Day. Polish Paintings.* T **594** and similar multicoloured designs. P 11.
2172   30 g. Type **594** 10 10
2173   40 g. "Ostafi Laskiewicz" (J. Metejko) 10 10
2174   60 g. "Summer Idyll" (W. Gerson) 10 10
2175   2 z. "The Neapolitan Woman" (A. Kotsis) 15 10
2176   2 z. 50, "Girl Bathing" (P. Szyndler) .. 20 10
2177   3 z. 40, "The Princess of Thum" (A. Grottger) 30 10
2178   4 z. "Rhapsody" (S. Wyspianski) .. 1·25 45
2179   8 z. 50 + 4 z. "Young Woman" (J. Malczewski) (*horiz*) .. 1·50 75
2172/2179   Set of 8 .. .. 3·25 1·40

1972 (2 Oct–17 Nov). *Provisionals. Nos. 1578/9 surch as* T **595**.
2180   50 g. on 40 g. red-brown (R.) (17.11) .. 10 10
2181   90 g. on 40 g. red-brown (R.) (17.11) .. 15 10
2182   1 z. on 40 g. red-brown (R.) .. 10 10
2183   1 z. 50 on 60 g. orange-red .. 10 10
2184   2 z. 70 on 40 g. red-brown (R.) .. 20 10
2185   4 z. on 60 g. orange-red .. 30 10
2186   4 z. 50 on 60 g. orange-red .. 30 10
2187   4 z. 90 on 60 g. orange-red .. 50 15
2180/2187   Set of 8 .. .. 1·60 55
On Nos. 2180/2 and 2184 the old denominations are obliterated by crosses.

(Des T. Michaluk. Litho)

1972 (16 Oct). *Children's Health Centre.* P 11½.
2188 **596** 60 g. black and pink 15 10

597 "Royal Castle, Warsaw" (E. J. Dahlberg, 1656)   **598** Chalet, Chocholowska Valley

(Des A. Heidrich. Photo)

1972 (16 Oct). *Restoration of Royal Castle, Warsaw.* P 11 × 11½.
2189 **597** 60 g. black, reddish violet & light blue 15 10

(Des A. Balcerzak. Photo)

1972 (13 Nov). *Tourism. Mountain Chalets.* T **598** and similar multicoloured designs. P 11.
2190   40 g. Type **598** 10 10
2191   60 g. Hala Ornak (*horiz*) .. 10 10
2192   1 z. 55, Hala Gasienicowa .. 10 10

2193	1 z. 65, Valley of Five Lakes (*horiz*)		−20	10
2194	2 z. 50, Morskie Oko		35	10
2190/2194	Set of 5		65	30

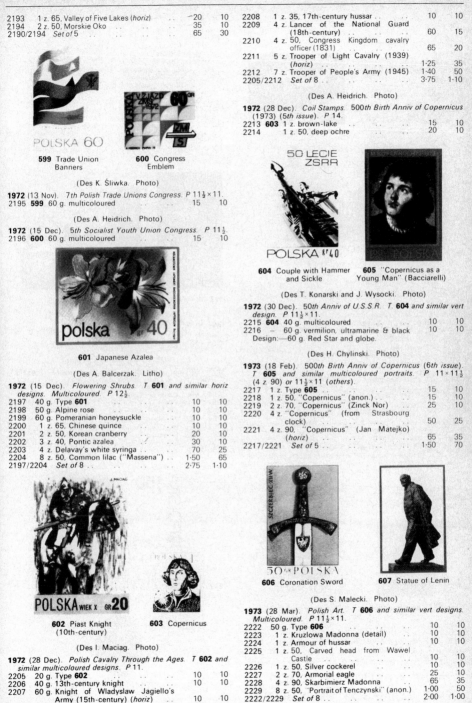

599 Trade Union Banners

600 Congress Emblem

(Des K. Śliwka. Photo)

1972 (13 Nov). *7th Polish Trade Unions Congress.* P 11½ × 11.

2195	**599**	60 g. multicoloured		15	10

(Des A. Heidrich. Photo)

1972 (15 Dec). *5th Socialist Youth Union Congress.* P 11½.

2196	**600**	60 g. multicoloured		15	10

601 Japanese Azalea

(Des A. Balcerzak. Litho)

1972 (15 Dec). *Flowering Shrubs.* T **601** *and similar horiz designs. Multicoloured.* P 12½.

2197	40 g. Type **601**		10	10
2198	50 g. Alpine rose		10	10
2199	60 g. Pomeranian honeysuckle		10	10
2200	1 z. 65, Chinese quince		10	10
2201	2 z. 50, Korean cranberry		20	10
2202	3 z. 40, Pontic azalea		30	10
2203	4 z. Delavay's white syringa		70	25
2204	8 z. 50, Common lilac ("Massena")		1·50	65
2197/2204	Set of 8		2·75	1·10

602 Piast Knight (10th-century)

603 Copernicus

(Des I. Maciag. Photo)

1972 (28 Dec). *Polish Cavalry Through the Ages.* T **602** *and similar multicoloured designs.* P 11.

2205	20 g. Type **602**		10	10
2206	40 g. 13th-century knight		10	10
2207	60 g. Knight of Wladyslaw Jagiello's Army (15th-century) (*horiz*)		10	10
2208	1 z. 35, 17th-century hussar		10	10
2209	4 z. Lancer of the National Guard (18th-century)		60	15
2210	4 z. 50, Congress Kingdom cavalry officer (1831)		65	20
2211	5 z. Trooper of Light Cavalry (1939) (*horiz*)		1·25	35
2212	7 z. Trooper of People's Army (1945)		1·40	50
2205/2212	Set of 8		3·75	1·10

(Des A. Heidrich. Photo)

1972 (28 Dec). *Coil Stamps. 500th Birth Anniv of Copernicus* (1973) (*5th issue*). P 14.

2213	**603**	1 z. brown-lake		15	10
2214		1 z. 50, deep ochre		20	10

604 Couple with Hammer and Sickle

605 "Copernicus as a Young Man" (Bacciarelli)

(Des T. Konarski and J. Wysocki. Photo)

1972 (30 Dec). *50th Anniv of U.S.S.R.* T **604** *and similar vert design.* P 11½ × 11.

2215	**604**	40 g. multicoloured		10	10
2216	—	60 g. vermilion, ultramarine & black		10	10

Design:—60 g. Red Star and globe.

(Des H. Chylinski. Photo)

1973 (18 Feb). *500th Birth Anniv of Copernicus* (*6th issue*). T **605** *and similar multicoloured portraits.* P 11 × 11½ (4 z. 90) *or* 11½ × 11 (*others*).

2217	1 z. Type **605**		15	10
2218	1 z. 50, "Copernicus" (anon.)		15	10
2219	2 z. 70, "Copernicus" (Zinck Nor)		25	10
2220	4 z. "Copernicus" (from Strasbourg clock)		50	25
2221	4 z. 90, "Copernicus" (Jan Matejko) (*horiz*)		65	35
2217/2221	Set of 5		1·50	70

606 Coronation Sword

607 Statue of Lenin

(Des S. Malecki. Photo)

1973 (28 Mar). *Polish Art.* T **606** *and similar vert designs. Multicoloured.* P 11½ × 11.

2222	50 g. Type **606**		10	10
2223	1 z. Kruzlowa Madonna (detail)		10	10
2224	1 z. Armour of hussar		10	10
2225	1 z. 50, Carved head from Wawel Castle		10	10
2226	1 z. 50, Silver cockerel		10	10
2227	2 z. 70, Armorial eagle		25	10
2228	4 z. 90, Skarbimierz Madonna		65	35
2229	8 z. 50, "Portrait of Tenczynski" (anon.)		1·00	50
2222/2229	Set of 8		2·00	1·00

(Des S. Malecki. Litho)

1973 (28 Apr). *Unveiling of Lenin's Statue, Nowa Huta.*
P 11×11½.
2230 **607** 1 z. multicoloured 15 10

608 Coded Letter

610 "Salyut"

609 Wolf

(Des H. Chylinski. Photo)

1973 (5 May). *Introduction of Postal Codes.* P 11×11½.
2231 **608** 1 z. 50, multicoloured 15 10

(Des I. Konarski and J. Wysocki. Photo)

1973 (21 May). *International Hunting Council Congress and 50th
Anniv of Polish Hunting Association. Game Animals.* T **609** *and
similar horiz designs. Multicoloured.* P 11.

2232	50 g. Type **609**	..	..	10	10
2233	1 z. Mouflon	..	..	10	10
2234	1 z. 50, Elk	..	..	10	10
2235	2 z. 70, Capercaillie	..	..	30	10
2236	3 z. Roe deer	..	..	30	10
2237	4 z. 50, Lynx ..	..	..	65	20
2238	4 z. 90, Red deer	..	..	1·75	35
2239	5 z. Wild boar	..	..	2·00	45
2232/2239	Set of 8 ..	..	..	4·75	1·25

(Des Z. Stasik. Photo)

1973 (20 June). *Cosmic Research.* T **610** *and similar horiz
design. Multicoloured.* P 11×11½.
2240 4 z. 90, Type **610** 45 25
2241 4 z. 90, "Copernicus" (U.S. satellite) .. 45 25
Nos 2240/1 were respectively issued in sheets of six stamps
plus two *se-tenant* stamp-sized labels depicting (No. 2240)
"Soyuz 11" or Soviet astronauts; (2241) Copernicus or
constellations.

611 Open Book and
Flame

612 Ancient Seal of
Poznan

(Des R. Dudzicki. Litho)

1973 (26 June). *2nd Polish Science Congress, Warsaw.* P 11½.
2242 **611** 1 z. 50, multicoloured 15 10

THE WORLD CENTRE FOR
FINE STAMPS IS 399 STRAND

(Des W. Andrzejewski. Eng E. Konecki (10 z.). Litho or recess
and litho (10 z.))

1973 (30 June–19 Aug). *"Polska 73" Philatelic Exhibition,
Poznan.* T **612** *and similar multicoloured designs.* P 11×11½ (4 z.)
or 11½×11 (*others*).

2243	1 z. Type **612**	..	..	10	10
2244	1 z. 50, Tombstone of N. Tomicki	..	10	10
2245	2 z. 70, Kalisz paten	..	..	25	10
2246	4 z. Bronze gates, Gniezno Cathedral (*horiz*)		..	40	20
2243/2246	Set of 4	..	..	75	35
MS2247	91×66 mm. 10 z. + 5 z. deep purple and pale olive. Imperf		..	2·00	1·10
MS2248	91×66 mm. 10 z. + 5 z. deep purple and pale lilac. Imperf		..	6·00	4·75

Design: 68×32 *mm*—10 z. Poznan in 1740.
No. **MS**2248 was sold only with entrance tickets to the
exhibition.

613 M. Nowotko

614 Cherry Blossom

(Des J. Wysocki. Litho)

1973 (8 Aug). *80th Birth Anniv of Marceli Nowotko (party
leader).* P 11½×11.
2249 **613** 1 z. 50, black and vermilion .. 15 10

(Des H. Matuszewska. Photo)

1973 (20 Aug). *Protection of the Environment.* T **614** *and
similar horiz designs. Multicoloured.* P 11.

2250	50 g. Type **614**	..	..	10	10
2251	90 g. Cattle in meadow	..	..	10	10
2252	1 z. White stork on nest	..	..	50	10
2253	1 z. 50, Fresh water life	..	..	15	10
2254	2 z. 70, Meadow flora	..	..	25	10
2255	4 z. 90, Ocean fauna ..	..	..	55	30
2256	5 z. Forest life	..	..	2·75	45
2257	6 z. 50, Agricultural produce ..	..	1·75	50
2250/2257	Set of 8 ..	..	..	5·50	1·50

615 Motor-cyclist

(Des W. Andrzejewski. Photo)

1973 (2 Sept). *World Speedway Championships, Chorzów.* P 11½.
2258 **615** 1 z. 50, multicoloured 15 10

616 "Copernicus" (M. Bacciarelli)

(Des A. Heidrich. Photo)

1973 (27 Sept). *Stamp Day.* P 11×11½.

| 2259 | 616 | 4 z.+2 z. multicoloured | .. | .. | 50 | 25 |

617 Tank

(Des T. Michaluk. Litho)

1973 (4 Oct). *30th Anniv of Polish People's Army.* T **617** and similar horiz designs. Multicoloured. P 12½.

2260	1 z. Type **617**		..	15	10
2261	1 z. Mikoyan Gurevich MiG-21D airplane		20	10
2262	1 z. 50, Guided missile ..		..	20	10
2263	1 z. 50, Missile boat	..	..	25	10
2260/2263	*Set of 4*	..	..	70	30

618 G. Piramowicz and Title Page

(Des S. Malecki. Eng E. Tirdiszek (1 z.) and B. Brandt (1 z. 50). Recess and photo)

1973 (13 Oct). *Bicentenary of National Education Commission.* T **618** and similar horiz design. P 12×11½.

| 2264 | 1 z. blackish brown and pale yellow | .. | 10 | 10 |
| 2265 | 1 z. 50, bronze-green & pale grey-green | 15 | 10 |

Design:—1 z. 50, J. Sniadecki, H. Kollataj and J. U. Niemcewicz.

619 Pawel Strzelecki (explorer) and Red Kangaroo

620 Polish Flag

(Des T. Michaluk. Photo)

1973 (30 Nov). *Polish Scientists.* T **619** and similar vert designs. Multicoloured. P 11.

2266	1 z. Type **619**		..	15	10
2267	1 z. Henryk Arctowski (polar explorer) and Adelie penguins		..	35	10
2268	1 z. 50, Stefan Rogoziński (explorer) and *Lucy-Margaret*		30	10
2269	1 z. 50, Benedykt Dybowski (zoologist) and sable, Lake Baikal	..	..	20	10
2270	2 z. Bronislaw Malinowski (anthropologist) and New Guinea dancers		25	10

2271	2 z. 70, Stefan Drzewiecki (oceanographer) and submarine	..	..	35	10
2272	3 z. Edward Strasburger (botanist) and classified plants	..	..	35	15
2273	8 z. Ignacy Domeyko (geologist) and Chilean desert landscape	..	..	1·40	50
2266/2273	*Set of 8*	..	..	3·00	90

(Des K. Śliwka. Photo)

1973 (15 Dec). *25th Anniv of Polish United Workers' Party.* P 11½×11.

| 2274 | 620 | 1 z. 50, red, ultramarine and gold | .. | 15 | 10 |

621 Jelcz-Berliet Coach

622 Iris

(Des T. Konarski and J. Wysocki. Photo)

1973 (28 Dec). *Polish Motor Vehicles.* T **621** and similar horiz designs. Multicoloured. P 11×11½.

2275	50 g. Type **621**	..	..	10	10
2276	90 g. Jelcz "316" truck	..	..	10	10
2277	1 z. Polski Fiat "126p" saloon	..	10	10
2278	1 z. 50, Polski Fiat "125p" saloon	..	10	10
2279	4 z. Nysa "M-521" utility van	..	40	40
2280	4 z. 50, Star "660" truck	..	75	50
2275/2280	*Set of 6*	..	..	1·40	95

(Des J. Brodowski. Eng B. Kowalska (50 g., 1 z.), E. Konecki (1 z. 50, 3 z.), A. Ostrowska (4 z., 4 z. 50). Recess)

1974 (22 Jan). *Flowers. Drawings by S. Wyspianski.* T **622** and similar vert designs. P 12×11½.

2281	50 g. purple	..	..	10	10
2282	1 z. turquoise-green ..		..	10	10
2283	1 z. 50, vermilion ..		..	10	10
2284	3 z. violet	..	..	35	10
2285	4 z. ultramarine	..	..	40	10
2286	4 z. 50, blue-green ..		..	60	25
2281/2286	*Set of 6*	..	..	1·40	50

Flowers:—1 z. Dandelion; 1 z. 50, Rose; 3 z. Thistle; 4 z. Cornflower; 4 z. 50, Clover.

623 Cottage, Kurpie

624 19th-century Mail Coach

(Des F. Winiarski. Photo)

1974 (5 Mar). *Wooden Architecture.* T **623** and similar horiz designs. Multicoloured. P 11×11½.

2287	1 z. Type **623**	..	..	10	10
2288	1 z. 50, Church, Sekowa	..	..	10	10
2289	4 z. Town Hall, Sulmierzyce	..	30	10
2290	4 z. 50, Church, Lachowice	..	35	10
2291	4 z. 90, Windmill, Sobienie Jeziory	..	55	20
2292	5 z. Orthodox Church, Ulucz	..	60	30
2287/2292	*Set of 6*	..	..	1·75	80

(Des T. Michaluk. Photo)

1974 (30 Mar). *Centenary of Universal Postal Union.* P 11½.

| 2293 | 624 | 1 z. 50, multicoloured | .. | .. | 15 | 10 |

625 Cracow Motif **626** Association Emblem

(Des H. Matuszewska. Photo)

1974 (7 May). "SOCPHILEX IV" International Stamp Exhibition, Katowice. Regional Floral Embroideries. T **625** and similar vert designs. Multicoloured. P 11½ × 11.

2294	50 g. Type **625**	..	10	10
2295	1 z. 50, Lowicz motif	..	10	10
2296	4 z. Silesian motif	..	35	15
MS2297	69×171 mm. No. 2296×3. Imperf			
	(sold at 17 z.)	..	1·40	1·10

The normal, imperforate, version of No. **MS**2297 has bluish violet borders, showing a lace pattern in white. The miniature sheet also exists perforated from a limited printing with white borders and the lace pattern in silver.

(Des K. Śliwka. Litho)

1974 (8 May). Fifth Congress of Fighters for Freedom and Democracy Association, Warsaw. P 11½.

2298	**626** 1 z. 50, red	..	15	10

627 Soldier and Dove **628** "Comecon" Headquarters, Moscow

(Des T. Michaluk. Litho)

1974 (9 May). 29th Anniv of Victory over Fascism in Second World War. P 11½ × 11.

2299	**627** 1 z. 50, multicoloured	..	15	10

(Des Z. Stasik. Litho)

1974 (15 May). 25th Anniv of Council for Mutual Economic Aid. P 11 × 11½.

2300	**628** 1 z. 50, ochre, red and cobalt	..	15	10

629 World Cup Emblem **630** Model of 16th-century Galleon

(Des H. Chyliński. Photo)

1974 (6 June). World Cup Football Championships, West Germany. T **629** and similar horiz design. Multicoloured. P 11×11½.

2301	4 z. 90, Type **629**	..	50	20
2302	4 z. 90, Players and Olympic Gold Medal of 1972	..	50	20
MS2303	116×83 mm. Nos. 2301/2×2	..	12·00	10·50

See also No. **MS**2315.

(Des W. Andrzejewski. Litho)

1974 (29 June). Sailing Ships. T **630** and similar vert designs. Multicoloured. P 11½×11.

2304	1 z. Type **630**	..	25	10
2305	1 z. 50, Trans-Atlantic sloop Dal (1934)	..	25	10
2306	2 z. 70, Yacht Opty (Teliga's circumnavigation, 1969)	..	35	10
2307	4 z. Cadet ship Dar Pomorza	..	65	25
2308	4 z. 90, Yacht Polonez (Baranowski's circumnavigation 1973)	..	95	35
2304/2308	Set of 5	..	2·25	80

631 Title page of Chess **632** Lazienkowska Road by Jan Kochanowski   Junction

(Des A. Heidrich. Litho)

1974 (15 July). 10th International Chess Festival, Lublin. T **631** and similar vert design. Multicoloured. P 11½×11.

2309	1 z. Type **631**	..	20	10
2310	1 z. 50, "Education" (engraving, D. Chodowiecki)	..	30	10

(Des M. Wieczorek. Litho)

1974 (21 July). Opening of Lazienkowska Road Junction. P 11×11½.

2311	**632** 1 z. 50, multicoloured	..	15	10

633 Face on Map of Poland **634** Strawberries

(Des J. W. Brzoza. Photo)

1974 (21 July). 30th Anniv of Polish People's Republic. T **633** and similar designs. P 11½×11.

2312	1 z. 50, black, gold and vermilion	..	15	10
2313	1 z. 50, multicoloured (silver background)	..	15	10
2314	1 z. 50, multicoloured (scarlet background)	..	15	10

Designs: 31×43 mm—Nos. 2313 and 2314, Polish "Eagle".

(Des H. Chyliński. Photo)

1974 (21 July). *Poland—Third Place in World Cup Football Championship. Sheet* 107 × 121 mm containing four stamps as No. 2301, but with inscr in silver instead of black, and two labels. P 11 × 11½.

MS2315 **629** 4 z. 90, × 4. multicoloured .. 3·75 1·90

(Des K. Śliwka. Photo)

1974 (10 Sept). *19th International Horticultural Congress, Warsaw. T* **634** *and similar vert designs. Multicoloured.* P 11½.

2316	50 g. Type **634**	..	10	10
2317	90 g. Blackcurrants	..	10	10
2318	1 z. Apples	..	10	10
2319	1 z. 50, Cucumbers	..	15	10
2320	2 z. 70, Tomatoes	..	25	10
2321	4 z. 50, Peas	..	60	20
2322	4 z. 90, Pansies	..	90	25
2323	5 z. Nasturtiums	..	1·25	30
2316/2323	*Set of 8* ..		2·25	1·00

635 Civic Militia and Security Service Emblem

636 "Child in Polish Costume" (L. Orlowski)

(Des W. Surowiecki. Photo)

1974 (3 Oct). *30th Anniv of Polish Civic Militia and Security Service.* P 11½ × 11.
2324 **635** 1 z. 50, multicoloured 15 10

(Des W. Andrzejewski. Photo)

1974 (9 Oct). *Stamp Day. Polish Paintings of Children. T* **636** *and similar vert designs. Multicoloured.* P 11½ × 11.

2325	50 g. Type **636**	..	10	10
2326	90 g. "Girl with Pigeon" (anon.)		10	10
2327	1 z. "Portrait of Girl" (S. Wyspiański)		10	10
2328	1 z. 50, "Orphan from Poronin" (W. Ślewiński)		10	10
2329	3 z. "Peasant Boy" (K. Sichulski)		25	10
2330	4 z. 50, "Florence Page" (A. Gierymski)		40	10
2331	4 z. 90, "Tadeusz and Dog" (P. Michalowski)		50	25
2332	6 z. 50, "Boy with Doe" (A. Kotsis)		70	40
2325/2332	*Set of 8*		1·90	90

637 "The Crib", Cracow

638 Angler and Fish

(Des S. Malecki. Litho)

1974 (2 Dec). *Polish Art. T* **637** *and similar vert designs. Multicoloured.* P 11½ × 11.

2333	1 z. Type **637**		10	10
2334	1 z. 50, "The Flight to Egypt" (15th-century polyptych)		15	10
2335	2 z. "King Sigismund III Vasa" (16th-century miniature) ..		20	10
2336	4 z. "King Jan Olbracht" (16th-century title-page)		80	25
2333/2336	*Set of 4* ..		1·10	40

(Des T. Michaluk. Eng B. Kowalska (1 z.). M. Kopecki (1 z. 50). Recess)

1974 (30 Dec). *Polish Folklore. 16th-century wood-carvings* (*1st series*). *T* **638** *and similar horiz design.* P 12 × 11.
2337 1 z. black 10 10
2338 1 z. 50, blue-black 15 10
Design:—1 z. 50, Hunter and wild animals.

639 "Pablo Neruda" (O. Guayasamin)

640 "Nike" Memorial and National Opera-house

(Des H. Chyliński. Litho)

1974 (31 Dec). *70th Birth Anniv of Pablo Neruda* (*Chilean poet*). P 11½ × 11.
2339 **639** 1 z. 50, multicoloured .. 15 10

(Des H. Chyliński. Photo)

1975 (17 Jan). *30th Anniv of Liberation of Warsaw.* P 11.
2340 **640** 1 z. 50, multicoloured 15 10

641 Male Lesser Kestrel (*Falco naumanni*)

642 Broken Barbed Wire

(Des J. Desselberger. Photo)

1975 (23 Jan). *Birds of Prey. T* **641** *and similar vert designs. Multicoloured.* P 11½ × 12.

2341	1 z. Type **641**		30	10
	a. Pair. Nos. 2341/2 ..		60	15
2342	1 z. Female lesser kestrel ..		30	10
2343	1 z. 50, Male red-footed falcon (*Falco vespertinus*) ..		35	10
	a. Pair. Nos 2343/4 ..		70	15
2344	1 z. 50, Female red-footed falcon ..		35	10
2345	2 z. European hobby (*Falco subbuteo*) ..		50	10
2346	3 z. Common kestrel (*Falco tinnunculus*)		80	10
2347	4 z. Merlin (*Falco columbarius*) ..		2·10	70
2348	8 z. Peregrine falcon (*Falco peregrinus*)		3·25	1·40
2341/2348	*Set of 8*		7·25	2·25

Nos. 2341/2 and 2343/4 were issued in *se-tenant* pairs within their sheets.

(Des Z. Stasik. Recess and photo)

1975 (27 Jan). *30th Anniv of Auschwitz Concentration Camp Liberation.* P 11½×11.
2349 **642** 1 z. 50, black and red 20 10

643 Hurdling   **644** "St Anne" (Veit Stoss)

(Des W. Andrzejewski. Litho (Nos. 2350/3) or recess and photo (**MS**2354))

1975 (8 Mar). *6th European Indoor Athletics Championships, Katowice.* T **643** *and similar horiz designs.* Multicoloured. P 11×11½.
2350	1 z. Type **643**	10	10
2351	1 z. 50, Pole vaulting	15	10
2352	4 z. Triple jump	30	10
2353	4 z. 90, Running	35	15
2350/2353	*Set of 4*	80	30

MS2354 72×63 mm. 10 z.+5 z. deep turquoise -green and silver (Montreal Olympics emblem) (26×31 mm). P 11½ .. .. 2·00 1·00
No. **MS**2354 has both the stamp and the outer edges of the sheet perforated.

(Des A. Heidrich. Photo)

1975 (15 Apr). *"Arphila 1975" International Stamp Exhibition, Paris.* P 11×11½.
2355 **644** 1 z. 50, multicoloured 15 10

645 Globe and "Radio Waves"   **646** Stone Pine and Tatra Mountains

(Des S. Malecki. Litho)

1975 (15 Apr). *International Amateur Radio Union Conference, Warsaw.* P 11½.
2356 **645** 1 z. 50, multicoloured 15 10

(Des A. Balcerzak. Photo)

1975 (30 Apr). *Centenary of National Mountain Guides' Association.* T **646** *and similar multicoloured designs.* P 11.
2357	1 z. Type **646**	10	10
	a. Pair. Nos. 2357/8	20	15
2358	1 z. Gentian and Tatra Mountains	10	10
2359	1 z. 50, Sudety Mountains (*horiz*)	15	10
	a. Pair. Nos. 2359/60	30	15
2360	1 z. 50, Yew-tree branch (*horiz*)	15	10
2361	4 z. Beskidy Mountains	40	15
	a. Pair. Nos. 2361/2	80	30
2362	4 z. Arnica blossoms	40	15
2357/2362	*Set of 6*	1·10	45

Designs of the same value were issued in *se-tenant* pairs forming composite designs.

647 Hands holding Tulips and Rifle   **648** Flags of Member Countries

(Des H. Chyliński. Photo)

1975 (9 May). *30th Anniv of Victory over Fascism.* P 11½×11.
2363 **647** 1 z. 50, multicoloured 15 10

(Des W. Surowiecki. Photo)

1975 (9 May). *20th Anniv of Warsaw Treaty Organisation.* P 11½×11.
2364 **648** 1 z. 50, multicoloured 15 10

649 Hens

(Des A. Balcerzak. Photo)

1975 (23 June). *26th European Zootechnical Federation Congress, Warsaw.* T **649** *and similar horiz designs.* Multicoloured. P 11½.
2365	50 g. Type **649**	10	10
2366	1 z. Geese	10	10
2367	1 z. 50, Cattle	15	10
2368	2 z. Cow	15	10
2369	3 z. Wielkopolska horse	30	10
2370	4 z. Arab horses	35	10
2371	4 z. 50, Pigs	1·25	40
2372	5 z. Sheep	1·75	60
2365/2372	*Set of 8*	3·75	1·10

650 "Apollo" and "Soyuz" Spacecraft linked   **651** Organisation Emblem

(Des R. Dudzicki. Photo)

1975 (30 June). *"Apollo-Soyuz" Space Link.* T **650** *and similar horiz designs.* Multicoloured. P 11×11½.
2373	1 z. 50, Type **650**	15	10
2374	4 z. 90, "Apollo" spacecraft	50	20
	a. Pair. Nos. 2374/5	1·00	40
2375	4 z. 90, "Soyuz" spacecraft	50	20

MS2376 119×156 mm. Nos. 2373×2, 2374×2 and 2375×2 .. .. 6·50 3·50
Nos. 2374/5 were issued together in *se-tenant* pairs within the sheet.

(Des K. Tarkowska. Photo)

1975 (12 July). *National Health Protection Fund.* P 11½×11.
2377 **651** 1 z. 50, blue, black and silver .. 15 10

652 U.N. Emblem

653 Polish Flag within
"E" for Europe

658 Mary and Margaret and
Polish Settlers

659 Frédéric Chopin

(Des A. Heidrich. Litho)

1975 (25 July). *30th Anniv of United Nations Organisation.*
P 11×11½.
2378 **652** 4 z. multicoloured 35 15

(Des H. Chyliński. Litho)

1975 (30 July). *European Security and Co-operation Conference, Helsinki.* P 11×11½.
2379 **653** 4 z. multicoloured .. 35 15

(Des T. Michaluk. Litho)

1975 (26 Sept). *Bicentenary of American Revolution.* T **658** and similar horiz designs. Multicoloured. P 11×11½.
2388 1 z. Type **658** 20 10
2389 1 z. 50, Polish Glass-works, Jamestown 15 10
2390 2 z. 70, H. Modrzejewska (actress) 15 10
2391 4 z. K. Pulaski (soldier) .. 30 10
2392 6 z. 40, T. Kościuszko (soldier) .. 70 30
2388/2392 *Set of 5* .. .. .. 1·25 45
MS2393 117×102 mm. 4 z. 90, Washington;
4 z. 90, Kościuszko; 4 z. 90, Pulaski. P 12 1·25 65

(Des S. Malecki. Photo)

1975 (7 Oct). *9th International Chopin Piano Competition.*
P 11½.
2394 **659** 1 z. 50, black, lavender and gold .. 15 10
No. 2394 was issued with se-tenant stamp-size label.

654 "Bolek and Lolek"

655 Institute Emblem

660 "Self-Portrait"

661 Market Place,
Kazimierz Dolny

(Des H. Matuszewska. Photo)

1975 (30 Aug). *Children's Television Characters.* T **654** and similar horiz designs. Multicoloured. P 11×11½.
2380 50 g. Type **654** 10 10
2381 1 z. "Jacek and Agatka" .. 15 10
2382 1 z. 50, "Reksio" 15 10
2383 4 z. "Telesfor" 55 15
2380/2383 *Set of 4* 75 25

(Des H. Matuszewska. Photo)

1975 (9 Oct). *Stamp Day and Birth Centenary of Xawery Dunikowski (sculptor).* T **660** and similar vert designs. Multicoloured. P 11½×11.
2395 50 g. Type **660** 10 10
2396 1 z. "Breath" 10 10
2397 1 z. 50, "Maternity" .. 15 10
2398 8 z.+4 z. "Silesian Insurrectionists" 90 45
2395/2398 *Set of 4* .. .. 1·10 55

(Des K. Rogaczewska. Litho)

1975 (1 Sept). *40th Session of International Institute of Statistics.* P 11½×11.
2384 **655** 1 z. 50, multicoloured 15 10

(Des S. Malecki. Photo)

1975 (11 Nov). *European Architectural Heritage Year.* T **661** and similar design. P 14.
2399 1 z. deep olive 10 10
2400 1 z. 50, lake 15 10
Design: *Vert*—1 z. 50, Town Hall, Zamosc.

656 Women's Faces

657 Albatros Biplane

662 "Łódź"
(W. Strzemiński)

663 Henry IV's Eagle
Gravestone Head
(14th-century)

(Des S. Malecki. Photo)

1975 (8 Sept). *International Women's Year.* P 11.
2385 **656** 1 z. 50, multicoloured 15 10

(Des J. Brodowski. Litho)

1975 (25 Sept). *50th Anniv of First Polish Airmail Stamps.* T **657** and similar horiz design. Multicoloured. P 11×11½.
2386 2 z. 40, Type **657** 20 10
2387 4 z. 90, Ilyushin Il-62 airplane .. 45 15

(Des Z. Stasik. Litho)

1975 (22 Nov). *"Łódź 1975" National Stamp Exhibition.* P 12½.

2401	**662**	4 z. 50, multicoloured		40	15
MS2402	80×101 mm. No. 2401			80	45

(Des H. Matuszewska. Eng M. Kopecki (1 z.). Des H. Matuszewska and K. Tarkowska. Eng M. Kopecki (1 z. 50,). Des K. Tarkowska. Eng W. Morycinska (4 z.))

1975 (29 Nov). *Piast Dynasty of Silesia. T* **663** *and similar horiz designs.* P 11½×12.

2403	1 z. deep dull green			10	10
2404	1 z. 50, sepia			10	10
2405	4 z. deep lilac			35	15

Designs:—1 z. 50, Prince Boleslaw seal (14th-century); 4 z. Prince Jerzy Wilhelm coin (17th-century).

664 Symbolised figure "7"   **665** Ski Jumping

(Des W. Surowiecki (1 z.), Z. Horodecki (1 z. 50). Photo)

1975 (8 Dec). *7th Polish United Workers' Party Congress. T* **664** *and similar design.* P 11½×11.

2406	1 z. multicoloured			10	10
2407	1 z. 50, vermilion, ultramarine and silver		15	10

Design: 32×43 *mm*—1 z. 50, Party Initials ("P.Z.P.R.").

(Des H. Matuszewska. Photo)

1975 (10 Jan). *Winter Olympic Games, Innsbruck. T* **665** *and similar horiz designs. Multicoloured.* P 11×11½.

2408	50 g. Type **665**			10	10
2409	1 z. Ice-hockey			15	10
2410	1 z. 50, Skiing			20	10
2411	2 z. Skating			20	10
2412	4 z. Tobogganing			35	10
2413	6 z. 40, Shooting (Biathlon)			50	25
2408/2413	Set of 6			1·40	45

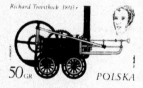

666 R. Trevithick's Steam Railway Locomotive, 1803

(Des S. Malecki. Photo)

1976 (13 Feb). *History of the Railway Locomotive. T* **666** *and similar horiz designs. Multicoloured.* P 11½.

2414	50 g. Type **666**			15	10
2415	1 z. Murray and Blenkinsop's steam locomotive, 1810			15	10
2416	1 z. 50, George Stephenson's locomotive *Rocket*, 1829			25	10
2417	1 z. 50, Polish "Universal" Type ET-22 electric locomotive, 1969			25	10
2418	2 z. 70, Robert Stephenson's locomotive *North Star*, 1837			30	10
2419	3 z. Joseph Harrison's steam locomotive, 1840			45	10
2420	4 z. 50, Thomas Roger's steam locomotive, 1855			2·00	45
2421	4 z. 90, Polish Chrzanów Works steam locomotive, 1922			2·00	45
2414/2421	Set of 8			5·00	1·25

667 Flags of Member Countries

(Des Z. Stasik. Litho)

1976 (8 Mar). *20th Anniv of International Nuclear Research Institute.* P 11½.

2422	**667**	1 z. 50, multicoloured		15	10

668 Early Telephone, Satellites and Radar   **669** Jantar Glider

(Des Z. Stasik. Photo)

1976 (10 Mar). *Telephone Centenary.* P 11.

2423	**668**	1 z. 50, multicoloured		15	10

(Des J. Brodowski. Recess)

1976 (27 Mar)**–78.** *AIR. Contemporary Aviation. T* **669** *and similar vert designs.* P 11½.

2424	5 z. deep blue-green			30	15
2425	10 z. sepia			60	30
2425a	20 z. blackish olive (15.2.77)			1·25	40
2425b	50 z. brown-lake (2.2.78)			3·00	1·50
2424/2425b	Set of 4			4·50	2·10

Designs:—10 z. Mil Mi-6 helicopter; 20 z. PZL-106 agricultural airplane; 50 z. PZL-Mielec TS-11 Iskra jet trainer over Warsaw Castle.

670 Player   **671** Polish U.N. Soldier

(Des T. Michaluk. Photo)

1976 (8 Apr). *World Ice Hockey Championships, Katowice. T* **670** *and similar vert design. Multicoloured.* P 11½×11.

2426	1 z. Type **670**			10	10
2427	1 z. 50, Player (*different*)			15	10

(Des B. Berg. Photo)

1976 (30 Apr). *Polish United Nations Troops in Sinai.* P 11×11½.

2428	**671**	1 z. 50, multicoloured		15	10

Issued with a *se-tenant* stamp-size label.

672 "Glory to the Sappers"
(S. Kulon)

673 "Interphil 76"

(Des K. Tarkowska. Photo)

1976 (8 May). *War Memorials. T* **672** *and similar vert design. Multicoloured.* P 11½.

2429	1 z. Type **672**			15	10
2430	1 z. 1st Polish Army Monument, Sandau/ Laba (B. Koniuszy)		..	15	10

(Des T. Michaluk. Litho)

1976 (20 May). *"Interphil 1976" International Stamp Exhibition, Philadelphia.* P 11½×11.

2431	**673** 8 z. 40, multicoloured			60	20

674 Wielkopolski and Tawny Owl

(Des J. Brodowski. Photo)

1976 (22 May). *National Parks. T* **674** *and similar horiz designs. Multicoloured.* P 11½.

2432	90 g. Type **674**			40	15
2433	1 z. Woliński and white-tailed sea eagle		..	40	15
2434	1 z. 50, Słowiński and seagull		..	50	15
2435	4 z. 50, Bieszczadzki and lynx		..	40	15
2436	5 z. Ojcowski and bat		..	40	15
2437	6 z. Kampinoski and elk		..	50	25
2432/2437	Set of 6 ..		..	2·25	65

675 Peace Dove within Globe

676 Fencing

(Des S. Malecki. Litho)

1976 (29 June). *25th Anniv of United Nations Postal Administration.* P 11×11½.

2438	**675** 8 z. 40, multicoloured		..	60	20

(Des T. Michaluk. Photo (Nos. 2439/44). Eng M. Kopecki. Recess and photo (**MS**2445))

1976 (30 June). *Olympic Games, Montreal. T* **676** *and similar horiz designs. Multicoloured.* P 11×11½.

2439	50 g. Type **676**			10	10
2440	1 z. Cycling ..		..	10	10
2441	1 z. 50, Football		..	10	10
2442	4 z. 20, Boxing		..	40	10
2443	6 z. 90, Weight-lifting		..	65	15
2444	8 z. 40, Athletics		..	75	25
2439/2444	Set of 6 ..		..	1·90	60

MS2445 78×94 mm. 10 z. +5 z. black and bright rose-red (Volleyball) (23×29 *mm*). P 11½ .. 1·60 80
No. **MS**2445 has both the stamp and the outer edges of the sheet perforated.

677 National Theatre

678 Aleksander Czekanowski and Baikal landscape

(Des S. Malecki. Litho)

1976 (12 July). *Centenary of National Theatre, Poznań.* P 11×11½.

2446	**677** 1 z. 50, deep yellow-green & orange	15	10

(Des T. Michaluk. Photo)

1976 (3 Sept). *Death Centenary of Aleksander Czekanowski (geologist).* P 11×11½.

2447	**678** 1 z. 50, multicoloured		..	15	10

679 "Sphinx"

680 Warszawa "M-20"

(Des H. Matuszewska. Photo)

1976 (30 Sept). *Stamp Day. Corinthian Vase Paintings (7th century B.C.). T* **679** *and similar multicoloured designs.* P 11½×11 (*vert*) or 11×11½ (*horiz*).

2448	1 z. Type **679**		..	10	10
2449	1 z. 50, "Siren" (*horiz*)		..	10	10
2450	2 z. "Lion" (*horiz*)		..	15	10
2451	4 z. 20, "Bull" (*horiz*)		..	30	10
2452	4 z. 50, "Goat" (*horiz*)		..	35	20
2453	8 z. +4 z. "Sphinx" (*different*)	..	1·10	50
2448/2453	Set of 6 ..		..	1·90	90

(Des W. Surowiecki. Photo)

1976 (6 Nov). *25th Anniv of Zeran Motor-car Factory, Warsaw. T* **680** *and similar horiz designs. Multicoloured.* P 11.

2454	1 z. Type **680**		..	10	10
2455	1 z. 50, Warszawa "223"		..	10	10
2456	2 z. Syrena "104"		..	15	10
2457	4 z. 90, Polski-Fiat "125-P"		..	40	20
2454/2457	Set of 4 ..		..	65	30
MS2458	137×109 mm. Nos. 2454/7 ..		..	1·10	50

681
Molten Steel Ladle

682
Congress Emblem

683
"Wirzbieto Epitaph"
(painting on wood,
1425)

(Des M. Zabaglo. Litho)
1976 (26 Nov). *Huta Katowice Steel Works.* P 11.
2459 **681** 1 z. 50, multicoloured 15 10

(Des S. Malecki. Photo)
1976 (6 Dec). *8th Polish Trade Unions Congress.* P 11.
2460 **682** 1 z. 50, red-orange, bistre & sepia 15 10

(Des S. Malecki. Litho)
1976 (15 Dec). *Polish Art. T* **683** *and similar vert design.
Multicoloured.* P 11×11½.
2461 1 z. Type **683** 10 10
2462 6 z. "Madonna and Child" (painted
carving, *c* 1410) 35 15

684 Tanker *Zawrat* at
Oil Terminal, Gdańsk

(Des S. Malecki. Photo)
1976 (29 Dec). *Polish Ports. T* **684** *and similar horiz designs.
Multicoloured.* P 11.
2463 1 z. Type **684** 20 10
2464 1 z. *Gryf* (ferry) at Gdansk ... 20 10
2465 1 z. 50, Loading *General Bem* (container
ship), Gdynia 40 10
2466 1 z. 50, *Stefan Batory* (liner) leaving
Gdynia 40 10
2467 2 z. *Ziemia Szczecinska* (bulk carrier)
loading at Szczecin ... 55 10
2468 4 z. 20, Loading coal, Swinoujście .. 70 15
2469 6 z. 90, Pleasure craft, Kolobrzeg .. 90 25
2470 8 z. 40, Coastal map ... ... 1·40 35
2463/2470 Set of 8 ... ... 4·25 1·00

685 Nurse and Patient

686 Order of Civil
Defence Service

(Des E. Nozko-Paprocka. Litho)
1977 (24 Jan). *Polish Red Cross.* P 11½×11.
2471 **685** 1 z. 50, multicoloured ... 15 10

(Des E. Nozko-Paprocka. Litho)
1977 (26 Feb). *Polish Civil Defence.* P 11.
2472 **686** 1 z. 50, multicoloured ... 15 10

687 Ball in Road

(Des J. Raczko. Photo)
1977 (12 Mar). *Child Road Safety Campaign.* P 11.
2473 **687** 1 z. 50, multicoloured 15 10

688 Dewberries
(*Rubus caesius*)

689 Computer Tape

(Des A. Balcerzak. Photo)
1977 (17 Mar). *Wild Fruits. T* **688** *and similar vert designs.
Multicoloured.* P 11½×11.
2474 50 g. Type **688** ... 10 10
2475 90 g. Cowberries (*Vaccinium vitis-idaea*) 10 10
2476 1 z. Wild strawberries (*Fragaria vesca*) 10 10
2477 1 z. 50, Bilberries (*Vaccinium
myrtillus*) ... 15 10
2478 2 z. Raspberries (*Rubus idaeus*) .. 20 10
2479 4 z. 50, Sloes (*Prunus spinosa*) .. 40 15
2480 6 z. Rose hips (*Rosa canina*) .. 50 15
2481 6 z. 90, Hazelnuts (*Corylus avellana*) 60 25
2474/2481 Set of 8 ... ... 1·90 70

(Des W. Surowiecki. Litho)
1977 (4 Apr). *30th Anniv of Russian-Polish Technical Co-
operation.* P 11½×11.
2482 **689** 1 z. 50, multicoloured 15 10

690 Pendulum Traces
and Emblem

691 "Toilet of Venus"

(Des K. Śliwka. Litho)
1977 (22 Apr). *Seventh Polish Congress of Technology.*
P 11½×11.
2483 **690** 1 z. 50, multicoloured 15 10

(Des T. Michaluk. Recess (8 z.), litho (others))

1977 (30 Apr). *400th Birth Anniv of Peter Paul Rubens* (*artist*). *T* **691** *and similar designs. Multicoloured. P* 11½.

2484	1 z. Type **691**	..	10	10
2485	1 z. 50, "Bathsheba at the Fountain" (detail)	..	10	10
2486	5 z. "Helena Fourment with Fur Coat"	..	40	20
2487	6 z. "Self-portrait"	..	55	35
2484/2487	*Set of 4*	..	1·00	60

MS2488 76×62 mm. 8 z. + 4 z. sepia ("The Stoning of St. Stephen") (21×26 mm). P 11½ 1·75 85

No. **MS**2488 has both the stamp and the outer edges of the sheet perforated. It also exists printed in black with the face value obliterated with wavy lines; this was not valid for postage.

692 Dove

693 Cyclist

(Des W. Freudenreich. Litho)

1977 (6 May). *World Peace Congress, Warsaw. P* 11×11½.
2489 **692** 1 z. 50, bright blue, black & lemon .. 15 10

(Des T. Michaluk. Photo)

1977 (6 May). *30th International Peace Cycle Race. P* 11×11½.
2490 **693** 1 z. 50, multicoloured .. 15 10

694 Wolf
(*Canis lupus*)

695 "The Violinist"
(Jacob Toorenvliet)

(Des H. Matuszewska. Photo)

1977 (12 May). *Endangered Animals. T* **694** *and similar vert designs. Multicoloured. P* 11½×11.

2491	1 z. Type **694**	..	10	10
2492	1 z. 50, Great bustard (*Otis tarda*)	..	40	15
2493	1 z. 50, Common kestrel (*Falco tinnunculus*)	..	40	15
2494	6 z. European otter (*Lutra lutra*)	..	50	20
2491/2494	*Set of 4*	..	1·10	35

1977 (16 May). *"Amphilex 77" International Stamp Exhibition, Amsterdam. P* 11½×11.
2495 **695** 6 z. multicoloured 40 25
Printed in sheets of six.

696 Midsummer's Day Bonfire

697 H. Wieniawski and Music Clef

(Des K. Tarkowska. Photo)

1977 (13 June). *Folk Customs. T* **696** *and similar designs from 19th-century wood engravings. Multicoloured. P* 11×11½ (*horiz*) *or* 11½×11 (*vert*).

2496	90 g. Type **696**		10	10
2497	1 z. Easter cock (*vert*)		10	10
2498	1 z. 50. "Śmigus" (dousing of women on Easter Monday. Miechów district) (*vert*)		10	10
2499	3 z. Harvest Festival, Sandomierz district (*vert*)		25	10
2500	6 z. Children with Christmas crib (*vert*)		50	15
2501	8 z. 40. Mountain wedding dance	..	70	20
2496/2501	*Set of 6*	..	1·50	50

(Des Z. Kaja. Litho)

1977 (30 June). *Wieniawski International Music Competition, Poznań. P* 11½×11.
2502 **697** 1 z. 50, black, gold and red-orange 20 10

698 Apollo (*Parnassius apollo*)

(Des J. Wysocki. Photo)

1977 (22 Aug). *Butterflies. T* **698** *and similar horiz designs. Multicoloured. P* 11.

2503	1 z. Type **698**	..	20	10
2504	1 z. Large tortoiseshell (*Nymphalis polychloros*)		20	10
2505	1 z. 50, Camberwell beauty (*Nymphalis antiopa*)		25	10
2506	1 z. 50, Swallowtail (*Papilio machaon*)	..	25	10
2507	5 z. High brown fritillary (*Fabriciana adippe*)		75	15
2508	6 z. 90, Silver-washed fritillary (*Argynnis paphia*)		1·40	65
2503/2508	*Set of 8*	..	2·75	1·00

699 Keyboard and Arms of Slupsk

700 Feliks Dzerzhinsky

(Des S. Malecki. Litho)

1977 (3 Sept). *Piano Festival, Słupsk. P* 11½.
2509 **699** 1 z. 50, bright mve, blk & grey-green 15 10

(Des W. Surowiecki. Litho)

1977 (10 Sept). *Birth Centenary of Feliks E. Dzerzhinsky* (*Russian politician*). *P* 11½×11.
2510 **700** 1 z. 50, bistre-brn & dp brn-ochre 15 10

701 "Sputnik" circling Earth

702 Silver Dinar (11th century)

(Des Z. Stasik. Litho)

1977 (1 Oct). *60th Anniv of Russian Revolution and 20th Anniv of First Artificial Satellite (1st issue).* P 11×11½.

2511	**701** 1 z. 50, ultramarine and cerise	15	10
MS2512	99×125 mm. No. 2511×3 plus three labels. P 12	80	55

No. 2511 was issued *se-tenant* with a label depicting the Winter Palace, Leningrad.

(Des Z. Horodecki. Photo)

1977 (9 Oct). *Stamp Day. Polish Coins. T **702** and similar vert designs. Multicoloured.* P 11½×11.

2513	50 g. Type **702**	10	10
2514	1 z. Cracow grosz, 14th century	10	10
2515	1 z. 50, Legnica thaler, 17th century	10	10
2516	4 z. 20, Gdańsk guilder, 18th century	35	10
2517	4 z. 50, Silver 5 z. coin, 1936	35	10
2518	6 z. Millenary 100 z. coin, 1966	60	25
2513/2518	*Set of 6*	1·40	60

703 Wolin Gate, Kamień Pomorski

704 "Sputnik 1" and "Mercury" Capsule

(Des J. Brodowski. Photo)

1977 (21 Nov). *Architectural Monuments. T **703** and similar designs. Multicoloured.* P 11½×11 (*vert*) or 11×11½ (*horiz*).

2519	1 z. Type **703**	10	10
2520	1 z. Larch church, Dębno	10	10
2521	1 z. 50, Monastery, Przasnysz (*horiz*)	10	10
2522	1 z. 50, Plock cathedral (*horiz*)	10	10
2523	6 z. Kórnik Castle (*horiz*)	40	10
2524	6 z. 90, Palace and garden, Wilanów (*horiz*)	50	25
2519/2524	*Set of 6*	1·10	45

1977 (12 Dec). *Polish Folklore. 16th-century Wood-carvings (2nd series). Horiz designs as T **638**. Recess.* P 11½×11.

2525	4 z. blackish olive	25	10
2526	4 z. 50, deep brown	30	10

Designs:—4 z. Bird snaring; 4 z. 50, Beekeeper and hives.

1977 (28 Dec). *20th Anniv of First Artificial Satellite (2nd issue). Photo.* P 11×11½.

2527	**704** 6 z. 90, multicoloured	45	35
	a. Tête-bêche (horiz pair)	90	70

No. 2527 was issued in sheets of six stamps and two different labels, depicting "Sputnik 1" or "Explorer 1". The sheet was arranged in four rows of two, the labels being in the top right and bottom left positions. The latter label and the three stamps of the right-hand vertical row were printed inverted.

705 DN Category Iceboats

(Des M. Raducki. Litho)

1978 (6 Feb). *Sixth World Ice Sailing Championships. T **705** and similar horiz design.* P 11.

2528	1 z. 50, black, pale grey-blue and azure	15	10
	a. Vert strip. Nos. 2528/9 plus label	30	20
2529	1 z. 50, black, pale grey-blue and azure	15	10

Design:—No. 2529, Close-up of DN iceboat.

Nos. 2528/9 were issued together *se-tenant* with an intervening label bearing the Championships emblem, within sheets of 16 stamps and 8 labels.

706 Electric Locomotive and Katowice Station

(Des S. Malecki. Photo)

1978 (28 Feb). *Railway Engines. T **706** and similar horiz designs. Multicoloured.* P 11½.

2530	50 g. Type **706**	10	10
2531	1 z. Locomotive Py 27 and route map of Żnin—Gąsawa narrow gauge railway	15	10
2532	1 z. Locomotive Pm 36 and Cegielski's factory, Poznań	15	10
2533	1 z. 50, Electric locomotive and Otwock station	15	10
2534	1 z. 50, Locomotive and Warsaw Stalowa station	15	10
2535	4 z. 50, Locomotive Ty 51 and Gdynia station	35	10
2536	5 z. Locomotive Tr 21 and locomotive factory, Chrzanów	40	15
2537	6 z. Cockerill locomotive and Vienna station	60	25
2530/2537	*Set of 8*	1·75	70

707 Czesław Tański and Glider

708 Tackle

(Des J. Brodowski. Photo)

1978 (15 Apr). *Aviation History and 50th Anniv of Polish Aero Club. T **707** and similar multicoloured designs.* P 11×11½ (*horiz*) or 11½×11 (*vert*).

2538	50 g. Type **707**	10	10
2539	1 z. Franciszek Zwirko and Stanislaw Wigura with RWD–6 aircraft (*vert*)	10	10
2540	1 z. 50, Stanislaw Skarzynski and RWD-5 bis monoplane (*vert*)	15	10
2541	4 z. 20 Mil Mi-2 helicopter (*vert*)	25	10
2542	6 z. 90, PZL-104 Wilga 35 monoplane	90	20
2543	8 z. 40 SZD-45 Ogar powered glider	80	20
2538/2543	*Set of 6*	2·10	60

1978 (12 May). *World Cup Football Championship, Argentina.*
T **708** *and similar horiz design. Multicoloured. P* 11½×11
(1 z. 50) *or* 11×11½ (6 z. 90).

2544	1 z. 50, Type **708**		10	10
2545	6 z. 90, Ball on field		45	20

709 Biennale Emblem

710 Kazimierz Stanislaw
Gzowski
(building engineer)

(Des W. Jankowski. Litho)

1978 (1 June). *Seventh International Poster Biennale, Warsaw.*
P 11½.

2546	**709** 1 z. 50, magenta, greenish yellow and bluish violet		10	10

(Des H. Matuszewska. Photo)

1978 (6 June). *"Capex 78" International Stamp Exhibition,*
Toronto. Sheet 68×79 *mm. P* 11½×11.

MS2547	**710** 8 z. 40+4 z. multicoloured		1·10	55

POLONEZ FSO

711 Polonez Saloon Car

1978 (10 June). *Car Production. Photo. P* 11.

2548	**711** 1 z. 50, multicoloured		15	10

712 Fair Emblem

713 Miroslaw Hermaszewski

(Des W. Freudenreich. Litho)

1978 (10 June). *50th International Fair, Poznań. P* 11.

2549	**712** 1 z. 50, multicoloured		10	10

1978 (27 June). *First Pole in Space. T* **713** *and similar horiz*
design. Multicoloured. P 11½×11 (1 z. 50) *or* 11×11½
(6 z. 90). A. *With date* "27.6.1978". B. *Without date.*

		A.		B.	
2550	1 z. 50, Type **713**	15	10	25	25
2551	6 z. 90, Hermaszewski and globe	55	15	2·00	2·00

Nos. 2550/1B were each printed in sheets of six stamps and
two different labels.

A similar set of stamps portraying Major Jankowski, the
stand-by cosmonaut, was prepared but not issued.

714 Globe containing Face

715 Flowers

(Des S. Malecki. Litho)

1978 (12 July). 11*th World Youth and Students' Festival,*
Havana. P 11½.

2552	**714** 1 z. 50, multicoloured		10	10

(Des S. Malecki. Photo)

1978 (20 July). 30*th Anniv of Polish Youth Union. Sheet*
69×79 *mm. P* 11½×11.

MS2553	**715** 1 z. 50, multicoloured		25	25

716 Mosquito and
Malaria Organisms

717 Pedunculate Oak
(*Quercus robur*)

(Des T. Konarski. Litho)

1978 (19 Aug). *Fourth International Congress of Parasitolo-*
gists, Warsaw and Cracow. T **716** *and similar vert design.*
Multicoloured. P 11½×11.

2554	1 z. 50, Type **716**		15	10
2555	6 z. Tsetse fly and sleeping sickness organisms		40	20

(Des J. Towpik. Photo German Bank Note Ptg Co, Leipzig)

1978 (6 Sept). *Environment Protection. Trees. T* **717** *and similar*
vert designs. Multicoloured. P 14.

2556	50 g. Norway maple (*Acer platanoides*)		10	10
2557	1 z. Type **717**		10	10
2558	1 z. 50, White poplar (*Populus alba*)		10	10
2559	4 z. 20, Scots pine (*Pinus silvestris*)		30	10
2560	4 z. 50, White willow (*Salix alba*)		30	10
2561	6 z. Birch (*Betula verrucosa*)		45	20
2556/2561	*Set of* 6		1·25	45

718 "The Battle of Grunwald"
(detail, Jan Matejko)

720 "Peace"
(André Le Brun)

719 Communications

(Des K. Tarkowska. Photo)

1978 (8 Sept). *"PRAGA 1978" International Stamp Exhibition.*
Sheet 69×79 mm. P 11½×11.

MS2562	**718**	6 z. multicoloured	75	40

(Des Z. Stasik. Litho)

1978 (20 Sept). *20th Anniv of Socialist Countries Communications Organization. P 11.*

2563	**719**	1 z. 50, dull vermilion, greenish blue and royal blue	10	10

(Des J. Brodowski. Litho)

1978 (30 Sept)–**79**. *P 12½ (others).*

2564	**720**	1 z. deep reddish violet	10	10
	a.	Perf 11½	10	10
2565		1 z. 50, deep turquoise-blue (28.4.79)	15	10
2565a		2 z. deep brown (30.11.79)	15	10
2565b		2 z. 50, ultramarine (5.11.79)	20	10
2564/2565b		Set of 4	50	20

721 Polish Unit of
UN Middle East Force

(Des T. Michaluk. Photo)

1978 (6 Oct). *35th Anniv of Polish People's Army. T* **721** *and similar horiz. designs. Multicoloured. P. 11½.*

2566		1 z. 50, Colour party of Tadeusz Kościuszko 1st Warsaw Infantry Division	15	10
2567		1 z. 50, Colour party of Mechanized Unit	15	10
2568		1 z. 50, Type **721**	15	10

724 Wojciech Boguslawski

725 Polish Combatants'
Monument and Eiffel Tower

(Des S. Malecki. Litho)

1978 (1 Nov). *Polish Dramatists. T* **724** *and similar square designs. Multicoloured. P 11½.*

2571		50 g. Type **724**	10	10
2572		1 z. Aleksander Fredro	10	10
2573		1 z. 50, Juliusz Slowacki	15	10
2574		2 z. Adam Mickiewicz	15	10
2575		4 z. 50, Stanislaw Wyspiański	30	10
2576		6 z. Gabriela Zapolska	50	20
2571/2576		Set of 6	1·10	35

(Des A. Heidrich. Photo)

1978 (2 Nov). *Monument to Polish Combatants in France, Paris. P 11×11½.*

2577	**725**	1 z. 50, multicoloured	15	10

726 Przewalski Horses

727 Party Flag

(Des J. Towpik. Photo)

1978 (10 Nov). *50th Anniv of Warsaw Zoo. T* **726** *and similar horiz designs. Multicoloured. P 11×11½.*

2578		50 g. Type **726**	10	10
2579		1 z. Polar bears	10	10
2580		1 z. 50, Indian elephants	20	10
2581		2 z. Jaguars	25	10
2582		4 z. 20, Grey seals	30	10
2583		4 z. 50, Hartebeests	30	10
2584		6 z. Mandrills	45	25
2578/2584		Set of 7	1·40	50

(Des W. Freudenreich. Photo)

1978 (15 Dec). *30th Anniv of Polish United Workers' Party. P 11×11½.*

2585	**727**	1 z. 50, orange-vermilion, gold & blk	10	10

722 "Portrait of a Young
Man" (Raphael)

723 Janusz Korczak with
Children

(Des J. Wysocki. Photo)

1978 (9 Oct). *Stamp Day. P 11.*

2569	**722**	6 z. multicoloured	35	20

(Des T. Konarski. Litho)

1978 (11 Oct). *Birth Centenary of Janusz Korczak (pioneer of children's education). P 11½×11.*

2570	**723**	1 z. 50, multicoloured	15	10

728 Stanislaw Dubois

729 Ilyushin Il-62M
and Fokker F.VIIb/3m

(Des J. Brodowski. Photo)

1978 (15 Dec). *Leaders of Polish Workers' Movement. T* **728** *and similar vert designs. P* 11½ × 11.

2586	1 z. 50, steel blue and cerise . .		. .	10	10
2587	1 z. 50, blackish lilac and cerise			10	10
2588	1 z. 50, deep brown-olive and cerise		. .	10	10
2589	1 z. 50, reddish brown and cerise		. .	10	10
2586/2589	*Set of* 4 . .	. .	. .	35	25

Portraits:—No. 2586, Type **728**; 2587, Aleksander Zawadzki; 2588, Julian Leński; 2589, Adolf Warski.

(Des J. Bokiewicz. Photo)

1979 (2 Jan). *50th Anniv of LOT Polish Airlines. P* 11 × 11½.

2590	**729**	6 z. 90, multicoloured . .	60	20

730 Train

(Des K. Tarkowska. Photo)

1979 (13 Jan). *International Year of the Child. T* **730** *and similar horiz designs showing children's paintings. Multicoloured. P* 11.

2591	50 g. Type **730** . .		. .	15	10
2592	1 z. Mother with children		. .	10	10
2593	1 z. 50, Children playing		. .	15	10
2594	6 z. Family group		. .	45	15
2591/2594	*Set of* 4 . .		. .	70	25

731 "Portrait of Artist's Wife with Foxgloves" (Karol Mondrala)

732 A. Frycz Modrzewski (political writer), King Stefan Batory and J. Zamoyski (chancellor)

(Des S. Malecki. Recess)

1979 (5 Mar). *Contemporary Graphics. T* **731** *and similar designs. P* 11½.

2595	50 g. deep lilac . .		. .	10	10
2596	1 z. blackish olive		. .	10	10
2597	1 z. 50, indigo		. .	10	10
2598	4 z. 50, purple-brown . .		. .	30	10
2595/2598	*Set of* 4 . .		. .	50	25

Designs: *Horiz*—50 g. "Lightning" (Edmund Bartlomiejczyk). *Vert*—1 z. 50, "The Musicians" (Tadeusz Kulisiewicz); 4 z. 50, "Head of a Man" (Władysław Skoczylas).

(Des T. Michaluk. Recess and photo)

1979 (12 Mar). *400th Anniv of Royal Tribunal in Piotrkow Trybunalski (1978). P* 11½.

2599	**732**	1 z. 50, pale grey-brown & blackish brown	15	10

733 Pole Vaulting

(Des E. Nozko-Paprocka (10 z.), M. Raducki (others). Recess and photo (10 z.), photo (others))

1979 (26 Mar–19 May). *60th Anniv of Polish Olympic Committee. T* **733** *and similar horiz designs. P* 11½.

2600	1 z. brown-lilac, dp brown & brt crimson		10	10
2601	1 z. 50, brown-lilac, dp brn & brt crimson		10	10
2602	6 z. brown-lilac, dp brown & brt crimson		40	15
2603	8 z. 40, brown-lilac, dp brn & brt crimson		60	25
2600/2603	*Set of* 4		1·00	45
MS2604	102 × 61 mm. 10 z. + 5 z. blackish brown. Imperf (May)		1·10	1·00

Designs:—1 z. 50, High jumping; 6 z. Skiing; 8 z. 40, Horse riding; 10 z. Olympic rings.

734 Flounder (*Platichthys flesus*)

(Des J. Brodowski. Photo)

1979 (26 Apr). *Centenary of Polish Angling. T* **734** *and similar horiz designs. Multicoloured. P* 11½.

2605	50 g. Type **734** . .		. .	10	10
2606	90 g. Perch (*Perca fluviatilis*) . .		. .	10	10
2607	1 z. Greyling (*Thymallus thymallus*) . .			10	10
2608	1 z. 50, Salmon (*Salmo salar*)		. .	10	10
2609	2 z. Trout (*Salmo trutta*)		. .	15	10
2610	4 z. 50, Pike (*Esox lucius*)		. .	25	10
2611	5 z. Carp (*Cyprinus carpio*) . .		. .	40	10
2612	6 z. Catfish (*Silurus glanis*)		. .	45	20
2605/2612	*Set of* 8 . .	. .	. .	1·40	50

735 "30 Years of RWPG"

736 Soldier, Civilian and Congress Emblem

(Des W. Freudenreich. Litho)

1979 (30 Apr). *30th Anniv of Council for Mutual Economic Aid. P* 11 × 11½.

2613	**735**	1 z. 50, orange-vermilion, ultramarine and greenish blue . .	15	10

(Des S. Malecki. Litho)

1979 (7 May). *Sixth Congress of Association of Fighters for Liberty and Democracy, Warsaw. P* 11.

2614	**736**	1 z. 50, orange-vermilion and black	15	10

737 St. George's Church,
Sofia

738 Pope and Auschwitz
Concentration Camp
Memorial

(Des Z. Stasik. Photo)

1979 (15 May). *"Philaserdica '79" International Stamp
Exhibition, Sofia, Bulgaria.* P 11 × 11½.
2615 **737** 1 z. 50, pale orange, reddish brown
and carmine-vermilion   15   10

(Des S. Malecki. Photo)

1979 (2 June). *Visit of Pope John Paul II.* T **738** *and similar
vert design. Multicoloured.* P 11½ × 11 (50 z.) or 11 (*others*).
2616   1 z. 50, Pope and St. Mary's Church,
Cracow   25   10
2617   8 z. 40, Type **738**   65   30
MS2618 68 × 79 mm. 50 z. Framed portrait of
Pope (26 × 35 *mm*)   ..   ..   6·50   5·25
No. **MS**2618 has a gold frame. A version with a silver frame
exists from a limited printing.

POLSKA 1

739 River Paddle-steamer *Ksiaze
Ksawery* and Old Warsaw

(Des S. Malecki. Litho)

1979 (15 June). *150th Anniv of Navigation on River Vistula.*
T **739** *and similar horiz designs. Multicoloured.* P 11.
2619   1 z. Type **739**   20   10
2620   1 z. 50, River paddle-steamer *General
Świerczewski* and Gdańsk   ..   25   10
2621   4 z. 50, River tug *Żubr* and Plock   70   10
2622   6 z. Passenger launch *Syrena* and modern
Warsaw   ..   ..   ..   1·25   20
2619/2622   Set of 4   ..   ..   ..   2·25   45

740 Statue of Tadeusz
Kościuszko (Marian Konieczny)

741 Mining Machinery

(Des J. Brodowski. Photo)

1979 (1 July). *Monument to Tadeusz Kościuszko in Philadelphia.*
P 11½.
2623 **740** 8 z. 40, multicoloured   50   20

(Des Z. Stasik. Photo German Bank Note Ptg Co, Leipzig)

1979 (14 July). *Wieliczka Salt Mine.* T **741** *and similar horiz
design.* P 14.
2624   1 z. orange-brown and black   10   10
2625   1 z. 50, deep turquoise-green & black ..   10   10
Design:—1 z. 50, Salt crystals.

742 Heraldic Eagle

743 Rowland Hill and
1860 Stamp

(Des J. Brodowski. Photo)

1979 (21 July–Sept). *35th Anniv of Polish People's Republic.*
T **742** *and similar vert design.* P 11½ × 11.
2626   1 z. 50, vermilion, black and silver   ..   15   10
2627   1 z. 50, vermilion, silver & greenish blue   15   10
MS2628 120 × 84 mm. Nos. 2626/7 plus label
(2.9.79)   45   45
Design:—No. 2626, Girl and stylized flag.
No. **MS**2628 was sold at the "Katowice '79" Stamp
Exhibition for 10 z. including admission.

(Des S. Malecki. Litho)

1979 (16 Aug). *Death Centenary of Rowland Hill.* P 11½ × 11.
2629 **743** 6 z. dull blue, black and orange   ..   45   15

744 "The Rape of Europa"
(Bernardo Strozzi)

745 Wojciech Jastrzebowski

(Des Z. Stasik. Photo)

1979 (20 Aug). *International Stamp Exhibitions. Sheet
86 × 63 mm.* P 11 × 11½.
MS2630 **744** 10 z. multicoloured   80   50

(Des J. Wysocki. Photo)

1979 (27 Aug). *Seventh Congress of International Ergonomic
Association, Warsaw.* P 11½ × 11.
2631 **745** 1 z. 50, multicoloured   15   10

746 Monument (Wincenty
Kućma)

747 Radio Mast and
Telecommunications Emblem

(Des A. Heidrich. Photo)

1979 (1 Sept). *Unveiling of Monument to Defenders of Polish Post, Gdańsk, and 40th Anniv of German Occupation.* P 11×11½.

2632	**746**	1 z. 50, brownish grey, sepia and orange-vermilion	15	10
MS2633	79×69 mm. **746**	10 z.+5 z. brownish grey, sepia and orange-vermilion. Imperf	1·10	80

(Des W. Freudenreich. Photo)

1979 (24 Sept). *50th Anniv of International Radio Communication Advisory Committee.* P 11×11½.

2634	**747**	1 z. 50, multicoloured	15	10

748 Violin

749 Statue of Kazimierz Pulaski, Buffalo (K. Danilewicz)

(Des W. Freudenreich. Photo)

1979 (25 Sept). *Wieniawski Young Violinists' Competition, Lublin.* P 11×11½.

2635	**748**	1 z. 50, deep ultramarine, red-orange and emerald	15	10

(Des J. Brodowski. Photo)

1979 (1 Oct). *Death Bicentenary of Kazimierz Pulaski (American Revolution hero).* P 11½.

2636	**749**	8 z. 40, multicoloured	60	20

750 Franciszek Jóźwiak (first Commander)

751 Post Office in Rural Area

(Des W. Surowiecki. Photo)

1979 (3 Oct). *35th Anniv of Civic Militia and Security Force.* P 11½×11.

2637	**750**	1 z. 50, blue and gold	15	10

(Des A. Balcerzak. Photo)

1979 (9 Oct). *Stamp Day. T **751** and similar horiz designs. Multicoloured.* P 11½.

2638	1 z. Type **751**			10	10
2639	1 z. 50, Parcel sorting machinery			10	10
2640	4 z. 50, Loading containers on train			40	10
2641	6 z. Mobile post office			50	20
2638/2641	*Set of 4*			90	35

752 "The Holy Family" (Ewelina Pekasowa)

753 "Soyuz 30–Salyut 6" Complex and Crystal

(Des H. Matuszewska. Photo)

1979 (4 Dec). *Polish Folk Art. Glass Paintings. T **752** and similar horiz design. Multicoloured.* P 11½×11 (2 z.) or 11×11½ (6 z. 90).

2642	2 z. Type **752**	15	10
2643	6 z. 90, "The Nativity" (Zdzislaw Walczak)	55	20

(Des Z. Stasik. Photo)

1979 (28 Dec). *Space Achievements. T **753** and similar vert designs. Multicoloured.* P 11½ ×11.

2644	1 z. Type **753** (First anniv of first Pole in space)	10	10
2645	1 z. 50, "Kopernik" and "Copernicus" satellites	15	10
2646	2 z. "Lunik 2"and "Ranger 7" spacecraft (20th anniv of first unmanned Moon landing)	15	10
2647	4 z. 50, Yuri Gagarin and "Vostok 1"	40	10
2648	6 z. 90, Neil Armstrong, lunar module and "Apollo 11" (10th anniv of first man on Moon)	50	20
2644/2648	*Set of 5*	1·10	40
MS2649	120 ×103 mm. Nos. 2644/8 plus label (sold at 20 z. 90)	1·50	1·10

754 Coach and Four

755 Slogan on Map of Poland

1980 (31 Jan). *150th Anniv of Sierakow Stud Farm. T **754** and similar vert designs. Multicoloured. Photo.* P 11½.

2650	1 z. Type **754**	15	10
2651	2 z. Horse and groom	20	10
2652	2 z. 50, Sulky racing	25	10
2653	3 z. Hunting	30	10
2654	4 z. Horse-drawn sledge	40	10
2655	6 z. Haywain	60	15
2656	6 z. 50, Grooms exercising horses	70	15
2657	6 z. 90, Show jumping	80	20
2650/2657	*Set of 8*	3·00	75

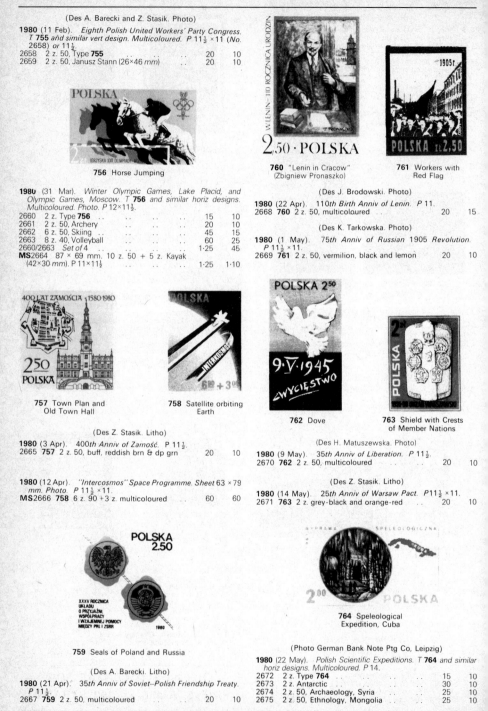

(Des A. Barecki and Z. Stasik. Photo)

1980 (11 Feb). *Eighth Polish United Workers' Party Congress.*
T **755** *and similar vert design. Multicoloured.* P 11½ ×11 (*No.*
2658) *or* 11½.
2658   2 z. 50, Type **755**   20   10
2659   2 z. 50, Janusz Stann (26×46 *mm*)   ..   20   10

756 Horse Jumping

1980 (31 Mar). *Winter Olympic Games, Lake Placid, and*
Olympic Games, Moscow. T **756** *and similar horiz designs.*
Multicoloured. Photo. P 12×11½.
2660   2 z. Type **756**   15   10
2661   2 z. 50, Archery   20   10
2662   6 z. 50, Skiing   45   15
2663   8 z. 40, Volleyball   60   25
2660/2663   *Set of* 4   ..   ..   1·25   45
MS2664   87 × 69 mm. 10 z. 50 + 5 z. Kayak
(42×30 *mm*). P 11×11½   ..   ..   1·25   1·10

757 Town Plan and   **758** Satellite orbiting
     Old Town Hall   Earth

(Des Z. Stasik. Litho)

1980 (3 Apr). *400th Anniv of Zamość.* P 11½.
2665 **757**   2 z. 50, buff, reddish brn & dp grn   20   10

1980 (12 Apr). *"Intercosmos" Space Programme. Sheet* 63 × 79
mm. Photo. P 11½ ×11.
MS2666 **758**   6 z. 90 + 3 z. multicoloured   ..   60   60

POLSKA
2.50

XXXV ROCZNICA
UKŁADU
O PRZYJAŹNI
WSPÓŁPRACY
I WZAJEMNEJ POMOCY
MIĘDZY PRL I ZSRR   1980

759 Seals of Poland and Russia

(Des A. Barecki. Litho)

1980 (21 Apr). *35th Anniv of Soviet–Polish Friendship Treaty.*
P 11½.
2667 **759**   2 z. 50, multicoloured   ..   20   10

760 "Lenin in Cracow"   **761** Workers with
   (Zbigniew Pronaszko)   Red Flag

(Des J. Brodowski. Photo)

1980 (22 Apr). *110th Birth Anniv of Lenin.* P 11.
2668 **760**   2 z. 50, multicoloured   ..   20   15

(Des K. Tarkowska. Photo)

1980 (1 May). *75th Anniv of Russian* 1905 *Revolution.*
P 11½ ×11.
2669 **761**   2 z. 50, vermilion, black and lemon   20   10

762 Dove   **763** Shield with Crests
                    of Member Nations

(Des H. Matuszewska. Photo)

1980 (9 May). *35th Anniv of Liberation.* P 11½.
2670 **762**   2 z. 50, multicoloured   ..   20   10

(Des Z. Stasik. Litho)

1980 (14 May). *25th Anniv of Warsaw Pact.* P 11½ ×11.
2671 **763**   2 z. grey-black and orange-red   ..   20   10

764 Speleological
Expedition, Cuba

(Photo German Bank Note Ptg Co, Leipzig)

1980 (22 May). *Polish Scientific Expeditions. T* **764** *and similar*
horiz designs. Multicoloured. P 14.
2672   2 z. Type **764**   15   10
2673   2 z. Antarctic   30   10
2674   2 z. 50, Archaeology, Syria   ..   25   10
2675   2 z. 50, Ethnology, Mongolia   ..   25   10

2676	6 z. 50, Mountaineering, Nepal	..	45	20
2677	8 z. 40, Palaeontology, Mongolia	..	60	25
2672/2677	Set of 6 ..	..	1·75	60

765 School and Arms

766 *Clathrus ruber*

2⁰⁰ POLSKA

769 *Atropa belladonna*   **770** Jan Kochanowski

(Des A. Heidrich. Photo)

1980 (7 June). *800th Anniv of Malachowski School, Plock.* P 11 ×11½.

2678	**765**	2 z. dull yellowish green and black	20	10

(Des A. Balcerzak. Photo)

1980 (30 June). *Fungi. T **766** and similar vert designs. Multicoloured. P 11½×11.*

2679	2 z. Type **766**	..	..	25	10
2680	2 z. *Xerocomus parasiticus*	..	..	25	10
2681	2 z. 50, Old man of the woods (*Strobilomyces floccopus*)	..	30	10
2682	2 z. 50, *Phallus hadriani*	..	..	30	10
2683	8 z. Cauliflower fungus (*Sparassis crispa*)	50	20
2684	10 z. 50, Giant puff-ball (*Langermannia gigantea*) ..	..	..	75	40
2679/2684	Set of 6 ..	..	..	2·10	70

767 T. Ziolkowski and *Lwow*   **768** Town Hall

(Des S. Malecki. Litho)

1980 (21 July). *Polish Merchant Navy School. Cadet Ships and their Captains. T **767** and similar horiz designs. P 11.*

2685	2 z. black, brt mauve & brt violet	30	10
2686	2 z. 50, black, greenish blue & new bl	35	10
2687	6 z. black, pale green and blue-green	55	15
2688	6 z. 50, black, olive-yellow & yell-ol	65	15
2689	6 z. 90, black, brnish grey & slate-grn	85	20
2690	8 z. 40, black, cobalt and blue-green	90	25
2685/2690	Set of 6 ..	3·25	85

Designs:—2 z. 50, A. Garnuszewski and *Antoni Garnuszewski;* 6 z. A. Ledóchowski and *Zenit;* 6 z. 50, K. Porebski and *Jan Turleski;* 6 z. 90, G. Kański and *Horyzont;* 8 z. 40, K. Maciejewicz and *Dar Pomorza.*

(Des S. Malecki. Photo)

1980 (26 July). *Millenary of Sandomir.* P 11 × 11½.

2691	**768**	2 z. 50, olive-brown and black	..	20	10

SET PRICES

Set prices are given for many issues generally those containing four stamps or more. Definitive sets include one of each value or major colour change but do not cover different perforations, die types or minor shades. Where a choice is possible the catalogue set prices are based on the cheapest versions of the stamps included in the listings.

1980 (15 Aug.). *Medicinal Plants. T **769** and similar vert designs. Multicoloured. Photo. P 11½ ×11.*

2692	2 z. Type **769** ..	..	..	20	10
2693	2 z. 50, *Datura innoxia*	..	..	25	10
2694	3 z. 40, *Valeriana officinalis*	..	35	10
2695	5 z. *Mentha piperita*	..	..	45	10
2696	6 z. 50, *Calendula officinalis*	..	55	15
2697	8 z. *Salvia officinalis*	..	..	70	30
2692/2697	Set of 6 ..	..	..	2·25	70

(Des W. Chomicz. Litho)

1980 (20 Aug). *450th Birth Anniv of Jan Kochanowski (poet).* P 11.

2698	**770**	2 z. 50, multicoloured	..	20	10

1980 (2 Sept). *POSTAGE DUE. As Type D **190** but redrawn without imprint at foot. Litho. P 12½.*

D2699	D **190**	1 z. Venetian red	..	..	10	10
D2700		2 z. drab	..	..	10	10
D2701		3 z. slate-lilac	..	..	25	10
D2702		5 z. brown	..	..	45	15
D2699/2702	Set of 4 ..	..	..	80	30

Polska 8,40

771 U.N. General Assembly

(Des J. Bokiewicz. Photo)

1980 (19 Sept). *35th Anniv of United Nations Organization.* P 11 ×11½.

2703	**771**	8 z. 40, dp brown, light blue & verm	70	25

772 Chopin and Trees

1980 (2 Oct). *Tenth International Chopin Piano Competition, Warsaw. Litho. P 11½.*

2704	**772**	6 z. 90, multicoloured	..	..	50	15

773 Postman emptying Post Box

(Des A. Balcerzak. Photo)

1980 (9 Oct). *Stamp Day. T* **773** *and similar horiz designs. Multicoloured. P* 11½.

2705	2 z. Type **773**				20	10
2706	2 z. 50, Mail sorting				20	10
2707	6 z. Loading mail on to airplane				50	15
2708	6 z. 50, Letter boxes				55	15
2705/2708	*Set of* 4				1·25	45
MS2709	123×94 mm. Nos. 2705/8				3·75	2·75

774 Child embracing Dove

(Des W. Freudenreich. Litho)

1980 (21 Nov). *United Nations Declaration on Preparation of Societies for Life in Peace. P* 11 ×11½

2710	**774**	8 z. 40, multicoloured			70	20

775 "Battle of Olszynka Grochowska" (Wojciech Kossak)

1980 (29 Nov). *150th Anniv of Battle of Olszynka Grochowska. Photo. P* 11.

2711	**775**	2 z. 50, multicoloured			20	10

776 Fire Engine

777 "Honour to Silesian Rebels" (statue, Jan Borowczak)

(Des J. Miller. Photo)

1980 (16 Dec). *Warsaw Horse-drawn Vehicles. T* **776** *and similar horiz designs. Multicoloured. P* 11.

2712	2 z. Type **776**				15	10
2713	2 z. 50, Omnibus				20	10
2714	3 z. Brewery dray				25	10
2715	5 z. Sledge-cab				40	10

2716	6 z. Tram				45	20
2717	6 z. 50, Droshky cab				60	30
2712/2717	*Set of* 6				1·90	70

(Des A. Heidrich. Recess)

1981 (22 Jan). *60th Anniv of Silesian Rising. P* 11½.

2718	**777**	2 z. 50, deep green			15	10

778 Picasso

779 Hydrogen/Hot Air Balloon of Pilatre de Rozier and Romain, 1785*

(Des W. Freudenreich. Photo)

1981 (10 Mar). *Birth Centenary of Pablo Picasso* (artist). *P* 11½ ×11.

2719	**778**	8 z. 40, multicoloured			90	25
MS2720	95 ×130 mm. No. 2719 ×2 plus two labels (sold at 20 z. 80)				2·10	1·25

No. 2719 was issued *se-tenant* with a label depicting Picasso's work "Weeping Woman".

(Des R. Dudzicki. Photo)

1981 (25 Mar). *Balloons. T* **779** *and similar vert designs. Multicoloured. P* 11½.

2721	2 z. Type **779**			20	10
2722	2 z. Balloon of J. Blanchard and J. Jeffries, 1785			20	10
2723	2 z. 50, Eugene Godard's quintuple "acrobatic" balloon, 1850			25	10
2724	3 z. F. Hynek and Z. Burzynski's Kosciuszko, 1933			30	10
2725	6 z. Z. Burzynski and N. Wysocki's Polonia II, 1935			55	15
2726	6 z. 50, Ben Abruzzo, Max Anderson and Larry Newman's Double Eagle II, 1978			55	20
2721/2726	*Set of* 6			1·90	55
MS2727	59×98 mm. 10 z. 50, Polish balloon L.O.P.P. and Gordon Bennett statuette. Imperf			90	90

*No. 2721 is wrongly inscr "Pilatre de Rozier D'Arlandes 1783".

780 "Iphigenia" (Anton Maulbertsch)

781 Wroclaw, 1493

(Des A. Barecki. Litho)

1981 (11 May). *"WIPA 1981" International Stamp Exhibition, Vienna. P* 11½.

2728	**780**	10 z. 50, multicoloured			90	35

(Des A. Barecki. Photo)

1981 (15 May–July). *Towns. T **781** and similar designs.*
P 11 ×11½ (4, 5 z.), 11½ ×11 (6, 8 z.) or 14 (6 z. 50).

2729	4 z. reddish violet (28.7.81)		30	10
2730	5 z. bright blue-green (28.7.81)		50	15
2731	6 z. red-orange (28.7.81)		60	15
2732	6 z. 50, bistre-brown		60	20
2733	8 z. blue (28.7.81)		70	25
2729/2733	Set of 5		2·40	75

Designs: *Vert*—4 z. Gdańsk, 1652; 5 z. Cracow, 1493. *Horiz*—6 z. Legnica, 1744; 8 z. Warsaw, 1618.

782 Sikorski

783 Faience Vase

(Des A. Balcerzak. Photo)

1981 (20 May). *Birth Centenary of Gen. Wladyslaw E. Sikorski (statesman).* P 11½ ×11.

2744	**782** 6 z. 50, multicoloured	55	20

(Des K. Tarkowska (1, 5 z., 8 z. 40), H. Matuszewska (others). Photo)

1981 (15 June). *Pottery. T **783** and similar vert designs. Multicoloured.* P 11½ ×11.

2745	1 z. Type **783**	15	10
2746	2 z. Porcelain cup and saucer in "Baranowka" design	25	10
2747	2 z. 50, Porcelain jug, Korzec manufacture	25	10
2748	5 z. Faience plate with portrait of King Jan III Sobieski by Thiele	50	15
2749	6 z. 50, Faience "Secession" vase	65	20
2750	8 z. 40, Porcelain dish, Cmielow manufacture	80	30
2745/2750	Set of 6	2·25	70

784 Congress Emblem   **785** Wild Boar, Rifle and Oak Leaves

(Des W. Freudenreich. Litho)

1981 (15 June). *Architects' Congress.* P 11½ ×11.

2751	**784** 2 z. 50, lemon, black & brt scarlet	20	10

(Des W. Surowiecki. Litho)

1981 (30 June). *Game Shooting. T **785** and similar multicoloured designs.* P 11 ×11½ (6 z. 50) or 11½ ×11 (others).

2752	2 z. Type **785**	25	10
2753	2 z. Elk, rifle and fir twigs	25	10
2754	2 z. 50, Red fox, shotgun, cartridges and fir branches	30	10
2755	2 z. 50, Roe deer, feeding rack, rifle and fir branches	30	10
2756	6 z. 50, Mallards, shotgun, basket and reeds	1·10	30

2757	6 z. 50, Barnacle goose, shotgun and reeds (*horiz*)		1·10	30
2752/2757	Set of 6		3·00	80

786 European Bison

787 Tennis Player

(Des K. Sliwka. Photo)

1981 (27 Aug). *Protection of European Bison. T **786** and similar vert designs. Multicoloured.* P 11½ ×11.

2758	6 z. 50, Type **786**	75	25
	a. Strip of 5. Nos. 2758/62	3·25	
2759	6 z. 50, Two bison (one grazing)	75	25
2760	6 z. 50, Bison with calf	75	25
2761	6 z. 50, Calf feeding	75	25
2762	6 z. 50, Two bison (both looking towards right)	75	25
2758/2762	Set of 5	3·25	1·10

Nos. 2758/62 were printed together in *se-tenant* strips of five within the sheet, each strip forming a composite design.

(Des W. Swierzy. Photo)

1981 (17 Sept). *60th Anniv of Polish Tennis Federation.* P 11 ×11½.

2763	**787** 6 z. 50, multicoloured	55	15

788 Boy with Model Airplane

(Des J. Brodowski. Photo German Bank Note Ptg Co, Leipzig)

1981 (24 Sept). *Model Making. T **788** and similar horiz designs. Multicoloured.* P 14.

2764	1 z. Type **788**	15	10
2765	2 z. Atlas 2 (tug)	30	10
2766	2 z. 50, Cars	30	10
2767	4 z. 20, Man with gliders	35	15
2768	6 z. 50, Racing cars	70	15
2769	8 z. Man with yachts	80	25
2764/2769	Set of 6	2·25	55

789 Disabled Pictogram

790 17th-cent. Flint-lock Pistol

(Des. R. Dudzicki. Litho)

1981 (25 Sept). *International Year of Disabled Persons.*
P 11½ × 11.
2770 **789** 8 z. 40, blue-green, light yellowish
green and black 75 20

(Des H. Chyliński. Photo German Bank Note Ptg Co, Leipzig)

1981 (9 Oct). *Stamp Day. Antique Weapons. T* **790** *and similar
vert design. Multicoloured. P* 14.
2771 2 z. 50, Type **790** 25 10
2772 8 z. 40, 17th-cent. gala sabre .. 70 20

791 H. Wieniawski
and Violin Head

792 Bronisław Wesołowski

(Des S. Malecki. Photo)

1981 (10 Oct). *Wieniawski Young Violinists' Competition.*
P 11½.
2773 **791** 2 z. 50, multicoloured 25 15

(Des Z. Stasik. Litho)

1981 (15 Oct). *Activists of Polish Workers' Movement. T* **792**
and similar horiz designs. P 11½.
2774 50 g. green and black 10 10
2775 2 z. blue and black 15 10
2776 2 z. 50, light brown and black 20 10
2777 6 z. 50, magenta and black 60 25
2774/2777 *Set of* 4 .. .. 95 30
Designs:—2 z. Malgorzata Fornalska; 2 z. 50, Maria Koszutska;
6 z. 50, Marcin Kasprzak.

793 F.A.O. Emblem
and Globe

794 Helena Modrzejewska
(actress)

(Des Z. Stasik. Litho)

1981 (16 Oct). *World Food Day. P* 11½ × 11.
2778 **793** 6 z. 90, bistre-brown, dull orange and
pale yellow 55 20

(Des J. Brodowski. Recess and photo)

1981 (17 Oct). *Bicentenary of Cracow Old Theatre. T* **794** *and
similar horiz designs. P* 12 × 11½.
2779 2 z. maroon, pale grey & bluish violet 15 10
2780 2 z. 50, dp blue, pale stone & ol-sep 20 10
2781 6 z. 50, dull violet, pale grey-blue and
brown-olive 50 20

2782 8 z. bistre-brown, pale sage green and
brown-lake 80 20
2779/2782 *Set of* 4 .. .. .. 1·50 45
Designs:—2 z. 50, Stanisław Koźmian (politician, writer and
theatre director); 6 z. 50, Konrad Swinarski (stage manager and
scenographer); 8 z. Old Theatre building.

795 Cracow and Vistula
River

796 Gdansk Memorial

(Des S. Malecki. Litho)

1981 (20 Nov). *Vistula River Project. Sheet* 62 × 51 *mm. P* 11½.
MS2783 **795** 10 z. 50, multicoloured .. .. 1·25 90

(Des S. Malecki. Litho)

1981 (16 Dec). *Memorials to Victims of 1970 Uprising. T* **796**
and similar vert design. P 11½ × 12 (2 z. 50) *or* 11½ × 11 (6 z. 50).
2784 2 z. 50 + 1 z. olive-grey, black & orge-verm 50 20
2785 6 z. 50 + 1 z. olive-grey, black & violet-blue 1·10 90
Design: 26 × 37 *mm*—6 z. 50, Gdynia memorial.

797 Epyphyllopsis gaertneri

798 Writing on Wall

(Des A. Balcerzak. Photo German Bank Note Ptg Co, Leipzig)

1981 (22 Dec). *Succulent Plants. T* **797** *and similar square
designs. Multicoloured. P* 13.
2786 90 g. Type **797** 15 10
2787 1 z. *Cereus tonduzii* 15 10
2788 2 z. *Cylindropuntia leptocaulis* .. 15 10
2789 2 z. 50, *Cylindropuntia fulgida* .. 20 10
2790 2 z. 50, *Caralluma lugardi* .. 20 10
2791 6 z. 50, *Nopalea chochenillifera* .. 60 60
2792 6 z. 50, *Lithops helmutii* .. 60 20
2793 10 z. 50, *Cylindropuntia spinosior* .. 1·00 35
2786/2793 *Set of* 8 .. .. .. 2·75 80

UNDERGROUND POST. Between 1982 and 1989, following the
imposition of martial law, a large number of unofficial stamps
were printed and circulated by the Solidarity Movement, camp
internees, and similar organizations. Although most of these were
used on clandestine mail some did pass through the normal mail
network.

(Des A. Barecki. Photo)

1982 (5 Jan). *40th Anniv of Polish Workers' Coalition. P* 11½ × 11.
2794 **798** 2 z. 50, salmon-pink, rosine and black 25 10
No. 2794 with overprint "13. XII. 1981r. WOJNA WRON Z
NARODEM 13. XII. 1982r." is a private issue.

799 Faience Plate, Wloclawek

800 Lukasiewicz and Lamp

(Des K. Tarkowska (6 z.), H. Matuszewska (others). Photo)

1982 (20 Jan). *Polish Ceramics. T* **799** *and similar vert designs. Multicoloured. P* 11½ × 11.

2795	1 z. Type **799**	15	10
2796	2 z. Porcelain cup and saucer, Korzec	20	10
2797	2 z. 50, Porcelain tureen and sauce-boat, Barnówka	25	10
2798	6 z. Porcelain inkpot, Horodnica	60	20
2799	8 z. Faience "Hunter's Tumbler", Lubartów	75	20
2800	10 z. 50, Faience figurine of nobleman, Biala Podlaska	1·10	40
2795/2800	*Set of* 6	2·75	80

(Des W. Andrzejewski. Photo)

1982 (22 Mar). *Death Centenary of Ignacy Lukasiewicz (inventor of petroleum lamp). T* **800** *and similar vert designs. Multicoloured. P* 11½ × 11.

2801	1 z. Type **800**	15	10
2802	2 z. Lamp with green shade	20	10
2803	2 z. 50, Lamp with pink shade	30	10
2804	3 z. 50, Two lamps	35	10
2805	9 z. Lamp with decorated shade	90	25
2806	10 z. Lamp with globe	95	30
2801/2806	*Set of* 6	2·40	80

801 Karol Szymanowski

802 RWD 6, 1932

(Des K. Sliwka. Photo)

1982 (8 Apr). *Birth Centenary of Karol Szymanowski (composer). P* 11½ × 11.

2807	**801** 2 z. 50, deep bistre-brown and gold	25	10

(Des J. Brodowski. Photo)

1982 (5 May). *50th Anniv of First Polish Victory in Tourist Aircraft Challenge Competition. T* **802** *and similar horiz design. Multicoloured. P* 11 × 11½.

2808	27 z. Type **802**	1·50	1·25
2809	31 z. RWD 9 (winner of 1934 Challenge)	1·90	1·75
MS2810	89×101 mm. Nos. 2808/9	3·50	3·50

ALBUM LISTS

Write for our latest lists of albums and accessories.

These will be sent free on request.

803 Henryk Sienkiewicz (literature, 1905)

804 Football as Globe

(Des W. Freudenreich. Litho)

1982 (10 May). *Polish Nobel Prize Winners. T* **803** *and similar vert designs. P* 11½ × 11.

2811	3 z. blackish olive and black	15	10
2812	15 z. sepia and black	65	25
2813	25 z. blue-black	1·50	30
2814	31 z. grey and black	1·25	70
2811/2814	*Set of* 4	3·25	1·25

Designs:—15 z. Wladyslaw Reymont (literature, 1924); 25 z. Marie Curie (physics, 1903, and chemistry, 1911); 31 z. Czeslaw Milosz (literature, 1980).

(Des J. Konarzewski (25 z.), K. Kosmowski (27 z.). Photo)

1982 (28 May). *World Cup Football Championship, Spain. T* **804** *and similar horiz design. Multicoloured. P* 11½ × 11 (25 z.) or 11 × 11½ (27 z.).

2815	25 z. Type **804**	1·10	40
2816	27 z. Bull and football (35 × 28 mm)	1·25	70

805 "Maria Kazimiera Sobieska"

806 Stanislaw Sierakowski and Boleslaw Domański (former Association presidents)

(Des J. Brodowski. Photo)

1982 (11 June). *"Philexfrance 82" International Stamp Exhibition, Paris. Sheet* 69 × 86 *mm. P* 11½ × 11.

MS2817	**805** 65 z. multicoloured	3·25	3·25

(Des S. Malecki. Litho)

1982 (20 July). *60th Anniv of Association of Poles in Germany. P* 11½ × 11.

2818	**806** 4 z. 50, orange-verm & bronze-grn	55	15

807 Text around Globe

(808)

(Des H. Chyliński. Photo)

1982 (9 Aug). *Second United Nations Conference on the Exploration and Peaceful Uses of Outer Space, Vienna.* P 11½×11.

2819 **807** 31 z. multicoloured 90 35

1982 (20 Aug). *No. 2732 surch with T **808**.*

2820 **781** 10 z. on 6 z. 50, bistre-brown .. 25 10

809 Father Augustyn Kordecki (prior)

810 Marchers with Banner

(Des R. Dudzicki. Photo)

1982 (26 Aug). *600th Anniv of "Black Madonna" (icon) of Jasna Góra. T **809** and similar multicoloured designs.* P 11.

2821   2 z. 50, Type **809** 10 10
2822   25 z. "Siege of Jasna Góra by Swedes,
     1655" (detail) (*horiz*) 40 20
2823   65 z. "Black Madonna" .. 1·25 60
MS2824 122×108 mm. No. 2823×2 (sold at
   140 z.) .. .. 12·00 12·00
   The premium on No. **MS**2824 was for benefit of the Polish Philatelic Federation.

(Des K. Kosmowski. Photo)

1982 (3 Sept). *Centenary of Proletarian Party.* P 11½×11.

2825 **810** 6 z. multicoloured 40 10

811 Norbert Barlicki

812 Dr. Robert Koch

(Des Z. Stasik. Photo)

1982 (10 Sept). *Activists of Polish Workers' Movement.* T **811** *and similar vert designs.* P 12×11½.

2826   5 z. light new blue, bright blue and black 15 10
2827   6 z. greenish grey, dull blue-green & blk 20 15
2828   15 z. salmon-pink, deep carmine & black 35 20
2829   20 z. mauve, reddish violet and black 60 30
2830   29 z. buff, orange-brown and black 75 45
2826/2830   Set of 5 .. .. 1·90 1·00
Designs:—6 z. Pawel Finder; 15 z. Marian Buczek; 20 z. Cezaryna Wojnarowska; 29 z. Ignacy Daszyński.

(Des K. Syta. Photo)

1982 (22 Sept). *Centenary of Discovery of Tubercle Bacillus.* T **812** *and similar vert design. Multicoloured.* P 11½×11.

2831   10 z. Type **812** 25 10
2832   25 z. Dr. Odo Bujwid 85 20

813 Head of Woman

813a Head of Ruler

814 Maximilian Kolbe (after M. Koscielniak)

(Des S. Skiba (2833/4), J. Konarzewski (others). Eng W. Zajdel (2840), B. Kowalska (2842), M. Kopecki (2843a). Photo German Bank Note Ptg Co, Leipzig (2836, 2841, 2843); recess (2840, 2842, 2843a) or photo (others) Govt Ptg Wks, Warsaw)

1982 (25 Sept)–**89**. *Carved Heads from Wawel Castle.*
   (a) T **813** *and similar vert design.* P 12×11½

2833   60 z. salmon and brown .. .. 1·50 50
2834   100 z. ochre and sepia .. .. 3·00 1·00
   Design:—100z. Man.

(b) T **813a** *and similar vert designs.* P 14 (2836, 2841, 2843) or
          11×12 (*others*)

2835   3 z. 50, reddish brown (24.1.85) .. 15 10
2836   5 z. deep bluish green (10.7.84) .. 20 10
2837   5 z. crimson (8.7.85) 20 10
2838   10 z. ultramarine (8.7.85) 25 10
2839   15 z. lake-brown (22.9.88) 15 10
2840   20 z. olive-grey (30.7.86) 45 15
2841   20 z. deep dull blue (31.3.89) .. 15 10
2842   40 z. agate (30.7.86) 75 25
2843   60 z. deep green (15.12.89) .. 15 10
2843a   200 z. black (11.11.86) .. .. 3·75 1·75
2833/2843a   Set of 12 .. .. 5·50 2·40
   Designs:—Nos. 2835, 2841, Type **813a**; 2836, Warrior; 2837, 2839, Woman wearing chaplet; 2838, Man in cap; 2840, Thinker; 2842, Man in beret; 2843, Young man; 2843a, Man.
   Nos. 2836, 2841 and 2843 were issued in coils, with every fifth stamp numbered on the back.

(Des K. Kosmowski. Photo)

1982 (10 Oct). *Sanctification of Maximilian Kolbe (Franciscan concentration camp victim).* P 11½×11.

2844 **814** 27 z. multicoloured 90 50

815 Polar Research Station

816 "Log Floats on Vistula River" (drawing by J. Telakowski)

(Des H. Matuszewska. Litho)

1982 (25 Oct). *50th Anniv of Polish Polar Research. P 11½.*
2845 **815** 27 z. multicoloured .. .. 2·50 60

(Des M. Piekarski. Photo)

1982 (2 Nov). *Views of Vistula River. T **816** and similar horiz designs. P 11½ × 12.*
2846 12 z. ultramarine 25 10
2847 17 z. cobalt 30 15
2848 25 z. deep blue 40 20
Designs:—17 z. "Kazimierz Dolny" (engraving by Andriollo); 25 z. "Danzig" (18th-century engraving).

817 Stanislaw Zaremba

(Des H. Chyliński. Photo)

1982 (23 Nov). *Mathematicians. T **817** and similar horiz designs. P 11 × 11½.*
2849 5 z. reddish purple, ultramarine & black 25 10
2850 6 z. orange, violet and black .. 25 10
2851 12 z. cobalt, olive-brown and black .. 40 10
2852 15 z. olive-yellow, deep chestnut & black 60 20
2849/2852 *Set of 4* .. .. .. 1·40 40
Designs:—6 z. Waclaw Sierpiński; 12 z. Zygmunt Janiszewski; 15 z. Stefan Banach.

818 Military Council Medal

1982 (13 Dec). *First Anniv of Military Council. Photo. P 12 × 11½.*
2853 **818** 2 z. 50, black, yellow and rosine .. 25 15

819 Deanery Gate

820 Bernard Wapowski Map, 1526

(Des A. Heidrich. Eng M. Kopecki (65 z.). Recess and photo (65 z.), litho (others))

1982 (20 Dec). *Renovation of Cracow Monuments (1st series). T **819** and similar vert design. P 11½×11.*
2854 15 z. black, yellow-olive and emerald .. 50 15
2855 25 z. black, dull purple and deep magenta 65 20
MS2856 75 × 93 mm. 65 z. pale blue-green, dull purple and sepia (22 × 27 mm). Imperf .. 1·10 1·10
Designs:—25 z. Gateway of Collegium Iuridicum; 65 z. Street plan of Old Cracow.
See also Nos. 2904/5, 2968/9, 3029/30, 3116 and 3153.

(Des J. Brodowski. Litho)

1982 (28 Dec). *Polish Maps. T **820** and similar square designs. P 11½.*
2857 5 z. multicoloured 15 10
2858 6 z. pale cinnamon, black and maroon .. 20 10
2859 8 z. multicoloured 25 10
2860 25 z. multicoloured 70 25
2857/2860 *Set of 4* .. .. .. 1·10 45
Designs:—6 z. Map of Prague, 1839; 8 z. Map of Poland from Eugen Romer's Atlas, 1908; 25 z. Plan of Cracow by A. Buchowiecki, 1703, and astrolabe.

821 "The Last of the Resistance" (Artur Grottger)

1983 (22 Jan). *120th Anniv of January Rising. Photo. P 12 × 11½.*
2861 **821** 6 z. deep brown 15 10

822 "Grand Theatre, Warsaw, 1838" (Maciej Zaleski)

1983 (24 Feb). *150th Anniv of Grand Theatre, Warsaw. Photo. P 11.*
2862 **822** 6 z. multicoloured 15 10

823 Wild Flowers

824 Karol Kurpiński (composer)

(Des S. Malecki. Litho)

1983 (24 Mar). *Environmental Protection. T **823** and similar square designs. Multicoloured. P 11½.*
2863 5 z. Type **823** 20 10
2864 6 z. River fishes and mute swan .. 35 10
2865 17 z. Hoopoe and trees .. .. 1·10 30
2866 30 z. Sea fishes .. .. 1·10 45
2867 31 z. European bison and roe deer .. 1·10 50
2868 38 z. Fruit .. .. 1·10 60
2863/2868 *Set of 6* .. .. .. 4·25 1·75

(Des H. Chyliński. Photo)

1983 (25 Mar). *Celebrities. T **824** and similar vert designs.* P 11½×11.

2869	5 z. cinnamon and reddish brown	20	10
2870	6 z. pale magenta and bluish violet	25	10
2871	17 z. pale bluish green and slate-green	60	20
2872	25 z. pale yellow-orange & dp orange-brn	75	20
2873	27 z. new blue and deep ultramarine	80	25
2874	31 z. reddish lilac and bright violet	90	25
2869/2874	*Set of* 6	3·25	90

Designs:—6 z. Maria Jasnorzewska Pawlikowska (poetess); 17 z. Stanisław Szober (linguist); 25 z. Tadeusz Banachiewicz (astronomer and mathematician); 27 z. Jarosław Iwaszkiewicz (writer); 31 z. Władysław Tatarkiewicz (philosopher and historian).

825 3000 Metres Steeplechase

826 Ghetto Heroes Monument (Natan Rappaport)

(Des W. Freudenreich. Photo)

1983 (5 Apr). *Sports Achievements. T **825** and similar horiz designs.* P 11×11½.

2875	5 z. pale pink and bright violet	20	10
2876	6 z. chestnut, pale pink and black	20	10
2877	15 z. stone and deep olive	45	15
2878	27 z.+5 z. dull violet-blue, dp blue & black	1·00	30
2875/2878	*Set of* 4	1·60	50

Designs:—6 z. Show jumping; 15 z. Football; 27 z.+5 z. Pole vaulting.

The 5, 6 and 27 z. commemorate gold medals won by Polish athletes at the Moscow Olympic Games, the 15 z. third place in World Cup Football Championship, Spain.

(Des M. Piekarski. Photo)

1983 (19 Apr). *40th Anniv of Warsaw Ghetto Uprising.* P 11½×11.

2879	**826** 6 z. buff and deep bistre-brown	15	10

No. 2879 was issued with *se-tenant* label showing the anniversary medal by K. Danielewicz.

827 Customs Officer and Suitcases

828 John Paul II and Jasna Góra Sanctuary

(Des K. Kosmowski. Photo)

1983 (28 Apr). *30th Anniv of Customs Co-operation Council.* P 11½×11.

2880	**827** 5 z. multicoloured	15	10

(Des R. Dudzicki. Photo)

1983 (16 June). *Papal Visit. T **828** and similar horiz design.* Multicoloured. P 11.

2881	31 z. Type **828**	1·00	30
2882	65 z. Niepokalanów Church and John Paul holding crucifix	2·25	80
MS2883	107×81 mm. No. 2882	2·00	1·75

829 Dragoons

830 Arrow piercing "E"

(Des R. Dudzicki. Photo)

1983 (5 July). *300th Anniv of Polish Relief of Vienna (1st issue). Troops of King Jan III Sobieski. T **829** and similar vert designs.* Multicoloured. P 11½×11.

2884	5 z. Type **829**	20	10
2885	5 z. Armoured cavalryman	20	10
2886	6 z. Infantry non-commissioned officer and musketeer	30	10
2887	15 z. Light cavalry lieutenant	40	20
2888	27 z. "Winged" hussar and trooper with carbine	1·00	40
2884/2888	*Set of* 5	1·75	80

See also Nos. 2893/**MS**2897.

(Des A. Barecki. Litho)

1983 (16 Aug). *50th Anniv of Deciphering "Enigma" Machine Codes.* P 11½×11.

2889	**830** 5 z. vermilion, grey and black	15	15

831 Toruń

(Des S. Malecki. Photo)

1983 (25 Aug). *750th Anniv of Toruń.* P 11.

2890	**831** 6 z. multicoloured	30	15
MS2891	142×116 mm. No. 2890×4	2·75	2·75

The gutter of No. **MS**2891 is inscribed for 14th Polish Philatelic Exhibition, Toruń.

832 Child's Painting

833 King Jan III Sobieski

(Des H. Matuszewska. Photo)

1983 (9 Sept). *"Order of the Smile" (politeness publicity campaign).* P 11½ × 12.
2892 **832** 6 z. multicoloured 15 10

(Des S. Malecki. Photo)

1983 (12 Sept). *300th Anniv of Polish Relief of Vienna (2nd issue).* T **833** *and similar vert designs. Multicoloured.* P 11.
2893 5 z. Type **833** 20 10
2894 6 z. King Jan III Sobieski (*different*) .. 20 10
2895 6 z. "King Jan III Sobieski on Horseback" (Francesco Trevisani) .. 20 10
2896 25 z. "King Jan III Sobieski" (Jerzy Eleuter) 90 35
2893/2896 *Set of 4* .. .. 1·25 45
MS2897 97×75 mm. 65 z.+10 z. "King Jan III Sobieski at Vienna" (Jan Matejko). Imperf .. 2·50 2·50

834 Wanda Wasilewska

835 Profiles and W.C.Y. Emblem

(Des W. Surowiecki (2898/9). Photo)

1983 (12 Oct). *40th Anniv of Polish People's Army.* T **834** *and similar designs.* P 12 × 11½ (2901) *or* 11½ × 12 (*others*).
2898 5 z. multicoloured 15 10
2899 5 z. greenish black, blue-green and black 15 10
2900 6 z. multicoloured 25 10
2901 6 z. multicoloured 25 10
2898/2901 *Set of 4* 70 25
Designs: *Vert*—No. 2899, General Zygmunt Berling; 2900, "The Frontier Post" (S. Poznanski). *Horiz*—No. 2901, "Taking the Oath" (S. Poznanski).

(Des N. Chyliński. Photo)

1983 (18 Oct). *World Communications Year.* P 11 × 11½.
2902 **835** 15 z. black, greenish blue and rosine 45 20

836 Boxing

837 Biskupiec Costume

(Des J. Brodowski. Litho)

1983 (9 Nov). *60th Anniv of Polish Boxing Federation.* P 11½ × 11.
2903 **836** 6 z. multicoloured 20 10

(Des A. Heidrich. Litho)

1983 (25 Nov). *Renovation of Cracow Monuments (2nd series). Designs as* T **819**. P 11 × 11½ (5 z.) *or* 11½ × 11 (6 z.).
2904 5 z. brown, purple and black .. 20 10
2905 6 z. black, olive-green and new blue .. 20 15
Design: *Horiz*—5 z. Cloth Hall. *Vert*—6 z. Town Hall tower.

(Des W. Świerzy. Photo)

1983 (16 Dec). *Women's Folk Costumes.* T **837** *and similar vert designs. Multicoloured.* P 11½ × 11.
2906 5 z. Type **837** 20 10
2907 5 z. Rozbark 20 10
2908 6 z. Warmia and Mazuria 25 10
2909 6 z. Cieszyn 25 10
2910 25 z. Kurpie .. .. .. 1·10 30
2911 38 z. Lubusk .. .. .. 1·60 60
2906/2911 *Set of 6* .. .. 3·25 1·10

838 Hand with Sword (poster by Zakrzewski and Krolikowski, 1945)

839 Badge of "General Bem" Brigade

(Des Z. Stasik. Photo)

1983 (31 Dec). *40th Anniv of National People's Council.* P 11½ × 11.
2912 **838** 6 z. multicoloured 20 10

(Des W. Surowiecki. Litho)

1983 (31 Dec). *40th Anniv of People's Army.* P 11½.
2913 **839** 5 z. multicoloured 20 10

840 Dulcimer

841 Wincenty Witos

(Des Z. Stasik. Photo)

1984 (10 Feb). *Musical Instruments (1st series).* T **840** *and similar vert designs. Multicoloured.* P 11½×11.
2914 5 z. Type **840** 20 10
2915 6 z. Kettle drum and tambourine .. 25 10
2916 10 z. Accordion 40 10
2917 15 z. Double bass 50 20
2918 17 z. Bagpipe 60 20
2919 29 z. Country band (wood carvings by Tadeusz Zak) .. .. 1·00 30
2914/2919 *Set of 6* .. .. 2·75 90
See also Nos. 2994/9.

(Des S. Malecki. Litho)

1984 (2 Mar). *110th Birth Anniv of Wincenty Witos (leader of Peasants' Movement).* P 11½ × 11.
2920 **841** 6 z. purple-brown and bright emerald 20 10

842 *Clematis lanuginosa*

(A. Balcerzak. Photo)

1984 (26 Mar). *Clematis. T* **842** *and similar horiz designs. Multicoloured. P* 11 × 11½.
2921	5 z. Type **842**		20	10
2922	6 z. *Clematis tangutica*		25	10
2923	10 z. *Clematis texensis*		30	15
2924	17 z. *Clematis alpina*		50	20
2925	25 z. Travellers' joy (*Clematis vitalba*)		1·00	30
2926	27 z. *Clematis montana*		1·10	35
2921/2926	*Set of* 6		3·00	1·00

843 "The Ecstasy of St. Francis" (El Greco)

(Des J. Konarzewski. Photo)

1984 (21 Apr). *"España 84" International Stamp Exhibition, Madrid. P* 11.
2927	**843** 27 z. multicoloured		90	25

844 Handball

(Des J. Brodowski. Litho)

1984 (25 Apr). *Olympic Games, Los Angeles, and Winter Olympics, Sarajevo. T* **844** *and similar horiz designs. Multicoloured. P* 11 × 11½.
2928	5 z. Type **844**		15	10
2929	6 z. Fencing		20	10
2930	15 z. Cycling		50	15
2931	16 z. Janusz Kusociński winning 10,000 metres race, 1932 Olympics, Los Angeles		70	20
2932	17 z. Stanisława Walasiewiczówna winning 100 metres race, 1932 Olympics, Los Angeles		70	20
2933	31 z. Women's slalom (Winter Olympics)		1·10	35
2928/2933	*Set of* 6		3·00	90
MS2934	129 × 78 mm. Nos. 2931/2. P 12 × 13 (sold at 43 z.)		1·25	1·25

The 10 z. premium on No. **MS**2934 was for benefit of the Polish Olympic Committee.

845 Monte Cassino Memorial Cross and Monastery

846 "German Princess" (Lucas Cranach)

(Des S. Malecki. Photo)

1984 (18 May). *40th Anniv of Battle of Monte Cassino. P* 11½ × 11.
2935	**845** 15 z. blackish olive & orange-verm		45	15

(Des R. Dudzicki. Photo)

1984 (15 June). *19th Universal Postal Union Congress, Hamburg. P* 11½ × 12.
2936	**846** 27 z. + 10 z. multicoloured		1·10	50

No. 2936 was issued with *se-tenant* label bearing text and U.P.U. emblem.

847 "Warsaw from Praga Bank" (detail) (Canaletto)

(Des J. Wysocki. Photo)

1984 (20 June). *Paintings of Vistula River. T* **847** *and similar horiz designs. Multicoloured. P* 11.
2937	5 z. Type **847**		20	10
2938	6 z. "Trumpet Festivity" (Aleksander Gierymski)		25	10
2939	25 z. "The Vistula River near Bielany District" (Józef Rapacki)		90	30
2940	27 z. "Steamship Harbour in Powiśle District" (Franciszek Kostrzewski)		1·00	35
2937/2940	*Set of* 4		2·10	70

848 Order of Grunwald Cross

849 Group of Insurgents

(Des J. Desselberger. Photo)

1984 (21 July). *40th Anniv of Polish People's Republic.* T **848** *and similar vert designs. Multicoloured.* P 11½.

2941	5 z. Type **848**		20	10
2942	6 z. Order of Revival of Poland		20	10
2943	10 z. Order of Banner of Labour, First Class		30	10
2944	16 z. Order of Builders of People's Poland		55	25
2941/2944	*Set of 4*		1·10	50
MS2945	156×101 mm. Nos. 2941/4		3·25	3·25

(Des W. Freudenreich. Photo)

1984 (1 Aug). *40th Anniv of Warsaw Uprising.* T **849** *and similar horiz designs. Multicoloured.* P 11×11½.

2946	4 z. Type **849**		20	10
2947	5 z. Insurgent on postal duty		20	10
2948	6 z. Insurgents fighting		20	10
2949	25 z. Tending wounded		90	35
2946/2949	*Set of 4*		1·25	45

850 Defence of Oksywie Holm and Col. Stanisław Dąbek

(Des A. Balcerzak. Photo)

1984 (1 Sept). *45th Anniv of German Invasion.* T **850** *and similar horiz design. Multicoloured.* P 12×11½.

2950	5 z. Type **850**		20	10
2951	6 z. Battle of Bzura River and Gen. Tadeusz Kutrzeba		25	10

See also Nos. 3004/5, 3062, 3126/8, 3172/4 and 3240/3.

851 "Broken Heart" (monument, Łódź Concentration Camp)

852 Militiaman and Ruins

(Des W. Surowiecki. Photo)

1984 (17 Sept). *Child Martyrs.* P 11½×11.

2952	**851** 16 z. deep bistre-brown, bright blue and blackish brown		45	15

(Des J. Kroll. Photo)

1984 (29 Sept). *40th Anniv of Civic Militia and Security Force.* T **852** *and similar horiz design. Multicoloured.* P 11×11½.

2953	5 z. Type **852**		20	10
2954	6 z. Militiaman in control centre		25	10

MINIMUM PRICE

The minimum price quoted is 10p which represents a handling charge rather than a basis for valuing common stamps. For further notes about prices see introductory pages.

853 First Balloon Flight, 1784 (after Chrostowski)

854 Weasel (*Mustela nivalis*)

(Des A. Balcerzak. Photo)

1984 (5 Nov). *Polish Aviation.* T **853** *and similar horiz designs.* P 11×11½.

2955	5 z. black, apple green and mauve		20	10
2956	5 z. multicoloured		20	10
2957	6 z. multicoloured		20	10
2958	10 z. multicoloured		30	15
2959	16 z. multicoloured		40	20
2960	27 z. multicoloured		90	40
2961	31 z. multicoloured		1·10	50
2955/2961	*Set of 7*		3·00	1·40

Designs:—No. 2956, Michal Scipio del Campo and biplane (first flight over Warsaw, 1911); 2957, Balloon *Polonez* (winner, Gordon Bennett Cup, 1983); 2958, PWS 101 and Jantar gliders (Lilienthal Medal winners); 2959, PZL-104 Wilga airplane (world precise flight champion, 1983); 2960, Jan Nagórski and Farman M.F.7 floatplane (Arctic zone flights, 1914); 2961, PZL P-37 Łoś and PZL P-7 aircraft.

(Des J. Brodowski. Photo)

1984 (4 Dec). *Fur-bearing Animals.* T **854** *and similar multicoloured designs.* P 11½×11½ (horiz) or 11½×11 (vert).

2962	4 z. Type **854**		20	10
2963	5 z. Stoat (*Mustela erminea*)		20	10
2964	5 z. Beech marten (*Martes foina*)		25	10
2965	10 z. Eurasian beaver (*Castor fiber*) (vert)		30	15
2966	10 z. Eurasian otter (*Lutra lutra*) (vert)		30	15
2967	65 z. Alpine marmot (*Marmota marmota*) (vert)		2·40	75
2962/2967	*Set of 6*		3·25	1·10

(Des A. Heidrich. Litho)

1984 (10 Dec). *Renovation of Cracow Monuments* (3rd series). Designs as T **819**. P 11½×11 (5 z.) or 11×11½ (15 z.).

2968	5 z. lake-brown, black & dp bluish green		20	10
2969	15 z. turquoise-blue, chestnut and black		40	15

Designs: *Vert*—5 z. Wawel cathedral. *Horiz*—15 z. Wawel Castle (royal residence).

855 Protestant Church, Warsaw

856 Steam Fire Hose (late 19th century)

(Des J. Wysocki. Photo)

1984 (28 Dec). *Religious Architecture.* T **855** *and similar multicoloured designs.* P 11½×12 (vert) or 12×11½ (horiz).

2970	5 z. Type **855**		15	10
2971	10 z. Saint Andrew's Roman Catholic church, Cracow		30	10
2972	15 z. Greek Catholic church, Rychwald		45	20
2973	20 z. St. Maria Magdalena Orthodox church, Warsaw		60	20

2974	25 z.	Tykocin synagogue, Kaczorów (*horiz*)		75	25
2975	31 z.	Tatar mosque, Kruszyniany (*horiz*)		95	40
2970/2975		*Set of 6*		2·75	1·00

(Des Z. Stasik. Photo)

1985 (25 Feb). *Fire Engines. T* **856** *and similar horiz designs. Multicoloured. P* 11×11½.

2976	4 z.	Type **856**		15	10
2977	10 z.	"Polski Fiat", 1930s		30	10
2978	12 z.	"Jelcz 315" fire engine		35	15
2979	15 z.	Manual fire hose, 1899		45	15
2980	20 z.	"Magirus" fire ladder on "Jelcz" chassis		60	25
2981	30 z.	Manual fire hose (early 18th century)		1·00	45
2976/2981		*Set of 6*		2·50	1·00

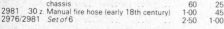

857 "Battle of Raclawice" (Jan Styka and Wojciech Kossak)

(Des A. Heidrich. Photo)

1985 (4 Apr). *P* 11.

2982	**857**	27 z. multicoloured	70	25

858 Wincenty Rzymowski

859 Badge on Denim

(Des Z. Stasik. Litho)

1985 (11 Apr). *35th Death Anniv of Wincenty Rzymowski (founder of Polish Democratic Party). P* 11½×11.

2983	**858**	10 z. deep blue-violet & dull vermilion	25	10

(Des H. Matuszewska and K. Tarkowska. Photo)

1985 (25 Apr). *International Youth Year. P* 11½×11.

2984	**859**	15 z. multicoloured	40	10

860 Boleslaw III, the Wry-mouthed, and Map

(Des. S. Malecki. Litho)

1985 (8 May). *40th Anniv of Return of Western and Northern Territories to Poland. T* **860** *and similar square designs. Multicoloured. P* 11½.

2985	5 z.	Type **860**	10	10
2986	10 z.	Wladyslaw Gomulka (vice-president of first post-war government) and map	35	10
2987	20 z.	Piotr Zaremba (Governor of Szczecin) and map	60	20

861 "Victory, Berlin 1945" (Józef Mlynarski)

(Des W. Surowiecki. Photo)

1985 (9 May). *40th Anniv of Victory over Fascism. P* 12×11½.

2988	**861**	5 z. multicoloured	15	10

862 Warsaw Arms and Flags of Member Countries

863 Wolves in Winter

(Des S. Tolodziecki. Litho)

1985 (14 May). *30th Anniv of Warsaw Pact. P* 11½.

2989	**862**	5 z. multicoloured	15	10

(Des J. Brodowski. Photo)

1985 (25 May). *Protected Animals. The Wolf* (Canis lupus). *T* **863** *and similar horiz designs. Multicoloured. P* 11×11½.

2990	5 z.	Type **863**		15	10
2991	10 z.	She-wolf with cubs		35	10
2992	10 z.	Close-up of wolf		35	10
2993	20 z.	Wolves in summer		70	20
2990/2993		*Set of 4*		1·40	40

(Des Z. Stasik. Photo)

1985 (25 June). *Musical Instruments* (2nd series). *Vert designs as T* **840**. *Multicoloured. P* 11½×11.

2994	5 z.	Rattle and tarapata		15	10
2995	10 z.	Stick rattle and berlo		30	10
2996	12 z.	Clay whistles		35	15
2997	20 z.	Stringed instruments		55	25
2998	25 z.	Cow bells		75	30
2999	31 z.	Wind instruments		90	45
2994/2999		*Set of 6*		2·75	1·10

864 *Iskra* (cadet ship)   **865** Tomasz Nocznicki

(Des M. Piekarski. Eng P. Naszarkowski. Recess and litho)

1985 (29 June). *40th Anniv of Polish Navy. P* 11½×11.
3000 **864** 5 z. dp violet-blue, greenish yell & blk   40   10

(Des J. Konarzewski. Eng W. Zajdel (10 z.), M. Kopecki (20 z.).
Recess)

1985 (26 July). *Leaders of Peasants' Movement. T* **865** *and
similar horiz design. P* 11×11½.
3001   10 z. slate green   25   10
3002   20 z. chocolate   50   20
    Design:—20 z. Maciej Rataj.

866 Hockey Players   **867** Type "20 K" Goods
Wagon

(Des J. Brodowski. Litho)

1985 (22 Aug). *60th Anniv (1986) of Polish Field Hockey
Association. P* 11½×11.
3003 **866** 5 z. multicoloured   15   10

(Des A. Balcerzak. Photo)

1985 (1 Sept). *46th Anniv of German Invasion. Horiz designs as
T* **850**. *Multicoloured. P* 12×11½.
3004   5 z. Defence of Wizna and Capt.
            Wladyslaw Raginis   20   10
3005   10 z. Battle of Mlawa and Col. Wilhelm
            Liszka-Lawicz   60   15

(Des H. Chyliński. Litho)

1985 (18 Sept). *PAFAWAG Railway Rolling Stock. T* **867** *and
similar horiz designs. Multicoloured. P* 11½×11.
3006   5 z. Type **867**   20   10
3007   10 z. Type "201 E" electric locomotive   40   15
3008   17 z. Type "OMMK" two-axle coal car   ..   65   25
3009   20 z. Type "111 A" passenger coach   ..   85   35
3006/3009   *Set of 4*   ..   ..   1·90   70

868 "Madonna with Child,
St. John and Angel"
(Sandro Botticelli)

(Des R. Dudzicki. Photo)

1985 (25 Sept). *"Italia '85" International Stamp Exhibition,
Rome. Sheet* 81×108 *mm. P* 11.
MS3010 **868** 65 z. + 15 z. multicoloured   ..   2·00   2·00
    A limited quantity of No. **MS**3010 has the additional inscription
"35 LAT POLSKIEGO ZWIAZKU FILATELISTÓW" beneath the
stamp.

869 Green-winged Teal
(*Anas crecca*)

(Des J. Desselberger. Photo)

1985 (21 Oct). *Wild Ducks. T* **869** *and similar horiz designs.
Multicoloured. P* 11×11½.
3011   5 z. Type **869**   15   10
3012   5 z. Garganey (*Anas querquedula*)   ..   15   10
3013   10 z. Tufted duck (*Aythya fuligula*)   ..   40   10
3014   15 z. Goldeneye (*Bucephala clangula*)   ..   50   15
3015   25 z. Eider (*Somateria mollissima*)   ..   90   30
3016   29 z. Red-crested pochard (*Netta rufina*)   1·25   40
3011/3016   *Set of 6*   ..   ..   3·00   95

870 U.N. Emblem and   **871** Ballerina
"Flags"

(Des H. Chyliński. Litho)

1985 (24 Oct). *40th Anniv of United Nations Organization.
P* 11½×11.
3017 **870** 27 z. multicoloured   70   25

(Des S. Malecki. Litho)

1985 (4 Dec). *Bicentenary of Polish Ballet. T* **871** *and similar vert
design. P* 11½×11.
3018   5 z. bronze grn, yell-orge & Venetian red   15   10
3019   15 z. purplish brown, bright reddish violet
            and reddish orange   45   10
    Design:—15 z. Male dancer.

872 "Marysia and   **873** Oliwa Church
Burek in Ceylon"   Organ and Bach

(Des K. Sliwka. Photo)

1985 (8 Dec). *Birth Centenary of Stanislaw Ignacy Witkiewicz (artist). T **872** and similar multicoloured designs. P 11×11½ (3021) or 11½×11 (others).*

3020	5 z. Type **872**	..	..	15	10
3021	10 z. "Woman with Fox" (*horiz*)	..		30	10
3022	10 z. "Self-portrait" (*horiz*)	..	..	30	10
3023	20 z. "Compositions"	..	..	55	25
3024	25 z. "Nena Stachurska"	..	..	70	30
3020/3024	Set of 5	..	..	1·75	70

(Des R. Dudzicki. Photo)

1985 (30 Dec). *300th Birth Anniv of Johann Sebastian Bach (composer). Sheet 67×79 mm. P 11½×11.*

MS3025 **873** 65 z. multicoloured .. .. 1·75 1·75

No. **MS**3025 also exists with additional inscription "300 rocznica urodzin Jana Sebastiana Bacha" from a limited printing.

874 Human Profile

875 Michal Kamieński and Planetary and Comet's Orbits

(Des K. Sliwka. Litho)

1986 (16 Jan). *Congress of Intellectuals for Defence of Peaceful Future of the World, Warsaw. P 11½×11.*

3026 **874** 10 z. dull ultram, dull vio-bl & dp cobalt 25 10

(Des Z. Stasik. Litho)

1986 (7 Feb). *Appearance of Halley's Comet. T **875** and similar horiz design. P 11×11½.*

3027	25 z. deep blue and orange-brown	60	25
	a. Pair. Nos. 3027/8	1·25	
3028	25 z. indigo, greenish blue & orange-brn	60	25

Design:—No. 3028, "Vega", "Planet A", "Giotto" and "Ice" space probes and comet.

Nos. 3027/8 were printed together in *se-tenant* pairs within the sheet.

(Des A. Heidrich. Litho)

1986 (20 Mar). *Renovation of Cracow Monuments (4th series). Vert designs as T **819**. P 11½×11.*

3029	5 z. bistre-brown, chestnut and black ..	10	10
3030	10 z. yellow-green, yellow-brown & black	30	10

Designs:—5 z. Collegium Maius (Jagiellonian University museum); 10 z. Kazimierz Town Hall.

876 Sun

877 Grey Partridge (*Perdix perdix*)

(Des H. Chyliński. Photo)

1986 (20 Mar). *International Peace Year. P 11½×11.*

3031 **876** 25 z. lemon, greenish blue and blue 55 20

(Des H. Chyliński. Photo)

1986 (15 Apr). *Game. T **877** and similar multicoloured designs. P 11×11½ (horiz) or 11½×11 (vert).*

3032	5 z. Type **877** ..	50	20
3033	5 z. Common rabbit (*Oryctolagus cuniculus*)	15	10
3034	10 z. Ring-necked pheasants (*Phasianus colchicus*) (*horiz*) ..	90	20
3035	10 z. Fallow deer (*Dama dama*) (*horiz*) ..	30	10
3036	20 z. Hare (*Lepus europaeus*) ..	60	20
3037	40 z. Argali (*Ovis ammon*) ..	1·25	45
3032/3037	Set of 6	3·25	1·10

878 Kulczyński

(Des R. Dudzicki. Eng P. Naszarkowski. Recess and photo)

1986 (3 May). *10th Death Anniv (1985) of Stanislaw Kulczyński (politician). P 11½×11.*

3038 **878** 10 z. stone and chocolate 25 10

879 "Warsaw Fire Brigade, 1871" (detail, Józef Brodowski)

(Des Z. Stasik. Eng M. Kopecki. Recess and litho)

1986 (16 May). *150th Anniv of Warsaw Fire Brigade. P 11.*

3039 **879** 10 z. deep brown and dull brown .. 25 10

880 Paderewski (composer)

881 Footballers

(Des W. Andrzejewski. Photo)

1986 (22 May). *"Ameripex '86" International Stamp Exhibition, Chicago. P 11½×11.*

3040 **880** 65 z. dp brt blue, blk & brownish grey 1·50 70

(Des R. Dudzicki. Litho)

1986 (26 May). *World Cup Football Championship, Mexico.* P 11½.
3041 **881** 25 z. multicoloured ..   50   20

882 *Wilanów*

(Des J. Brodowski. Photo)

1986 (18 June). *Passenger Ferries.* T **882** *and similar horiz designs. Multicoloured.* P 11.
3042 10 z. Type **882**   55   20
3043 10 z. *Wawel*   55   20
3044 15 z. *Pomerania*   70   30
3045 25 z. *Rogalin*   ..   ..   1·25   50
3042/3045 *Set of 4* ..   ..   ..   2·75   1·10
MS3046 Two sheets, each 116 × 98 mm. (a) Nos. 3042/3 (sold at 30 z.); (b) Nos. 3044/5 (sold at 55 z.)   ..   ..   4·50   4·50
Nos. 3042/5 were each issued with *se-tenant* half stamp-size label depicting features of various harbours.

883 A. B. Dobrowolski, Map and Research Vessel *Kopernik*

(Des S. Malecki. Litho)

1986 (23 June). *25th Anniv of Antarctic Agreement.* T **883** *and similar horiz design.* P 11½×11.
3047 5 z. turquoise-green, olive-black & verm   40   25
3048 40 z. lavender, dp violet & reddish orange   3·50   85
Design:—40 z. H. Arctowski, map and research vessel *Profesor Siedlecki.*

884 Workers and Emblem   **885** "Paulinite Church on Skalka in Cracow" (detail), 1627

(Des A. Szczepaniak. Photo)

1986 (29 June). *Tenth Polish United Workers' Party Congress, Warsaw.* P 11×11½.
3049 **884** 10 z. steel blue and red   ..   25   10

(Des A. Heidrich. Photo)

1986 (15 Aug). *Treasures of Jasna Góra Monastery.* T **885** *and similar vert designs. Multicoloured.* P 11½×11.
3050 5 z. Type **885**   15   10
3051 5 z. "Tree of Jesse", 17th-century   15   10
3052 20 z. Chalice, 18th-century   ..   40   20
3053 40 z. "Virgin Mary" (detail, chasuble column), 15th-century   ..   1·00   40
3050/3053 *Set of 4* ..   ..   ..   1·50   60

886 Precision Flying   **887** "Bird" in National
(Waclaw Nycz)   Costume carrying Stamp

(Des J. Brodowski. Litho)

1986 (21 Aug). *1985 Polish World Championship Successes.* T **886** *and similar horiz designs. Multicoloured.* P 11×11½.
3054 5 z. Type **886**   20   10
3055 10 z. Windsurfing (Malgorzata Palasz-Piasecka)   50   10
3056 10 z. Glider aerobatics (Jerzy Makula) ..   40   10
3057 15 z. Wrestling (Bogdan Daras)   ..   40   15
3058 20 z. Individual road cycling (Lech Piasecki)   60   20
3059 30 z. Women's modern pentathlon (Barbara Kotowska)   ..   1·00   35
3054/3059 *Set of 6* ..   ..   ..   2·75   85

(Des W. Freudenreich. Photo)

1986 (28 Aug). *"Stockholmia 86" International Stamp Exhibition.* P 11×11½.
3060 **887** 65 z. multicoloured ..   ..   1·50   55
MS3061 94×80 mm. No. 3060   ..   1·50   1·50

(Des A. Balcerzak. Photo)

1986 (1 Sept). *47th Anniv of German Invasion. Horiz design as* T **850**. *Multicoloured.* P 12×11½.
3062 10 z. Battle of Jordanów and Col. Stanislaw Maczek   ..   25   10

888 Schweitzer   **889** Airliner and
Postal Messenger

(Des J. Wysocki. Eng T. Lis. Recess and photo)

1986 (26 Sept). *20th Death Anniv (1985) of Albert Schweitzer (medical missionary).* P 12×11½.
3063 **888** 5 z. agate, cinnamon and ultramarine   10   10

(Des S. Malecki. Litho)

1986 (9 Oct). *World Post Day.* P 11×11½.
3064 **889** 40 z. sepia, ultramarine and orange-red   80   35
MS3065 81×81 mm. No. 3064×2 (sold at 120 z.)   10·50   10·50

890 Basilisk | **891** Kotarbiński

894 Star | **895** Trip to Bielany, 1887

(Des Elzbieta Gaudasińska. Photo)

1986 (28 Oct). *Folk Tales. T* **890** *and similar multicoloured designs. P* 11×11½ *(horiz)* or 11½×11 *(vert).*

3066	5 z. Type **890**				15	10
3067	5 z. Duke Popiel (*vert*)				15	10
3068	10 z. Golden Duck				25	10
3069	10 z. Boruta the Devil (*vert*)				25	10
3070	20 z. Janosik the Robber (*vert*)				40	20
3071	50 z. Lajkonik (*vert*)				1·10	50
3066/3071	Set of 6				2·00	90

(Des J. Wysocki. Litho)

1986 (19 Nov). *Birth Centenary of Tadeusz Kotarbiński (philosopher). P* 12×11½.

3072	**891** 10 z. agate and brown			20	10

892 20th-century Windmill, Zygmuntów | **893** Mieszko (Mieczyslaw) I

(Des M. Piekarski. Photo)

1986 (26 Nov). *Wooden Architecture. T* **892** *and similar horiz designs. Multicoloured. P* 11½×11 (3073) or 11×11½ *(others).*

3073	5 z. Type **892**			10	10
3074	5 z. 17th-century church, Bączal Dolny			10	10
3075	10 z. 19th-century Oravian cottage, Zubrzyca Górna			25	10
3076	15 z. 18th-century Kashubian arcade cottage, Wdzydze			30	15
3077	25 z. 19th-century barn, Grzawa			60	20
3078	30 z. 19th-century water-mill, Siolkowice Stare			90	30
3073/3078	Set of 6			2·00	80

(Des S. Malecki. Eng P. Naszarkowski (10 z.), W. Zajdel (25 z.). Recess and photo)

1986 (4 Dec). *Polish Rulers (1st series). T* **893** *and similar vert design showing drawings by Jan Matejko. P* 11.

3079	10 z. agate and brown-olive		20	10
3080	25 z. brownish black and reddish purple		50	20

Design:—25 z. Queen Dobrawa (wife of Mieszko I).
See also Nos. 3144/5, 3193/4, 3251/2, 3341/2, 3351/2, 3387/8, 3461/4 and 3511/12.

GIBBONS STAMP MONTHLY

—finest and most informative magazine for all collectors. Obtainable from your newsagent or by postal subscription—details on request.

(Des W. Freudenreich. Photo)

1986 (12 Dec). *New Year. P* 11×11½.

3081	**894** 25 z. multicoloured			45	35

(Des W. Surowiecki. Litho)

1986 (19 Dec). *Centenary of Warsaw Cyclists' Society. T* **895** *and similar designs. P* 13×12½ (3082) or 12½×13 *(others).*

3082	5 z. multicoloured			10	10
3083	5 z. bistre-brown, grey-brown and black			10	10
3084	10 z. multicoloured			25	10
3085	10 z. multicoloured			25	10
3086	30 z. multicoloured			60	25
3087	50 z. multicoloured			1·10	40
3082/3087	Set of 6			2·10	90

Designs: *Vert*—No. 3083, Jan Stanislaw Skrodzki (1895 touring record holder); 3084, Dynasy (Society's headquarters, 1892–1937); 3085, Mieczyslaw Barański (1896 road cycling champion); 3086, Karolina Kocięcka; 3087, Henryk Weiss (Race champion).

896 Lelewel

(Des J. Wysocki. Photo)

1986 (22 Dec). *Birth Bicentenary of Joachim Lelewel (historian). P* 11×12.

3088	**896** 10 z. + 5 z. multicoloured		30	15

The premium was for the benefit of the National Committee for School Aid fund.

897 Krill (*Euphausia superba*) and *Antoni Garnuszewski* (supply ship) | **898** "Portrait of a Woman"

(Des S. Malecki. Litho)

1987 (13 Feb). *Tenth Anniv of Henryk Arctowski Antarctic Station, King George Island, South Shetlands. T* **897** *and similar square designs. Multicoloured. P* 11½.

3089	5 z. Type **897**			10	10
3090	5 z. *Nototenia marmurkowa, Notothenia rossi* (fishes) and *Zulawy* (supply ship)			10	10

3091 10 z. Southern fulmar (*Fulmarus glacialoides*) and *Pogoria* (cadet brigantine) 50 20
3092 10 z. Adelie penguin (*Pigoscelis adeliae*) and *Gedania* (yacht) 50 20
3093 30 z. Fur seal (*Arctocephalus*) and *Dziunia* (research vessel) 70 25
3094 40 z. Leopard seal (*Hydrurga leptonyx*) and *Kapitan Ledóchowski* (research vessel) 90 35
3089/3094 *set of 6* .. .. 2·50 1·00

(Des W. Surowiecki. Photo)

1987 (20 Mar). *50th Death Anniv* (1986) *of Leon Wyczólkowski (artist).* T **898** *and similar multicoloured designs.* P 11.
3095 5 z. "Cineraria Flowers" (*horiz*) .. 10 10
3096 10 z. Type **898** 20 10
3097 10 z. "Wooden Church" (*horiz*) .. 20 10
3098 25 z. "Beetroot Lifting" .. 45 20
3099 30 z. "Wading Fishermen" (*horiz*) .. 50 25
3100 40 z. "Self-portrait" (*horiz*) .. 70 40
3095/3100 *Set of 6* .. .. 1·90 90

899 "Ravage" (from "War Cycle") and Grottger

(Des W. Surowiecki. Photo)

1987 (26 Mar). *150th Birth Anniv of Artur Grottger (artist).* P 11.
3101 **899** 15 z. brown and stone 20 10

900 Świerczewski

901 Strzelecki

(Des J. Konarzewski. Eng P. Naszarkowski. Recess and photo)

1987 (27 Mar). *90th Birth Anniv of General Karol Świerczewski.* P 11½×12.
3102 **900** 15 z. olive-green and yellow-olive .. 20 10

(Des M. Piekarski. Photo)

1987 (23 Apr). *190th Birth Anniv of Pawel Edmund Strzelecki (scientist and explorer of Tasmania).* P 11½×11.
3103 **901** 65 z. blackish olive 90 45

902 Emblem and Banner

(Des A. Szczepaniak. Litho)

1987 (8 May). *Second Patriotic Movement for National Revival Congress.* P 11×11½.
3104 **902** 10 z. vermilion, ultramarine and drab 15 10

903 CWS "T-1" Motor Car, 1928

(Des J. Brodowski. Photo)

1987 (19 May). *Polish Motor Vehicles.* T **903** *and similar horiz designs. Multicoloured.* P 12×11½.
3105 10 z. Type **903** 15 10
3106 10 z. Saurer-Zawrat bus, 1936 .. .. 15 10
3107 15 z. Ursus-A lorry, 1928 .. .. 25 10
3108 15 z. Lux-Sport motor car, 1936 .. 25 10
3109 25 z. Podkowa "100" motor cycle, 1939 35 20
3110 45 z. Sokól "600 RT" motor cycle, 1935 65 50
3105/3110 *Set of 6* .. .. 1·60 90

904 Royal Palace, Warsaw

(Des S. Malecki. Photo)

1987 (5 June). P 12×11½.
3111 **904** 50 z. multicoloured 75 35
A miniature sheet containing No. 3111 and two labels showing Pope John Paul II and Pres. Jaruzelski exists from a limited printing.

905 Pope John Paul II

(Des W. Andrzejewski (50 z.), J. Wysocki (others). Photo)

1987 (8 June). *Third Papal Visit.* T **905** *and similar vert. designs. Multicoloured.* P 11.
3112 15 z. Type **905** 30 10
    a. Pair. Nos. 3112/13 .. .. 1·25
3113 45 z. Pope and signature 70 35
MS3114 77×66 mm. 50 z. Profile of Pope (21×27 mm). P 12×11½ .. 80 60
Nos. 3112/13 were printed together in *se-tenant* pairs within the sheet.

906 Polish Settler at Kasubia, Ontario

(Des R. Dudzicki. Photo)

1987 (13 June). *"Capex '87" International Stamp Exhibition, Toronto.* P 12×11½.

3115 **906** 50 z. + 20 z. multicoloured .. 95 45
The premium was for the benefit of the Polish Philatelic Union.

(Des A. Heidrich. Litho)

1987 (6 July). *Renovation of Cracow Monuments* (5th series). *Horiz design as T 819.* P 11×11½.

3116 10 z. magenta, black and yellowish green 15 10
Design:—10 z. Barbican.

907 Ludwig Zamenhof (inventor) and Star
908 "Poznań Town Hall" (Stanislaw Wyspiański)

(Des A. Szczepaniak. Litho)

1987 (25 July). *Centenary of Esperanto (invented language).* P 11×11½.

3117 **907** 45 z. grey-brown, emerald and black 80 30

(Des A. Heidrich. Litho)

1987 (8 Aug). *"Poznań 87" National Stamp Exhibition.* P 11½×11.

3118 **908** 15 z. black and salmon 20 10

909 Queen Bee
910 1984 Olympic Stamp and Laurel Wreath

(Des K. Sliwka. Photo)

1987 (20 Aug). *"Apimondia '87" International Bee Keeping Congress, Warsaw.* T **909** *and similar vert designs. Multicoloured.* P 11½×11.

3119	10 z. Type **909** ..	..	..	20	10
3120	10 z. Worker bee	..	..	20	10
3121	15 z. Drone	..	..	25	15
3122	15 z. Hive in orchard	..	..	25	15
3123	40 z. Worker bee on clover flower	..	70	30
3124	50 z. Forest bee keeper collecting honey	90	50
3119/3124	*Set of 6* ..	..	..	2·25	1·10

(Des H. Chyliński. Litho German Bank Note Ptg Co, Leipzig)

1987 (28 Aug). *"Olymphilex '87" Olympic Stamps Exhibition, Rome. Sheet* 83×57 mm. P 14.

MS3125 **910** 45 z. + 10 z. multicoloured .. 80 50
The premium was for the benefit of the Polish Olympic Committee's fund.

(Des B. Wróblewski and A. Balcerzak. Photo)

1987 (1 Sept). *48th Anniv of German Invasion. Horiz designs as T 850. Multicoloured.* P 12×11½.

3126	10 z. Battle of Mokra and Col. Julian Filipowicz ..	..	20	10
3127	10 z. Fighting at Oleszyce and Brig.-Gen. Józef Rudolf Kustroń	..	20	10
3128	15 z. PZL P-7 aircraft over Warsaw and Col. Stefan Pawlikowski ..	..	40	15

911 Hevelius and Sextant
912 High Jump (World Acrobatics Championships, France)

(Des J. Brodowski. Litho)

1987 (15 Sept). *300th Death Anniv of Jan Hevelius (astronomer). T 911 and similar multicoloured design.* P 11½×11 (15 z.) or 11×11½ (40 z.).

3129	15 z. Type **911** ..	..	..	30	15
3130	40 z. Hevelius and map of constellations (horiz) ..	..	..	70	25

(Des H. Chyliński. Litho German Bank Note Ptg Co, Leipzig)

1987 (24 Sept). *1986 Polish World Championship Successes. T 912 and similar horiz designs. Multicoloured.* P 14.

3131	10 z. Type **912** ..	..	..	15	10
3132	15 z. Two-man canoe (World Canoeing Championships, Canada) ..	..	25	10
3133	20 z. Marksman (Free pistol event, World Marksmanship Championships, East Germany) ..	..	..	40	15
3134	25 z. Wrestlers (World Wrestling Championships, Hungary) ..	..	50	20
3131/3134	*Set of 4* ..	..	..	1·10	50

913 "Stacionar 4" Telecommunications Satellite
914 Warsaw Post Office and Ignacy Przebendowski (Postmaster General)

(Des Z. Stasik. Photo)

1987 (2 Oct). *30th Anniv of Launch of "Sputnik 1" (first artificial satellite). Sheet* 67×82 mm. P 11½×11.

MS3135 **913** 40 z. multicoloured 60 50

(Des S. Malecki. Litho)

1987 (9 Oct). *World Post Day. P 11½×11.*
3136 **914** 15 z. olive-green and brown-lake .. 20 10

915 *The Little Mermaid*

916 Col. Stanislaw Wieckowski (founder)

919 Composition

920 17th-century Friesian Wall Clock with Bracket Case

(Des Emilia Freudenreich. Photo)

1987 (16 Oct). *"Hafnia 87" International Stamp Exhibition, Copenhagen. Hans Christian Andersen's Fairy Tales. T* **915** *and similar horiz designs. Multicoloured. P 11×11½.*
3137 10 z. Type **915** 15 10
3138 10 z. *The Nightingale* 15 10
3139 20 z. *The Wild Swans* 30 15
3140 20 z. *The Little Match Girl* .. 30 15
3141 30 z. *The Snow Queen* 50 25
3142 40 z. *The Brave Tin Soldier* .. 70 30
3137/3142 *Set of 6* .. .. .. 1·90 90

(Des M. Piekarski. Eng P. Naszarkowski. Recess and photo)

1987 (16 Oct). *50th Anniv of Democratic Clubs. P 12×11½.*
3143 15 z. black and blue 20 10

(Des S. Malecki. Eng M. Kopecki (10 z.), W. Zajdel (25 z.). Recess and photo)

1987 (4 Dec). *Polish Rulers (2nd series). Vert designs as T* **893** *showing drawings by Jan Matejko. P 11.*
3144 10 z. blackish olive and turquoise-blue .. 10 10
3145 15 z. deep violet-blue and ultramarine .. 25 10
Designs:—10 z. Boleslaw I, the Brave; 15 z. Mieszko (Mieczyslaw) II.
No. 3144 was issued with *se-tenant* inscribed label.

917 Santa Claus with Christmas Trees

918 Emperor Dragonfly *(Anax imperator)*

(Des Emilia and W. Freudenreich. Photo)

1987 (14 Dec). *New Year. P 11×11½.*
3146 **917** 15 z. multicoloured 20 10

(Des B. Wróblewski. Photo)

1988 (23 Feb). *Dragonflies. T* **918** *and similar multicoloured designs. P 11×11½ (horiz) or 11½×11 (vert).*
3147 10 z. Type **918** 20 10
3148 15 z. Four-spotted libellula (*Libellula quadrimaculata*) (*vert*) .. 35 10
3149 15 z. Banded agrion (*Calopteryx splendens*) 35 10
3150 20 z. *Cordulegaster annulatus* (*vert*) .. 35 10
3151 30 z. *Sympetrum pedemontanum* .. 50 15
3152 50 z. *Aeschna viridis* (*vert*) .. 90 25
3147/3152 *Set of 6* .. .. .. 2·40 60

(Des A. Heidrich. Litho)

1988 (8 Mar). *Renovation of Cracow Monuments (6th series). Vert design as T* **819**. *P 11½×11.*
3153 15 z. greenish yellow, chestnut and black 15 10
Design:—15 z. Florianska Gate.

(Des W. Freudenreich. Photo)

1988 (28 Apr). *International Year of Graphic Design. P 11×11½.*
3154 **919** 40 z. multicoloured 45 15

(Des S. Zieliński. Photo)

1988 (19 May). *Clocks and Watches. T* **920** *and similar multicoloured designs. P 11½×12 (vert) or 12×11½ (horiz).*
3155 10 z. Type **920** 15 10
3156 10 z. 20th-century annual clock (*horiz*) .. 15 10
3157 15 z. 18th-century carriage clock .. 20 10
3158 15 z. 18th-century French rococo bracket clock 20 10
3159 20 z. 19th-century pocket watch (*horiz*) 25 10
3160 40 z. 17th-century tile-cased clock from Gdańsk by Benjamin Zoll (*horiz*) .. 50 25
3155/3160 *Set of 6* .. .. .. 1·25 60

921 Salmon and Reindeer

(Des J. Brodowski. Photo)

1988 (1 June). *"Finlandia 88" International Stamp Exhibition, Helsinki. P 12×11½.*
3161 **921** 45 z. + 20 z. multicoloured .. 85 30
The premium was for the benefit of the Polish Philatelic Union.

922 Triple Jump

923 Kukuczka

(Des J. Konarzewski. Photo)

1988 (27 June). *Olympic Games, Seoul. T* **922** *and similar horiz designs. Multicoloured. P 11×11½.*
3162 15 z. Type **922** 20 10
3163 20 z. Wrestling 25 10
3164 20 z. Canoeing 25 10
3165 25 z. Judo 30 15
3166 40 z. Shooting 50 25
3167 55 z. Swimming 65 35
3162/3167 *Set of 6* .. .. .. 1·90 90

(Des J. Konarzewski. Photo)

1988 (17 Aug). *Award of Special Olympic Silver Medal to Jerzy Kukuczka for Mountaineering Achievements. Sheet 84×66 mm. P 11×11½.*

MS3168 **923** 70 z. + 10 z. multicoloured . . 90 60
The premium was for the benefit of the Polish Olympic Committee's fund.

924 Wheat as Graph on VDU

925 PZL P-37 Loś

(Des S. Malecki. Photo)

1988 (22 Aug). *16th European Conference of Food and Agriculture Organization, Cracow. T **924** and similar vert design. Multicoloured. P 11½×11.*
3169 15 z. Type **924** 20 10
3170 40 z. Factory in forest 45 20

(Des A. Szczepaniak. Photo)

1988 (23 Aug). *70th Anniv of Polish Republic (1st issue). 60th Anniv of Polish State Aircraft Works. P 11×11½.*
3171 **925** 45 z. multicoloured 80 20
See also Nos. 3175, 3177, 3181/**MS**3189 and 3190/2.

(Des B. Wróblewski and A. Balcerzak. Photo)

1988 (1 Sept). *49th Anniv of German Invasion. Horiz designs as T **850**. Multicoloured. P 12×11½.*
3172 15 z. Battle of Modlin and Brig.-Gen. Wiktor Thommée .. 20 10
3173 20 z. Battle of Warsaw and Brig.-Gen. Walerian Czuma .. 20 10
3174 20 z. Battle of Tomaszów Lubelski and Brig.-Gen. Antoni Szylling .. 20 10

(Des A. Szczepaniak. Photo)

1988 (5 Sept). *70th Anniv of Polish Republic (2nd issue). 50th Anniv of Stalowa Wola Ironworks. Horiz design as T **925**. Multicoloured. P 11×11½.*
3175 15 z. View of plant 15 10

926 Postal Emblem and Tomasz Arciszewski (Postal Minister, 1918–19)

927 On the Field of Glory Medal

(Des S. Malecki. Litho)

1988 (9 Oct). *World Post Day. P 11½×11.*
3176 **926** 20 z. multicoloured 20 10
Issued both in sheets of 30 stamps and in sheets of 15 stamps and 15 labels showing current postal emblem.

(Des A. Szczepaniak. Photo)

1988 (12 Oct). *70th Anniv of Polish Republic (3rd issue). 60th Anniv of Military Institute for Aviation Medicine. Horiz design as T **925**. Multicoloured. P 11×11½.*
3177 20 z. Hanriot XIV hospital aircraft (38×28 mm) 30 10

(Des R. Dudzicki. Photo)

1988 (12 Oct). *Polish People's Army Battle Medals (1st series). T **927** and similar vert design. Multicoloured. P 11½×11.*
3178 20 z. Type **927** 25 10
3179 20 z. Battle of Lenino Cross 25 10
See also Nos. 3249/50.

928 "Stanislaw Malachowski" and "Kazimierz Nestor Sapieha"

(Des A. Heidrich. Photo)

1988 (16 Oct). *Bicentenary of Four Years Diet (political and social reforms). Paintings of Diet Presidents by Józef Peszko. P 11.*
3180 **928** 20 z. multicoloured 20 10

929 Ignacy Daszyński (politician)

930 Snowman

(Des M. Piekarski. Photo)

1988 (11 Nov). *70th Anniv of Polish Republic (4th issue). Personalities. T **929** and similar vert designs. P 12×11½.*
3181 15 z. olive-green, rosine and black .. 10 10
3182 15 z. olive-green, rosine and black .. 10 10
3183 20 z. brown, vermilion and black .. 20 10
3184 20 z. brown, vermilion and black .. 20 10
3185 20 z. brown, vermilion and black .. 20 10
3186 200 z. slate-purple, bright scarlet & black 1·75 50
3187 200 z. slate-purple, bright scarlet & black 1·75 50
3188 200 z. slate-purple, bright scarlet & black 1·75 50
3181/3188 *Set of 8* .. . . 5·50 1·75
MS3189 102×60 mm. Nos. 3186/8 .. 13·00 13·00
Designs:—No. 3182, Wincenty Witos (politician); 3183, Julian Marchlewski (trade unionist and economist); 3184, Stanislaw Wojciechowski (politician); 3185, Wojciech Korfanty (politician); 3186, Ignacy Paderewski (musician and politician); 3187, Marshal Józef Pilsudski; 3188, Gabriel Narutowicz (President, 1922).

(Des A. Szczepaniak. Photo)

1988 (28 Nov–Dec). *70th Anniv of Polish Republic (5th issue). Horiz designs as T **925**. Multicoloured. P 11×11½.*
3190 15 z. Coal wharf, Gdynia Port (65th anniv) (38×28 mm) (12 Dec) 10 10
3191 20 z. Hipolit Cegielski (founder) and steam locomotive (142nd anniv of H. Cegielski Metal Works, Poznań) (38×28 mm) 20 10
3192 40 z. Upper Silesia Tower (main entrance) (60th anniv of International Poznań Fair) (21 Dec) 45 20

(Des S. Malecki. Eng M. Kopecki (10 z.), P. Naszarkowski (15 z.). Recess and photo)

1988 (4 Dec). *Polish Rulers (3rd series). Vert designs as T* **893** *showing drawings by Jan Matejko. P* 11.
3193   10 z. deep chocolate and lake-brown   ..   10   10
3194   15 z. deep chocolate and brown   ..   15   10
Designs:— 10 z. Queen Rycheza; 15 z. Kazimierz (Karol Odnowiciel) I.

(Des W. Freudenreich. Photo)

1988 (9 Dec). *New Year. P* 11×11½.
3195 **930** 20 z. multicoloured   20   10

931 Flag

932 *Blysk*

(Des J. Wysocki. Photo)

1988 (15 Dec). *40th Anniv of Polish United Workers' Party. P* 11½×12.
3196 **931** 20 z. bright scarlet and black   ..   20   10

(Des M. Piekarski. Litho German Bank Note Ptg Co, Leipzig)

1988 (29 Dec). *Fire Boats. T* **932** *and similar horiz designs. Multicoloured. P* 14.
3197   10 z. Type **932**   15   10
3198   15 z. Plomień   25   10
3199   15 z. Żar   25   10
3200   20 z. Strażak 11   40   10
3201   20 z. Strażak 4   40   10
3202   45 z. Strażak 25   80   50
3197/3202   *Set of* 6   ..   ..   ..   2·25   70

933 Ardennes

934 Wire-haired Dachshund

(Des H. Chyliński. Photo)

1989 (6 Mar). *Horses. T* **933** *and similar multicoloured designs. P* 11.
3203   15 z. Lippizaner (*horiz*)   10   10
3204   15 z. Type **933**   10   10
3205   20 z. English thoroughbred (*horiz*)   ..   20   10
3206   20 z. Arab   20   10
3207   30 z. Great Poland racehorse (*horiz*)   ..   35   10
3208   70 z. Polish horse   75   50
3203/3208   *Set of* 6   ..   ..   ..   1·50   75

(Des J. Wysocki. Photo)

1989 (3 May). *Hunting Dogs. T* **934** *and similar vert designs. Multicoloured. P* 11½×11.
3209   15 z. Type **934**   10   10
3210   15 z. Cocker spaniel   10   10

3211   20 z. Czech fousek pointer   15   10
3212   20 z. Welsh terrier   15   10
3213   25 z. English setter   20   10
3214   45 z. Pointer   40   25
3209/3214   *Set of* 6   ..   ..   ..   1·00   50

935 Gen. Wladyslaw Anders and Plan of Battle

936 Marianne

(Des H. Chyliński. Photo)

1989 (18 May). *45th Anniv of Battle of Monte Cassino. P* 11½×12.
3215 **935** 80 z. multicoloured   45   20
See also Nos. 3227, 3247, 3287 and 3327.

A 50 z. stamp showing Gen. Broni Grzegorz Korczyński was prepared in 1989 but not issued.

(Des J. Wysocki. Litho)

1989 (3 July). *Bicentenary of French Revolution. P* 11½×11.
3216 **936** 100 z. brownish blk, brt scar & ultram   60   30
MS3217 93×118 mm. No. 3216×2 plus two labels (sold at 270 z.)   ..   ..   ..   1·75   90
No. 3216 was issued with *se-tenant* label bearing the exhibition emblem.
The premium on No. **MS**3217 was for the benefit of the Polish Philatelic Union.

937 Polonia House

(Des A. Szczepaniak. Photo)

1989 (16 July). *Opening of Polonia House (cultural centre), Pultusk. P* 12×11½.
3218 **937** 100 z. multicoloured   60   30

938 Monument (Bohdan Chmielewski)

939 Xaweri Dunikowski (artist)

(Des Z. Stasik. Photo)

1989 (21 July). *45th Anniv of Civic Militia and Security Force.* P 11×11½.
3219 **938** 35 z. slate-blue and yellow-brown .. 70 25

(Des J. Wysocki. Photo)

1989 (21 July). *Recipients of Order of Builders of the Republic of Poland. T **939** and similar vert designs. Multicoloured.* P 11½×11.
3220 35 z. Type **939** 25 10
3221 35 z. Stanislaw Mazur (farmer) 25 10
3222 35 z. Natalia Gąsiorowska (historian) .. 25 10
3223 35 z. Wincenti Pstrowski (initiator of worker performance contests) .. 25 10
3220/3223 *Set of 4* 90 30

940 Astronaut   **941** Firemen

(Des Z. Stasik. Photo)

1989 (21 July). *20th Anniv of First Manned Landing on Moon.* P 11×11½.
3224 **940** 100 z. multicoloured 60 30
MS3225 85×85 mm. No. 3224 60 60
No. **MS**3225 also exists imperforate from a limited printing.

(Des W. Surowiecki. Photo)

1989 (25 July). *World Fire Fighting Congress, Warsaw.* P 11½×11.
3226 **941** 80 z. multicoloured 45 20

(Des H. Chyliński. Photo)

1989 (21 Aug). *45th Anniv of Battle of Falaise. Horiz design as T **935**. Multicoloured.* P 12×11½.
3227 165 z. Plan of battle and Gen. Stanislaw Maczek 90 45

942 Daisy   **943** Museum Emblem

(Des S. Malecki. Litho (700 z.) or photo (others))

1989 (25 Aug)–**91**. *Plants. T **942** and similar vert design.* P 14 (700 z.) or 11×12 (others).
3229 **942** 40 z. grey-green .. 10 10
3230 — 60 z. deep violet 15 10
3231 **942** 150 z. brown-lake (4.12.89) .. 20 10
3232 — 500 z. deep mauve (19.12.89) .. 25 15
3233 — 700 z. deep bluish green (26.4.91) 15 10
3234 — 1000 z. blue (19.12.89) 80 30
3229/3234 *Set of 6* .. .. 1·50 70
Designs:—60 z. Juniper; 500 z. Wild rose; 700 z. Lily of the valley; 1000 z. Blue cornflower.
For similar designs printed by lithography and self-adhesive, see Nos. 3297/8.

Nos. 3235/9 are vacant.

(Des L. Wróblewski (3243), B. Wróblewski and A. Balcerzak (others). Photo)

1989 (1 Sept). *50th Anniv of German Invasion. Horiz designs as T **850**.* P 12×11½.
3240 25 z. slate, orange and black .. 15 10
3241 25 z. multicoloured 15 10
3242 35 z. multicoloured 25 10
3243 35 z. multicoloured 25 10
3240/3243 *Set of 4* 70 30
Designs:—No. 3240, Defence of Westerplatte and Captain Franciszek Dąbrowski; 3241, Defence of Hel and Captain Zbigniew Przybyszewski; 3242, Battle of Kock and Brig.-Gen. Franciszek Kleeberg; 3243, Defence of Lwow and Brig.-Gen. Wladyslaw Langner.

(Des E. Lipiński. Photo)

1989 (15 Sept). *Caricature Museum.* P 11½×11.
3244 **943** 40 z. multicoloured 15 10

944 Rafal Czerwiakowski (founder of first university Surgery Department)   **945** Emil Kaliński (Postal Minister, 1933–39)

(Des J. Konarzewski. Photo)

1989 (18 Sept). *Polish Surgeons' Society Centenary Congress, Cracow. T **944** and similar horiz design.* P 11½×12.
3245 40 z. dull ultramarine and black .. 20 10
3246 60 z. blue-green and black 25 10
Design:—60 z. Ludwik Rydygier (founder of Polish Surgeons' Society).

(Des H. Chyliński. Photo)

1989 (25 Sept). *45th Anniv of Landing at Arnhem. Vert design as T **935**. Multicoloured.* P 11½×12.
3247 210 z. Gen. Stanislaw Sosabowski and plan of battle 80 40

(Des S. Malecki. Photo)

1989 (9 Oct). *World Post Day.* P 12×11½.
3248 **945** 60 z. multicoloured 15 10
No. 3248 was issued with *se-tenant* label depicting Polish Mail emblem.

(Des R. Dudzicki. Photo)

1989 (12 Oct). *Polish People's Army Battle Medals (2nd series). Vert designs as T **927**. Multicoloured.* P 11½×11.
3249 60 z. "For Participation in the Struggle for the Rule of the People" Medal .. 20 10
3250 60 z. Warsaw 1939–45 Medal 20 10

(Des S. Malecki. Eng P. Naszarkowski (20 z.), M. Kopecki (30 z.). Recess and photo)

1989 (18 Oct). *Polish Rulers (4th series). Vert designs as T **893** showing drawings by Jan Matejko.* P 11.
3251 20 z. slate-black and olive-grey .. 10 10
3252 30 z. sepia and yellow-brown .. 10 10
Designs:—20 z. Boleslaw II, the Bold; 30 z. Wladyslaw I Herman.

946 Stamps

947 Cross and Twig

(Des W. Andrzejewski. Photo)

1989 (14 Nov). "World Stamp Expo '89" International Stamp Exhibition, Washington D.C. P 11×11½.
3253 **946** 500 z. multicoloured .. .. 1·40 70
No. 3253 also exists imperforate.

(Des W. Andrzejewski. Photo)

1989 (17 Nov). 70th Anniv of Polish Red Cross. P 11½×11.
3254 **947** 200 z. rosine, bright green and black 55 25

948 Ignacy Paderewski and Roman Dmowski (Polish signatories)

949 Photographer and Medal depicting Maksymilian Strasz

(Des J. Wysocki. Photo)

1989 (21 Nov). 70th Anniv of Treaty of Versailles. P 11×11½.
3255 **948** 350 z. multicoloured 95 45

(Des S. Malecki. Photo)

1989 (27 Nov). 150th Anniv of Photography. T **949** and similar multicoloured design. P 12×11½ (40 z.) or 11½×12 (60 z.).
3256 40 z. Type **949** 15 10
3257 60 z. Lens shutter as pupil of eye (horiz) 20 10

500

(950)

951 Painting by Jan Ciągliński

1989 (30 Nov). No. 2729 surch with T **950**.
3258 500 z. on 4 z. reddish violet .. .. 1·40 70

(Des S. Malecki. Photo German Bank Note Ptg Co, Leipzig)

1989 (18 Dec). Flower Paintings. T **951** and similar square designs showing paintings by artists named. Multicoloured. P 13.
3259 25 z. Type **951** 10 10
3260 30 z. Wojciech Weiss 10 10
3261 35 z. Antoni Kolasiński 15 10
3262 50 z. Stefan Nacht-Samborski .. 15 10
3263 60 z. Józef Pankiewicz 20 10
3264 85 z. Henryka Beyer 30 10
3265 110 z. Wladyslaw Slewiński .. 40 20
3266 190 z. Czeslaw Wdowiszewski .. 50 30
3259/3266 Set of 8 .. .. .. 1·60 90

952 Christit

(953)

=

350 zł

(Des R. Dudzicki. Photo)

1989 (21 Dec). Icons (1st series). T **952** and similar multicoloured designs. P 11.
3267 50 z. Type **952** 20 15
3268 60 z. Two saints with books 20 15
3269 90 z. Three saints with books .. 30 20
3270 150 z. Displaying scriptures (vert) .. 60 30
3271 200 z. Madonna and child (vert) .. 70 30
3272 350 z. Christ with saints and angels (vert) 80 40
3267/3272 Set of 6 .. .. .. 2·50 1·25
See also Nos. 3345/50.

REPUBLIC OF POLAND

1990 (31 Jan). No. 2839 surch with T **953**.
3273 350 z. on 15 z. lake-brown 15 10

954 Krystyna Jamroz

955 High Jumping

(Des M. Piekarski. Photo)

1990 (9 Feb). Singers. T **954** and similar vert designs. Multicoloured. P 12×11½.
3274 100 z. Type **954** 10 10
3275 150 z. Wanda Werminska 10 10
3276 350 z. Ada Sari 15 10
3277 500 z. Jan Kiepura 20 10
3274/3277 Set of 4 .. .. 50 20

(Des J. Brodowski. Photo)

1990 (29 Mar). Sports. T **955** and similar horiz designs. Multicoloured. P 11×11½.
3278 100 z. Yachting 20 10
3279 200 z. Rugby 20 10
3280 400 z. Type **955** 20 10
3281 500 z. Ice skating 25 10
3282 500 z. Diving 25 10
3283 1000 z. Gymnastics 40 20
3278/3283 Set of 6 .. .. .. 1·25 50

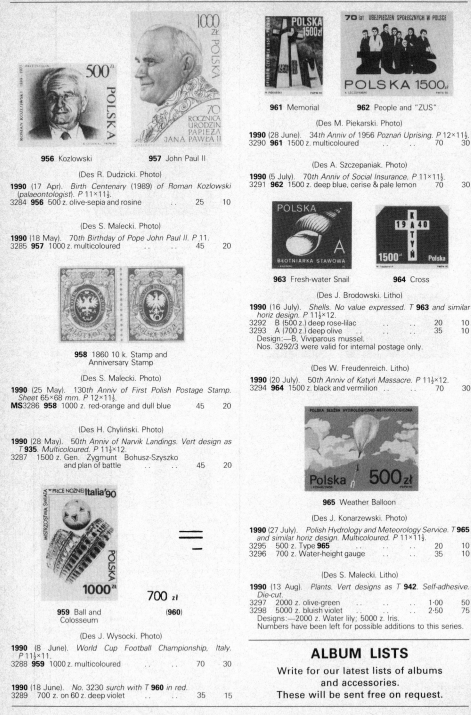

956 Kozlowski   **957** John Paul II

(Des R. Dudzicki. Photo)

1990 (17 Apr). *Birth Centenary* (1989) *of Roman Kozlowski* (*palaeontologist*). *P* 11×11½.
3284 **956** 500 z. olive-sepia and rosine   ..   25   10

(Des S. Malecki. Photo)

1990 (18 May). *70th Birthday of Pope John Paul II. P* 11.
3285 **957** 1000 z. multicoloured   45   20

958 1860 10 k. Stamp and
Anniversary Stamp

(Des S. Malecki. Photo)

1990 (25 May). *130th Anniv of First Polish Postage Stamp.* *Sheet* 65×68 *mm. P* 12×11½.
MS3286 **958** 1000 z. red-orange and dull blue   45   20

(Des H. Chyliński. Photo)

1990 (28 May). *50th Anniv of Narvik Landings. Vert design as T* **935**. *Multicoloured. P* 11½×12.
3287 1500 z. Gen. Zygmunt Bohusz-Szyszko
and plan of battle   45   20

959 Ball and   **(960)**
Colosseum

(Des J. Wysocki. Photo)

1990 (8 June). *World Cup Football Championship, Italy.* *P* 11½×11.
3288 **959** 1000 z. multicoloured   70   30

1990 (18 June). *No.* 3230 *surch with T* **960** *in red.*
3289   700 z. on 60 z. deep violet   35   15

961 Memorial   **962** People and "ZUS"

(Des M. Piekarski. Photo)

1990 (28 June). *34th Anniv of 1956 Poznań Uprising. P* 12×11½.
3290 **961** 1500 z. multicoloured   70   30

(Des A. Szczepaniak. Photo)

1990 (5 July). *70th Anniv of Social Insurance. P* 11×11½.
3291 **962** 1500 z. deep blue, cerise & pale lemon   70   30

963 Fresh-water Snail   **964** Cross

(Des J. Brodowski. Litho)

1990 (16 July). *Shells. No value expressed. T* **963** *and similar horiz design. P* 11½×12.
3292   B (500 z.) deep rose-lilac   20   10
3293   A (700 z.) deep olive   35   10
Design:—B, Viviparous mussel.
Nos. 3292/3 were valid for internal postage only.

(Des W. Freudenreich. Litho)

1990 (20 July). *50th Anniv of Katyń Massacre. P* 11½×12.
3294 **964** 1500 z. black and vermilion   70   30

965 Weather Balloon

(Des J. Konarzewski. Photo)

1990 (27 July). *Polish Hydrology and Meteorology Service. T* **965** *and similar horiz design. Multicoloured. P* 11×11½.
3295   500 z. Type **965**   20   10
3296   700 z. Water-height gauge   35   10

(Des S. Malecki. Litho)

1990 (13 Aug). *Plants. Vert designs as T* **942**. *Self-adhesive.* *Die-cut.*
3297 2000 z. olive-green   ..   ..   1·00   50
3298 5000 z. bluish violet   ..   ..   2·50   75
Designs:—2000 z. Water lily; 5000 z. Iris.
Numbers have been left for possible additions to this series.

ALBUM LISTS

Write for our latest lists of albums
and accessories.
These will be sent free on request.

966 Women's Kayak Pairs **967** Victory Sign

(Des R. Dudzicki. Photo)

1990 (22 Aug). *23rd World Canoeing Championships. T* **966** *and similar horiz design. Multicoloured. P* 11×11½.

3305	700 z. Type **966**			30	20
3306	1000 z. Men's kayak singles			50	20

A miniature sheet containing No. 3306 and an inscribed label was sold only with the Championship programme.

(Des J. Konarzewski. Litho)

1990 (31 Aug). *Tenth Anniv of Solidarity Trade Union. P* 11½×11.

3307	**967** 1500 z. grey, black and vermilion		70	30

968 Jacob's Ladder
(*Polemonium coeruleum*)

969 Serving Dish, 1870–87

(Des A. Balcerzak. Photo)

1990 (24 Sept). *Flowers. T* **968** *and similar vert designs. Multicoloured. P* 11½×11.

3308	200 z. Type **968**		10	10
3309	700 z. Floating heart water fringe (*Nymphoides peltata*)		30	15
3310	700 z. Dragonhead (*Dracocephalum ruyschiana*)		30	15
3311	1000 z. *Helleborus purpurascens*		50	20
3312	1500 z. *Daphne cneorum*		90	30
3313	1700 z. Campion (*Dianthus superbus*)		1·25	40
3308/3313	*Set of 6*		3·00	1·00

(Des R. Dudzicki. Photo)

1990 (31 Oct). *Bicentenary of Cmielów Porcelain Works. T* **969** *and similar multicoloured designs. P* 11×11½ (*horiz*) or 11½×11 (*vert*).

3314	700 z. Type **969**		30	15
3315	800 z. Plate, 1887–90 (*vert*)		40	20
3316	1000 z. Cup and saucer, 1887		50	20
3317	1000 z. Figurine of dancer, 1941–44 (*vert*)		50	20
3318	1500 z. Chocolate box, 1930–90		90	30
3319	2000 z. Vase, 1979 (*vert*)		1·00	40
3314/3319	*Set of 6*		3·25	1·25

970 Little Owl
(*Athene noctua*)

971 Wałęsa

(Des J. Desselberger. Litho)

1990 (6 Nov). *Owls. T* **970** *and similar vert designs. Multicoloured. P* 14.

3320	200 z. Type **970**		10	10
3321	500 z. Tawny owl (*Strix aluco*) (value at left)		30	10
3322	500 z. Tawny owl (*different*) (value at right)		30	10
3323	1000 z. Short-eared owl (*Asio flammeus*)		60	20
3324	1500 z. Long-eared owl (*Asio otus*)		90	30
3325	2000 z. Barn owl (*Tyto alba*)		1·25	40
3320/3325	*Set of 6*		3·00	1·00

(Des M. Piekarski. Litho)

1990 (12 Dec). *Lech Wałęsa, 1984 Nobel Peace Prize Winner and new President. P* 11×11½.

3326	**971** 1700 z. multicoloured			80	40

(Des H. Chyliński. Photo)

1990 (21 Dec). *50th Anniv of Battle of Britain. Vert design as T* **935**. *Multicoloured. P* 11½×12.

3327	1500 z. Emblem of 303 Squadron, Polish Fighter Wing, R.A.F. and Hawker Hurricane		70	30

972 Collegiate Church, Tum (12th century)

973 "King Zygmunt II August" (anon)

(Des J. Wysocki. Litho)

1990 (28 Dec). *Historic Architecture. T* **972** *and similar vert designs. Multicoloured. P* 11½×11.

3328	700 z. Type **972**		30	15
3329	800 z. Reszel castle (14th century)		40	20
3330	1500 z. Chelmno Town Hall (16th century)		90	30
3331	1700 z. Church of the Nuns of the Visitation, Warsaw (18th century)		1·00	40
3328/3331	*Set of 4*		2·40	90

No. 3331 was issued with *se-tenant* label bearing "Polska'93" International Stamp Exhibition emblem.

(Des A. Szczepaniak. Photo)

1991 (11 Jan). *Paintings. T* **973** *and similar vert designs. Multicoloured. P* 11.

3332	500 z. Type **973**		10	10
3333	700 z. "Adoration of the Magi" (Pultusk Codex)		15	10
3334	1000 z. "St. Matthew" (Pultusk Codex)		20	10
3335	1500 z. "Expelling of Merchants from Temple" (Mikolaj Haberschrack)		30	15
3336	1700 z. "The Annunciation" (miniature)		35	15
3337	2000 z. "The Three Marys" (Mikolaj Haberschrack)		40	20
3332/3337	*Set of* 6		1·25	70

978 Battle (detail of miniature, Schlackenwerth Codex, 1350) **979** Title Page of Constitution

(Des F. Lüdtke. Recess and litho State Ptg Wks, Berlin)

1991 (9 Apr). *750th Anniv of Battle of Legnica. P* 14.

3344	**978** 1500 z. multicoloured	35	15

974 Silver Fir (*Abies alba*)   **975** Radziwill Palace

(Des R. Dudzicki. Photo)

1991 (22 Apr). *Icons* (2nd series). *Vert designs as T* **952**. *Multicoloured. P* 11.

3345	500 z. "Madonna of Nazareth"		10	10
3346	700 z. "Christ the Acheirophyte"		15	10
3347	1000 z. "Madonna of Vladimir"		25	10
3348	1500 z. "Madonna of Kazan"		35	15
3349	2000 z. "St. John the Baptist"		50	20
3350	2200 z. "Christ the Pentocrator"		60	25
3345/3350	*Set of* 6		1·75	75

(Des A. Balcerzak. Photo)

1991 (22 Feb). *Cones. T* **974** *and similar vert design. Multicoloured. P* 12×11½.

3338	700 z. Type **974**	15	10
3339	1500 z. Weymouth pine (*Pinus strobus*)	30	15

See also Nos. 3483/4.

(Des S. Malecki. Eng W. Zajdel (1000 z.), M. Kopecki (1500 z.). Recess and photo)

1991 (30 Apr). *Polish Rulers* (6th series). *Vert designs as T* **893** *showing drawings by Jan Matejko. P* 11.

3351	1000 z. blue-black and brown-red	25	10
3352	1500 z. brownish black and new blue	35	15

Designs:—1000 z. Boleslaw IV, the Curly; 1500 z. Mieszko (Mieczyslaw) III, the Old.

(Des J. Wysocki. Litho)

1991 (15 Mar). *Admission of Poland into European Postal and Telecommunications Conference. P* 11×12.

3340	**975** 1500 z. multicoloured	30	15

(Des A. Heidrich. Photo (3000 z.) or litho (others))

1991 (2 May). *Bicentenary of 3rd May Constitution. T* **979** *and similar vert designs. P* 11½×11.

3353	2000 z. deep brown, buff and vermilion	50	20
3354	2500 z. deep brown, stone and vermilion	60	25
MS3355	85×85 mm. 3000 z. multicoloured	75	55

Designs:—2500 z. "Administration of Oath by Gustav Taubert" (detail, Johann Friedrich Bolt); 3000 z. "Constitution, 3 May 1791" (Jan Matejko).

1500 z

(976)   **977** Chmielowski

(Des S. Malecki. Eng W. Zajdel (1000 z.), P. Naszarkowski (1500 z.). Recess and photo)

1991 (25 Mar). *Polish Rulers* (5th series). *Vert designs as T* **893** *showing drawings by Jan Matejko, surch as T* **976** *in red. P* 11.

3341	1000 z. on 40 z. brownish black and bronze green	25	10
3342	1500 z. on 50 z. blue-black and crimson	40	15

Designs:—1000 z. Boleslaw III, the Wry Mouthed; 1500 z. Wladyslaw II, the Exile.

Nos. 3341/2 were not issued unsurcharged.

980 Satellite in Earth Orbit   **981** Map and Battle Scene

(Des J. Wysocki. Litho)

1991 (6 May). *Europa. Europe in Space. P* 12×11.

3356	**980** 1000 z. multicoloured	25	10

(Des M. Piekarski. Litho)

1991 (29 Mar). *75th Death Anniv of Adam Chmielowski* ("*Brother Albert*") (*founder of Albertine Sisters*). *P* 12×11½.

3343	**977** 2000 z. multicoloured	50	15

(Des J. Brodowski. Photo)

1991 (27 May). *50th Anniv of Participation of* Piorun (*destroyer*) *in Operation against* Bismarck (*German battleship*). *P* 12×11½.

3357	**981** 2000 z. multicoloured	50	20

982 Arms of   983 Pope John Paul II
Cracow

(Des S. Malecki. Litho)

1991 (28 May). *European Security and Co-operation Conference Cultural Heritage Symposium, Cracow.* P 12×11½.
3358 **982** 2000 z. deep claret & deep ultramarine   50   20

(Des J. Wysocki. Litho)

1991 (1 June). *Papal Visit. T* **983** *and similar vert design. Multicoloured.* P 11½×11.
3359   1000 z. Type **983**   25   10
3360   2000 z. Pope in white robes   50   20

984 Chinstrap   985 Making Paper
Penguin

(Des S. Malecki. Litho)

1991 (21 June). *30th Anniv of Antarctic Treaty.* P 12×11½.
3361 **984** 2000 z. multicoloured   50   20

(Des Z. Stasik. Litho)

1991 (8 July). *500th Anniv of Paper Making in Poland.* P 11½.
3362 **985** 2500 z. turquoise-blue and brown-lake   60   25

986 Prisoner   987 Pope John Paul II

(Des W. Freudenreich. Litho)

1991 (28 July). *Commemoration of Victims of Stalin's Purges.* P 11½×12.
3363 **986** 2500 z. bright scarlet and black   60   25

(Des J. Wysocki. Photo)

1991 (15 Aug). *Sixth World Youth Day, Częstochowa.* P 11½×11.
MS3364 **987** 3500 z. multicoloured   75   35

988 Ball and Basket   989 "Self-portrait"
(Leon Wyczółkowski)

(Des J. Konarzewski. Litho)

1991 (19 Aug). *Centenary of Basketball.* P 11×11½.
3365 **988** 2500 z. multicoloured   60   25

(Des R. Dudzicki. Photo)

1991 (7 Sept). *"Bydgoszcz '91" National Stamp Exhibition.* P 11½×12.
3366 **989** 3000 z. brown-olive and sepia   ..   70   30
MS3367   155×92 mm. No. 3366×4   ..   3·25   3·25

990 Twardowski

(Des J. Konarzewski. Photo)

1991 (10 Oct). *125th Birth Anniv of Kazimierz Twardowski (philosopher).* P 11×11½.
3368 **990** 2500 z. black and brownish grey   ..   50   20

991 Swallowtail
(*Papilio machaon*)

(Des O. Opresco. Hologram and litho (**MS**3375) or litho (others))

1991 (16 Nov). *Butterflies and Moths. T* **991** *and similar horiz designs. Multicoloured.* P 12½.
3369   1000 z. Type **991**   20   10
       a. Block of 6. Nos. 3369/74   ..   1·75
3370   1000 z. Dark crimson underwing (*Mormonia sponsa*)   ..   20   10
3371   1500 z. Painted lady (*Vanessa cardui*)   ..   30   15
3372   1500 z. Scarce swallowtail (*Iphiclides podalirius*)   30   15
3373   2500 z. Scarlet tiger moth (*Panaxia dominula*)   50   25

3374   2500 z. Peacock (*Nymphalis io*)   ..   50   25
3369/3374   Set of 6   ..   ..   ..   1·75   85
MS3375   127×63 mm. 15000 z. Black-veined
white (*Aporia crataegi*) (46×33 mm) plus label
for "Phila Nippon '91" International Stamp
Exhibition   ..   ..   ..   3·00   3·00
Nos. 3369/74 were issued together in *se-tenant* blocks of 6
within the sheet.

995 Lord Baden-Powell   **996** Sébastien Bourdon
(founder)

(Des M. Piekarski. Photo)

1991 (30 Dec).   *80th Anniv of Scout Movement in Poland.* T **995**
and similar vert designs. P 12×11½.
3383   1500 z. greenish yellow and emerald   ..   35   10
3384   2000 z. new blue and bright lemon   ..   50   20
3385   2500 z. brt bluish violet & chrome yellow   60   20
3386   3500 z. bistre-brown and orange-yellow   75   25
3383/3386   Set of 4   ..   ..   ..   2·00   60
Designs:—2000 z. Andrzej Malkowski (Polish founder); 2500 z.
"Watch on the Vistula" (Wojciech Kossak); 3500 z. Polish scout in
Warsaw Uprising, 1944.

992 "The Shepherd's Bow"
(Francesco Solimena)

(Des R. Dudzicki. Photo)

1991 (25 Nov).   *Christmas.* P 11.
3376   **992**   1000 z. multicoloured   20   10

(Des S. Malecki. Eng W. Zajdel (1500 z.), T. Zlotkowski (2000 z.).
Recess and photo)

1992 (15 Jan).   *Polish Rulers (7th series). Vert designs as* T **893**
showing drawings by Jan Matejko. P 11.
3387   1500 z. sepia and brown-olive   ..   35   10
3388   2000 z. blue-black & deep turquoise-blue   50   20
Designs:—1500 z. Kazimierz II, the Just; 2000 z. Leszek I, the
White.

993 Gen. Stanislaw Kopański and   **994** Brig.-Gen.
Battle Map   Michal Tokarzewski-
                 Karaszewicz

(Des J. Brodowski. Photo)

1991 (10 Dec).   *50th Anniv of Participation of Polish Troops in
Battle of Tobruk.* P 12×11½.
3377   **993**   2000 z. multicoloured   45   20

(Des M. Piekarski. Photo)

1992 (16 Jan).   *Self-portraits.* T **996** *and similar vert designs.*
Multicoloured. P 11.
3389   700 z. Type **996**   15   10
3390   1000 z. Sir Joshua Reynolds   ..   20   10
3391   1500 z. Sir Godfrey Kneller   ..   25   10
3392   2000 z. Bartolomé Estéban Murillo   ..   40   15
3393   2200 z. Peter Paul Rubens   ..   45   15
3394   3000 z. Diego de Silva y Velázquez   ..   60   25
3389/3394   Set of 6   ..   ..   ..   1·90   75

(Des S. Malecki. Litho)

1991 (20 Dec).   *World War II Polish Underground Army
Commanders.* T **994** *and similar vert designs.* P 12×11½.
3378   2000 z. blue-black and vermilion   ..   50   20
3379   2500 z. crimson and violet   ..   60   20
3380   3000 z. deep violet and bright magenta   70   25
3381   5000 z. brown and deep olive   ..   1·25   40
3382   6500 z. deep brown and orange-brown   1·60   50
3378/3382   Set of 5   ..   ..   ..   4·25   1·40
Designs:—2500 z. Gen. Broni Kazimierz Sosnowski; 3000 z.
Lt.-Gen. Stefan Rowecki; 5000 z. Lt.-Gen. Tadeusz Komorowski;
6500 z. Brig.-Gen. Leopold Okulicki.

997 Skiing

(Des J. Konarzewski. Litho)

1992 (8 Feb).   *Winter Olympic Games, Albertville.* T **997** *and
similar horiz design. Multicoloured.* P 11×11½.
3395   1500 z. Type **997**   25   10
3396   2500 z. Ice hockey   45   15

998 Manteuffel

999 Nicolas Copernicus (astronomer)

(Des M. Jędrysik. Photo)

1992 (5 Mar). *90th Birth Anniv of Tadeusz Manteuffel (historian). P 11½×11.*
3397	**998**	2500 z. light brown	..	45	15

(Des J. Wysocki. Photo)

1992 (3 May). *Famous Poles. T **999** and similar horiz designs. Multicoloured. P 11×11½.*
3398	1500 z. Type **999**		25	10
3399	2000 z. Frédéric Chopin (composer)	..	40	15
3400	2500 z. Henryk Sienkiewicz (writer)	..	45	15
3401	3500 z. Marie Curie (physicist)	..	65	25
3398/3401	*Set of 4*		1·60	60
MS3402	80×81 mm. 5000 z. Kazimierz Funk (biochemist) ..		90	90

No. **MS**3402 commemorates "Expo '92" World's Fair, Seville.

1000 Columbus and Left-hand Detail of Map

(Des J. Wysocki. Litho)

1992 (5 May). *Europa. 500th Anniv of Discovery of America by Christopher Columbus. T **1000** and similar horiz design. Multicoloured. P 11×11½.*
3403	1500 z. Type **1000**		25	10
	a. Horiz pair. Nos. 3403/4	..	75	40
3404	3000 z. *Santa Maria* and right-hand detail of Juan de la Costa map, 1500		50	25

Nos. 3403/4 were issued together in horizontal *se-tenant* pairs within the sheet, each pair forming a composite design.

1001 River Czarna Wiselka

1002 Prince Józef Poniatowski

(Des J. Brodowski. Photo)

1992 (12 June). *Environmental Protection. River Cascades. T **1001** and similar vert designs. Multicoloured. P 11½×12.*
3405	2000 z. Type **1001**	..	..	40	15
3406	2500 z. River Swider		..	45	15
3407	3000 z. River Tanew		..	60	20
3408	3500 z. Mickiewicz waterfall	..		65	30
3405/3408	*Set of 4*	..	..	1·90	70

(Des M. Jędrysik. Litho (**MS**3411) or photo (others))

1992 (18 June). *Bicentenary of Order of Military Virtue. T **1002** and similar vert designs. Multicoloured. P 11.*
3409	1500 z. Type **1002**		25	10
3410	3000 z. Marshal Józef Pilsudski	..	50	25
MS3411	108×93 mm. 20000 z. "Virgin Mary of Częstochowa" (icon) (36×57 mm). Imperf	..	4·50	4·50

1003 Family and Heart

1004 Fencing

(Des J. Wysocki. Litho)

1992 (26 June). *Children's Drawings. T **1003** and similar vert design. Multicoloured. P 11½×11.*
3412	1500 z. Type **1003**	..	25	10
	a. Pair. Nos 3412/13	..	75	40
3413	3000 z. Butterfly, sun, bird and dog	..	50	25

Nos. 3412/13 were issued together in *se-tenant* pairs within the sheet.

(Des J. Konarzewski. Litho)

1992 (25 July). *Olympic Games, Barcelona. T **1004** and similar horiz designs. Multicoloured. P 11×11½.*
3414	1500 z. Type **1004**	..	25	10
3415	2000 z. Boxing ..	..	40	15
3416	2500 z. Running	..	45	20
3417	3000 z. Cycling	..	55	25
3414/3417	*Set of 4*	..	1·50	60

1005 Runners

(Des H. Chyliński. Photo)

1992 (29 July). *"Olymphilex '92" Olympic Stamps Exhibition, Barcelona. Sheet 86×81 mm. P 11×11½.*
MS3418	**1005** 20000 z. multicoloured	..	4·50	4·50

No. **MS**3418 also exists imperforate from a limited issue.

MINIMUM PRICE

The minimum price quoted is 10p which represents a handling charge rather than a basis for valuing common stamps. For further notes about prices see introductory pages.

1006 Statue of Korczak   **1007** Flag and "V"

(Des J. Brodowski. Photo)

1992 (5 Aug). *50th Death Anniv of Janusz Korczak (educationist*). P 11×11½.
3419 **1006** 1500 z. black, lake-brn & chrome yell   30   10

(Des F. Winiarski. Photo)

1992 (14 Aug). *Fifth Polish Veterans World Meeting*. P 11½×11.
3420 **1007** 3000 z. multicoloured   ..   60   30

1008 Wyszyński   **1009** National Colours encircling World Map

(Des M. Jędrysik. Litho)

1992 (15 Aug). *11th Death Anniv of Stefan Wyszyński (Primate of Poland*) (3421) *and First Anniv of Sixth World Youth Day* (3422). *T* **1008** *and similar vert design. Multicoloured.* P 11½×11.
3421   1500 z. Type **1008**   30   10
      a. Block. Nos. 3421/2 plus 2 labels   90
3422   3000 z. Pope John Paul II embracing
        youth   60   30
   Nos. 3421/2 were issued together in blocks of two stamps and two labels showing the arms of either Wyszyński or the Pope.

(Des A. Szczepaniak. Photo)

1992 (19 Aug). *World Meeting of Expatriate Poles, Cracow.* P 12×11½.
3423 **1009** 3000 z. multicoloured   ..   60   30

(Des H. Chyliński. Photo)

1992 (15 Sept). *150th Anniv of Polish Settlement at Adampol, Turkey.* P 11×11½.
3424 **1010** 3500 z. multicoloured   ..   65   35

(Des Z. Stasik. Photo)

1992 (9 Oct). *World Post Day.* P 11½×11.
3425 **1011** 3500 z. multicoloured   ..   65   35

1012 "Dedication" (self-portrait)

(Des J. Konarzewski. Litho)

1992 (26 Oct). *Birth Centenary of Bruno Schulz (writer and artist*). P 11×11½.
3426 **1012** 3000 z. multicoloured   ..   60   30

1013 "Seated Girl" (Henryk Wiciński)

(Des H. Chyliński. Litho)

1992 (29 Oct). *Polish Sculptures. T* **1013** *and similar square designs. Multicoloured.* P 11½.
3427   2000 z. Type **1013**   ..   40   15
3428   2500 z. "Portrait of Tytus Czyżewski"
       (Zbigniew Pronaszko) ..   45   20
3429   3000 z. "Polish Nike" (Edward Wittig) ..   60   30
3430   3500 z. "The Nude" (August Zamoyski)   65   35
3427/3430   *Set of 4* ..   ..   ..   1·90   90
MS3431   107×90 mm. Nos. 3427/30 ..   1·90   1·90
   No. **MS**3431 commemorates "Polska'93" International Stamp Exhibition.

1010 Polish Museum, Adampol   **1011** 18th-century Post Office Sign, Slonim   **1014** "10th Theatrical Summer in Zamość" (Jan Mlodożeniec)   **1015** Girl skipping with Snake

(Des K. Kupczyk. Litho)

1992 (30 Oct). *Poster Art (1st series).* T **1014** *and similar multicoloured designs.* P 13½.

3432	1500 z. Type **1014**		25	10
3433	2000 z. "Red Art" (Franciszek Starowieyski) (*horiz*)		40	15
3434	2500 z. "Circus" (Waldemar Świerzy)		45	20
3435	3500 z. "Mannequin" (Henryk Tomaszewski)		65	35
3432/3435	*Set of 4*		1·60	70

See also Nos. 3502/3 and 3523/4.

(Des E. Lutczyn. Photo)

1992 (16 Nov). *"Polska'93" International Stamp Exhibition, Poznań (1st issue).* T **1015** *and similar vert designs. Multicoloured.* P 11.

3436	1500 z. Type **1015**		25	10
3437	2000 z. Boy on rocking horse with upside-down runners		40	15
3438	2500 z. Boy firing bird from bow		45	20
3439	3500 z. Girl placing ladder against clockwork giraffe		65	35
3436/3439	*Set of 4*		1·60	70

See also Nos. 3452, 3453/**MS**3457, 3466/9 and **MS**3476.

1016 Medal and Soldiers   **1017** Church and Star

(Des J. Wysocki. Litho)

1992 (20 Nov). *50th Anniv of Formation of Polish Underground Army.* T **1016** *and similar multicoloured designs.* P 13½.

3440	1500 z. Type **1016**		25	10
	a. Pair. Nos. 3440/1		90	50
3441	3500 z. Soldiers		65	35
MS3442	75×95 mm. 20000 z. + 500 z. "WP AK" (26×32 mm)		4·25	4·25

Nos. 3440/1 were issued together in *se-tenant* pairs within the sheet.

(Des J. Brodowski. Photo)

1992 (25 Nov). *Christmas.* P 11½×12.

3443	**1017** 1000 z. multicoloured		20	10

1018 Wheat   **1019** Arms of Sovereign Military Order

(Des M. Jędrysik. Photo)

1992 (5 Dec). *International Nutrition Conference, Rome.* T **1018** *and similar vert design. Multicoloured.* P 11½×11.

3444	1500 z. Type **1018**		25	10
3445	3500 z. Glass, bread, vegetables and jug on table		60	30

(Des A. Heidrich. Litho)

1992 (10 Dec). *Postal Agreement with Sovereign Military Order of Malta.* P 11½×11.

3446	**1019** 3000 z. multicoloured		50	25

1020 Arms, 1295   **1021** Exhibition Emblem and Stylised Stamp

(Des H. Chyliński. Photo)

1992 (14 Dec). *History of the White Eagle (Poland's arms).* T **1020** *and similar vert designs. Each black, orange-vermilion and orange-yellow.* P 11½.

3447	2000 z. Type **1020**		30	10
3448	2500 z. 15th-century arms		40	15
3449	3000 z. 18th-century arms		50	25
3450	3500 z. Arms, 1919		60	30
3451	5000 z. Arms, 1990		80	35
3447/3451	*Set of 5*		2·25	1·00

(Des J. Wysocki. Litho)

1993 (6 Jan). *Centenary of Polish Philately and "Polska'93" International Stamp Exhibition, Poznań (2nd issue).* P 11½.

3452	**1021** 1500 z. multicoloured		20	10

1022 Amber   **1023** Downhill Skier

(Des A. Jeziorkowski. Litho)

1993 (29 Jan). *"Polska'93" International Stamp Exhibition, Poznań (3rd issue). Amber.* T **1022** *and similar multicoloured designs.* P 13½.

3453	1500 z. Type **1022**		20	10
3454	2000 z. Pinkish amber		30	10
3455	2500 z. Amber in stone		40	25
3456	3000 z. Amber containing wasp		50	30
3453/3456	*Set of 4*		1·25	70
MS3457	82×88 mm. 20000 z. Detail of map with necklace representing amber route (44×29 mm)		3·00	3·00

(Des H. Chyliński. Litho)

1993 (5 Feb). *Winter University Games, Zakopane.* P 11½×11.

3458	**1023** 3000 z. multicoloured		50	30

1024 Flower-filled
Heart

1025 Arsenal

(Des S. Malecki. Litho)

1993 (14 Feb). *St. Valentine's Day. T* **1024** *and similar vert design. Multicoloured. P* 11½×11.
3459	1500 z. Type **1024**	..	..	20	15
3460	3000 z. Heart in envelope	..	..	50	30

(Des S. Malecki. Eng W. Zajdel (1500, 3000 z.), T. Zlotkowski (2000 z.), M. Kopecki (2500 z.). Recess and photo)

1993 (25 Mar). *Polish Rulers* (8th series). *Vert designs as T* **893** *showing drawings by Jan Matejko. P* 11.
3461	1500 z. blackish brown and yellow-olive		20	15
3462	2000 z. blue-black and deep magenta	..	30	20
3463	2500 z. black and slate-green	..	40	25
3464	3000 z. deep brown and orange-brown		50	30
3461/3464	Set of 4	..	1·25	80

Designs:—1500 z. Wladyslaw Laskonogi; 2000 z. Henryk I; 2500 z. Konrad I of Masovia; 3000 z. Boleslaw V, the Chaste.
No. 3464 was issued with *se-tenant* label commemorating "Polska'93" International Stamp Exhibition.

(Des A. Szczepaniak. Photo)

1993 (26 Mar). *50th Anniv of Action by Szare Szeregi* (formation of Polish Scouts in the resistance forces) *on Warsaw Arsenal. P* 12×11½.
3465	**1025** 1500 z. multicoloured	..	..	20	15

1026 Jousters with Lances

(Des F. Winiarski. Photo)

1993 (29 Mar). *"Polska'93" International Stamp Exhibition, Poznań* (4th issue). *Jousting at Golub Dobrzyń. T* **1026** *and similar horiz designs each showing a modern and a medieval jouster. Multicoloured. P* 11×11½.
3466	1500 z. Type **1026**	..	..	20	15
3467	2000 z. Jousters	..	..	30	20
3468	2500 z. Jousters with swords	..	..	40	25
3469	3500 z. Officials	..	..	60	30
3466/3469	Set of 4	..	..	1·40	80

1027 Szczecin

1028 Jew and
Ruins

(Des M. Jędrysik. Litho)

1993 (3 Apr). *750th Anniv of Granting of Town Charter to Szczecin. P* 11½×11.
3470	**1027** 1500 z. multicoloured	..	..	20	15

(Des Ruth Avrahami. Litho)

1993 (18 Apr). *50th Anniv of Warsaw Ghetto Uprising. P* 14.
3471	**1028** 4000 z. black, lemon and azure	..	65	40

No. 3471 was issued in sheets with a row of half stamp-size inscribed labels.

1029 Works by A. Szapocznikow
and J. Lebenstein

(Des J. Wysocki. Litho)

1993 (30 Apr). *Europa. Contemporary Art. T* **1029** *and similar horiz design. Multicoloured. P* 11×11½.
3472	1500 z. Type **1029**	..	..	20	15
	a. Pair. Nos. 3472/3	..	..	85	60
3473	4000 z. "CXCIX" (S. Gierowski) and "Red Head" (B. Linke)	..	..	65	40

Nos. 3472/3 were issued together in *se-tenant* pairs within the sheet.

1030 "King Alexander Jagiellonczyk in
the Sejm" (Jan Laski, 1505)

(Des A. Jeziorkowski. Photo)

1993 (2 May). *500th Anniv of Parliament. P* 11.
3474	**1030** 2000 z. multicoloured	..	..	30	20

1031 Nullo

(Des R. Dudzicki. Photo)

1993 (5 May). *130th Death Anniv of Francesco Nullo* (Italian volunteer in January 1863 Rising). *P* 11×11½.
3475	**1031** 2500 z. multicoloured	..	..	40	25

1032 Lech's Encounter with the White Eagle after Battle of Gniezno

(Des A. Jeziorkowski. Eng C. Slania. Recess)

1993 (7 May). *"Polska'93" International Stamp Exhibition, Poznań* (5th issue). *Sheet* 103×86 *mm. P* 13½.
MS3476 **1032** 50000 z. deep brown .. .. 8·00 8·00
No. **MS**3476 also exists imperforate from a limited issue.

1033 Cap

1034 Copernicus and Solar System

(Des J. Wysocki. Litho)

1993 (21 May). *Third World Congress of Cadets of the Second Republic. P* 11×11½.
3477 **1033** 2000 z. multicoloured 30 15

(Des J. Konarzewski. Litho)

1993 (24 May). *450th Death Anniv of Nicolas Copernicus* (*astronomer*). *P* 11×11½.
3478 **1034** 2000 z. multicoloured 30 15

1035 Fiki Miki and Lion

1036 Tree Sparrow (*Passer montanus*)

(Des H. Chyliński. Litho)

1993 (1 June). *40th Death Anniv of Kornel Makuszyński* (*writer of children's books*). T **1035** *and similar horiz designs. Multicoloured. P* 11×11½.
3479 1500 z. Type **1035** 25 15
3480 2000 z. Billy goat 35 20
3481 3000 z. Fiki Miki 50 30
3482 5000 z. Billy goat riding ostrich .. 80 45
3479/3482 *Set of 4* .. .. .. 1·75 1·00

(Des A. Balcerzak. Photo)

1993 (30 June). *Cones. Vert designs as T 974. Multicoloured. P* 12×11½.
3483 10000 z. Arolla pine (*Pinus cembra*) .. 1·60 80
3484 20000 z. Scots pine (*Pinus sylvestris*) .. 3·25 1·60

(Des K. Rogaczewska. Litho)

1993 (15 July). *Birds.* T **1036** *and similar vert designs. Multicoloured. P* 11½×11.
3485 1500 z. Type **1036** 25 10
3486 2000 z. Pied wagtail (*Motacilla alba*) .. 35 15
3487 3000 z. Syrian woodpecker (*Dendrocopos syriacus*) 50 25
3488 4000 z. Goldfinch (*Carduelis carduelis*) .. 70 30
3489 5000 z. Common starling (*Sturnus vulgaris*) 80 40
3490 6000 z. Bullfinch (*Pyrrhula pyrrhula*) .. 1·00 50
3485/3490 *Set of 6* .. .. .. 3·25 1·50

1037 Soldiers Marching

(Des M. Jędrysik. Photo)

1993 (20 July). *Bicentenary of Dabrowski's Mazurka* (*national anthem*) (1st issue). *P* 11×11½.
3491 **1037** 1500 z. multicoloured 15 10
See also No. 3526.

1038 "Madonna and Child" (St. Mary's Basilica, Leśna Podlaska)

1039 Armstrong Whitworth Whitley and Parachutes

(Des J. Wysocki. Litho)

1993 (15 Aug). *Sanctuaries to St. Mary.* T **1038** *and similar vert design. Multicoloured. P* 11×11½ (*with one elliptical hole on each vert side*).
3492 1500 z. Type **1038** 15 10
3493 2000 z. "Madonna and Child" (St. Mary's Church, Swieta Lipka) 20 15
Each issued in sheets of 9 stamps.

(Des M. Jędrysik. Litho)

1993 (15 Sept). *The Polish Rangers* (*Second World War air troop*). *P* 11×11½ (*with one elliptical hole on each horiz side*).
3494 **1039** 1500 z. multicoloured 15 10

1040 Trumpet Player   **1041** Postman

(Des J. Konarzewski. Litho)

1993 (27 Sept). *"Jazz Jamboree '93" International Jazz Festival, Warsaw. P* 11½ (*with one elliptical hole on each horiz side*).
3495 **1040** 2000 z. multicoloured   20   15

(Des S. Malecki. Eng T. Zlotkowski. Recess and photo)

1993 (9 Oct). *World Post Day. P* 11½×11.
3496 **1041** 2500 z. agate, lavender-grey and blue   25   15

1042 St. Jadwiga   **1043** Pope John Paul II
(miniature, Schlacken-
werther Codex)

(Des A. Heidrich. Litho State Ptg Wks, Berlin)

1993 (14 Oct). *750th Death Anniv of St. Jadwiga of Silesia. P* 14.
3497 **1042** 2500 z. multicoloured   25   15

(Des J. Wysocki. Litho)

1993 (16 Oct). *15th Anniv of Election of Pope John Paul II. Sheet 70×92 mm. P* 11½×11 (*with one elliptical hole on each vert side*).
MS3498 **1043** 20000 z. multicoloured   ..   2·00   2·00

1044 Eagle and   **1045** St. Nicholas
Crown

(Des J. Wysocki. Litho)

1993 (11 Nov). *75th Anniv of Republic. T* **1044** *and similar vert design. Multicoloured. P* 11½×11 (*with one elliptical hole on each vert side*).
3499   4000 z. Type **1044**   40   25
MS3500   66×89 mm. 20000 z. Silhouette and
shadow of flying eagle (31×38 mm) ..   ..   2·00   2·00
On No. **MS**3500 the perforations on each vertical side, as well as containing an elliptical hole, are interrupted along that part of the design showing the eagle.

(Des A. Gosik. Litho)

1993 (25 Nov). *Christmas. P* 12×11½ (*with one elliptical hole on each vert side*).
3501 **1045** 1500 z. multicoloured   15   10

(Des Krystyna Hoffman-Pagowska. Litho)

1993 (10 Dec). *Poster Art* (2nd series). *Vert designs as T* **1014**. *Multicoloured. P* 11×11½ (*with one elliptical hole on each vert side*).
3502   2000 z. "Come   and   see   Polish
mountains" (M. Urbaniec)   ..   20   15
3503   5000 z. Production   of   Alban   Berg's
Wozzeck (J. Lenica)   50   30

1046 Daisy shedding   **1047** Cross-country
Petals   Skiing

(Des A. Gosik. Litho)

1994 (14 Jan). *Greetings Stamp. P* 11½×11 (*with one elliptical hole on each vert side*).
3504 **1046** 1500 z. multicoloured   15   10

(Des M. Urbaniec. Photo)

1994 (12 Feb). *Winter Olympic Games, Lillehammer, Norway. T* **1047** *and similar vert designs. Multicoloured. P* 11½×11.
3505   2500 z. Type **1047**   25   10
3506   5000 z. Ski jumping   50   30
MS3507   81×80 mm. 10000 z. Downhill skiing   1·00   1·00
The miniature sheet also commemorates the centenary of the International Olympic Committee.

1048 Bem and Cannon   **1049** Jan Zamojski
(founder)

(Des J. Wysocki. Litho)

1994 (14 Mar). *Birth Bicentenary of General Józef Bem. P* 11½ (*with one elliptical hole on each horiz side*).
3508 **1048** 5000 z. multicoloured   50   30

(Des Y. Erol. Litho)

1994 (15 Mar). *400th Anniv of Zamojski Academy, Zamość. P* 11½×11 (*with one elliptical hole on each vert side*).
3509 **1049** 5000 z. violet-grey, black & lt brown   50   30

**THE WORLD CENTRE FOR
FINE STAMPS IS 399 STRAND**

1050 Cracow Battalion Flag and Scythes

1051 Oil Lamp, Open Book and Spectacles

1054 Mazurka **1055** Cogwheels

(Des M. Jedrysik. Litho)

1994 (24 Mar). *Bicentenary of Tadeusz Kosciuszko's Insurrection. P 11½×11 (with one elliptical hole on each vert side).*
3510 **1050** 2000 z. multicoloured 20 10

(Des S. Malecki. Eng T. Zlotkowski (2500 z.), W. Zajdel (5000 z.). Recess and photo)

1994 (15 Apr). *Polish Rulers (9th series). Vert designs as T 893 showing drawings by Jan Matejko. P 11.*
3511 2500 z. black and new blue 25 10
3512 5000 z. blue-black, dull vio & reddish vio 50 30
Designs:—2500 z. Leszek II, the Black; 5000 a. Przemysl II.

(Des T. Boguslawski. Litho)

1994 (30 Apr). *Europa. Inventions and Discoveries. T 1051 and similar vert design. Multicoloured. P 11½×11 (with one elliptical hole on each vert side).*
3513 2500 z. Type **1051** (invention of modern oil lamp by Ignacy Lukasiewicz) 25 10
3514 6000 z. Illuminated filament forming "man in the moon" (astronomy) 60 40

1052 "Madonna and Child"

1053 Abbey Ruins and Poppies

(Des Z. Stasik. Litho)

1994 (16 May). *St. Mary's Sanctuary, Kalwaria Zebrzydowska. P 11½×11 (with one elliptical hole on each vert side).*
3515 **1052** 4000 z. multicoloured 40 25

(Des A. Heidrich. Litho)

1994 (18 May). *50th Anniv of Battle of Monte Cassino. P 11×11½ (with one elliptical hole on each horiz side).*
3516 **1053** 6000 z. multicoloured 60 40

A regular new issue supplement to this catalogue appears each month in

GIBBONS STAMP MONTHLY

—from your newsagent or by postal subscription
—sample copy and details on request.

(Des A. Heidrich. Litho)

1994 (25 May). *Traditional Dances. T 1054 and similar vert designs showing paintings by Zofia Strvieńska. Multicoloured. P 11½ (with one elliptical hole on each vert side).*
3517 3000 z. Type **1054** 30 20
3518 4000 z. Coralski 40 25
3519 9000 z. Krakowiak 90 60

(Des H. Chyliński. Litho)

1994 (7 June). *75th Anniv of International Labour Organization. P 11½ (with one elliptical hole on each horiz side).*
3520 **1055** 6000 z. greenish bl, brt new bl & blk 60 40

1056 Optic Fibre Cable

(Des J. Górski. Litho)

1994 (10 June). *75th Anniv of Polish Electricians Association. P 11×11½ (with one elliptical hole on each horiz side).*
3521 **1056** 4000 z. multicoloured 40 25

1057 Map of Americas on Football **1058** Znaniecki

(Des M. Nadolski. Litho)

1994 (17 June). *World Cup Football Championship, U.S.A. P 11½×11 (with one elliptical hole on each horiz side).*
3522 **1057** 6000 z. multicoloured 60 40

1994 (4 July). *Poster Art (3rd series). Multicoloured designs as T 1014. Litho. P 11×11½ (4000 z.) or 11½×11 (6000 z.) (each with one elliptical hole on one side).*
3523 4000 z. "Monsieur Fabre" (Wiktor Górka) 40 25
3524 6000 z. "8th OISTAT Congress" (Hubert Hilscher) (horiz) 60 40

(Des A. Gosik. Litho)

1994 (15 July). 36*th Death Anniv of Professor Florian Znaniecki*.
P 11½ (*with one elliptical hole on each vert side*).
3525 **1058** 9000 z. deep olive, bistre and yellow   90   60

(Des M. Jędrysik. Litho)

1994 (20 July). *Bicentenary of Dabrowski's Mazurka (2nd issue)*.
Horiz designs as T **1037**. *Multicoloured.* P 11×11½.
3526 2500 z. Troops preparing to charge   ..   25   10

GERMAN OCCUPATION, 1915–18

A German offensive in Galicia on 1 May 1915 broke through the Russian lines and all Poland was in German hands by the end of August. In 1916 Poland was named the "General-Government, Warsaw" and on 5 November 1916, Germany and Austria proclaimed a "Polish Kingdom"; Pilsudski sat on the Council of State of this till he resigned in protest against German control. On 15 October 1917, the Germans set up a Regency Council, which exercised control under German supervision, and took charge of affairs on 12 October 1918 when the Central Powers were on the verge of collapse.

100 Pfennig=1 Mark

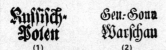

(1)   (2)

Contemporary stamps of Germany overprinted.

1915 (12 May). *With T* **1**.

1	**17**	3 pf. brown		60	25
2		5 pf. green		75	35
3		10 pf. carmine		75	35
4		20 pf. ultramarine		1·10	50
5		40 pf. black and carmine		6·00	2·50
1/5		*Set of 5*		8·25	3·50

Nos. 1/5 were for use in the Lodz region.

1916 (1 Aug)–**17**. *With T* **2**.

6	**24**	2½ pf. grey		15	15
7	**17**	3 pf. brown		55	25
8		5 pf. green		55	50
9	**24**	7½ pf. orange		40	10
10	**17**	10 pf. carmine		55	15
11	**24**	15 pf. yellow-brown		2·50	1·00
12		15 pf. slate-violet (1917)		35	15
13	**17**	20 pf. deep blue		80	35
		a. Violet-blue		20·00	20·00
		b. Ultramarine		90	90
14		30 pf. black and orange/*buff*		3·75	1·75
15		40 pf. black and carmine		1·40	10
16		60 pf. magenta		1·75	70
6/16		*Set of 11*		11·50	4·75

The area north-east of Warsaw was part of the German Eastern Command Area, which also included the Baltic Provinces of Russia. German stamps overprinted "Postgebiet Ob. Ost" were used in this area; these are listed in Part 7 (*Germany*) of this catalogue.

During the period of German occupation several municipal councils organized local postal delivery services. Most issued handstamps to indicate payment but the following towns issued stamps, some of which were quickly suppressed by the military authorities: Sosnowiec, Warsaw, Zawiercie, Bialystok (in the Eastern Command Area). Przedborz and Zarki in the Austrian occupied area also issued stamps.

PUZZLED ?

Then you need
PHILATELIC TERMS ILLUSTRATED
to tell you all you need to know about printing
methods, papers, errors, varieties, watermarks,
perforations, etc. 192 pages, some in full
colour, soft cover. Third Edition.

POLISH MILITARY POST

I. POLISH CORPS IN RUSSIA, 1918

In 1917 Poles serving in the Russian Army were transferred into Polish units so that an autonomous Polish Army could be organized. The Polish First Corps was formed on 21 August 1917. By January 1918 the Corps was based at Bobruisk, virtually surrounded by German troops.

An agreement with the Germans in February 1918 established an area of "Polish Occupation" and the forwarding of Polish mail to Warsaw by the German field post. Post offices operated from 1 April to 29 June 1918, after which the Corps was disbanded.

100 Kopeks=1 Rouble

(M 1)   (M 2)

1918 (March). *1912–18 stamps of Russia optd with Type M* **1**, *by Mr Podzuinski, Bobruisk. No wmk.*

M 1	**22**	3 k. carmine-red		40·00	38·00
M 2	**23**	4 k. red		40·00	38·00
M 3	**22**	5 k. brown-lilac		13·00	10·00
M 4	**23**	10 k. deep blue		13·00	10·00
M 5	**22**	10 k. on 7 k. deep blue (170)		£400	£450
M 6	**10**	15 k. blue and purple-brown		2·75	2·50
M 7	**14**	20 k. scarlet and blue		5·25	3·75
M 8	**10**	25 k. violet and deep green		65·00	50·00
M 9		35 k. deep green and brown-purple		2·75	2·50
M10	**14**	50 k. green and dull purple		10·50	7·50

          (*b*) *Imperf*

M11	**10**	70 k. vermilion and brown		£180	£150

1918 (March). *Stamps of Russia surch as Type M* **2**, *by the Corps Ptg Wks. No wmk. A. Perf* 14×14½. *B. Imperf.*

			A		B	
M12	**22**	10 k. on 3 k. carm-red	2·50	2·50	90	90
M13		35 k. on 1 k. orange	40·00	40·00	40	40
		a. Surch inverted	†		£130	—
M14		50 k. on 2 k. lt green	2·75	2·75	90	90
		a. Surch inverted	£130	—	†	
M15		1 r. on 3 k. carm-red	50·00	50·00	1·90	1·90
		a. Surch inverted	†		£130	

II. POLISH ARMY IN RUSSIA, 1942

After the German invasion of Russia in 1941, Polish prisoners of war taken by the Russians in 1939 were released and formed into an army which, after training in the Soviet Union, went to fight in Italy.

M 3 "We Shall Return"

(Eng Polkowski. Typo)

1942 (18 Aug). *Issued at Jangi-Jul, near Tashkent. Thick carton paper. Imperf×perf* 11½. *Edges of sheet also imperf.*

M16	**M 3**	50 k. brown (*shades*)		£130	£300
		a. Tête-bêche (pair)		£300	£650

Stamps with no full point after "KOP" are forgeries.

Polish Post Offices Abroad

A. CONSTANTINOPLE

100 Fenigów = 1 Marka

The following were used for franking correspondence handed in to the Polish Consulate at Constantinople.

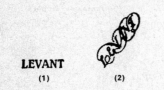

LEVANT

(1)   (2)

1919 (May). *Stamps of Poland optd as T* **1** (*larger on mark values*), *in carmine. P* 11½.

1	**15**	3 f. brown		1·40
2		5 f. yellow-green		1·40
3		10 f. purple		1·40
4		15 f. lake		1·40
5	**16**	20 f. blue		1·40
6		25 f. olive		1·40
7		50 f. green		1·40
8	**17**	1 m. violet		1·40
9		1 m. 50, green		1·40
10		2 m. brown		1·40
11	**18**	2 m. 50, red-brown		1·40
12	**19**	5 m. violet		1·40
1/12		*Set of 12*		15·00

The above prices are for the second printing of October 1919. The first printing, issued in May, is difficult to distinguish and has also been forged, but the genuine overprint was made with aniline ink which shows under the lamp. This does not apply to the forgeries or reprints. (*Prices for original printing, Nos* 1/12 £42 *each un.*)

1921 (25 May). *Stamps of Poland surch as T* **2** (*larger on T* **19**), *in red-brown.*

13	**25**	1 m. carmine		60
14		2 m. green		1·10
15		3 m. pale blue		1·00
16		4 m. rose		1·40
17	**19**	6 m. rose-carmine		1·60
18		10 m. vermilion		3·25
19		20 m. green		4·75
13/19		*Set of 7*		12·00

Nos. 13/19 were not issued.

This office was closed down in 1923 under the terms of the Treaty of Lausanne.

B. DANZIG

100 Groszy = 1 Zloty

The Poles operated a postal service in Danzig with a post office by the harbour.

From 1934 Danzig stamps were valid for use throughout Poland.

Stamps of Poland overprinted

PORT	**PORT**	**PORT**
GDAŃSK	**GDAŃSK**	**GDAŃSK**
(R 1)	(R 2)	(R 3)

1925 (5 Jan). *Nos.* 218/28 (*Arms*) *optd with Type* R **1.**

R 1	**40**	1 g. yellow-brown			30	60
R 2		2 g. grey-brown			35	1·60
R 3		3 g. orange			35	60
R 4		5 g. sage-green			8·75	3·75
R 5		10 g. blue-green			3·00	1·25
R 6		15 g. scarlet			18·00	3·00
R 7		20 g. light blue			1·00	60
R 8		25 g. claret			1·00	60
R 9		30 g. bright violet			1·25	60
R10		40 g. slate			1·25	60
R11		50 g. magenta			3·25	80
R1/11		*Set of 11*			35·00	12·50

1926 (12 Apr). *Nos.* 244/5 *optd with Type* R **1.**

R12	**44**	5 g. green (Town Hall, Poznán)		30·00	22·00
R13	**45**	10 g. violet (King Sigismund Monument, Warsaw)		7·25	8·75

1926–29. *Optd with Type* R **2.**

R14	**44**	5 g. green (244a)		1·25	1·00
R15	**45**	10 g. violet (245a) (1927)		1·25	1·00
R16	**46**	15 g. carmine (246a) (Wawel Castle)		2·40	2·25
		a. Optd on No. 246		35·00	32·00
R17	**48**	20 g. carmine (Ship) (15.2.28)		1·90	1·40
R18	**51**	25 g. yellow-brown (Marshal Pilsudski) (15.2.28)		2·75	90
R19	**57**	1 z. slate-black/cream (Pres. Moscicki) (30.11.29)		18·00	18·00
R14/19		*Set of 6*		25·00	22·00

Inverted overprints of Nos. R14/15, R17 and R24 are now believed to be private productions made from the original cliches.

1929 (28 May)–**30.** *Optd with Type* R **3.**

R21	**61**	5 g. violet (Arms)		95	80
R22		10 g. green (1930)		95	80
R23	**59**	15 g. deep blue (Sienkiewicz) (5.1.30)		1·75	2·40
R24	**61**	25 g. red-brown		1·60	80
R21/24		*Set of 4*		4·75	4·25

See note below No. R19.

PORT GDAŃSK

(R 4)   (R 5)   R 6 Port of Danzig

1933 (1 July). *No.* 273a (*Moscicki*) *optd with Type* R **4.** *P* 11½.

R25	**57**	1 z. slate-black/cream (V.)		48·00	60·00

1934 (22 Sept)–**35.** *Nos.* 284a/285a (*Arms*) *optd with Type* R **3.**

R26	**65**	5 g. violet		1·90	2·25
R27		10 g. green (30.10.35)		20·00	65·00
R28		15 g. claret		1·90	2·25

1936–37. *Nos.* 313, 315, 317, 319 *and* 321 *optd as Type* R **5** *in one or* (*Nos.* R30 *and* R31) *in two lines.*

(a) Typo (Aug–Sept 1936)

R29	**79**	5 g. violet-blue (Dog's Rock) (15.8.36)		2·00	1·75
R30	–	15 g. greenish blue (Pilsudski) (liner) (10.9.36)		2·00	2·75

(b) Recess (Sept 1936–June 1937)

R31	**5**	15 g. violet (Czestochowa) (5.6.37)		65	1·00
R32	–	15 g. brown-lake (Lwow University) (5.6.37)		65	1·00
R33	–	25 g. deep blue-green (Belvedere Palace) (10.9.36)		2·00	1·25